Everyday Mathematics

The University of Chicago School Mathematics Project

Meeting All Expectations

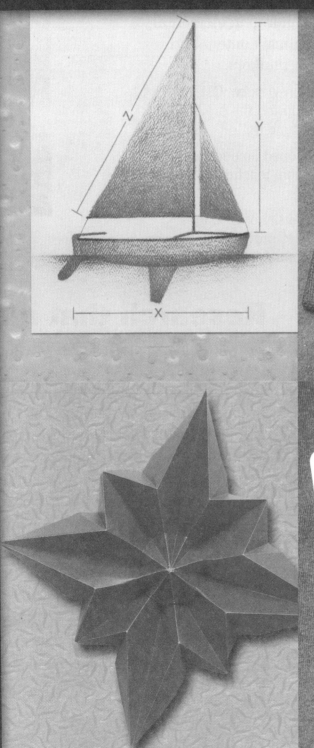

Everyday Mathematics *Meeting* all expectations

An inspired mission

Everyday Mathematics was developed through the University of Chicago School Mathematics Project (UCSMP) in order to enable children in elementary grades to learn more mathematical content and become life-long mathematical thinkers.

✦ The National Science Foundation, Amoco, GTE and other leading corporations supported the project through substantial, long-term funding.

✦ A strong partnership was developed among researchers, mathematics educators, classroom teachers, students and administrators.

✦ A core author team at the University of Chicago collaborates on all grade levels to provide a cohesive and well-articulated K-6 curriculum.

Research that matters

Everyday Mathematics begins with the premise that young children can, and must, learn more mathematics than has been expected from them in the past. This premise is based on the research the UCSMP author team undertook prior to writing the curriculum. Here are some of the major findings of this research:

✦ The typical U.S. mathematics curriculum is arithmetic-driven, slow-paced with isolated instruction, and broad without depth of content.

✦ International studies show that U.S. students learn much less mathematics than students in other countries.

✦ Children are capable of learning more mathematics in a richer curriculum.

✦ All children can be successful mathematical thinkers.

✦ Mathematics is meaningful to children when it is varied, rich, and rooted in real world problems and applications.

Instruction with impact

The *Everyday Mathematics* instructional design was carefully crafted to capitalize on student interest and maximize student learning.

- ✦ High expectations for all students
- ✦ Concepts and skills developed over time and in a wide variety of contexts
- ✦ Balance among mathematical strands
- ✦ Dynamic applications
- ✦ Multiple methods and strategies for problem solving
- ✦ Concrete modeling as a pathway to abstract understanding
- ✦ Collaborative learning in partner and small group activities
- ✦ Cross-curricular applications

Field test validation

Everyday Mathematics was originally field tested for one full year per grade level in hundreds of classrooms across the U.S. Prior to second edition development, additional classroom observation and research was conducted. One research component included evaluation of all first edition lessons by numerous teachers using the curriculum. Second edition content was then developed and field tested in a variety of educational settings.

Based on teacher and student feedback, and classroom observation by authors, revisions were made prior to publication.

Everyday Mathematics Doing more with mathematics

Everyday Mathematics is organized into six mathematical content strands that cover a number of skills and concepts. This provides a rich yet balanced curriculum—attention to numeration and computation without neglecting geometry, data, and algebraic thinking.

Every strand is addressed throughout all grade levels of the program. Each grade level builds on and extends concept understanding so that children approach each new challenge from a firmly established foundation.

Within the content of *Everyday Mathematics*, emphasis is placed on

✦ Establishing links from past experience

✦ Discussing and sharing ideas

✦ Using and comparing equivalent expressions

✦ Expressing numbers in context by including units

✦ Learning about the reversibility of most things

By becoming a part of everyday work and play, these ideas gradually shape children's ways of thinking about mathematics and foster the development of mathematical intuition and understanding.

content strands

OPERATIONS & COMPUTATION	NUMERATION	PATTERNS, FUNCTIONS & ALGEBRA	DATA & CHANCE	MEASUREMENT & REFERENCE FRAMES	GEOMETRY
Facts	Counting	Number and Visual Patterns	Mean	Linear Measures	Two Dimensional
Mental Math	Order	Properties	Median	Weight	Three Dimensional
Algorithms	Relations	Sequences	Range	Capacity	
Estimation	Estimation	Functions	Mode	Money	Symmetry
Number Stories	Odd/Even	Number Sentences	Tally Charts	Time	Congruence
Money	Fractions	Line Plots		Temperature	Angles
Powers of Ten	Decimals	Equations and Inequalities	Graphs	Perimeter	
Exponents	Percents	Variables	Probability	Area	
		Formulas		Volume	
				Diameter and Circumference	
				Angle	

Everyday Mathematics *Providing* classroom support

Everyday Mathematics was written in collaboration with teachers, for teachers as well as for students. *Everyday Mathematics* provides all the tools needed for instruction.

student materials

components

Student Reference Book (Grades 3–6)

Students use this hardbound reference book to access mathematical information and procedures that support the program. Game rules, ongoing routines, reference tables, a glossary of terms and calculator usage information are all included.

Student Math Journal, Volumes 1 & 2 (Grades 1–6)

These consumable books provide lesson support material for students to solve and complete. They provide a long-term record of each student's mathematical development.

Teacher's Lesson Guide, Volumes 1 & 2 (Grades 1–6)

Easy-to-follow three-part daily lesson plans. A unit organizer provides learning goals, planning tips, content highlights, and suggestions on problem solving, cross-curricular links, and support for special student populations.

Minute Math+ (Grades1–3)

Brief activities for transition time and for spare moments throughout the day.

Math Masters (Grades 1–6)

Blackline masters that support daily lesson activities. Includes Home/Study Link and Assessment Masters.

---

teacher resources

Teacher's Reference Manual

Contains comprehensive background information about mathematical content and program management for Grades K–3 and 4–6.

Home Connection Handbook

Provides suggestions for enhancing home-school communication and involvement in the program for Grades K–6.

Assessment Handbook

Grade level specific handbook that provides ideas for portfolio, ongoing, and product assessment.

grade specific K–6

---

kindergarten materials

Teacher's Guide to Activities

Classroom activities and ongoing daily routines. Includes detailed notes, illustrations, and progress guideposts.

Program Guide and Activity Masters

Teacher support material including program overview and philosophy, activity listings by mathematical content strand, curriculum and classroom management strategies and a comprehensive glossary. Ready-to-use masters provide printed material for student activities and Home Links.

Minute Math

Contains brief activities for transition time and for spare moments through-out the day.

Everyday Mathematics Unit Organizer

Each Unit begins with comprehensive support information to assist in successful implementation and instruction. In addition to the sections detailed on the following pages, the Unit Organizer also includes:

✦ Unit Overview
✦ Table of Contents
✦ Problem Solving Opportunities
✦ Cross-Curricular Links
✦ Materials Chart
✦ Detailed Content Highlights

Program Content Links
Connections to prior and future content both within and across grade levels.

Unit 9
Multiplication & Division

learning goals in perspective

learning goals	links to the past	links to the future
9a Beginning Goal Solve number stories involving positive and negative numbers. **(Lesson 9.13)**	In second grade, children experienced negative numbers by working with temperatures, number lines, and number grids. *(Related Grade 3 lessons: 4.1–4.4, 7.4, 7.5, 7.9, 8.7)*	In fourth grade, children will use positive and negative numbers in "credits and debits" number stories. *(Related Grade 3 lesson: 11.9)*
9b Beginning/Developing Goal Multiply multidigit numbers by 1- or 2-digit numbers. **(Lessons 9.4, 9.5, 9.9, 9.11, and 9.12)**	In second grade, children developed their own strategies for solving multidigit multiplication problems. In Grade 3 Unit 2, children worked with addition and subtraction algorithms. *(Related Grade 3 lessons: 2.7, 2.8, 4.8, 7.1–7.3, 7.6, 7.8)*	In fourth grade, children will review the basic principles of multiplication with multidigit numbers, and practice using the partial-products algorithm. The partial-products algorithm is used in later grades, in algebra, to find the products of binomials, such as $(x + 2)(x + 5)$. *(Related Grade 3 lessons: 10.2, 10.6)*
9c Beginning/Developing Goal Find factors of a number. **(Lesson 9.6)**	Skip counting by 2s, 5s, and 10s in previous grades prepared children to learn multiplication by these factors. Children were also introduced to multiplication/division fact families in second grade. *(Related Grade 3 lessons: 1.8, 4.2, 4.4–4.8, 7.1–7.3, 7.6, 7.8)*	In later grades, children will further explore factors and products in a branch of mathematics called number theory. Children will develop factoring skills by using arrays to identify all the possible factor pairs for a given number.
9d Beginning/Developing Goal Interpret remainders in division problems. **(Lesson 9.8)**	Second graders used counters to solve real-life division problems, and were introduced to the idea of remainders. *(Related Grade 3 lessons: 3.1, 4.3, 4.4, 4.6, 7.6)*	Children will continue to interpret remainders in division problems throughout the grades.
Developing Goal Solve	In second grade, children worked with	Children will continue to work with fact ... in *Fourth Grade Everyday ...matics.*

Unit Learning Goals
Indicates developmental level expected and lesson reference.

...out the grades, children will continue ...e and solve division number stories.

assessment
ongoing • product • periodic

✓ Informal Assessment

Math Boxes These *Math Journal* pages provide opportunities for cumulative review or assessment of concepts and skills.

Ongoing Assessment: Kid Watching Use the Ongoing Assessment suggestions in the following lessons to make quick, on-the-spot observations about children's understanding of:
• Operations and Computation **(Lessons 9.4–9.13)**
• Measurement and Reference Frames **(Lessons 9.7 and 9.13)**

Portfolio Ideas Samples of children's work may be obtained from the following assignments:
• Solving an Allowance Problem **(Lesson 9.2)**
• Using Count-By Patterns **(Lesson 9.4)**
• Sharing Money **(Lesson 9.7)**
• Multiplying and Dividing Multiples of 10 in the Context of Time **(Lesson 9.9)**
• Finding Number Patterns by Filing Equilateral Triangles **(Lesson 9.10)**

✓ Unit 9 Review and Assessment

Math Message Use the question in Lesson 9.14 to assess children's progress toward the following learning goal: Goal 9b

Slate Assessments Use oral or slate assessments during Lesson 9.14 to assess children's progress toward the following learning goals: Goals 9e and 9f

Written Assessment Use a written review during Lesson 9.14 to assess children's progress toward the following learning goals: Goals 9a, 9b, 9c, 9d, 9e, and 9f

Performance/Group Assessment Use a small-group activity in Lesson 9.14 to assess children's progress toward the following learning goals: Goals 9c, 9e, and 9f

Assessment Support
Suggestions for informal assessments and use of the Assessment Handbook are also included.

Ongoing Assessment
Built-in evaluation techniques and opportunities teachers may use to assess student attainment of unit learning goals.

assessment handbook

For more information on how to use different types of assessment in Unit 9, see the Assessment Overview on pages 69–71 in the *Assessment Handbook.* The following Assessment Masters can be found in the *Math Masters* book:
• Unit 9 Checking Progress, pp. 386 and 387
• Unit 9 Class Checklist, p. 420
• Unit 9 Individual Profile of Progress, p. 421
• Class Progress Indicator, p. 441

Examples from Third Grade, Unit 9

meeting INDIVIDUAL needs

✦ RETEACHING

The following features provide additional instructional support:

Adjusting the Activity

- **Lesson 9.1, Part 1**
- **Lesson 9.2, Part 1**
- **Lesson 9.4, Part 1**
- **Lesson 9.5, Parts 1, 2**
- **Lesson 9.6, Part 2**
- **Lesson 9.7, Part 1**
- **Lesson 9.8, Part 2**
- **Lesson 9.9, Part 1**
- **Lesson 9.10, Part 1**
- **Lesson 9.11, Part 1**
- **Lesson 9.12, Part 1**
- **Lesson 9.13, Part 1**

✦ ENRICHMENT

The following features suggest enrichment and extension activities:

Adjusting the Activity	Options for Individualizing
• **Lesson 9.5, Part 1**	• **Lesson 9.1** Finding Out More about Animals
• **Lesson 9.6, Part 1**	• **Lesson 9.2** Solving an Allowance Problem
• **Lesson 9.7, Part 1**	• **Lesson 9.4** Using Count-By Patterns
• **Lesson 9.8, Part 1**	• **Lesson 9.8** Solving Division Number Stories
• **Lesson 9.13, Part 1**	• **Lesson 9.9** Multiplying and Dividing Multiples of 10 in the Context of Time
	• **Lesson 9.12** Using the Lattice Method to Multiply 3-Digit Numbers by 2-Digit Numbers
	• **Lesson 9.13** Using Data Expressed with Positive and Negative Numbers from a Table

✦ MULTIAGE CLASSROOM

The following chart lists related lessons from Grades 2 and 4 that can help you meet your instructional needs:

Grade 2	7.3 10.8 11.5	7.4 12.4	8.1 8.2 9.8	5.3 6.10 11.5	4.6 7.4 11.3	6.7 11.7 12.5	6.8 6.11 7.6	1.10 6.11 11.4	5.3 6.10 11.5	5.2 6.9 6.10	5.3 6.10 11.5	5.3 6.10 11.5	1.9 4.3 4.4
Grade 3	9.1	9.2	9.3	9.4	9.5	9.6	9.7	9.8	9.9	9.10	9.11	9.12	9.13
Grade 4	3.4 5.9	3.1	5.1	5.5	5.5		5.1	3.4	5.7	1.3 5.1	5.6	5.6	

planning tips

Pacing
Pacing depends on a number of factors, such as children's individual needs and how long your school has been using *Everyday Mathematics*. At the beginning of Unit 9, review your Content by Strand Poster to help you set a monthly pace.

	◄—————— MOST CLASSROOMS ——————►	
FEBRUARY	MARCH	APRIL

Using the Projects
Use Project 2, Watermelon Feast and Seed-Spitting Contest, during Units 3, 4, 7, or 9 to measure the distances children spit watermelon seeds, and to find landmarks of the data. The Projects can be found at the back of this book.

Home Communication
Share Home Links 9.1–9.13 with families to help them understand the content and procedures in this unit. At the end of the unit, use Home Link 9.14 to introduce Unit 10. Supplemental information can be found in the *Home Connection Handbook*.

NCTM Standards

Standard	1	2	3	4	5	6	7	8	9	10
Unit 9 Lessons	1–13	1–13	3, 4, 10–12	3, 5, 7, 10, 12	2	1–13	1–13	1–13	1–13	1–13

Content Standards	Process Standards
1 Number and Operations	**6** Problem Solving
2 Algebra	**7** Reasoning and Proof
3 Geometry	**8** Communication
4 Measurement	**9** Connections
5 Data Analysis and Probability	**10** Representation

PRACTICE *through* Games

Everyday Mathematics uses games to help children develop good fact power and other math skills.

- Comparing fractions with *Fraction Top-It* (**Lesson 9.3**)
- Identifying the factors of whole numbers in *Factor Bingo* (**Lessons 9.6, 9.7, and 9.10**)
- Practicing multiplication facts pictured on dot arrays in *Array Bingo* (**Lesson 9.6**)
- ...rements with *Angle Race* (**Lesson 9.11**)

Everyday Mathematics Lesson Highlights

Each lesson has been designed to follow an easy-to-use three-part plan. This assists teachers in focusing on lesson objectives, provides ongoing practice for all students, and addresses individual student needs for a variety of populations.

Lesson Summaries
A concise chart which provides a summary of lesson activities and materials, content strand coverage, background information and references, advance preparation needed, and lesson vocabulary.

Getting Started
Contains quick mental math activities, Math Message (an independent warm-up for the lesson), and Home/Study Link follow-up suggestions.

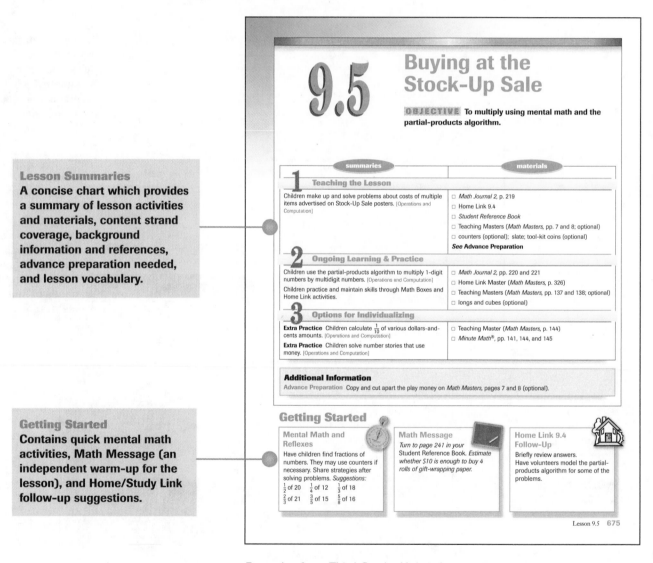

9.5 Buying at the Stock-Up Sale

OBJECTIVE To multiply using mental math and the partial-products algorithm.

summaries	materials
1 Teaching the Lesson	
Children make up and solve problems about costs of multiple items advertised on Stock-Up Sale posters. [Operations and Computation]	□ *Math Journal 2*, p. 219 □ Home Link 9.4 □ *Student Reference Book* □ Teaching Masters (*Math Masters*, pp. 7 and 8; optional) □ counters (optional); slate; tool-kit coins (optional) **See Advance Preparation**
2 Ongoing Learning & Practice	
Children use the partial-products algorithm to multiply 1-digit numbers by multidigit numbers. [Operations and Computation] Children practice and maintain skills through Math Boxes and Home Link activities.	□ *Math Journal 2*, pp. 220 and 221 □ Home Link Master (*Math Masters*, p. 326) □ Teaching Masters (*Math Masters*, pp. 137 and 138; optional) □ longs and cubes (optional)
3 Options for Individualizing	
Extra Practice Children calculate $\frac{1}{10}$ of various dollars-and-cents amounts. [Operations and Computation] **Extra Practice** Children solve number stories that use money. [Operations and Computation]	□ Teaching Master (*Math Masters*, p. 144) □ *Minute Math®*, pp. 141, 144, and 145

Additional Information
Advance Preparation Copy and cut apart the play money on *Math Masters*, pages 7 and 8 (optional).

Getting Started

Mental Math and Reflexes
Have children find fractions of numbers. They may use counters if necessary. Share strategies after solving problems. *Suggestions:*
$\frac{1}{2}$ of 20 $\frac{1}{4}$ of 12 $\frac{1}{3}$ of 18
$\frac{2}{3}$ of 21 $\frac{3}{5}$ of 15 $\frac{5}{8}$ of 16

Math Message
Turn to page 241 in your Student Reference Book. Estimate whether $10 is enough to buy 4 rolls of gift-wrapping paper.

Home Link 9.4 Follow-Up
Briefly review answers. Have volunteers model the partial-products algorithm for some of the problems.

Lesson 9.5   675

Examples from Third Grade, Unit 9, Lesson 5

◆ *Student Reference Book,* p. 241

▼ Backs of bills are provided on *Math Masters,* page 8.

$1 Bills

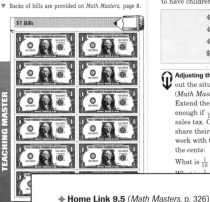

676 Unit

1 Teaching the Lesson

◆ **Math Message Follow-Up**
(*Student Reference Book,* p. 241;
Math Masters, pp. 7 and 8)

WHOLE-CLASS DISCUSSION

Discuss children's answers. Possible estimation strategies:

▷ $4 \times \$2.50 = \$10.00$ (double $2.50 twice). I could buy
4 rolls if they were $2.50 a roll. Since $2.50 is more
than $2.35, the cost of 4 rolls at $2.35 is less than $10.

▷ Change $2.35 to a close but easier amount, such as
$2.40. $4 \times \$2.00 = \$8.00$, and $4 \times \$0.40 = \$1.60$.
Therefore, $4 \times \$2.40 = \$9.60$. Since $2.40 is more than
$2.35, the cost is less than $10.

Remind children that many problems can be solved with
estimation instead of exact calculation. An efficient
estimation strategy requires simple mental math and
gives an answer reasonably close to the exact answer. For
most people, the most efficient estimation strategy for the
problem above would probably be the first one listed.

Now ask children to work in small groups to find the exact
cost, using mental math or an algorithm. $9.40 Take time
to have children share strategies. *For example:*

$$4 \times \$2.00 = \$8.00$$
$$4 \times \$0.30 = \$1.20$$
$$4 \times \$0.05 = \$0.20$$
$$\$8.00 + \$1.20 + \$0.20 = \$9.40$$

Adjusting the Activity Some children may want to act
out the situation with play money. Provide dollar bills
(*Math Masters,* pages 7 and 8) and tool-kit coins.
Extend the problem by asking if $10 will still be
enough if $\frac{1}{10}$ or 10% of the $9.40 cost is added for
sales tax. Children try to solve this problem and then
share their strategies. If only a few are successful,
work with the class first on the dollars and then on
the cents:

What is $\frac{1}{10}$ of $9.00? 9 dimes: $0.90

◆ **Solving Stock-Up Sale Stories**
(*Math Journal 2,* p. 219;
Student Reference Book, p. 240)

PARTNER ACTIVITY

Children work together in partnerships to solve the
problems on journal page 219 using the information on
page 240 in their *Student Reference Book.* Some problems
call for an exact answer, while others require only an
estimate. Children should show the number models that
they are using to make their estimates.

2 Ongoing Learning & Practice

◆ **Using the Partial-Products Algorithm to
Multiply** (*Math Journal 2,* p. 220;
Math Masters, pp. 137 and 138)

INDEPENDENT ACTIVITY

Circulate and assist as necessary.

Adjusting the Activity Children who are still confused
by the partial-products algorithm should write the
number model next to each partial product.

$$\begin{array}{r} 68 \\ \times\ 2 \\ \end{array}$$
$$2 \ [60s] \rightarrow\ \ 120$$
$$2 \ [8s] \rightarrow\ \underline{+\ 16}$$
$$120 + 16 \rightarrow\ \ 136$$

Children may also use the array grid (*Math Masters,*
pages 137 and 138) with base-10 blocks to model the
problems.

◆ **Math Boxes 9.5** (*Math Journal 2,* p. 221)

INDEPENDENT ACTIVITY

Mixed Review This journal page provides
opportunities for cumulative review or
assessment of concepts and skills.

◆ **Home Link 9.5** (*Math Masters,* p. 326)

Home Connection Children use mental
math or the partial-products algorithm to
solve multiplication number stories.

3 Options for Individualizing

◆ **EXTRA PRACTICE** Calculating $\frac{1}{10}$ of Amounts
of Money (*Math Masters,* p. 144)

INDEPENDENT ACTIVITY   5–15 min

Children find $\frac{1}{10}$ of various dollars-and-cents amounts.

◆ **EXTRA PRACTICE** Minute Math

SMALL-GROUP ACTIVITY   5–15 min

To offer children more experience with calculating with
money, see the following pages in *Minute Math:*
Number Stories: pp. 141, 144, and 145

◆ *Math Masters,* p. 144

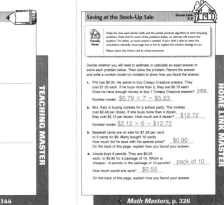

◆ *Math Masters,* p. 326

Sidebar (right margin)

Teaching the Lesson
**Main instructional
activities for the
lesson, where most
new content is
introduced.**

**Ongoing Learning
& Practice**
**Essential for
developing and
maintaining skills,
these activities
provide review and
practice in the form
of Math Journal
assignments, Math
Boxes, Home/Study
Links and games.**

**Options for
Individualizing**
**Optional activities
for reteaching,
extra skill practice,
enrichment, and
meeting the needs
of particular popu-
lations (ESL, etc.)
Usually extensions
of "Teaching the
Lesson" section.**

Lesson 9.5 **679**

Everyday Mathematics
Student Reference Book
Grades 3–6

The grade-specific Student Reference Book contains

✦ **Mathematical Essays** Sections organized around mathematical topics which provide explanations and examples. Students may use these pages during lesson instruction and when they need information to complete independent work.

✦ **Game Section** Provides directions for games introduced at each grade level. They are helpful for clarification of rules, adaptations for various abilities, and home use.

✦ **Data Section** Contains charts, tables, and other information provided for use with student lesson activities and projects.

In addition, a comprehensive glossary, an answer key for every **Check Your Understanding,** and an index are found at the back of the book.

Title Bar
Highlights page contents

Vocabulary
Notes words that may also be found in the glossary

Examples
Provides examples of mathematical processes

Check Your Understanding
Problems for students to try and check before returning to their work.

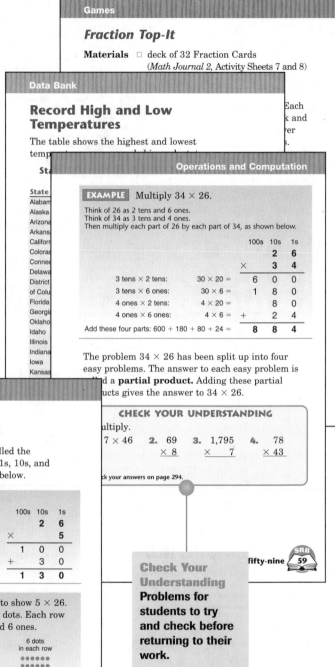

Games

Fraction Top-It

Materials ☐ deck of 32 Fraction Cards
(*Math Journal 2,* Activity Sheets 7 and 8)

Data Bank

Record High and Low Temperatures

The table shows the highest and lowest temp...

State

| State |
| Alabam |
| Alaska |
| Arizona |
| Arkans |
| Californ |
| Colorad |
| Connec |
| Delawa |
| District |
| of Colu |
| Florida |
| Georgia |
| Oklaho |
| Idaho |
| Illinois |
| Indiana |
| Iowa |
| Kansas |

Operations and Computation

EXAMPLE Multiply 34 × 26.

Think of 26 as 2 tens and 6 ones.
Think of 34 as 3 tens and 4 ones.
Then multiply each part of 26 by each part of 34, as shown below.

		100s	10s	1s
			2	6
	×		3	4
3 tens × 2 tens:	30 × 20 =	6	0	0
3 tens × 6 ones:	30 × 6 =	1	8	0
4 ones × 2 tens:	4 × 20 =		8	0
4 ones × 6 ones:	4 × 6 = +		2	4
Add these four parts: 600 + 180 + 80 + 24 =		8	8	4

The problem 34 × 26 has been split up into four easy problems. The answer to each easy problem is ...ed a **partial product.** Adding these partial ...ucts gives the answer to 34 × 26.

CHECK YOUR UNDERSTANDING
...ultiply.

...7 × 46   **2.** 69   **3.** 1,795   **4.** 78
            × 8   × 7   × 43

...ck your answers on page 294.

Operations and Computation

Partial-Products Multiplication Method

One way to multiply numbers is called the **partial-products method.** Write 1s, 10s, and 100s above the columns, as shown below.

EXAMPLE Multiply 5 × 26.

Think of 26 as 2 tens and 6 ones.
Then multiply each part of 26 by 5.

		100s	10s	1s
			2	6
	×			5
5 ones × 2 tens:	5 × 20 =	1	0	0
5 ones × 6 ones:	5 × 6 = +		3	0
Add these two parts:	100 + 30 =	1	3	0

EXAMPLE Use an array diagram to show 5 × 26. There are 5 rows. Each row has 26 dots. Each row has been divided to show 2 tens and 6 ones.

20 dots in each row   6 dots in each row

5 rows

Multiply each part: 5 × 20 = 100   5 × 6 = 30
Add these two parts: 5 × 26 = 100 + 30, which is 130.

Examples from Third Grade
Student Reference Book

Assessment Handbook

The grade-specific Assessment Handbook provides ideas to make assessment and instruction more manageable, productive, and exciting, as well as offer a more complete picture of each child's progress and instructional needs. It guides teachers as they develop a plan that balances techniques and tools from four different assessment areas.

✦ **Ongoing Assessment** Informal student observation and anecdotal record keeping during teacher-guided instruction, strategy sharing, game play, and slate routines.

✦ **Product Assessment** Samples of student work from Math Boxes, Math Journals, Explorations, and Projects.

✦ **Periodic Assessment** Unit, mid-year and end-of-year assessments and Math Boxes.

✦ **Outside Tests** School, district, or state assessments and standardized achievement tests.

Unit 9
Assessment Overview

At this stage in *Everyday Mathematics*, children are expected to be at a Beginning/Developing level for multiplying multidigit numbers by 1- or 2-digit numbers. Because this is such a critical skill, five ongoing assessment opportunities are provided in Unit 9 (see Goal 9b in the chart below).

By this time, perhaps you have tried several different types of assessment strategies. Remember, as you use a balance of assessment approaches, the overall effectiveness of your assessment plan should improve. If there is still a major type of assessment, such as Ongoing, Product, or Periodic, that you haven't used, this unit might be a good time to try it.

Ongoing Assessment Opportunities

Ongoing assessment opportunities are opportunities to observe children during regular interactions, as they work independently and in groups. You can conduct ongoing assessment during teacher-guided instruction, Math Boxes sessions, mathematical mini-interviews, games, Mental Math and Reflexes sessions, strategy sharing, and slate work. The chart below provides a summary of ongoing assessment opportunities in Unit 9, as they relate to specific Unit 9 learning goals.

Beginning Goal Solve number stories involving positive and negative numbers. (Lesson 9.13)	Lesson 9.13, p. 722
Beginning/Developing Goal Multiply multidigit numbers by 1- or 2-digit numbers. (Lessons 9.2, 9.4, 9.5, 9.9, 9.11, and 9.12)	Lesson 9.2, p. 860 / Lesson 9.4, p. 672 / Lesson 9.9, p. 699 / Lesson 9.11, p. 710 / Lesson 9.12, p. 715
Beginning/Developing Goal Find factors of a number. (Lessons 9.6 and 9.10)	Lesson 9.6, p. 681 / Lesson 9.10, p. 705
Beginning/Developing Goal Interpret remainders in division problems. (Lesson 9.6)	Lesson 9.6, p. 693

Ongoing Assessment
Suggestions from lesson activities throughout the unit. Refers teachers back to unit learning goals and development levels.

Product Assessment Opportunities

Math Journals, Math Boxes, activity sheets, masters, Math Logs, and the results of Explorations and Projects all provide product assessment opportunities. Here is an example of how you might use a rubric to assess children's abilities to solve equal-sharing problems.

Lesson 9.7, p. 689

EXTRA PRACTICE Sharing Money

Circulate around the room as children work in pairs to complete *Math Masters*, page 148. Children record the problem, a number model, and the answer. This activity can help you assess children's ability to solve equal-sharing problems with remainders. The sample rubric below will help you evaluate children's work.

Sample Rubric

Beginning (B)
The pair of children is able to set up the problem by rolling the die and drawing two cards. However, the number model may be written incorrectly or children may need teacher assistance. Problems b–f are difficult for partners to solve without teacher assistance. Children may get through only one of the equal-sharing problems.

Developing (D)
The pair of children sets up the problem without teacher assistance using the die and number cards. The number model is written correctly in both problems and the numbers of $10 bills and $1 bills are correct. It may be difficult for children to calculate how many cents each friend would receive if the leftover money were shared equally (Problem e). Therefore, their final answer may be incorrect.

Secure (S)
The pair of children sets up and solves the problems without teacher assistance. The number sentences are written correctly, and the numbers of $10 bills and $1 bills are correct. Children are able to calculate how the leftover money can be shared equally; thus they have a correct total for the amount that each friend would receive. Children may also be able to solve more than two problems.

Product Assessment
Detailed sample rubric for a product assessment opportunity.

Periodic Assessment Opportunities

Here is a summary of the periodic assessment opportunities that are provided in Unit 9. Refer to Lesson 9.14 for details.

Oral and Slate Assessment

In Lesson 9.14, you will find oral and slate assessment problems on pages 725–727.

Written Assessment

In Lesson 9.14, you will find written assessment problems on pages 727–728 (*Math Masters*, pages 386 and 387).

See the chart on the next page to find slate and written assessment problems that address specific learning goals.

Periodic Assessment
Suggestions for recording students' periodic progress from the unit assessment lesson. Refers teachers back to unit learning goals and development levels.

Examples from Third Grade
Assessment Handbook

Everyday Mathematics
Making a mark in education

Everyday Mathematics is used in a variety of settings throughout the United States as shown here on the map.

Over 2 million students in 100,000 classrooms are engaged in this exciting curriculum.

Look for users in your area.

WASHINGTON
Northshore SD 417
Longview SD 122
Franklin Pierce SD 402
South Kitsap SD 402
Silverdale Elementary

MONTANA
Livingston SD 1 & 4
Bigfork SD 38

OREGON
Beavertown SD 48J
Portland Jewish
  Academy

IDAHO
Coeur D'Alene SD 271
Lewiston ISD 1

SOUTH DAKOTA
Beresford SD 61-2
Pierre Indian School

WYOMING
Sheridan County SD 2

CALIFORNIA
Rocklin SD
Glendale SD
Poway SD
Hacienda-La Puente
  Unified SD
Center for Early Education

UTAH
Rolling Meadows
  School
Park City SD

COLORADO
Douglas County
  SD R-1
Cherry Creek SD 5
Julesburg SD R-1
Eagleton Elementary
Lewis-Palmer SD 38

ARIZONA
Kyrene Elementary
  SD 28

NEW MEXICO
Rio Rancho Public SD
Bloomfield SD
Taos Day School–Bureau
  of Indian Affairs
Bernalillo Public SD
Pojoaque Valley SD

ALASKA
Anchorage SD

HAWAII
Waipahu Elementary
Nanakuli Elementary
Ewa Beach Elementary

VERMONT
Addison Rutland
   Supervisory Union 4
Barre Town SD
Colchester SD
East Montpelier SD
Montpelier SD 45

MICHIGAN
Ann Arbor Public SD
Troy SD
Rochester Community SD
Kalamazoo Public SD
Walled Lake
   Consolidated SD

NEW YORK
Bronx SD 11
Staten Island SD 31
Valley Stream SD 30
Monroe Woodbury
   Central SD
Williamsville Central SD

ILLINOIS
Rockford SD 205
Sunset Ridge SD 29
Community
   Consolidated SD 93
Aptakisic-Tripp SD 102
Mt. Prospect SD 57

NEW HAMPSHIRE
District 8 Concord
District 24 Weare
District 41 Hollis
District 46 Merrimack
   Valley

NEBRASKA
Millard Public
   Schools 17
Westside Community
   SD 66
Hebron City SD 7
Seward Public SD 9
Tri-County SD 300

WISCONSIN
Kenosha USD
Sheboygan Area SD
Oak Creek-Franklin SD
Wauwatosa SD
Menasha Joint SD

OHIO
Worthington SD
Upper Arlington City SD
Northwest Local SD
Clyde-Green Springs
   Exempt Village SD
Lakewood City SD

MAINE
Cape Elizabeth SD
Sanford SD
School Administration
   District 60 North
   Berwick
York School District

INDIANA
Penn Harris
   Madison SD
Lafayette Christian
   School

PENNSYLVANIA
Abington SD
Haverford Township SD
Butler Area SD
Pittsburgh Public SD
Quaker Valley SD

MASSACHUSETTS
Lexington SD
Lynnfield SD
Newton Public SD
Reading Public SD
Westborough SD

MINNESOTA
Minneapolis Public SD 1
Edina Public SD 273
Wayzata SD 284
Brainerd ISD 181
Moorhead ISD 152

RHODE ISLAND
Barrington Town SD
East Providence City SD
Middletown Public SD
Tivertown SD
West Warwick Town SD

IOWA
College Community SD
Bettendorf Community SD
Sheldon Community SD
Pleasant Valley
   Community SD
Cedar Rapids Catholic
   Schools

CONNECTICUT
New Milford SD
Norwich SD
Old Saybrook SD
South Windsor Public SD
Wilton Public SD
Colchester Public SD

KANSAS
Winfield USD 465
Geary County USD 475
Cheney USD 268
Bonner Springs
   USD 204

MISSOURI
Melhville SD R9
Webster Groves SD
Affton SD 101
Blue Spring SD R4

MARYLAND
Cecil County SD

NEW JERSEY
Hackensack Public
   Schools
South Orange
   Maplewood SD
Tenafly SD
East Brunswick Public SD
Spotswood SD

KENTUCKY
Brandeis Elementary
Sayre School
The Lexington School
Grapevine Elementary
East View Elementary

OKLAHOMA
Holland Hall School

ARKANSAS
Corning SD 8

VIRGINIA
Virginia Beach City SD

NORTH CAROLINA
Charlotte Country Day
   School
McDougle Elementary
Mangum Primary
The Summit School

MISSISSIPPI
St. Andrew's Episcopal
   School

GEORGIA
Lovett School
Westminster Lower
   School
Trinity School
Greater Atlanta
   Christian School

TEXAS
Leander ISD
Temple ISD
Houston ISD
Lockhart ISD
River Oaks Baptist
   School

ALABAMA
Birmingham City
   Public SD
Vestavia Hills City SD
Randolph School

SOUTH CAROLINA
Fort Mill Primary
Heathwood Hall
   Episcopal
Hilton Head Primary &
   Elementary
Memminger Elementary
Richland County SD 2

FLORIDA
Dunbar Magnet School
Gene Witt Elementary
   School
Osceola Magnet School
Putnam County SD

TENNESSEE
Memphis City SD
Hamilton County Schools
Oak Ridge SD
Bright School
St. Mary's Episcopal
   School

Everyday Mathematics Acknowledgments

The first edition of the K–6 *Everyday Mathematics* program was made possible by sustained support over several years from the GTE Corporation and the National Science Foundation. Additional help came from the Amoco Foundation through its support of the University of Chicago School Mathematics Project (UCSMP).

Earlier projects supported by the National Science Foundation, the National Institute of Education, and the Benton Foundation provided us with insights into the often surprising capabilities of young children.

This second edition of the K–6 *Everyday Mathematics* program is funded by Everyday Learning Corporation and by the authors.

For both editions, feedback and advice from teachers willing to take risks in trying development versions have been essential and enormously helpful. There are too many such teachers to list, but their contributions are gratefully acknowledged.

For both editions, many University of Chicago and UCSMP colleagues have been helpful. Finally, we acknowledge dedicated and resourceful help on production and technical tasks by many people on our various development staffs and also at Everyday Learning Corporation.

James McBride
Director, Second Edition

Max Bell
Director, First Edition

Second Grade

Everyday Mathematics®

Teacher's Lesson Guide
Volume 1

The University of Chicago
School Mathematics Project

EVERYDAY
LEARNING

Chicago, Illinois

UCSMP Elementary Materials Component

Max Bell, Director

Authors

Max Bell
Jean Bell
John Bretzlauf*
Amy Dillard*
Robert Hartfield
Andy Isaacs*
James McBride, Director
Kathleen Pitvorec*
Peter Saecker

Technical Art

Diana Barrie*

Second Edition only

Everyday Learning Development Staff

Editorial: Anna Belluomini, Mary Cooney, Julie Crawford, Christine Fraser, Elizabeth Glosniak, Bernadette Lopez, Michael Murphy
Design: Fran Brown, Jess Schaal
Production: Annette Davis, Tina Dunlap, Elizabeth Gabbard, Silvana Valenzuela

Additional Credits

Donna Antkowiak, Elizabeth Allen, Nancy Baty, Kathy Burke, Lindaanne Donohoe, Susan Halko, Herman Adler Design Group, Scott LaPierre, Made in Chicago Design, Yoshi Miyake, Point West, Inc., Precision Graphics, Randi Robin Design, Adam Sugarman, Katie Telser, Regina Thoeming, Cathy Wacaser

Photo Credits

Phil Martin/Photography
Jack Demuth/Photography
Cover: Bill Burlingham/Photography
Photo Collage: Herman Adler Design Group

Contributors

Librada Acosta, Carol Arkin, Robert Balfanz, Sharlean Brooks, Jean Callahan, Anne Coglianese, Ellen Dairyko, Tresea Felder, James Flanders, Dorothy Freedman, Rita Gronbach, Deborah Arron Leslie, William D. Pattison, LaDonna Pitts, Danette Riehle, Marie Schilling, Robert Strang, Sadako Tengan, Therese Wasik, Leeann Wille, Michael Wilson

Permissions

page 438, Project 5: Snow Crystals, 2453 Illustrations,
    W. A. Bentley and W. J. Humphreys, Dover Publications, Inc.
page 447, Myrleen Ferguson Cate/PhotoEdit
page 894, http://vraptor.jpl.nasa.gov/voyager/gold.gif
page 899, Myrleen Ferguson Cate/PhotoEdit

ISBN 1-57039-828-3

Everyday Learning Corporation
P.O. Box 812960
Chicago, IL 60681
www.everydaylearning.com

2 3 4 5 6 7 8 9 QW 05 04 03 02 01

Contents

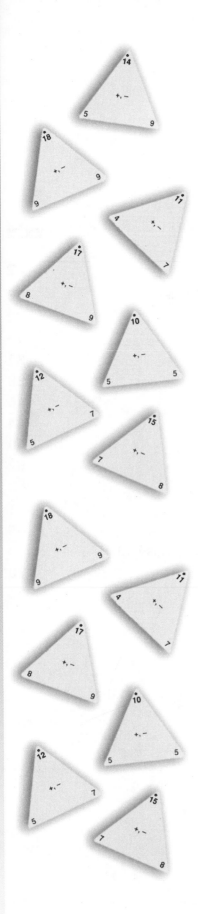

Volume 2

Welcome to *Everyday Mathematics,* the elementary school mathematics curriculum developed by the University of Chicago School Mathematics Project (UCSMP). *Everyday Mathematics* offers you and your children a broad background and rich experiences in mathematics.

Second Grade Everyday Mathematics content emphasizes the following content strands, skills and concepts:

- ❖ **Numeration** Counting; reading and writing numbers; identifying place-value; comparing numbers; working with fractions; using money to develop place-value and decimal concepts.
- ❖ **Operations and Computation** Recalling addition and subtraction facts; exploring fact families; adding and subtracting with tens and hundreds; beginning multiplication and division; exchanging money amounts.
- ❖ **Data and Chance** Collecting, organizing, and interpreting data using tables, charts, and graphs; exploring concepts of chance.
- ❖ **Geometry** Exploring 2- and 3-dimensional shapes; classifying polygons.
- ❖ **Measurement and Reference Frames** Using tools to measure length, capacity, weight, and volume; using U.S. customary and metric measurement units.
- ❖ **Patterns, Functions, and Algebra** Exploring number patterns, rules for number sequences, relations between numbers, and attributes.

Within the content of *Everyday Mathematics,* emphasis is placed on:

- ❖ A problem-solving approach based on everyday situations that develops critical thinking.
- ❖ Frequent practice of basic skills through ongoing program routines and mathematical games.
- ❖ An instructional approach that revisits topics regularly to ensure full concept development.
- ❖ Activities that explore a wide variety of mathematical content and offer opportunities for students to apply their basic fact skills to geometry, measurement, and algebra.

Everyday Mathematics will provide you with ample opportunities to monitor implementation. At the beginning of the school year, focus on Parts 1 and 2 of the three-part lesson plan and try at least one assessment technique from each of the four sources: ongoing, product, and periodic assessment and outside tests. As the school year progresses, incorporate activities from Part 3 of your lesson plan as appropriate for your children and try some of the other assessment suggestions to gain a clearer picture of student development. During your first year, you will become increasingly comfortable with the content, components, and strategies of *Second Grade Everyday Mathematics.*

You and your children will incorporate mathematical processes as a part of everyday work and play. These processes will gradually shape children's ways of thinking about mathematics and foster the development of mathematical intuition and understanding.

Have an exciting year!

Professional Preparation

Components for *Second Grade Everyday Mathematics*

Go to...	*When you need...*
Teacher's Lesson Guide	Daily lessons; unit support information; key vocabulary; scope and sequence Grades 1–3
Math Masters	Blackline masters for Math Boxes, Home Links, projects, and assessments
Assessment Handbook	Suggestions for portfolio, ongoing, and product assessment
Teacher's Reference Manual	Background on mathematical content; ideas for curriculum and classroom management for K–3
Home Connection Handbook	Suggestions for home-school communication for K–6
Minute Math®	Quick activities for transition time throughout the day
Content by Strand Poster	Skills organized by content strand and paced by month (side one); learning goals organized by unit for the year (side two)
Student Math Journal	Lesson support material for students to analyze and complete; a year-long record of each student's mathematical development

Suggested Reading & Lesson Preparation

In order to prepare for effective classroom and curriculum management, we suggest that the following activities take place before you teach *Everyday Mathematics* for the first time.

Reading and Planning

❏ Review each of the components in your Teacher's Resource Package (TRP). Take time to analyze where information and materials are located so that you may access them as needed throughout the school year. See the chart above.

❏ Read Unit 1 Organizer and the first three to four lessons in your *Teacher's Lesson Guide.*

❏ Prepare a general daily math schedule. This schedule should include time for morning routines (calendar, weather, attendance, etc.), Teaching the Lesson, and Ongoing Learning and Practice activities such as games and Math Boxes.

Materials Preparation

Prepare materials as indicated for the first three to four lessons. Special items for consideration include:

❑ Review the *Addition Top-It* and *Coin Top-It Games.* See *Teacher's Lesson Guide* Unit 1, Lesson 4, page 31. Make note of the game skills you will need to teach before play begins. Try the game with a colleague. Consider any adaptations you may need to make for various abilities.

❑ Create Tool Kits. See *Teacher's Lesson Guide,* Unit 1 Lesson 2, page 22.

❑ Prepare slates for student use. See *Teacher's Lesson Guide,* Unit 1, Lesson 5, page 36.

❑ Write and copy a list of coins for each student to bring from home (10 pennies, 5 nickels, 10 dimes, 2 quarters). Suggest that students bring the coins in either a small plastic bag or a 35 mm plastic film container. An additional class collection of pennies is also useful.

❑ Prepare a supply of paper:
    Blank $8\frac{1}{2} \times 11$ (full, half, and quarter size sheets)
    Primary grade handwriting paper
    Colored construction paper
    Graph paper (1-inch)

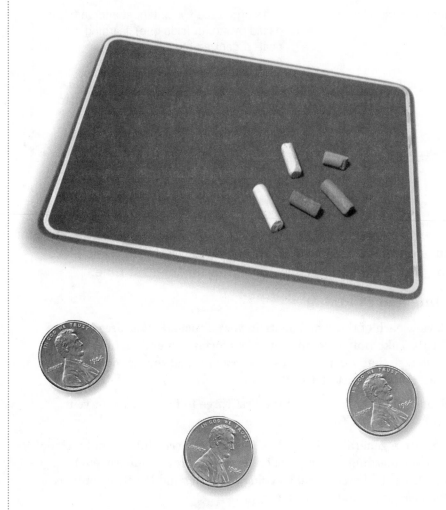

Organizing Your Classroom

Items for Display

Before the school year begins, we suggest that you prepare the following items for classroom display. By taking time to prepare these items your first year and laminating them if possible, you will be able to re-use them year after year. Refer to the Management Guide of your *Teacher's Reference Manual* for more information.

- ❑ Number cards with words
- ❑ Number Line (−35 −180)
- ❑ Number Grid Poster (In your TRP)
- ❑ Monthly Calendar
- ❑ Weather/Temperature Recording Chart
- ❑ Attendance Chart
- ❑ Daily Class Schedule
- ❑ Job Chart
- ❑ N, S, E, W directional indicators
- ❑ Class Data Pad

Classroom Set-Up

The following items should be considered as you set-up your *Everyday Mathematics* classroom. Try several configurations until you find one that is comfortable and effective for both you and your students. Visit other classrooms in your building to observe and discuss what works for your colleagues.

- ❑ Prepare and label a location in the classroom where students may deposit their written work: Math Messages, and Home Links.
- ❑ Arrange classroom desks/tables to allow for easy access to manipulatives and to facilitate efficient transitions for individual, partner, and small group activities.
- ❑ Organize class and individual manipulatives for easy access and efficient use of storage space.
- ❑ Allow (table) space for math center(s). Particular games and activities may then be left in this space for ongoing practice or free exploration.

Manipulatives for *Second Grade Everyday Mathematics* Activities

The following list has been organized to highlight the items that are used on a regular basis throughout *Second Grade Everyday Mathematics*. Some lessons call for minor additional materials, which you or students may bring in at the appropriate time.

Quantity	Item
1 set	Attribute Blocks
1 set	Base-10 Blocks
10 sets	Play Money Bills
1 per student	Calculator* (TI-108 recommended)
1 per student	Clock Face
1 set	Clock Face Stamps
1 set	Coin Stamps, heads
1 pkg. (2,000)	Connectors (twist ties)
1 pkg. (1,000)	Counting (Craft) Sticks
1 pkg. (16 total)	Dice, blanks
1 per student	Die, dot
3 pkg. (18 total)	Dice, polyhedra
5 sets	Dominoes, Double-9
15 decks	Everything Math Decks
8	Geoboards
10	Meter Sticks, dual scale
1	Number Line (−35–180)
2 sets	Pattern Blocks
1 per student	Pattern Block Template
1 pkg.	Rubber Bands (for geoboards)
1 per student	Ruler, 6-inch
1 per student	Slate (chalk or marker board)
2	Stamp Pads
1 pkg. (500)	Straws
15	Tape Measures, retractable
1	Thermometer (°F and °C)
1 per student	Tool-Kit Bag*

All of the above items are available from Everyday Learning Corporation. They may be purchased either as a comprehensive classroom manipulative kit or by individual components. The Everyday Learning classroom kit provides appropriate quantities for a class of 25 and comes packaged in durable plastic tubs with labels.

* *Calculators and tool-kit bags available from Everyday Learning Corporation for individual purchase only.*

nstruction

he following sections introduce instructional methods and
uggestions for successful *Everyday Mathematics* implementation.
eachers are encouraged to read these pages and refer to them as
eeded throughout the school year.

aily Routines

hildren learn a great deal of mathematics through daily routines
at they perform independently and with the class. These daily
tivities may include tracking attendance, calendar, weather,
mperature, and choral counting. Numerous mathematical
ncepts are reinforced on a daily basis and help children become
vare of how mathematics pervades our everyday lives.

ost of the daily routines in *Second Grade Everyday Mathematics*
e introduced within the lessons of Unit 1 and should be
aintained throughout the school year. Refer to Unit 1 lessons
d the Management Guide in the *Teacher's Reference Manual*
r more information.

rogram Routines

veryday Mathematics uses a number of program routines that are
corporated throughout all grade levels. These allow for ongoing
evelopmental practice in a number of skill and content areas.
elow is a list of the routines you will encounter in *Second Grade
veryday Mathematics*. The unit and lesson in which each routine
first used have been noted. Refer to the Management Guide in
e *Teacher's Reference Manual* for more information.

Mental Math and Reflexes (Unit 1, Lesson 1)
Math Message (Unit 1, Lesson 1)
Games (Unit 1, Lesson 4)
Math Boxes (Unit 1, Lesson 7)
Home Links (Unit 1, Lesson 12)
Name Collection Boxes (Unit 2, Lesson 9)
Frames and Arrows (Unit 2, Lesson 10)
"What's My Rule?"/Function Machines (Unit 2, Lesson 11)

All of the above routines are used in *First Grade Everyday Mathematics*

Explorations

You will find an Explorations lesson in virtually every unit in *Second Grade Everyday Mathematics*. The term "Exploration" is used to indicate independent, small-group activities that are informal and open-ended. The Explorations have been designed so that you can position the various activities at different stations around the room and have small groups rotate among them.

Each Explorations lesson suggests three exploratory activities, with the option of adding other familiar activities as desired. In each set of activities, Exploration A contains the main content of the lesson and requires the most teacher facilitation, especially at the outset.

Explorations are not intended as optional activities for children to do when they have finished their other work. Be sure to set aside enough class time so that all children can experience the Explorations. They provide critical initial exposure to content that is developed later in *Everyday Mathematics*.

Refer to the Management Guide in the *Teacher's Lesson Manual* for more information.

Projects

The projects outlined in this program cover an array of mathematics activities and concepts, and are built around various themes that interest children. Projects also incorporate science, social studies, art and language arts skills. Projects are suggested in Unit Organizers in the *Teacher's Lesson Guide* at appropriate times throughout the year. They typically take one to two days to complete, depending upon how many of the suggested activities you incorporate. This time is well spent as it allows the teacher to assess the children in mathematics applications and in cross-curricular skills. They also are memorable events for children.

Refer to the Management Guide of the *Teacher's Reference Manual* and Unit Organizers in the *Teacher's Lesson Guide* for more information.

Assessment

Everyday Mathematics encourages a balanced approach to student assessment, one that reveals the development of a child's mathematical understanding while giving the teacher useful feedback about instructional needs. They also provide information and documentation to help assign grades.

Refer to the *Assessment Handbook* and the Unit Organizers in the *Teacher's Lesson Guide* for detailed information regarding ongoing, product, and periodic assessment.

Providing for Home-School Connections

Comprehensive and consistent home-school communication regarding program content, routines and student assessment is essential for successful implementation. *Everyday Mathematics* provides a number of support materials to facilitate this communication. The *Home Connection Handbook* is a tool that can help you introduce parents and primary caregivers to the *Everyday Mathematics* curriculum. Grade specific Family Letters and Home Links serve as a basis for ongoing communication as well as a vehicle to engage parents as partners in the learning process. Individual assessment checklists enable teachers to describe in detail the developmental progress of each child. They are a valuable communication tool during conferences.

Refer to the *Home Connection Handbook* for more information.

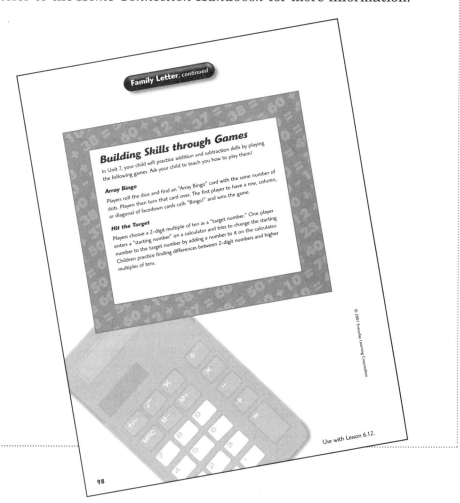

Family Letter, continued

Building Skills through Games

In Unit 7, your child will practice addition and subtraction skills by playing the following games. Ask your child to teach you how to play them!

Array Bingo

Players roll the dice and find an "Array Bingo" card with the same number of dots. Players then turn that card over. The first player to have a row, column, or diagonal of facedown cards calls "Bingo!" and wins the game.

Hit the Target

Players choose a 2-digit multiple of ten as a "target number." One player enters a "starting number" on a calculator and tries to change the starting number to the target number by adding a number to it on the calculator. Children practice finding differences between 2-digit numbers and higher multiples of tens.

© 2001 Everyday Learning Corporation

Use with Lesson 6.12.

98

K–3 Games Correlation Chart

Skill and Concept Areas

Game	K Title Page #	Grade 1 Lesson	Grade 2 Lesson	Grade 3 Lesson	Numeration	Mental Math	Basic Facts	Operations	Patterns	Geometry	Money	Time	Probability	Calculator
Addition Card Draw			12.5			■	■	■						
Addition Spin			4.2			■	■							
Addition Top-It		6.1	1.4	1.4			■	■						
Addition Top-It with Dominoes			2.5				■	■						
Angle Race				6.9						■				
Animal Weight Top-It		5.5			■									
Array Bingo			6.10	9.6			■	■						
Attribute Rule Game			7.2						■	■				
Attribute Train Game		7.2	7.2						■	■				
Base-10 Exchange		8.4			■									
Baseball Multiplication				4.7		■	■	■						
Basketball Addition			7.4			■		■						
Beat the Calculator		5.11	2.2	1.8			■							■
Before and After		3.1			■									
The Block-Drawing Game				11.6						■			■	
Broken Calculator			1.10	*										■
Buyer and Vendor Game		10.3		1.9							■			
Class Clock Game			1.3									■		
Clock Concentration			5.1									■		
Coin-Dice		3.12									■			
Coin Exchange	194	6.10	1.4		■						■			
Coin Top-It		2.10	1.4		■						■			
Concentration with Number Cards & Dominoes	89				■									
Dice-Roll and Tally Game		1.8	1.5		■			■					■	
Difference Game		5.7			■			■						
Digit Discovery			1.12		■									
Digit Game	267		3.2		■									
Dime-Nickel-Penny Grab		3.12									■			
Disappearing Train	217				■									
Division Arrays				4.3				■						
Division Coin-Drop								■						
Dollar Rummy			3.4								■			
Domino Top-It		3.14			■			■						
Double-Digit Dice Game	268				■									
Equivalent Fractions Game			8.5	8.4	■									
Fact Power Game		6.4				■	■							
Fact Triangle Flip				4.6			■							
Factor Bingo				9.6			■							
Fraction Top-It			8.6	8.5	■									
Guess the Rule		7.2							■					
High Roller	297	2.12			■									
Hit the Target			7.3			■								■
Less Than You!				1.3				■						
Magic Bag Game		5.10								■				
Making Change			3.8								■			
Matching Coin Game	40										■			
Memory Addition/Subtraction				10.9		■		■						■
Missing Terms				*										
Money Exchange Game ($)			1.6		■						■			
Monster Squeeze Game	84				■									

Number indicates first exposure at grade level. *Additional games available in *Student Reference Book*

Game	K Title Page #	Grade 1 Lesson	Grade 2 Lesson	Grade 3 Lesson	Numeration	Mental Math	Basic Facts	Operations	Patterns	Geometry	Money	Time	Probability	Calculator
Multiplication Bingo				7.3		■	■	■						
Multiplication Coin-Drop						■	■				■			
Multiplication Draw			11.5	✳		■	■	■						
Multiplication Top-It				10.5	■									
Name That Number			2.9	1.6				■						
Nickel/Penny Grab		2.11			■						■			
Number-Grid Game	216	9.2	1.11		■									
Number-Line Squeeze*		1.2			■									
Number Top-It				5.2	■									
One-Dollar Exchange Game		8.2									■			
One-Dollar Game	266										■			
$1, $10, $100 Exchange Game		10.3									■			
Ones, Tens, Hundreds Game	295				■			■						
Paper Money Exchange	292										■			
Penny-Cup		2.8	1.7		■		■							
Penny-Dice Game		1.3			■						■			
Penny-Drop Addition		2.11			■						■			
Penny Grab		2.8	6.2	2.6	■						■			
Penny Guessing		2.9			■						■			
Penny-Dime Exchange				5.8	■						■			
Penny-Nickel Exchange		2.10			■						■			
Penny-Nickel Dime Exchange		5.13			■						■			
Pick-a-Coin			10.3	✳							■			
Pin the Number (Number Grid)	216		1.11		■									
Plus or Minus Game	227					■		■						
Pocket Game	201							■						
Prize Time			3.3									■		
Raft Game	221				■									
Robot Game				6.3						■				
Rolling for 50		2.1			■	■								
Scissors, Paper, Stone		1.8											■	
Secret Number		5.3			■									
Shaker Addition Top-It		4.12			■									
Shopping			4.6					■			■			
Spin a Number (1–10)	80				■									
Spinning for Money			3.2								■			
Spinning to Win				11.5									■	
Stand Up If.....		7.7							■	■				
Subtraction Top-It				3.6	■									
Tens-and-Ones Trading Game		5.3			■									
3, 2, 1 Game		8.5			■				■					
Three Addends			6.1	2.9	■	■								
Tic-Tac-Toe Addition		10.4						■						
Time Match		4.4										■		
Top-It	170	1.6			■									
Touch-and-Match Quadrangles				6.5						■				
Turn-Around Facts Game		5.10			■		■							
Two-Fisted Penny Addition		2.3	1.7	2.4			■				■			
"Who Am I Thinking Of?"		7.1							■					
"What's My Rule?" Fishing	99		2.11	2.3					■	■				
"What's My Attribute Rule?"			5.1						■	■				

Number indicates first exposure at grade level. *Additional games available in *Student Reference Book*

Unit 1
Numbers and Routines

overview

The organization of *Everyday Mathematics*® is based on the observation that children learn best when they build on prior knowledge. At the beginning of the school year, when children have been away from concentrated mathematics experiences for the summer, they might not recall all that they have learned in the past. Therefore, before they are introduced to new material, children will retrieve past learnings through brief reminders and reviews. To that end, Unit 1 suggests a number of review activities for mathematics that children have encountered in first grade. These will provide you with a snapshot of their mathematics background and capabilities as they begin a new school year.

In addition, Unit 1 also establishes routines meant to be used all year to promote an active and cooperative learning environment.

contents

learning goals
in perspective

learning goals	links to the past	links to the future
1a **Developing Goal** Find values of coin and bill combinations. **(Lessons 1.2 and 1.6)**	Children were introduced to coins and bills in Kindergarten and counted combinations of coins in first grade.	Children will continue to develop money counting and change-making skills and strategies throughout second grade. *(Related Grade 2 lessons: 3.2, 3.8, 4.3, 4.6, 5.3)*
1b **Developing Goal** Know "easy" addition facts (sums to 10). **(Lesson 1.2)**	Children practiced +1, +0, doubles, and sums of 10 addition facts during first grade.	Children will work on "harder" addition facts and construct fact families in Unit 2. Addition will also be practiced through games and in a variety of problem solving situations throughout second grade. *(Related Grade 2 lessons: 2.1–2.6, 2.8, 2.10, 3.2, 3.7, 4.1, 4.6, 4.8, 4.9, 6.1, 6.4, 7.4)*
1c **Developing Goal** Identify place value for ones, tens, and hundreds. **(Lesson 1.9)**	In first grade, children were introduced to place value for 10s and 1s using base-10 blocks (longs and cubes).	Place value concepts will be revisited in Unit 3 and used later to develop mental arithmetic strategies for adding and subtracting two- and three-digit numbers. *(Related Grade 2 lessons: 3.1, 3.4)*
1d **Developing Goal** Complete number sequences; identify and use number patterns to solve problems. **(Lessons 1.1 and 1.8)**	Beginning in Kindergarten and continuing in first grade, children worked with patterns including calendar patterns, even and odd, and skip counting by 2s, 5s, and 10s. Children used calculators, number lines, and number grids to explore patterns.	In Unit 2, children will use patterns to help develop strategies for learning addition facts. Identifying patterns will also be key to determining solutions for "What's My Rule?" and Frames-and-Arrows problems. *(Related Grade 2 lessons: 2.3–2.5, 2.10, 2.11, 2.13, 3.6, 7.1–7.3, 7.5)*
1e **Developing Goal** Find equivalent names for numbers. **(Lessons 1.10 and 1.11)**	Children began using different names for the same number in Kindergarten. First graders used name-collection boxes and played *Broken Calculator*.	Throughout second grade, children will find different combinations of coins for the same value, make fact families from Fact Triangles, and play *Broken Calculator*. Children will review name-collection boxes in Unit 2. *(Related Grade 2 lessons: 2.8, 2.9, 3.2, 3.8, 4.6, 5.3)*
1f **Developing Goal** Compare numbers; write the symbols $<$, $>$, or $=$. **(Lesson 1.12)**	Very young children understand the ideas of more and less. In Kindergarten, children compared number size and ordered numbers. The symbols $<$ and $>$ were introduced in first grade.	Comparisons are fundamental for understanding many mathematical relationships, number stories, and analyzing data. Children will make comparisons on many types throughout the grades. *(Related Grade 2 lessons: 3.5, 4.1, 4.4, 6.2, 6.4, 7.7–7.9)*
1g **Secure Goal** Count by 2s, 5s, and 10s. **(Lesson 1.11)**	In Kindergarten and first grade, children began skip counting by 2s, 5s, and 10s.	Proficiency with skip counting will help children to count money, tell time using analog clocks, find number patterns, and learn multiplication facts in subsequent grades. *(Related Grade 2 lessons: 3.2, 3.3, 3.4, 3.7, 3.8, 5.3, 7.1, 7.2, 7.5)*
1h **Secure Goal** Make tallies and give the total. **(Lesson 1.5)**	Children were introduced to the use of tally marks to count and record numbers of things in Kindergarten and first grade.	Children will continue to use tallies to record data throughout the grades. *(Related Grade 2 lessons: 3.5, 6.3)*

assessment
ongoing • product • periodic

☑ Informal Assessment

Math Boxes These *Math Journal* pages provide opportunities for cumulative review or assessment of concepts and skills.

Ongoing Assessment: Kid Watching Use the Ongoing Assessment suggestions in the following lessons to make quick, on-the-spot observations about children's understanding of:
- Numeration **(Lessons 1.1, 1.4, and 1.12)**
- Operations and Computation **(Lessons 1.4, 1.6, and 1.10)**
- Measurement and Reference Frames **(Lesson 1.3)**

Portfolio Ideas Samples of children's work may be obtained from the following assignments:
- Using Tally Marks to Record Survey Responses **(Lesson 1.5)**
- Making Individual Number Scrolls **(Lesson 1.8)**
- Creating Number-Grid Puzzles **(Lesson 1.14)**

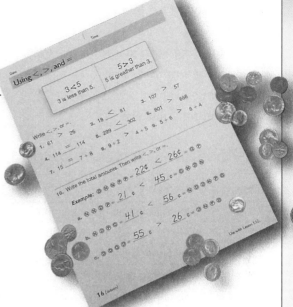

☑ Unit 1 Review and Assessment

Math Message Use the problem in Lesson 1.14 to assess children's progress toward the following learning goal: **Goal 1e**

Oral and Slate Assessments Use oral or slate assessments during Lesson 1.14 to assess children's progress toward the following learning goals: **Goals 1a, 1b, 1c, 1d, 1e, 1f, and 1g**

Written Assessment Use a written review during Lesson 1.14 to assess children's progress toward the following learning goals: **Goals 1a, 1b, 1c, 1d, 1e, and 1h**

Performance/Group Assessment Use a small-group activity in Lesson 1.14 to assess children's progress toward the following learning goals: **Goals 1a and 1c**

assessment handbook

For more information on how to use different types of assessment in Unit 1, see the Assessment Overview on pages 40–42 in the *Assessment Handbook*. The following Assessment Masters can be found in the *Math Masters* book:

- Unit 1 Checking Progress, p. 419
- Unit 1 Class Checklist, p. 448
- Unit 1 Individual Profile of Progress, p. 449
- Class Progress Indicator, p. 488
- Math Logs, pp. 493–495
- Self-Assessment Forms, pp. 496–497
- Interest Inventory, pp. 491 and 492

problem solving

A process of modeling everyday situations using tools from mathematics

Encourage children to use a variety of strategies when attacking a given problem—and to explain those strategies. *Strategies children might use in this unit:*

- Modeling with manipulatives
- Using a number line
- Using a table
- Finding a pattern
- Listing possibilities
- Acting out the problem
- Using computation

Four Problem-Solving REPRESENTATIONS

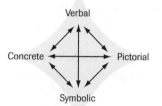

Lessons that teach *through* problem solving, not just *about* problem solving

Lesson	Activity	Lesson	Activity
1.1	Finding missing numbers on number lines	1.8	Making a class number scroll
1.2	Finding values of coin combinations	1.10	Solving *Broken Calculator* problems
1.3	Building a monthly calendar	1.12	Acting as a pan balance for comparing numbers
1.3	Displaying time using the tool-kit clock	1.12	Acting out place value by playing *Digit Discovery*
1.4	Exploring number-grid patterns	1.13	Reading and displaying temperature on a thermometer
1.7	Naming parts of a total in *Penny Cup*	1.14	Solving simple number stories

For more information about problem solving in *Everyday Mathematics,* see the *Teacher's Reference Manual,* pp. 197–208.

cross-curricular links

literature

- Read *A Day with No Math*, a book about a young boy who experiences a frustrating and funny day without math. **(Lesson 1.1)**

language arts

- Discuss the limited number of suffixes used for ordinal numbers and see if children find patterns for the ordinal words. **(Lesson 1.3)**

science

- Children identify and learn to read "°F" as "degrees Fahrenheit." Children also learn that the Fahrenheit temperature scale is named for Gabriel Daniel Fahrenheit, the physicist who developed it. **(Lesson 1.13)**

meeting
INDIVIDUAL needs

UNIVERSAL ACCESS

◆ RETEACHING

The following features provide additional instructional support:

Adjusting the Activity
- **Lesson 1.1, Parts 1, 2**
- **Lesson 1.3, Parts 1, 2**
- **Lesson 1.4, Part 2**
- **Lesson 1.5, Part 1**
- **Lesson 1.7, Part 2**
- **Lesson 1.9, Parts 1, 2**
- **Lesson 1.13, Part 1**

Options for Individualizing
- **Lesson 1.1** Using Objects to Identify Number Lines
- **Lesson 1.3** Saying and Writing Ordinal Numbers
- **Lesson 1.5** Playing the *Dice-Roll and Tally Game*
- **Lesson 1.7** Playing *Two-Fisted Penny Addition*
- **Lesson 1.9** Filling in Pieces of a Number Grid
- **Lesson 1.12** Showing Equalities and Inequalities with a Pan Balance

◆ ENRICHMENT

The following features suggest some enrichment and extension activities found in this unit:

Adjusting the Activity
- **Lesson 1.1, Part 1**
- **Lesson 1.4, Part 1**
- **Lesson 1.5, Part 2**
- **Lesson 1.6, Part 2**
- **Lesson 1.7, Part 2**
- **Lesson 1.11, Part 1**
- **Lesson 1.12, Part 1**
- **Lesson 1.13, Part 1**

Options for Individualizing
- **Lesson 1.1** Counting Aloud to Estimate Seconds
- **Lesson 1.2** Arranging Children in Order Using their Tool-Kit Numbers
- **Lesson 1.5** Using Tally Marks to Record Survey Responses
- **Lesson 1.8** Making Individual Number Scrolls
- **Lesson 1.9** Making Number-Grid Puzzle Pieces
- **Lesson 1.10** Finding Counting Patterns in a Number Grid
- **Lesson 1.11** Playing *Pin the Number on the Number Grid*
- **Lesson 1.12** Playing *Digit Discovery*

◆ LANGUAGE DIVERSITY

The following features suggest some ways to support children who are acquiring proficiency in English:

Adjusting the Activity
- **Lesson 1.2, Part 1**
- **Lesson 1.3, Parts 1, 2**
- **Lesson 1.7, Part 2**
- **Lesson 1.12, Part 1**

Options for Individualizing
- **Lesson 1.3** Playing Games Using Ordinal-Number Words
- **Lesson 1.10** Illustrating Equivalencies Using a Pan Balance and Identical Objects
- **Lesson 1.11** Counting by 2s, 5s, and 10s

◆ MULTIAGE CLASSROOM

The following chart lists related lessons from Grades 1 and 3 that can help you meet your instructional needs:

Grade 1	3.3 3.5 4.1	1.3 1.11	1.9 2.5 6.10	1.10 4.11	1.4 1.7	5.1 8.3	2.3	1.10 3.3	2.1 3.3 9.1	3.10 6.2	3.2– 3.5 9.1	1.6 5.3 5.6	1.12 2.7 4.1
Grade 2	1.1	1.2	1.3	1.4	1.5	1.6	1.7	1.8	1.9	1.10	1.11	1.12	1.13
Grade 3	1.11	1.9	1.12 11.8	2.1 2.2		5.1 5.5 9.1	5.1	1.11	1.2	1.6	1.11	1.9	5.6 5.7 11.9

m_aterials_

lesson	math masters pages	manipulative kit items	other items
1.1	Home Link Masters, pp. 231–234 Teaching Master, p. 1 (optional) **_See_ Advance Preparation, p. 16**	Class Number Line	calculator (optional) Class Data Pad (optional) objects showing number line segments stick-on notes
1.2		Pattern-Block Template	Lost-and-Found Box coins **_See_ Advance Preparation, p. 22**
1.3		number cards 1–12	tool-kit clock and coins demonstration clock (optional) 2 pieces of yarn large wall calendar
1.4	Teaching Masters, pp. 2 and 3 (optional) **_See_ Advance Preparation, p. 31**	number cards 0–10 per partnership Class Number Grid Poster	Working with a Partner Poster coins
1.5		slate per partnership: number cards, dominoes, or dice craft sticks **_See_ Advance Preparation, p. 36**	half-sheets of paper

1.6	transparency of
	   Teaching Master, p. 4
	Teaching Masters, pp. 4–11 and 227
	See Advance Preparation, p. 40
		slate
		per partnership: number cards,
		   dominoes, or 1 die
		base-10 blocks
			envelope
			15 pennies and 15 dimes
			one $1 bill

1.7	Teaching Master, p. 12, per partnership (optional)	slate	1 container per partnership 20 tool-kit pennies per partnership **_See_ Advance Preparation, p. 44**
1.8	Teaching Masters, pp. 13 and 14 **_See_ Advance Preparation, p. 48**	slate Class Number Grid Poster per partnership: number cards, dominoes; or dice (optional)	demonstration clock Rules for Small Groups Poster paste or tape
1.9	Teaching Masters, pp. 15–17	Class Number Grid Poster **_See_ Advance Preparation, p. 52**	grease pencil or washable marker

1.10	Teaching Masters, pp. 4–11
	   and 227
	Teaching Master, p. 18
		die, bills, tool-kit coins, or base-10
		   blocks
		pan balance
			calculator
			18 small, identical objects
			See Advance Preparation, p. 56

1.11		slate Class Number Grid Poster	calculator stick-on notes
1.12	Home Link Masters, pp. 235 and 236	pan balance number cards slate dominoes or dice (optional)	40 small, identical objects (optional) colored chalk (optional) **_See_ Advance Preparation, p. 65**

1.13	Home Link Master, p. 237
	Teaching Masters, pp. 19–21,
	   1 each per station
		per station: Class Thermometer
		   Poster, outdoor thermometer,
		   base-10 blocks, number cards,
		   double-9 dominoes
			quarter-sheets of paper per station

1.14	Home Link Masters, pp. 238–241 Assessment Master, p. 419	slate number cards 0–9 **_See_ Advance Preparation, p. 77**	demonstration clock overhead calculator (optional) calculator 1 set of tool-kit coins colored chalk grease pencil or washable marker

planning tips

Pacing

Pacing depends on a number of factors, such as children's individual needs and how long your school has been using *Everyday Mathematics*. At the beginning of Unit 1, review your Content by Strand Poster to help you set a monthly pace.

	←——MOST CLASSROOMS——→	
AUGUST	SEPTEMBER	OCTOBER

Home Communication

Share Home Links 1.1, 1.12, and 1.13 with families to help them understand the content and procedures in this unit. At the end of the unit, use Home Link 1.14 to introduce Unit 2. Supplemental information can be found in the *Home Connection Handbook*.

NCTM Standards

Standard	1	2	3	4	5	6	7	8	9	10
Unit 1 Lessons	1–13	1, 8–12	2, 13	2, 3, 6, 13	4, 5, 13	1–13	1–13	1–13	1–13	1–13

Content Standards
1. Number and Operation
2. Patterns, Functions, and Algebra
3. Geometry and Spatial Sense
4. Measurement
5. Data Analysis, Statistics, and Probability

Process Standards
6. Problem Solving
7. Reasoning and Proof
8. Communication
9. Connections
10. Representations

PRACTICE *through* Games

Everyday Mathematics uses games to help children develop good fact power and other math skills.

- Practice finding the values of coin combinations in *Coin Top-It* **(Lesson 1.4)**
- Practice tallying with the *Dice-Roll and Tally Game* **(Lesson 1.5)**
- Practice addition in *Addition Top-It* **(Lessons 1.4, 1.5, 1.6, 1.8, 1.12, and 1.13)**
- Practice making exchanges with coins in the *Money Exchange Game* **(Lessons 1.6 and 1.10)**
- Practice subtraction in *Penny Cup* **(Lesson 1.7)**
- Practice naming parts of a whole with *Two-Fisted Penny Addition* **(Lesson 1.7)**
- Practice numeration in *Pin the Number on the Number Grid* **(Lesson 1.11)**
- Practice place-value with *Digit Discovery* **(Lesson 1.12)**

unit 1 content highlights

The notes below highlight the major content ideas presented in Unit 1. These notes may help you establish instructional priorities.

Routines and Devices

Most of the routines and devices initiated in Unit 1 and in later units have been introduced in prior grades. If you have not used *Everyday Mathematics* before, you are urged to read the Organizing Routines and Displays section of the Management Guide, which is found in the *Teacher's Reference Manual.*

The following tables list routines and devices that initially appear in Unit 1:

A Mathematics All Around bulletin board

Routines	Lesson
Family Letters	1.1
Math Message	1.1
Mental Math and Reflexes	1.1
Oral counting	1.1
School days on the Class Number Line	1.1
Mathematics All Around bulletin board	1.1
Monthly calendar	1.3
Partner activities	1.4
Math Boxes	1.7
Home Links	1.12

Devices	Lesson
Class Number Line	1.1
Class Data Pad	1.1
Tool kits, coins, Pattern-Block Template	1.2
Clocks (demonstration and tool-kit)	1.3
Everything Math Deck	1.4
Class Number Grid Poster	1.4
Slates	1.5
Money (bills)	1.6
Number scrolls	1.8
Calculators	1.10

Reminders and Review Activities

We all tend to "forget" concepts and skills we have "learned," especially if we have not used them for an extended period of time. Therefore, when assessing children's level of mastery of previously taught concepts and skills, briefly review the topics before conducting the actual assessment. Without such review, children may not be able to demonstrate the full extent of their knowledge.

The following table lists the topics reviewed in Unit 1:

Reminders and Review	Lesson
Number sequences	1.1
Number line	1.1
Counts by 2s, 5s, 10s	1.1
Coin values	1.2
Months, weeks, days	1.3
Time of day	1.3
Addition facts	1.4, 1.7
Number-grid patterns	1.4, 1.8, 1.9
Tallies	1.5
Money values	1.6
Place value	1.6, 1.9
Equivalent names for numbers	1.10
Skip counting	1.10, 1.11
Comparing numbers ($<$, $>$, $=$)	1.12

Math Message and Number Sequences (Lesson 1.1)

The Math Message and Mental Math and Reflexes routines are introduced in this first lesson. Most Math Messages are designed to start children thinking about the main topic of the day. Some Math Messages may also review ideas covered in prior lessons.

The Mental Math and Reflexes routine focuses, for the most part, on quick mental-mathematics activities. In this lesson, the routine involves whole-class, oral responses. Starting in Lesson 1.5, children will often display their individual responses on slates.

The first lesson of the year emphasizes counting and number sequences, especially sequences on a number line. Children look for examples of number lines in everyday life (rulers, for example) and begin keeping

track of the number of school days on the Class Number Line. Children also share ideas about mathematics. The first Family Letter should be sent home to inform families about *Everyday Mathematics* in general and Unit 1 in particular.

Before beginning Unit 1, read about the following routines and devices in the Management Guide, which is located in the Teacher's Reference Manual: *Daily Routines, Math Messages, Mental Math and Reflexes, Class Data Pad, and Home Links and Family Letters.*

Also decide on the following:

▷ *where you will post the Math Message.*

▷ *how children will respond to the Math Message.*

▷ *where you will post the current date.*

▷ *how to keep track of the number of school days on the Class Number Line. Marking days can be a daily job for one of the children.*

Tool Kits (Lesson 1.2)

In the Mental Math and Reflexes section of Lesson 1.3, children find ways to represent 35¢.

Doing mathematics involves much more than working with pencil and paper. It involves using mathematical tools, such as rulers to measure length, straightedges and templates to draw shapes, calculators to compute, random-number generators to play mathematical games and to perform probability experiments, and counters to model problem situations. In this lesson, children receive tool kits, which are convenient devices designed to store their individual materials. You may already have filled their kits with tools, or you may prefer to add to them as tools are needed. Children use coins in their tool kits to find the value of coin collections and to explore making shape designs using the Pattern-Block Template. You may want to read more about tool kits in the Management Guide, which is located in the *Teacher's Reference Manual.*

Calendars and Clocks (Lesson 1.3)

Children practice telling time. Most children should be able to tell time to 15-minute intervals; a few children may even be able to tell time to 5-minute intervals. Adjust examples to suit the level of your class. Telling time will be covered again in later units. Children fill in a calendar for the current month—a routine that can be done each month. The calendar is used to review ordinal numbers.

Pattern-Block Template

Partner Study Routines (Lesson 1.4)

Because children will often work with partners, it is important to agree on guidelines for working together early in the year. You will want to establish a supportive classroom environment in which conversation and movement are welcome but wasting time and bothering others are not. In this lesson, children pair up to play a game that gives them practice with basic addition facts. Children also explore patterns on the Class Number Grid Poster, which displays the numbers 0 through 110.

Before beginning this lesson, read about Games and Cooperative Groupings in the Management Guide in the Teacher's Reference Manual.

Working with a Partner
- Be polite.
- Help each other.
- Share.
- Listen to your partner.
- Praise your partner.
- Take turns.
- Talk about problems.
- Speak quietly.

You may want to display a poster like this one in your classroom.

Slate Routines (Lesson 1.5)

Slates will be used often this year, especially in Mental Math and Reflexes activities. Slates provide a quick way to check children's work as they respond to questions and display their answers on their slates. In this lesson, procedures for storing and retrieving slates are determined, and slates are used for recording tallies.

Before beginning Lesson 1.5, read about slates in the Management Guide in the Teacher's Reference Manual.

Grouping by Tens—$1, $10, $100 (Lesson 1.6)

Children cut out the $1, $10, and $100 bills provided in their journals (or you can supply play money from another source). After counting the total amount of money, children strengthen their place-value skills by playing various versions of the *Money Exchange Game*. In this game, groups of ten bills are exchanged for one bill of the next-higher denomination.

Math Boxes (Lesson 1.7)

Math Boxes have proved to be a popular and effective routine for review and practice. Starting with this lesson, each lesson will have one page of Math Boxes problems. Usually, Math Boxes problems will be based on skills developed earlier, not on the content of the current lesson.

Before beginning this lesson, read about Math Boxes in the Management Guide in the Teacher's Reference Manual.

Children also practice exchanging 10 "ones" for 1 "ten" using base-10 blocks.

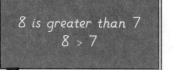

Working in Small Groups (Lesson 1.8)

In this lesson, the rules for working with partners established in Lesson 1.4 are extended to working in small groups. Children work in small groups to make a scroll of the numbers to 1,000. There is an opportunity to discuss even and odd numbers, as well as other patterns found in number grids.

Number Grids (Lesson 1.9)

Children find patterns on number grids and use place-value skills to fill in missing numbers. It is helpful for children to have their own laminated number grids, which can be used several times. *Math Masters,* page 17 is available for this purpose.

Before beginning this lesson, read about semipermanent chalk in the Organizing Routines and Displays section of the Management Guide, which is located in the Teacher's Reference Manual.

The Class Number Grid Poster helps children visualize numbers as they count by 2s, 5s, and 10s.

Equivalent Names for Numbers (Lesson 1.10); Counting Patterns (Lesson 1.11)

One of the basic ideas of mathematics is that any number can be named in a variety of ways. For example, $4 + 6$, $20 - 10$, 2×5, $100 \div 10$, $\frac{30}{3}$, and $2^3 + 2$ are all names for the number 10. This idea is reinforced in Lesson 1.10 in several ways—one of which is by solving "broken calculator" problems, in which one or more calculator keys are "broken" and numbers must be obtained without using the numbers on those keys.

Calculators are incorporated into instruction in Lessons 1.10 and 1.11. Children use calculators to skip count and explore patterns. The authors of *Everyday Mathematics* believe that calculators can make a significant contribution to children's mathematical growth in Grades 1–6, especially when used for solving problems, analyzing data, and exploring number patterns. Before beginning Lesson 1.10, you may want to read about calculators in the *Teacher's Reference Manual.*

Relations ($<$, $>$, $=$) and Home Links (Lesson 1.12)

Children compare numbers by first writing the phrases *is less than, is greater than,* or *is equal to* between pairs of numbers and then by writing the symbols $<$, $>$, or $=$. Mnemonic devices are reviewed to help children remember the meanings of $<$ and $>$.

Home Links are described in detail in the Management Guide. The Home Links routine is begun in this lesson. Home Links, which include activities and problems for children to complete outside of school, are provided in each lesson.

Exploring Temperatures, Base-10 Structures, and Dominoes (Lesson 1.13)

Explorations are discussed in the Managing the Curriculum section of the Management Guide, which is located in the *Teacher's Reference Manual.*

You will need to decide how you will organize the Explorations. Remember that Explorations are designed to be small-group activities. If you are going to run them simultaneously, you will need a plan for managing several different activities at the same time. Parent volunteers can be helpful.

In the first Exploration, children read and mark temperatures on the Class Thermometer Poster.

In the second Exploration, children review the values that base-10 blocks represent. Then children build structures with the blocks and calculate the values of the structures.

In this unit's final Exploration, children develop addition facts by sorting dominoes according to the sums of the dots.

Children build structures with cubes, longs, and flats. Then they find the numerical value of these structures based on the following system:

1 cube = 1
1 long = 10
1 flat = 100

Review and Assessment (Lesson 1.14)

Each unit in *Second Grade Everyday Mathematics* ends with a review and assessment lesson. The commentary for each review and assessment lesson includes a list of unit goals, and other goals if appropriate, as well as suggestions for oral and slate evaluation questions. *Math Masters,* page 419 contains review items for children to complete in writing; each item is keyed to one or more learning goals. There is more information about assessment in *Everyday Mathematics* in the *Assessment Handbook.*

For **additional information** on the following topics, see the *Teacher's Reference Manual:*

- calculators
- calendars
- counting: plain and fancy
- games for practice
- managing the curriculum
- number grids, scrolls, and lines

- organizing routines and displays
- organizing students
- relations
- temperature
- time

1.1

Math Message and Number Sequences

OBJECTIVES To introduce the Math Message routine; and to review number sequences and number lines.

summaries | materials

1 Teaching the Lesson

Children are introduced to the Math Message routine.

Children complete and extend number sequences and number lines. [Patterns, Functions, and Algebra]

- □ *Math Journal 1*, p. 1
- □ Teaching Master (*Math Masters*, p. 1; optional)
- □ Class Number Line; half-sheet of paper; calculator (optional)

2 Ongoing Learning & Practice

Children share ideas about what mathematics is through discussion and through drawing pictures for the Mathematics All Around bulletin board. [multiple strands]

- □ Class Data Pad (optional)
- □ Home Link Masters (*Math Masters*, pp. 231–234)
- □ *A Day with No Math* (optional)

***See* Advance Preparation**

3 Options for Individualizing

Reteaching Children use objects to identify number lines and their uses. [Patterns, Functions, and Algebra]

Enrichment Children revisit number sequences starting with 1,000. [Patterns, Functions, and Algebra]

Enrichment Children use Roman numerals to count the days of school. [Numeration]

- □ objects showing number-line segments, such as a ruler, a thermometer, or a measuring cup marked in ounces
- □ Class Number Line
- □ Class Data Pad
- □ stick-on notes

Additional Information

Advance Preparation Provide for each child a copy of the introductory Family Letter found on pages 231–234 in *Math Masters*. Send the letter home with children to introduce the family to *Everyday Mathematics*. Start a Mathematics All Around bulletin board. Post items that show a variety of numbers and shapes—for example, advertisements with quantities and prices, schedules that list times, and pictures of designs and structures. For the Literature Link on page 20, you may want to obtain *A Day with No Math* by Marilyn Kaye (Harcourt, Brace, Jovanovich, 1992).

Vocabulary • **Math Message** • **number line**

Getting Started

Mental Math and Reflexes

Count by 2s, 5s, and 10s.

Do "stop and start" counting. Have a group of children begin counting at a number you name; stop them; point at another group to continue where the count left off.

Repeat. If children are comfortable, try 3-digit counting.

Math Message

Write the following in the place where the Math Message will be posted regularly:

We are going to mark school days on a number line. Where would you mark today on the number line?

Sample answer: Under the numeral 1

1 Teaching the Lesson

◆ Math Message Follow-Up

WHOLE-CLASS ACTIVITY

Point out the **Math Message.** Tell children that every day they will complete a Math Message before the math lesson begins.

Have children suggest how to keep track of the number of school days by marking each day on the Class Number Line. Decide where to mark *today* on the **number line.** If today is the first day of school, the number 1 would be marked.

Have children describe other ways in which number lines can be used. Number lines are often used as scales for measuring things. The axes on a graph resemble number lines. Ask children to think of objects that remind them of number lines. Ruler, thermometer, measuring cup, weighing scale, radio dial

> **Adjusting the Activity** Challenge children by asking, *What number names the day before the first day of school?* 0 More difficult: *What number names the day before the day before the first day of school?* −1 *What are numbers less than 0 called?* Negative numbers

◆ Writing Numbers in Sequence

WHOLE-CLASS ACTIVITY

Write a partial sequence of numbers on the board. *For example:*

163, <u>164</u>, <u>165</u>, <u>166</u>, 167, <u>168</u>, ...

Ask children to copy the sequence on a piece of paper and fill in the blanks. When most children have finished:

▷ Have a volunteer name the missing numbers.

▷ Ask whether anyone can explain the meaning of the ellipsis—the three dots—at the end. The dots show that the sequence goes on.

▷ Ask children to write the next few numbers in the sequence on their half-sheets.

Adapt the size of the numbers to your children's abilities. Pose problems like the following:

• 727, 728, <u>729</u>, <u>730</u>, <u>731</u>

• 42, 43, <u>44</u>, <u>45</u>, <u>46</u>

• 310, 311, <u>312</u>, <u>313</u>, <u>314</u>

Collect and evaluate completed work.

> **Adjusting the Activity** If children get stuck on which number to write next, remind them that they can also use their calculators by keying in ON/C [any number] (+) (1) (=) (=) and so on. The key presses and what children would say are:
>
> (7) (2) (7) (+) (1) (=) (=) (=) (=)
>
> "727 plus 1, 728, 729, 730, 731"
>
> Consider posing some problems orally; for example, *On your paper, write 163 and the next five numbers after 163.*

ONGOING ASSESSMENT

Vary the numbers so that you can observe the range of numbers with which different children are comfortable. If children have used *First Grade Everyday Mathematics,* they should be fairly comfortable with 3-digit numbers.

✦ Reviewing Number Sequences Starting with 1,000

WHOLE-CLASS ACTIVITY

Write 1,000 on the board. Ask a volunteer to write the number that comes next while the class says the number in unison.

Remind children not to say "and" when reading large whole numbers. The number 1,001 is read "one thousand one," NOT "one thousand and one."

> NOTE: The word "and" is used to indicate the decimal point when reading numbers.

✦ Introducing the Journal (*Math Journal 1*)

WHOLE-CLASS DISCUSSION

Distribute *Math Journal 1* and have children write their names on the back cover. Briefly discuss how the journals will be used and stored.

Take a tour of the journal. Ask questions, such as the following:

* What information is in the table of contents?
* What information is inside the front cover?
* What should be recorded at the top of every journal page?

✦ Missing Numbers on Number Lines (*Math Journal 1*, p. 1; *Math Masters*, p. 1)

INDEPENDENT ACTIVITY

Have children turn to journal page 1. Remind them to write the date and time at the top of the page. Show them where the current date will be displayed in the classroom.

Have children fill in the missing numbers for the number lines. When most children have finished, briefly review answers by counting in unison.

> **Adjusting the Activity** If the range of numbers on the journal page is too easy or too difficult, use *Math Masters*, page 1 to create number lines that meet the needs of individual children.

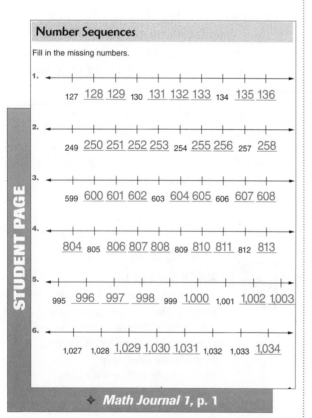

Number Sequences

Fill in the missing numbers.

1. 127 _128_ _129_ 130 _131_ _132_ _133_ 134 _135_ _136_

2. 249 _250_ _251_ _252_ _253_ 254 _255_ _256_ 257 _258_

3. 599 _600_ _601_ _602_ 603 _604_ _605_ 606 _607_ _608_

4. _804_ 805 _806_ _807_ _808_ 809 _810_ _811_ 812 _813_

5. 995 _996_ _997_ _998_ 999 _1,000_ 1,001 _1,002_ _1,003_

6. 1,027 1,028 _1,029_ _1,030_ _1,031_ 1,032 1,033 _1,034_

✦ *Math Journal 1, p. 1*

STUDENT PAGE

◆ Sharing Ideas about Mathematics

WHOLE-CLASS DISCUSSION

Ask the children to talk about mathematics—what they think it is, how it is used, what they expect to learn about it in second grade, and so on. Sample answers: Mathematics is the study of numbers, measures, shapes, and patterns. People use mathematics to help them make things, buy things, measure, label, solve problems, understand the world, and so on.

You may want to record the children's ideas on the Class Data Pad. As the year progresses, add ideas as they come up. Refer to the pad whenever a link can be made to a topic under discussion.

> Counting
> Measuring Distances and
>   Lengths
> Measuring Amounts
> Buying Things
> Knowing Shapes and Patterns
> Solving Problems

The Class Data Pad can be used to list children's ideas about mathematics.

Adjusting the Activity If children have difficulty naming ways in which numbers are used, ask a few questions; for example: *How old are you? How do you use the telephone? What is your address? What number is on our classroom door? Why is this particular number on our door? What numbers are on other classroom doors? Is there a system for using these numbers?*

Continue the discussion by having children tell what they like about mathematics. Have them find numbers, shapes, and other mathematical objects in the classroom.

Children's ideas for the Mathematics All Around
bulletin board

◆ Adding to the Mathematics All Around Bulletin Board

INDEPENDENT ACTIVITY

Call children's attention to the Mathematics All Around bulletin board. Have them draw things that have to do with numbers, shapes, or patterns. Attach their efforts to the bulletin board.

Ask children to bring pictures from home for the Mathematics All Around bulletin board. Periodically over the next month or so, ask them to bring additional pictures.

Literature Link You may want to share with children *A Day with No Math* by Marilyn Kaye (Harcourt, Brace, Jovanovich, 1992). The book is about a young boy who wishes for and then experiences a frustrating and sometimes funny day without math.

◆ Home Link Family Letter
(*Math Masters*, pp. 231–234)

Home Connection Distribute copies of the beginning-of-the-year Family Letter for children to take home.

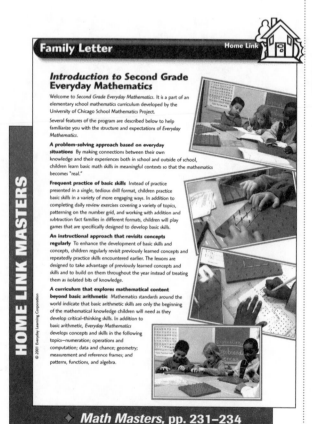

Math Masters, pp. 231–234

3 Options for Individualizing

◆ RETEACHING Using Objects to Identify Number Lines

WHOLE-CLASS ACTIVITY   5–15 min

Display objects that show number lines, such as a ruler, a thermometer, a measuring cup, and a coordinate grid. Ask children to identify the number line on each object and to explain how that number line is used. Sample answer: The number line on a ruler is used to measure the lengths of objects.

◆ ENRICHMENT Counting Aloud to Estimate Seconds

WHOLE-CLASS ACTIVITY 5–15 min

People sometimes estimate the passage of time in seconds by counting aloud: *one thousand one; one thousand two; one thousand three,* and so on. Have children check the accuracy of this method by watching the second hand on the classroom clock while they count from 1,001. Ask: *When would you count seconds?* Sample answer: When playing hide-and-seek

◆ ENRICHMENT Counting School Days with Roman Numerals

WHOLE-CLASS ACTIVITY 5–15 min

Display a table of Roman numerals (as shown below) on the board or Class Data Pad. Discuss the patterns in the Roman numeral system.

I = 1	XX = 20 (2 tens)
II = 2	
III = 3	XL = 40 (50 less 10)
IV = 4	**L = 50**
V = 5	LX = 60 (50 plus 10)
VI = 6	
VII = 7	XC = 90 (100 less 10)
VIII = 8	**C = 100**
IX = 9	CX = 110 (100 plus 10)
X = 10	
	D = 500
	M = 1,000

Use Roman numerals along with the routine of keeping track of the number of school days. Roman numerals could be written on large stick-on notes and attached to the Class Number Line.

PLANNING AHEAD
Beginning in Lesson 1.2, children will need 20 pennies, 5 nickels, 10 dimes, and 4 quarters. Be prepared to distribute either real or play coins for children to add to their tool kits in Lesson 1.2. Consider sending a note to parents requesting real coins for their children to use in class.

1.2 Tool Kits

OBJECTIVES To introduce the tool kits; and to find the values of coin combinations.

summaries	materials

1 Teaching the Lesson

The teacher distributes and discusses tool kits.

Children find the values of coin combinations.
[Numeration; Measurement and Reference Frames]

- □ *Math Journal 1*, p. 2
- □ tool kit; Lost-and-Found Box
- □ 20 pennies, 5 nickels, 10 dimes, and 4 quarters
- □ overhead coins (optional)

***See* Advance Preparation**

2 Ongoing Learning & Practice

The teacher distributes and discusses the Pattern-Block Template. [Geometry]

Children identify template shapes as well as make and color designs with the template. [Geometry]

- □ Pattern-Block Template

3 Options for Individualizing

Enrichment Children line up sequentially using their tool-kit numbers. [Numeration]

Extra Practice Children count coins forward and backward. [Numeration]

- □ tool kit
- □ *Minute Math®*, p. 35

Additional Information

Advance Preparation Put a Lost-and-Found Box in a prominent place in the room. Before distributing the tool kits in Part 1, assign a number to each child. Some teachers assign numbers in the thousands. If there is more than one section of second grade, each classroom might have a different thousands digit. Label the tool kits and their contents with corresponding numbers, using a permanent, fine-point marker. Be prepared to distribute either real or play coins in case children did not bring enough from home.

Vocabulary • **tool kit** • **Lost-and-Found Box** • **Pattern-Block Template**

Getting Started

Mental Math and Reflexes

Do "stop and start" counting. Have the class count by 10s from a multiple of 10 that you name; stop them; tell them to continue but to count on by 5s; stop them; tell them to continue but to count on by 1s.

Math Message

How much are these coins worth?

Q Q D D N

1 Teaching the Lesson

◆ Math Message Follow-Up

WHOLE-CLASS ACTIVITY

Have children share strategies for solving the Math Message problem. Children might share the following:

Strategy 1

I put the coins in order by what they're worth and counted up: 25, 50, 60, 70, 75 cents.

Strategy 2

I traded each quarter for 2 dimes and 1 nickel. Then I had 6 dimes and 3 nickels. I know that 2 nickels equal 1 dime, so I traded 2 nickels for 1 dime. Then I had 7 dimes and 1 nickel. I counted the 7 dimes—10, 20, 30, 40, 50, 60, 70 cents—and counted 1 nickel to get 75 cents.

Strategy 3

I know that two quarters are 50 cents. Then I counted up 10 for each dime—60, 70 cents. Finally I counted the nickel to get 75 cents.

◆ Distributing Tool Kits

WHOLE-CLASS DISCUSSION

Ask questions such as the following:

- Who uses tools? Doctors? Plumbers? Who else?
- What tools do they use?
- What do they use their tools for?
- What tools belong in a tool box for mathematics?

Tell children that they will each have a **tool kit** to help in their work with mathematics.

Distribute the tool kits. Point out that each tool kit has a number written on the outside of it. Explain that the numbers will help identify the owners of misplaced items. Show the **Lost-and-Found Box** and explain its purpose. Talk about the items now in the tool kits, identifying each item.

Call out the names of the children and have them say their tool-kit numbers. Be sure to keep a master list of children's names along with their tool-kit numbers.

Adjusting the Activity If your children did not use *First Grade Everyday Mathematics*, you may wish to have them count this group of coins instead: Ⓠ Ⓓ Ⓝ 40 cents

Other small items, such as a ruler, tape measure, dice, play bills, clock face, and calculator, will be added to the tool kit as they are introduced.

NOTE: You might want to distribute tool kits at random, or you might want to assign children their numbers (for example, in alphabetical order according to first names) ahead of time and then match children with tool-kit numbers. This matching provides opportunities for comparing the order of letters in the alphabet with the order of numbers.

◆ Finding the Values of Coin Combinations

WHOLE-CLASS ACTIVITY

Have children show 2 quarters. Ask: *How much money do you have?* 50 cents Then have each child show 2 dimes and 2 nickels. Ask: *How much money do you have now?* 30 cents Continue with simple combinations as needed. You might model these combinations on the overhead if you have overhead coins.

Ask children to show more complex coin combinations in random order of value; for example, 2 dimes, 1 quarter, 2 pennies. Ask: *How much money do you have?* 47 cents Have children share strategies for solving this problem. If no one mentions it, have children line their coins up in order of value from greatest to least and count as a class: 25, 35, 45, 46, 47 cents.

◆ More Oral Coin-Counting (*Math Journal 1*, p. 2)

INDEPENDENT ACTIVITY

Have children turn to journal page 2. They may use their coins to help them complete the page. Draw

Ⓟ Ⓝ Ⓓ Ⓠ

on the board, and remind children that these symbols stand for penny, nickel, dime, and quarter.

When most children have finished the problems on the journal page, briefly review the answers.

Adjusting the Activity If children are having difficulty counting a group of coins, have them record the value of each coin above the coin:

For the problems in which coins are displayed in random order, have children model the problems by placing real coins in order of value.

Coins

1. = _27_ ¢
2. = _32_ ¢
3. = _80_ ¢
4. = _46_ ¢
5. = _50_ ¢
6. = _38_ ¢
7. = _31_ ¢

◆ *Math Journal 1, p. 2*

STUDENT PAGE

Ongoing Learning & Practice

◆ Exploring the Pattern-Block Template

INDEPENDENT ACTIVITY

Distribute the **Pattern-Block Templates.** Point to shapes on the Pattern-Block Template and ask children to name the shapes as you point to them.

Review how to use the Pattern-Block Template to draw shapes. Then let children play freely with their Pattern-Block Templates, creating and coloring their designs.

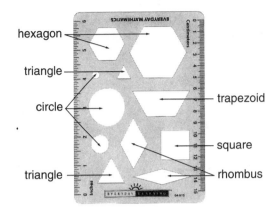

Pattern-Block Template

Options for Individualizing

◆ ENRICHMENT Arranging Children in Order Using their Tool-Kit Numbers

WHOLE-CLASS ACTIVITY   **5–15 min**

Follow this procedure:

1. In their own small groups, have children stand in line from the lowest to the highest tool-kit numbers.

2. Ask the members from the group with the lowest tool-kit number to raise their hands. Have the group stand in front of the room in order.

3. Determine the group with the next lowest number. Have the group with that number line up with the first group, placing themselves in the correct order in the sequence.

4. Repeat the process until the entire class is in order according to tool-kit numbers. Have children count off from the lowest to the highest number.

◆ EXTRA PRACTICE Minute Math

SMALL-GROUP ACTIVITY   **5–15 min**

To offer children more experience with counting coins, see the following page in *Minute Math:*

Counting: p. 35

1.3 Calendars and Clocks

OBJECTIVES To review months, weeks, and days; and to review telling time.

summaries	materials

1 Teaching the Lesson

Children number and name months in a year, begin to build a calendar for the current month, and say and write ordinal numbers. [Numeration; Measurement and Reference Frames]

Children tell time using clocks found in their tool kits and on their journal pages. [Measurement and Reference Frames]

- ☐ *Math Journal 1*, pp. 3, 4, and 164
- ☐ tool-kit coins; tool-kit clock; a large wall calendar
- ☐ demonstration clock (optional)

See **Advance Preparation**

2 Ongoing Learning & Practice

Children complete the calendar for the current month.
[Numeration; Measurement and Reference Frames]

- ☐ *Math Journal 1*, p. 3

3 Options for Individualizing

Reteaching Children say and write ordinal numbers.
[Numeration]

Language Diversity Children describe their positions in a line by playing ordinal-number games.
[Numeration; Measurement and Reference Frames]

Extra Practice The class practices telling time by simulating a large clock. [Measurement and Reference Frames]

- ☐ number cards 1–12 (from the Everything Math Deck, if available)
- ☐ 2 pieces of yarn

Additional Information

Advance Preparation Consider writing the names of the months on the board if they are not posted in the classroom.

Vocabulary • calendar • ordinal numbers

Getting Started

Mental Math and Reflexes

Children can use their coins to help with these problems. Try to have children present different solutions and solution strategies for each problem.

- Judy has 52 cents. Which coins does she have?
- Tommy has 29 cents. Which coins does he have?
- Mohammed has 40 cents. Which coins does he have?
- Kelly has 35 cents. Which coins does she have?

Math Message

How many months are in a year? Can you name the months? 12; January, February, March, April, May, June, July, August, September, October, November, December

Teaching the Lesson

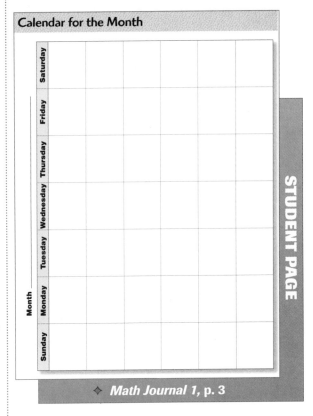

Calendar for the Month

STUDENT PAGE

Month

Sunday | Monday | Tuesday | Wednesday | Thursday | Friday | Saturday

✦ *Math Journal 1, p. 3*

✦ Math Message Follow-Up
(*Math Journal 1*, p. 164)

WHOLE-CLASS ACTIVITY

Have children turn to journal page 164 and find the number of months in a year.

Have children name as many of the months as they can. Prompt them by asking questions like the following: *In what month were you born? What month is it now? In what month do we celebrate Valentine's Day?*

Say the months of the year in order together. If the months are displayed in the classroom, point to each name as you say it. If they are not displayed, write the names on the board as you say them.

✦ Building a Calendar for the Month
(*Math Journal 1*, p. 3)

WHOLE-CLASS DISCUSSION

Show children a large wall calendar, preferably one with more than one month. Remind them that we use a **calendar** to keep track of days, weeks, and months in a year.

Ask questions, such as the following, about the calendar:

• How many days are in a week? 7 days

• How many days are in a month? 28, 29, 30, or 31 days

• How many days does this month have?

• On what day of the week did this month begin? Do all months begin on the same day?

• What year, month, and day is today?

Mention that people usually use **ordinal numbers** to say a date; for example, "September fifth," not "September five."

Show children how to write today's date. Have them write it at the top of the journal page. Then have them rotate the page and write the month at the top of the calendar. Next, children write the first seven numbers on the calendar. *How many days are in this month?* 30 or 31 days Count the spaces on the calendar until you reach the space for the last day of the month. Have children write 30 or 31 in that space.

NOTE: As you give the correct answers, always attach a unit to the number. One of the ongoing ideas in *Everyday Mathematics* is that numbers almost always occur in context.

Adjusting the Activity For number-line and calendar activities, emphasize ordinal-number words. For example, use expressions such as, "Today is September 12th. This is the 4th day of school, the 3rd day of the week, the 1st hour of the school day, the 21st minute of the hour," and so on.

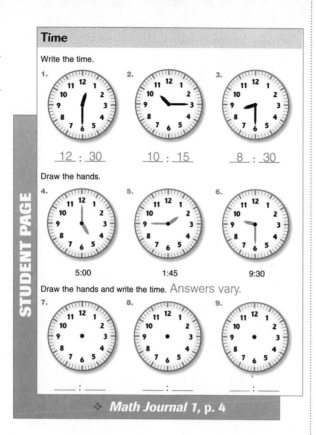

STUDENT PAGE

Time

Write the time.

1.   `12` : `30`

2.   `10` : `15`

3.   `8` : `30`

Draw the hands.

4.   5:00

5.   1:45

6.   9:30

Draw the hands and write the time. Answers vary.

7.

8.

9.

___ : ___   ___ : ___   ___ : ___

◆ *Math Journal 1, p. 4*

ONGOING ASSESSMENT

As children complete journal page 4, watch for

· children who can tell time to 15-minute intervals.

· children who can tell time to 5-minute intervals.

· children who draw the hour hand in the appropriate position in relationship to the minute hand. (At this point, it is acceptable for the hour hand to simply point to the correct hour.)

The majority of children in your class should be comfortable with telling time to 15-minute intervals.

Tell children that they will finish the calendar independently at the end of today's lesson. They can use the last day written on the calendar to check their own work.

◆ Telling Time (*Math Journal 1*, p. 4)

WHOLE-CLASS ACTIVITY 🏃🏃🏃

Distribute tool-kit clocks. Have children check that the number on their clocks is the same as the number on their tool kits.

Ask a volunteer to tell what time it is now and to explain how he or she knows what time it is. Sample answers: By using the hour and minute hands on the classroom clock or by reading a digital watch or clock.

Quickly review the functions of the hour hand and minute hand. Remind children that when people tell time it is always an estimate because as soon as they say or write the time, the time in seconds has changed, and the time in minutes may have also changed.

Tell children times to show on their clocks, such as 4:00, 3:30, 8:15, 7:45, 1:00, ten minutes to twelve, half-past six, quarter to five, and so on.

 Adjusting the Activity To help children who confuse hours and minutes, say an hour and have them set the hour hand for that time. Tell them to set the minute hand at 12, and then count off the minutes past the hour as they move the minute hand. Have children adjust the hour hand accordingly.

After children show each time on their clocks, you may want to display the correct time on your demonstration clock so that children can check their own clocks.

Have children write the date and current time at the top of journal page 4. Tell them that from now on, they should always record the date and time when they begin a journal page.

Children complete journal page 4. Briefly go over the answers.

 Adjusting the Activity For children having difficulty telling time, spend a few extra minutes each day asking questions such as:

• What time is it now?

• What time will it be in 5 minutes? 10 minutes? 1 hour?

• What time was it 5 minutes ago?

Ongoing Learning & Practice

✦ Completing Calendar Pages
(*Math Journal 1*, p. 3)

INDEPENDENT ACTIVITY

Children finish filling in the dates on the calendar page. They should mark any special events, holidays, or days to remember. For example, they might circle the first day of school, write in the names of classmates or others who have birthdays this month, and note any special events that will take place at school.

Adjusting the Activity Children can record special events or activities by drawing small pictures instead of writing words.

Month September						
Sunday	Monday	Tuesday	Wednesday	Thursday	Friday	Saturday
			1 School starts	2	3	4
5	6 Labor Day holiday	7	8	9	10	11
12	13	14	15	16 Ann's birthday	17	18
19	20	21	22	23	24 Field trip to the zoo	25
26	27	28	29 storyteller assembly	30		

Children fill in dates and special days on the calendar.

Options for Individualizing

✦ RETEACHING Saying and Writing Ordinal Numbers

WHOLE-CLASS DISCUSSION 👥👥👥 15–30 min 🕐

Language Arts Link Make a list of ordinal numbers up to 30th. Talk about the limited number of suffixes (*-st, -nd, -rd, -th*) and the fact that the teen ordinal numbers all use the suffix *-th*.

Ask children if they see a pattern for the ordinal words beyond 19th. Sample answer: 20th and 30th use the same suffix as 10th; 21st through 29th use the same suffixes as 1st through 9th.

Discuss which number words do not sound like the ordinal words. One, first; two, second Beyond that, most number and ordinal words do sound alike.

✦ LANGUAGE DIVERSITY Playing Games Using Ordinal-Number Words

SMALL-GROUP ACTIVITY   5–15 min

Arrange children in a line and assign them an ordinal number. As you point to children, they say their ordinal numbers. Briskly repeat several times using the ordinal number words. For example, give the following instructions:

- First person, clap your hands once.

- Third person, raise your hand.

- Thirteenth person, stomp your foot once (or clap your hands three times).

- Tenth person, find the fifteenth person; shake his or her hand and then return to your place in line.

To finish the activity and get children seated, give instructions such as the following:

- First person and (ordinal for last) person, take your seats.

- If your number ends in -rds, take your seats (3rd, 23rd, and so on).

✦ EXTRA PRACTICE Simulating a Large Clock

WHOLE-CLASS ACTIVITY   5–15 min

Children with number cards 1 to 12 position themselves to form a clock face. Children with yarn act as the hands of the clock, with a child in the center holding both pieces of yarn, one of which is shorter.

Begin with one child acting as the hour hand. You or a volunteer call out times for the "clock" to represent. After a few minutes, add another child for the minute hand.

NOTE: Teachers report that this activity, used over several weeks, is an excellent way to reinforce learning about clock movement.

PLANNING AHEAD

Slates are introduced in Lesson 1.5. You may wish to send home a note asking that children bring clean, old socks to school. The socks can be used as erasers for slates. If you do not have children bring socks, you may want to have them use tissues or paper towels as erasers.

Simulated clock face

1.4 Partner Study Routines

OBJECTIVES To practice addition facts; and to establish partnership principles.

summaries

materials

1 Teaching the Lesson

Children review addition facts and then practice by playing *Addition Top-It*. [Numeration; Operations and Computation]

Children discuss and practice working with partners and explore the Everything Math Deck.

- ☐ *Math Journal 1*, p. 5
- ☐ Working with a Partner Poster (optional)
- ☐ four each of the number cards 0–10 (from the Everything Math Deck, if available) per partnership

2 Ongoing Learning & Practice

Children explore patterns on a number grid. They use the patterns to solve problems. [Numeration; Patterns, Functions, and Algebra]

- ☐ *Math Journal 1*, p. 5
- ☐ Teaching Master (*Math Masters*, p. 2; optional)
- ☐ Class Number Grid Poster

See **Advance Preparation**

3 Options for Individualizing

Enrichment Children play *Coin Top-It* to practice finding the values of coin combinations. [Operations and Computation; Measurement and Reference Frames]

- ☐ Teaching Master (*Math Masters*, p. 3)
- ☐ scissors
- ☐ per partnership: 8 quarters, 8 dimes, 2 nickels, 8 pennies (optional)

See **Advance Preparation**

Additional Information

Advance Preparation Before children review number grids in Part 2, you may find it helpful to provide small laminated grids for children to keep in their desks. *Math Masters*, page 2 can be used for this purpose. Also, display the Class Number Grid Poster.

For Part 3, you may wish to copy the *Coin Top-It* cards from *Math Masters*, page 3 on tagboard instead of paper.

Getting Started

Mental Math and Reflexes

Children go to the board. Dictate numbers and ask children to write the next-larger number. Start with numbers like 29, 99, 105, 200, 782, 999. Continue as time allows.

Math Message

Write the date and time on the top of journal page 5. Then do Problems 1 through 7.

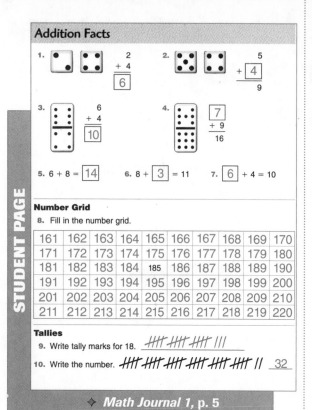

Addition Facts

1. $\begin{array}{r} 2 \\ +\ 4 \\ \hline \boxed{6} \end{array}$

2. $\begin{array}{r} 5 \\ +\ \boxed{4} \\ \hline 9 \end{array}$

3. $\begin{array}{r} 6 \\ +\ 4 \\ \hline \boxed{10} \end{array}$

4. $\begin{array}{r} 7 \\ +\ 9 \\ \hline 16 \end{array}$

5. $6 + 8 = \boxed{14}$

6. $8 + \boxed{3} = 11$

7. $\boxed{6} + 4 = 10$

Number Grid

8. Fill in the number grid.

161	162	163	164	165	166	167	168	169	170
171	172	173	174	175	176	177	178	179	180
181	182	183	184	185	186	187	188	189	190
191	192	193	194	195	196	197	198	199	200
201	202	203	204	205	206	207	208	209	210
211	212	213	214	215	216	217	218	219	220

Tallies

9. Write tally marks for 18. ~~HHT~~ ~~HHT~~ ~~HHT~~ ///

10. Write the number. ~~HHT~~ ~~HHT~~ ~~HHT~~ ~~HHT~~ ~~HHT~~ ~~HHT~~ // _32_

✦ *Math Journal 1,* p. 5

Teaching the Lesson

✦ **Math Message Follow-Up** (*Math Journal 1,* p. 5)

WHOLE-CLASS DISCUSSION

Briefly review answers. Discuss the different formats of the addition-fact problems.

✦ **Discussing Partnership Principles**

WHOLE-CLASS DISCUSSION

Review the partnership principles: Guide, Check, and Praise.

Ask children for suggestions to help make the classroom more pleasant while working as partners in a room full of people.

Show children the list of rules for working with a partner (see page 13) and discuss why each rule will help them work effectively.

Reinforce the partnership principles frequently. This will ensure that important partnership and small-group work can be carried on in the best possible environment.

✦ **Exploring the Everything Math Deck**

PARTNER ACTIVITY

Form partnerships and distribute one Everything Math Deck to each pair. Allow time for children to explore the organization of the cards. Then bring the class together to discuss what has been found. Expect observations like the following:

▷ There are two colors on white—black or blue.

▷ There are four cards for each of the numbers 0 through 10 and one card for each of the numbers 11 through 20.

▷ There are geometric figures with the appropriate number of sides on cards 0 through 10.

▷ There are rectangular and triangular dot patterns on cards 0 through 10.

▷ A fraction is on one side of the cards 0 through 10. The fraction is pictured with blue shading.

▷ The fraction on each of the cards 0 through 10 is also shown using a number line.

◆ Demonstrating and Playing *Addition Top-It*

PARTNER ACTIVITY

Have partners remove all the cards with numbers greater than 10 from the Everything Math Deck and put them aside.

Explain the following rules of *Addition Top-It:*

Rules _____

1. Play in partnerships.

2. Mix or shuffle the cards and place them in a pile facedown between the two players.

3. One player turns over two cards and says the sum of the numbers.

4. The other player turns over the next two cards and says the sum of the numbers.

5. The player with the higher sum takes all four cards.

6. In case of a tie, each player draws one more card to add to the sum. The higher sum wins all the cards.

7. Play ends when not enough cards remain for both players to have another turn. The winner is the player with more cards.

Circulate and observe how well children are following the partnership principles. Interrupt from time to time to comment on positive things you are seeing.

NOTE: To vary the game, toss a coin to determine whether the player with more or fewer cards is the winner.

ONGOING ASSESSMENT
Observe how children find the sums as they play *Addition Top-It. For example:*

- The child has instant recall of the addition facts.
- The child "counts on." For example, to find 5 + 6, the child says, "5" and then counts "6, 7, 8, 9, 10, 11" or uses fingers to count.
- The child counts all the symbols on the cards. For example, to find 5 + 6, the child points to each symbol and says, "1, 2, 3, 4, 5" and then "6, 7, 8, 9, 10, 11."

By the end of Unit 2, children should have instant recall of the "easy" addition facts (sums to 10) and almost all the other addition facts. Also, children should know the "easy" subtraction facts.

 Adjusting the Activity Children who are ready can play with all of the cards, using the numbers 0 through 20.

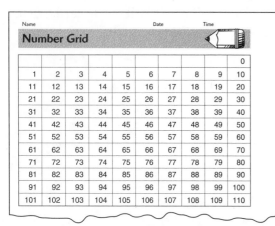

Number Grid

									0
1	2	3	4	5	6	7	8	9	10
11	12	13	14	15	16	17	18	19	20
21	22	23	24	25	26	27	28	29	30
31	32	33	34	35	36	37	38	39	40
41	42	43	44	45	46	47	48	49	50
51	52	53	54	55	56	57	58	59	60
61	62	63	64	65	66	67	68	69	70
71	72	73	74	75	76	77	78	79	80
81	82	83	84	85	86	87	88	89	90
91	92	93	94	95	96	97	98	99	100
101	102	103	104	105	106	107	108	109	110

Children can use the Class Number Grid Poster and *Math Masters,* page 2 to practice counting numbers.

Adjusting the Activity Remind children that when they count up or down on a number grid, they are counting the grid boxes (or spaces). For example, moving from 0 to 1 begins the count by 1s. Children can use *Math Masters,* page 2 to work with individual grids.

Number Grid

8. Fill in the number grid.

161	162	163	164	165	166	167	168	169	170
171	172	173	174	175	176	177	178	179	180
181	182	183	184	185	186	187	188	189	190
191	192	193	194	195	196	197	198	199	200
201	202	203	204	205	206	207	208	209	210
211	212	213	214	215	216	217	218	219	220

Ongoing Learning & Practice

◆ Exploring Number-Grid Patterns
(*Math Masters,* p. 2)

WHOLE-CLASS ACTIVITY

Have children describe patterns they see or things they notice about the Class Number Grid Poster. Expect observations like the following:

▷ Every other number across is odd.

▷ Every number in the far-right column is a multiple of 10.

▷ The grid starts at 0 and ends at 110.

▷ The grid is like a chopped-up number line.

▷ Each number down a specific column has the same digit in the 1s place.

▷ Each number across a specific row has the same digit in the 10s place (except for the last number in the row).

Do counting-up and counting-down exercises, such as the following, on the Class Number Grid Poster:

• If I start at 1 and count up 6, where do I stop? 7

• If I start at 8 and count down 2, where do I stop? 6

• If I start at 7 and count up 10, where do I stop? 17

• If I start at 15 and count down 5, where do I stop? 10

• If I start at 20 and count up 3, where do I stop? 23

As children answer questions, have them describe how they solved each problem.

◆ Completing a Number Grid
(*Math Journal 1,* p. 5)

WHOLE-CLASS ACTIVITY

Children fill in numbers less than 185 and greater than 185 to complete the number grid. (See the margin.) You might complete some of the grid together, giving hints as to what numbers to fill in next. *For example:*

• What number goes right above 185? 175

• What number goes 1 space to the right of 179? 180

• What number goes right below 179? 189

NOTE: Children complete Problems 9 and 10 on journal page 5 during Lesson 1.5.

Options for Individualizing

◆ ENRICHMENT Playing *Coin Top-It*
(*Math Masters*, p. 3)

PARTNER ACTIVITY   **5–15 min**

Each player cuts apart a copy of *Math Masters*, page 3.
Partners combine their cards.

Explain the following rules of *Coin Top-It*:

Rules _____

1. Players mix the 32 cards and place them facedown
   between themselves.

2. Each player draws a card and says the total amount
   of the coins shown on his or her card. The player
   with the greater amount collects and keeps both
   cards. (Players draw again if the amounts are equal.)

3. The game ends when there are no cards left to draw.
   The winner is the player who collected more cards.

 Adjusting the Activity Children may find it helpful to
use their tool-kit coins to model the combinations
pictured on the cards.

1.5

Slate Routines

OBJECTIVES To introduce the slate routine; and to practice making and counting tallies.

summaries	**materials**
1 Teaching the Lesson	
Children are introduced to slate routines and use their slates to record tallies. [Numeration]	☐ *Math Journal 1*, p. 5 ☐ slate; chalk; eraser ***See* Advance Preparation**
2 Ongoing Learning & Practice	
Children review addition facts by playing *Addition Top-It*. [Numeration; Operations and Computation]	☐ four each of the number cards 0–10 (from the Everything Math Deck, if available) per partnership ☐ 1 set of double-9 dominoes per partnership (optional) ☐ 1 die or 3 dice per partnership (optional)
3 Options for Individualizing	
Language Diversity Children use craft sticks to tally the number of children in class. [Numeration] **Enrichment** Children take a survey and tally the results. [Numeration; Data and Chance] **Reteaching** Children practice tallying by playing the *Dice-Roll and Tally Game*. [Numeration; Data and Chance]	☐ craft sticks ☐ 1 die per partnership ☐ half-sheet of paper

Additional Information

Advance Preparation Before beginning the teaching activities in Part 1, decide how to manage the slates. Some teachers number them to correspond to tool-kit numbers; children keep their slates with their numbers. Other teachers stack the slates in a special spot in the classroom and have children take them when needed. Still others make passing out slates a classroom job that rotates among the children.

Vocabulary • **tally marks**

Getting Started

Mental Math and Reflexes

Do "stop and start" counting by 10s. Have the class begin at 10; count by 10s to 70; count by 5s from 70 to 95; and then count by 1s from 95 to 100.

Repeat as time allows, starting with numbers like 50, 110, and 180.

Math Message

Take a slate, a piece of chalk, and an eraser. Make tally marks to show how many children are here today.

1 Teaching the Lesson

✦ Math Message Follow-Up

WHOLE-CLASS ACTIVITY

Have children share responses to the Math Message. Record the correct number of tallies on the board, and have the class count them together. Be sure to count the groups of 5s; for example, 5, 10, 15, 20, 25, 26, 27.

Adjusting the Activity If children are not familiar with how to make **tally marks,** begin by making a separate mark for each child in attendance. Count the total by 1s. Now show children how to make four marks with a fifth mark placed across the others ("four standing tall; then one takes a fall"). Make a tally count for the class total. Then count by 5s for each group of tallies.

✦ Introducing the Slate Routine

WHOLE-CLASS ACTIVITY

Discuss the care and use of slates. Explain where slates will be kept and how they will be distributed.

Explain that during whole-class activities, the slates will provide everyone with a chance to answer quietly and at the same time.

Practice a routine, such as "Listen, Think, Write, Show, Erase." You may want to use some of the suggestions below to practice this routine. Encourage children to erase their slates completely between problems.

• Write the number that comes before 200. 199

• Write the number that comes before 1,001. 1,000

• Write the number that comes after 509. 510

Continue as time allows.

Children may use a sock for an eraser.

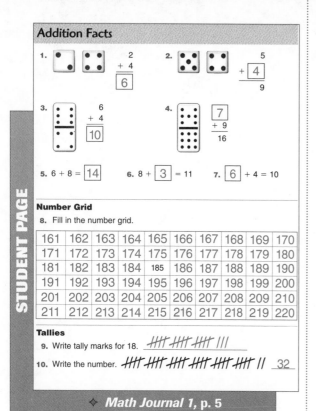

Addition Facts

1. [dice images] $\frac{\begin{array}{r} 2 \\ +\ 4 \end{array}}{\boxed{6}}$ 2. [dice images] $\frac{\begin{array}{r} 5 \\ +\ \boxed{4} \end{array}}{9}$

3. [domino image] $\frac{\begin{array}{r} 6 \\ +\ 4 \end{array}}{\boxed{10}}$ 4. [domino image] $\frac{\begin{array}{r} \boxed{7} \\ +\ 9 \end{array}}{16}$

5. $6 + 8 = \boxed{14}$ 6. $8 + \boxed{3} = 11$ 7. $\boxed{6} + 4 = 10$

Number Grid

8. Fill in the number grid.

161	162	163	164	165	166	167	168	169	170
171	172	173	174	175	176	177	178	179	180
181	182	183	184	185	186	187	188	189	190
191	192	193	194	195	196	197	198	199	200
201	202	203	204	205	206	207	208	209	210
211	212	213	214	215	216	217	218	219	220

Tallies

9. Write tally marks for 18. //// //// //// ///

10. Write the number. //// //// //// //// //// //// // _32_

◆ *Math Journal 1*, p. 5

◆ Making Tally Marks for 30 Seconds

WHOLE-CLASS DISCUSSION

Ask children to estimate how many tally marks they can make on their slates in 30 seconds. Record their estimates on the board. Then have them check their estimates by making as many tally marks—grouping by 5s—as they can in 30 seconds. Explain that this is not a competitive activity, and that neatness is important.

Call out "start" and "stop" to time the 30-second period. When time is up, children count their tally marks and write their totals using numerals. Then they compare their totals to their estimates.

Ask children to show their slates if they think they would win the "neatness" award. Show several of these and praise the careful work.

Take a survey to find out what the highest number of tally marks is. Draw that tally count on the board and count together with the class.

◆ Representing Numbers with Tally Marks (*Math Journal 1*, p. 5)

PARTNER ACTIVITY

Partners choose numbers between 0 and 30 for each other to tally on their slates. They check by counting the tally marks together. Then they do Problems 9 and 10 on journal page 5.

2 Ongoing Learning & Practice

◆ Playing *Addition Top-It*

PARTNER ACTIVITY

Partners play the game as it was introduced in Lesson 1.4, or they play one of the following variations:

▷ Use double-9 dominoes instead of number cards.

▷ Draw three cards on each turn instead of two.

▷ Roll one die three times, or roll three separate dice together, to generate three addends.

Adjusting the Activity If children are able, have them write number models for each round of the game.

3 Options for Individualizing

◆ LANGUAGE DIVERSITY Using Craft Sticks to Tally the Number of Children

INDEPENDENT ACTIVITY   5–15 min

Children unfamiliar with tally marks may benefit from modeling tally counts with craft sticks.

Have children represent the number of children in class today with craft sticks. Encourage children to bundle their sticks in groups of five.

Children can model tallying with craft sticks.

◆ ENRICHMENT Using Tally Marks to Record Survey Responses

INDEPENDENT ACTIVITY   15–30 min

Children survey friends and family members to find their answers to one or more questions. They tally the results and then share the results with the class.

Portfolio Ideas

Make sure each question has different possible categories for answers. Most questions require an Other column. Children can make up their own questions or use questions like the following:

▷ What is your favorite season?

▷ What is your favorite sport?

▷ What is your favorite color?

▷ What is your favorite dessert?

Help children set up tally charts in which to record their survey responses.

Favorite Colors

Blue	
Red	
Yellow	
Green	
Purple	
Other	

Children set up tally charts in which to record their survey responses.

◆ RETEACHING Playing the *Dice-Roll and Tally Game*

PARTNER ACTIVITY   5–15 min

The *Dice-Roll and Tally Game* is a simple way for children to practice making tally marks.

Each partner sets up a table with the numbers 1 through 6 in the first column and blank spaces in the second column.

Partners take turns rolling a die and putting a tally mark next to the appropriate number on their half-sheets of paper. The first player to have at least five tally marks next to each number is the winner.

Rolls of the Die

1	卌 ‖
2	‖‖
3	卌 ‖‖
4	卌 卌
5	‖‖
6	卌	

This player needs two rolls of 2 and two rolls of 5 to win the game.

1.6 Grouping by Tens— $1, $10, $100

OBJECTIVES To review grouping by tens; and to practice exchanging $1, $10, and $100 bills.

summaries	materials

1 Teaching the Lesson

Children find the total values of combinations of $1, $10, and $100 bills. [Operations and Computation; Measurement and Reference Frames]

Children play the *Money Exchange Game* with $1, $10, and $100 bills. [Numeration; Measurement and Reference Frames]

- ☐ *Math Journal 1,* p. 6
- ☐ Teaching Masters (*Math Masters,* pp. 4–7)
- ☐ Teaching Master transparency (*Math Masters,* p. 4; optional)
- ☐ envelope or other device for storing play money
- ☐ scissors
- ☐ 1 die per partnership
- ☐ slate

See **Advance Preparation**

2 Ongoing Learning & Practice

Children play *Addition Top-It.* [Operations and Computation]

- ☐ per partnership: four each of the number cards 0–10 (from the Everything Math Deck, if available); 1 set of double-9 dominoes, or 1 die or 3 dice (optional)

3 Options for Individualizing

Reteaching Children play the *Money Exchange Game* with base-10 blocks. [Numeration; Measurement and Reference Frames]

Extra Practice Children play the *Money Exchange Game* with pennies, dimes, and $1 bills. [Numeration; Measurement and Reference Frames]

Enrichment Children play the *Money Exchange Game* with $10 bills, $100 bills, and $1,000 bank drafts. [Numeration; Measurement and Reference Frames]

- ☐ Teaching Masters (*Math Masters,* pp. 5–11 and 227)
- ☐ 1 die per partnership (2 dice optional)
- ☐ 15 cubes, 15 longs, 1 flat
- ☐ 15 pennies and 15 dimes
- ☐ one $1 bill

See **Advance Preparation**

Additional Information

Advance Preparation Before using the Math Message, you may want each child to cut out the paper money from a copy of *Math Masters,* pages 5–7. You can shorten this preparation by having parent volunteers or other helpers (for example, upper-grade students) cut out the money ahead of time. An alternative is to provide play money, which is available from many sources.

For the *Money Exchange Game* activity in Part 1, you might want to make an overhead transparency of *Math Masters,* page 4. You should also decide how you want children to store their paper money. Many teachers have found that small envelopes work well. The envelopes can be labeled with children's tool-kit numbers. Some teachers have children bundle the bills with paper clips or rubber bands.

For the optional Enrichment activity in Part 3, have each child cut out the $100 bills and the $1,000 bank drafts from *Math Masters,* pages 8 and 9. Then have children write $10, $100, and $1,000 in the cells along the top row on *Math Masters,* page 227.

Getting Started

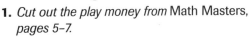

Mental Math and Reflexes

Tell simple number stories. Let children make pictures or tallies on their slates to solve the stories.

- Joan had $8. She gave $3 to Martin. She gave $1 to Diana. How much money did Joan have left? $4
- Malik won the first 5 rounds of *Addition Top-It*. He won 6 of the next 8 rounds. How many rounds did he win in all? 11 rounds

Math Message

1. *Cut out the play money from* Math Masters, *pages 5–7.*
2. *Count the money. How much do you have?*
3. *Take an envelope. Write your tool-kit number on the front of it. Put the money inside.*

1 Teaching the Lesson

◆ Math Message Follow-Up

WHOLE-CLASS ACTIVITY

Have children put their money into three piles—$100s, $10s, and $1s—and count all the money beginning with the $100s. $576

◆ Counting Money (*Math Journal 1*, p. 6)

INDEPENDENT ACTIVITY

Make sure children write the date and time at the top of journal page 6.

Children work alone or with a partner to do the problems on the journal page.

When most of the children have finished the page, go over the answers. For Problem 5, discuss how to rearrange the bills to make the problem easier to solve. Sample answer: Group the bills by value and then count, beginning with bills of the greatest value.

Adjusting the Activity Have some children use their tool-kit bills to model the problems.

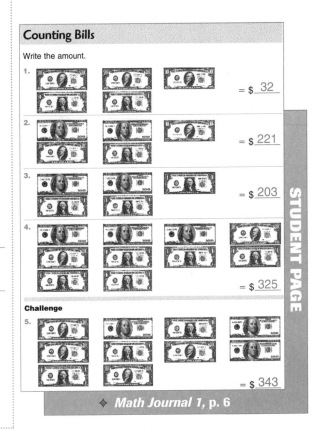

Counting Bills

Write the amount.

1. = $ 32
2. = $ 221
3. = $ 203
4. = $ 325

Challenge

5. = $ 343

◆ *Math Journal 1,* p. 6

STUDENT PAGE

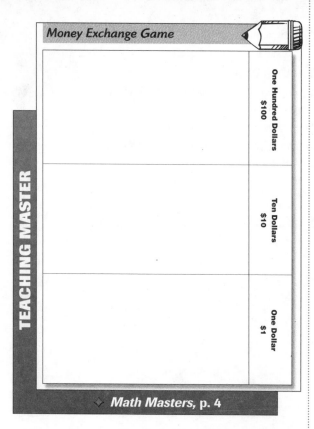

Money Exchange Game

| One Hundred Dollars $100 | Ten Dollars $10 | One Dollar $1 |

Math Masters, p. 4

ONGOING ASSESSMENT

As children play the *Money Exchange Game*, circulate and ask them to describe the bill exchanges they are making.

Bills cut out from *Math Masters*, pages 5–7

Adjusting the Activity If children are able, have them write number models for each round of *Addition Top-It*.

◆ Playing the *Money Exchange Game* with $100 Bills (*Math Masters,* pp. 4–7)

PARTNER ACTIVITY

Provide each player with *Math Masters,* page 4 and the bills used in the Math Message Follow-Up. Show the class how to play the *Money Exchange Game* with $1, $10, and $100 bills. The rules are as follows:

Rules

1. Partners put all of their bills together to form a "bank."

2. Player 1 rolls one die and takes from the bank the number of $1 bills shown on the die.

3. Player 1 places the $1 bills in the right-hand column (the $1 column) on his or her Place-Value Mat.

4. Player 2 repeats Steps 2 and 3.

5. Players continue in this way, taking turns.

6. Whenever possible, players trade ten $1 bills for one $10 bill and ten $10 bills for one $100 bill. They put the new bills in the correct column on their Place-Value Mats.

7. The first player to trade for a $100 bill wins.

Show the class how to collect and exchange bills. Have a volunteer roll a die to tell how much money to take. You might record the totals with tally marks on an overhead transparency of *Math Masters,* page 4. Act out the exchanges with bills when the total is $10 or more.

Most games last from 18 to 24 rounds.

2 Ongoing Learning & Practice

◆ Playing *Addition Top-It*

PARTNER ACTIVITY

Partners play the game as it was introduced in Lesson 1.4, or they play one of the following variations:

▷ Use double-9 dominoes instead of number cards.

▷ Draw three cards on each turn instead of two.

▷ Roll one die three times, or roll three separate dice together, to generate three addends.

3 Options for Individualizing

◆ RETEACHING Playing the *Money Exchange Game* with Base-10 Blocks (*Math Masters*, p. 10)

PARTNER ACTIVITY   5–15 min

The rules are modified as follows: Two players have a "bank" of base-10 blocks. Players take turns rolling a die, taking from the bank the number of cubes (ones) shown on the die, and placing that number of cubes on the game mat in the right-hand ($1) column. Whenever possible, players trade ten cubes for one long ($10), or ten longs for one flat ($100), and put the new block in the correct column. The first player to trade for a flat wins.

◆ EXTRA PRACTICE Playing the *Money Exchange Game* with Coins and $1 Bills (*Math Masters*, pp. 5, 7, and 11)

PARTNER ACTIVITY   5–15 min

The rules are modified as follows: Two players put all of their coins in the "bank." Players take turns rolling a die, taking from the bank the number of pennies shown on the die, and placing that number of pennies on the game mat in the One Cent column. Whenever possible, players trade ten pennies for a dime and place the dime in the Ten Cents column; they trade ten dimes for a $1 bill and place the $1 bill in the One Dollar column. The first player to trade for a $1 bill wins.

◆ ENRICHMENT Playing the *Money Exchange Game* with $1,000 Bank Drafts (*Math Masters*, pp. 6–9 and 227)

PARTNER ACTIVITY   5–15 min

There are currently no $1,000 bills in circulation. Instead, people use bank drafts.

The rules are modified as follows: Two players put all of their bills and drafts in the "bank." Players take turns rolling a die, taking from the bank the number of $10 bills shown on the die, and placing the $10 bills on the game mat in the right-hand ($10) column. Whenever possible, they trade ten $10 bills for one $100 bill and place the $100 bill in the $100 column; they trade ten $100 bills for a $1,000 bank draft and place it in the $1,000 column. The first player to trade for a $1,000 bank draft wins.

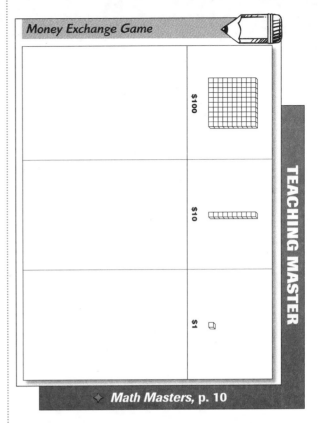

◆ *Math Masters*, p. 10

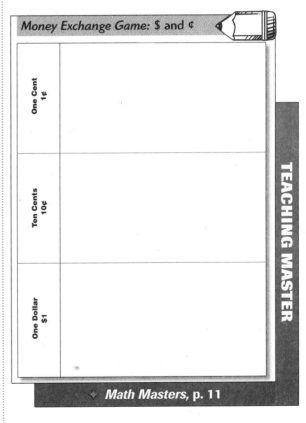

◆ *Math Masters*, p. 11

NOTE: Each partnership will need to add two bank drafts for $1,000 and 12 more $100 bills (*Math Masters*, pages 8 and 9) to its money supply.

1.7 Math Boxes

OBJECTIVES To review place value; and to introduce the Math Boxes routine.

summaries	materials

1 Teaching the Lesson

Children review addition facts. [Operations and Computation]

Children are introduced to the Math Boxes routine and complete the first Math Boxes page. [multiple strands]

☐ *Math Journal 1*, p. 7
☐ slate

2 Ongoing Learning & Practice

Children play *Penny Cup* to practice naming parts of a whole. [Numeration; Operations and Computation]

Per partnership:
☐ Teaching Master (*Math Masters*, p. 12; optional)
☐ cup, can, or other container; 20 tool-kit pennies
***See* Advance Preparation**

3 Options for Individualizing

Reteaching Children practice naming parts of a whole by doing *Two-Fisted Penny Addition*. [Numeration; Operations and Computation]

Extra Practice Children review addition facts and place value. [Numeration; Operations and Computation]

☐ 20 pennies
☐ *Minute Math®*, pp. 9, 23, 32, and 33

Additional Information

Advance Preparation For *Penny Cup* in Part 2, obtain cups, cans, or other open-top, opaque containers. During the game, containers will be turned upside down and as many as 20 pennies will be stacked or piled on the containers' bottoms. Make sure the bottom of each container is wide and sturdy enough to hold the pennies.

Vocabulary • **digit** • **Math Boxes**

Getting Started

Mental Math and Reflexes

- Name all the 1-**digit** numbers. 0, 1, 2, …, 9 How many are there? 10
- Name some 2-digit numbers and 3-digit numbers.
- Write a 3-digit number on the board, and have children name the digits in the ones, tens, and hundreds places.

Use exercises like the following:

- Write 38 on your slate. Circle the digit in the 10s place. 3 Put an X on the digit in the 1s place. 8 Show your slate.

Continue as time allows. Vary the difficulty of the numbers to get a feel for the level of the class's place-value skills. Use numbers in the thousands if children are able.

Math Message

2 + 2 = __4__	3 + 3 = __6__	4 + 4 = __8__	2 + 3 = __5__	3 + 4 = __7__	4 + 5 = __9__
1 + 3 = __4__	2 + 4 = __6__	3 + 5 = __8__	1 + 4 = __5__	5 + 2 = __7__	6 + 3 = __9__

1 Teaching the Lesson

◆ Math Message Follow-Up

WHOLE-CLASS ACTIVITY

Briefly review answers. Ask children how they can improve their ability to give the answers to addition facts. Sample answer: Learn the facts and practice them.

◆ Introducing Math Boxes

WHOLE-CLASS DISCUSSION

Ask children to name activities that people practice. Sample answers: Dancing, singing, playing a musical instrument, speaking a foreign language, basketball and other sports, and so on.

Ask children, *What would happen if people never practiced? Is anyone familiar with the expression, "Practice makes perfect"? What does this mean?*

Explain that practice is necessary in mathematics, too. In *Everyday Mathematics,* one of the ways to practice is by doing a page of problems called **Math Boxes.**

◆ Completing a Math Boxes Page
(*Math Journal 1,* p. 7)

INDEPENDENT ACTIVITY

Mixed Review Go over each problem so that children understand what to do. Children complete the journal page independently or with a partner.

When children have finished, briefly discuss the answers.

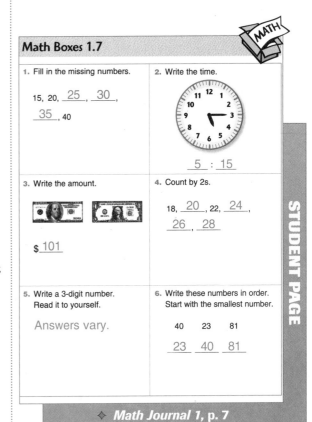

Math Boxes 1.7

1. Fill in the missing numbers.

   15, 20, __25__, __30__, __35__, 40

2. Write the time.

   __5__ : __15__

3. Write the amount.

   $ __101__

4. Count by 2s.

   18, __20__, 22, __24__, __26__, __28__

5. Write a 3-digit number. Read it to yourself.

   Answers vary.

6. Write these numbers in order. Start with the smallest number.

   40   23   81

   __23__   __40__   __81__

STUDENT PAGE

◆ Math Journal 1, p. 7

Penny Cup Record Sheet

Example

We started with __20__ pennies.

We could see __6__ pennies on top.

We figured there were __14__ pennies inside.

We counted __14__ pennies inside.

? inside

Round 1	**Round 2**
We started with _____ pennies.	We started with _____ pennies.
We could see _____ pennies on top.	We could see _____ pennies on top.
We figured there were _____ pennies inside.	We figured there were _____ pennies inside.
We counted _____ pennies inside.	We counted _____ pennies inside.
Round 3	**Round 4**
We started with _____ pennies.	We started with _____ pennies.
We could see _____ pennies on top.	We could see _____ pennies on top.
We figured there were _____ pennies inside.	We figured there were _____ pennies inside.
We counted _____ pennies inside.	We counted _____ pennies inside.

◆ *Math Masters, p. 12*

TEACHING MASTER

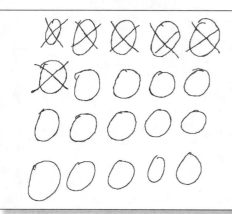

Children name the two parts of 20 shown here: 6 and 14.

Ongoing Learning & Practice

◆Playing *Penny Cup* (*Math Masters,* p. 12)

PARTNER ACTIVITY

Each partnership has 20 pennies and a cup, can, or other container. To play *Penny Cup,* Player 1 turns the container upside down, hides some of the 20 pennies under the cup, and puts the rest on top of the cup. Player 2 counts the pennies on top and figures out, or guesses, how many are hidden under the cup. If the number is correct, Player 2 gets a point. Partners trade roles. The first player to get 5 points wins.

Players keep a tally of their points.

NOTE: *Math Masters,* page 12 can be used to make a game record.

Another Way to Play

Each partnership is a team. Partners count out a total number of pennies appropriate to their level of play. Player 1 grabs a bunch of pennies without counting them, puts them under the cup, and puts the rest of the pennies on top of the cup. Players work together to figure out, or guess, how many pennies are under the cup. If the number is correct, they get a team point. The object of the game is to improve the team total each time partners play.

Adjusting the Activity If children are having difficulty determining the number of pennies, suggest that they draw circles to represent all of the pennies. (If they play with 20 pennies, they draw 20 circles.) Then children use one of the following strategies to help figure out how many pennies are under the cup:

▷ Cross off one circle for each penny on top of the cup. Count the uncrossed circles to find the number of pennies under the cup.

▷ Use a second set of pennies as markers. Cover one circle for each penny on top of the cup. Count the uncovered circles to find the number of pennies under the cup.

You may wish to have more able children write a number model to show how they solved the problem.

3 Options for Individualizing

◆ RETEACHING Playing *Two-Fisted Penny Addition*

PARTNER ACTIVITY   5–15 min

If children are having difficulty with the missing-part concept in *Penny Cup,* they may need to practice naming parts of a whole.

Children count out 10 pennies and split them between their two hands. Help children identify their left and right hands.

Call on several children to share amounts. For example: "My left hand has 1 penny, and my right hand has 9 pennies," "... left hand 3 and right hand 7," "... left hand 4 and right hand 6," "... left hand 5 and right hand 5." The various splits can be recorded on the board.

Repeat with other numbers of pennies. Partners can continue to practice using different total numbers of pennies—9, 12, 20, and so on.

◆ EXTRA PRACTICE Minute Math

SMALL-GROUP ACTIVITY   5–15 min

To offer children more experience with complements of 10, as well as with 2-, 3-, and 4-digit numbers, see the following pages in *Minute Math:*

Basic Routines: pp. 9 and 23

Counting: pp. 32 and 33

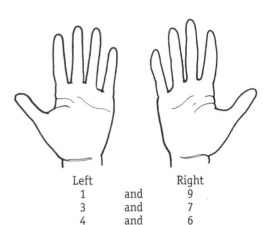

Left		Right
1	and	9
3	and	7
4	and	6
5	and	5

1.8 Working in Small Groups

OBJECTIVES To establish rules for working in small groups; and to review number patterns and sequences.

summaries	**materials**
1 Teaching the Lesson	
Children describe and continue number sequences as well as explore patterns on the Class Number Grid Poster. [Numeration; Patterns, Functions, and Algebra] Children learn rules for working in small groups. Children make a class number scroll from 0 to 1,000. [Numeration; Patterns, Functions, and Algebra]	☐ Teaching Masters (*Math Masters,* pp. 13 and 14) ☐ Class Number Grid Poster ☐ demonstration clock ☐ slate ☐ Rules for Small Groups Poster ***See* Advance Preparation**
2 Ongoing Learning & Practice	
Children review addition facts by playing *Addition Top-It.* [Numeration; Operations and Computation] Children practice and maintain skills through Math Boxes.	☐ *Math Journal 1,* p. 8 ☐ per partnership: four each of the number cards 0–10 (from the Everything Math Deck, if available); double-9 dominoes; or dice (optional)
3 Options for Individualizing	
Enrichment Children make number scrolls using greater numbers. [Numeration; Patterns, Functions, and Algebra] **Extra Practice** Children use number patterns to practice counting. [Numeration; Patterns, Functions, and Algebra]	☐ Teaching Masters (*Math Masters,* pp. 13 and 14) ☐ *Minute Math®,* pp. 3, 5, 7, 27, 29, and 31 ☐ paste or tape ***See* Advance Preparation**

Additional Information

Advance Preparation For the *Establishing Rules for Small-Group Work* activity in Part 1, consider making a poster of rules like the one shown on page 49.

For the Class Number Scroll activity in Part 1 and the optional Enrichment activity in Part 3, the class will need 1 copy of *Math Masters,* page 13 to begin the scroll and at least 9 copies of *Math Masters,* page 14 to continue it. Make several extra copies of *Math Masters,* page 14 for children who wish to continue scrolling.

Vocabulary • number scroll • even number • odd number

Getting Started

Mental Math and Reflexes

Set the hands on your demonstration clock to various times. Children write these times on their slates. *Suggestions:* 2:30, 5:45, 12:00, 9:45, 8:00, 6:30

Math Message

Write the next 3 numbers on a piece of paper.

34, 36, 38, __40__ , __42__ , __44__

Teaching the Lesson

✦ **Math Message Follow-Up**

WHOLE-CLASS ACTIVITY

Go over the answers. Ask someone to describe the pattern.
Counting by 2s

✦ **Exploring Counting Patterns on the Class Number Grid Poster**

WHOLE-CLASS ACTIVITY

Count by 2s in unison, starting at 0. Point to the numbers
on the Class Number Grid Poster as you count. *What
patterns do the count-by-2 numbers make on the grid?*
Sample answers: They are every other number, the even
numbers, the numbers in every other column, and so on.

Next, count by 5s and review the patterns. All of the
numbers fall in the middle column and end in 5 or in the
last column and end in 0. Finally, count by 10s and review
the patterns. All of the numbers fall in the last column,
with numbers ending in 0.

Adjusting the Activity Ask a volunteer to color or cross
out the multiples of 2 while the class counts by 2s.
When the pattern begins to emerge, ask if there is an
easier way to mark the 2s. Mark or color every other
column. Use different colors or different marks for the
5s and 10s patterns.

✦ **Establishing Rules for Small-Group Work**

WHOLE-GROUP DISCUSSION

Teaching and reinforcing orderly small-group interactions
is well worth the time and effort. Effective small groups
encourage cooperative learning and reduce children's
reliance on you for answers.

Review the partnership principles: Guide, Check, and
Praise. Have the class suggest additional rules that might
help when doing activities in small groups.

Emphasize that children should ask you for help only
when no one in the group can solve the problem or answer
the question. This is very important for developing good
group interaction.

Class Number Grid

									0
1	2	3	4	5	6	7	8	9	10
11	12	13	14	15	16	17	18	19	20
21	22	23	24	25	26	27	28	29	30
31	32	33	34	35	36	37	38	39	40
41	42	43	44	45	46	47	48	49	50
51	52	53	54	55	56	57	58	59	60
61	62	63	64	65	66	67	68	69	70
71	72	73	74	75	76	77	78	79	80
81	82	83	84	85	86	87	88	89	90
91	92	93	94	95	96	97	98	99	100
101	102	103	104	105	106	107	108	109	110

Class Number Grid Poster

Rules for Working in Small Groups

- Use quiet voices.
- Be polite.
- Share materials.
- Take turns.
- Help each other.

NOTE: Some teachers use green and red
plastic cups for small-group management. Each
group has one red and one green cup. The cups
are stacked and displayed to indicate the
following:

▷ Green cups: Everything is running smoothly.

▷ Red cups: We need help.

No group should display a red cup until every
group member has tried to solve the problem or
answer the question.

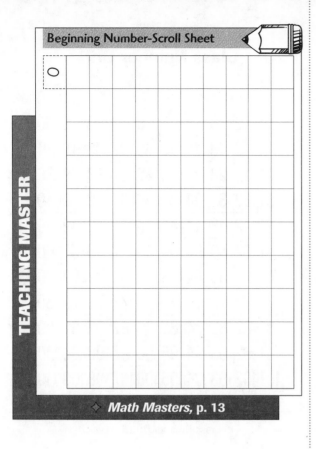

Math Masters, p. 13

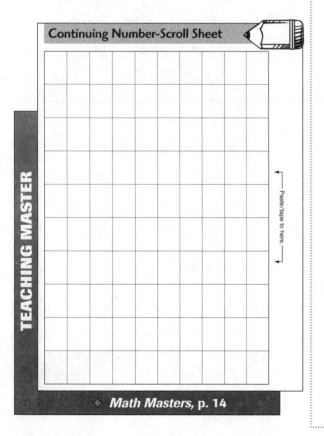

Math Masters, p. 14

✦ Making a Class Number Scroll from 1 to 1,000 (*Math Masters*, pp. 13 and 14)

SMALL-GROUP ACTIVITY

Children work in small groups to create a **number scroll** for the numbers up to 1,000. The scroll will be made from separate number grids.

Have children count off into ten small groups with 2 to 4 children per group. Give one group a copy of *Math Masters*, page 13 to begin the scroll. Give each of the other groups a copy of *Math Masters*, page 14. Assign each group a different 3-digit number ending in 1 (101, 201, 301, and so on, up to 901).

Each group begins filling in the scroll by using its special 3-digit number.

As children work, circulate and ask questions about patterns on the grid. *For example:*

• Who can show me some **even numbers**?

• Some **odd numbers**?

• What is the pattern for counting by 10s?

> **Adjusting the Activity** Write several numbers on each grid before distributing the grids. Children can check their own work as they fill in the remaining numbers. If children get stuck on what number to write next, remind them that they can use their calculators by keying in a sequence such as **ON/C** [the number they know] **+** **1** **=** **=** and so on.

After all groups have completed their grids, bring the class together to review the completed grids. Tape or paste them together to make the number scroll.

NOTE: Some children may have completed individual number scrolls in *First Grade Everyday Mathematics* using rather large numbers.

2 Ongoing Learning & Practice

✦ Playing *Addition Top-It*

PARTNER ACTIVITY

Partners continue to play the game as it was introduced in Lesson 1.4, or they play one of the following variations:

▷ Use double-9 dominoes instead of number cards.

▷ Draw three cards on each turn instead of two.

▷ Roll three dice, or one die three times, to generate three addends.

✦ Math Boxes 1.8 (*Math Journal 1*, p. 8)

INDEPENDENT ACTIVITY

Mixed Review This journal page provides opportunities for cumulative review or assessment of concepts and skills.

3 Options for Individualizing

✦ ENRICHMENT Making Individual Number Scrolls (*Math Masters*, pp. 13 and 14)

INDEPENDENT ACTIVITY 🯄   15–30 min

As a variation on making a class number scroll to 1,000, children can make individual scrolls. Let children select any starting numbers they are comfortable with.

Portfolio Ideas

Everyone who participates will need multiple copies of *Math Masters*, page 14. The first page of individual scrolls can be taped to empty paper-towel rolls for storage.

✦ EXTRA PRACTICE Minute Math

SMALL-GROUP ACTIVITY   5–15 min

To offer children more experience with number patterns, see the following pages in *Minute Math*:

Basic Routines: pp. 3, 5, and 7

Counting: pp. 27, 29, and 31

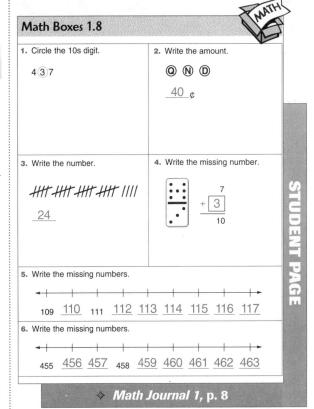

Math Boxes 1.8

1. Circle the 10s digit.

   4 ③ 7

2. Write the amount.

   Ⓠ Ⓝ Ⓓ

   __40__ ¢

3. Write the number.

   ̶H̶H̶T̶ ̶H̶H̶T̶ ̶H̶H̶T̶ ̶H̶H̶T̶ ||||

   __24__

4. Write the missing number.

   $\begin{array}{r} 7 \\ +\;\boxed{3} \\ \hline 10 \end{array}$

5. Write the missing numbers.

   109 __110__ 111 __112__ __113__ __114__ __115__ __116__ __117__

6. Write the missing numbers.

   455 __456__ __457__ 458 __459__ __460__ __461__ __462__ __463__

✦ *Math Journal 1, p. 8*

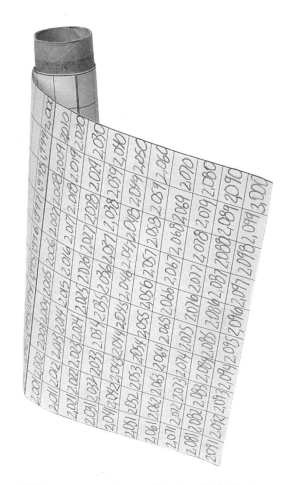

Children make number scrolls using *Math Masters*, pages 13 and 14.

1.9 Number Grids

To explore place-value patterns on number grids.

summaries	materials
1 Teaching the Lesson	
Children identify various number-grid patterns, such as 1 more, 10 more, 1 less, and 10 less. Children practice place-value skills by completing number-grid puzzles. [Numeration; Patterns, Functions, and Algebra]	☐ *Math Journal 1*, p. 9 ☐ Class Number Grid Poster ***See* Advance Preparation**
2 Ongoing Learning & Practice	
Children practice place-value skills by identifying missing numbers on a number grid. [Numeration; Patterns, Functions, and Algebra] Children practice and maintain skills through Math Boxes.	☐ *Math Journal 1*, pp. 10 and 11
3 Options for Individualizing	
Enrichment and Reteaching Children use place-value patterns to create number-grid puzzles. [Numeration; Patterns, Functions, and Algebra]	☐ Teaching Masters (*Math Masters*, pp. 15–17) ☐ scissors ☐ grease pencil or washable marker ***See* Advance Preparation**

Additional Information

Advance Preparation Before beginning the activities in Part 1, draw a semipermanent 3-by-3 blank number grid on the board.

For the optional Reteaching activity in Part 3, cut out and laminate the number-grid pieces from *Math Masters,* page 16.

Getting Started

Mental Math and Reflexes

Use the Class Number Grid Poster and ask questions like the following:

- Is 6 an even or odd number? even
- I am counting by 4s, what number comes after 16? 20
- My finger is on 21. What number will I land on if I move down one row? 31
- What digit is always in the 1s place in the last column on the right? (Signal which direction is right.) 0
- What happens as I move my finger from the top of the number grid to the bottom? The numbers increase.

Math Message

What number is 1 more than 46?

What number is 10 more than 46?

What number is 1 less than 46?

What number is 10 less than 46?

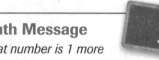

Teaching the Lesson

✦ Math Message Follow-Up

WHOLE-CLASS ACTIVITY

Ask a volunteer to point to a number that is 1 more than 46 on the Class Number Grid Poster. 47 Ask other volunteers to point to the other answers for the Math Message. 56; 45; 36

Have children choose other numbers on the Class Number Grid Poster and repeat this routine.

✦ Finding Patterns on a Number Grid

WHOLE-CLASS DISCUSSION

Write 55 in the center of the 3-by-3 grid on the board. (See the margin.) Ask for volunteers to write in the grid the number that is 1 more than 55; 1 less than 55; 10 more than 55; 10 less than 55. *What numbers go in the other squares on the grid?* 44; 46; 64; 66

Let the children choose other beginning numbers and repeat this procedure.

Tell the children to think of any number on the grid. Ask:

• Where is the number that is 1 more? To the right, or at the left end of the next row below Where is the number that is 1 less? To the left, or at the right end of the previous row above

• Where is the number that is 10 more? One row down, directly below Where is the number that is 10 less? One row up, directly above

✦ Completing Number-Grid Puzzles
(*Math Journal 1*, p. 9)

INDEPENDENT ACTIVITY

Check to be sure children have recorded the date and time on the top of journal page 9.

Children work alone or with a partner to complete the number-grid puzzles.

Adjusting the Activity If a child is having difficulty completing the number-grid puzzles, provide hints by filling in several of the surrounding blue boxes. (See the margin.)

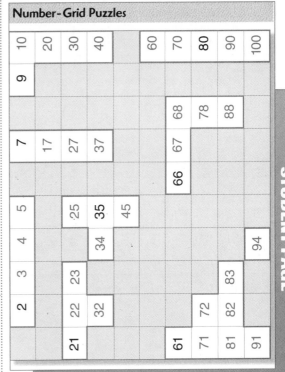

Number-Grid Puzzles

✦ *Math Journal 1*, p. 9

STUDENT PAGE

	45	
54	55	56
	65	

21			24	
		33		35

65	66		
	76		

Number-grid puzzles

Number-Grid Hunt

401		403	△	□	○	408	△	△
○	△	□		415		○		419	□
421	○		424		△		△		△
□	△		⏢	□	○	437		△	440
⏢	442	⏢	○		446		○	⏢
△		△		455		⏢	□	459	○
	462	○	□	⏢		□	△		470
□			474	△	476		○	□	⏢
⏢	□	483			□	⏢	488		○
491	○	⏢	△	○		497		△

Draw the shape (⏢, ○, □, or △) for the number.

1.	406	□	2.	422	○	3.	448	○
4.	500	△	5.	431	□	6.	486	□
7.	430	⏢	8.	479	□	9.	457	⏢
10.	492	○	11.	493	⏢	12.	468	△

✦ Math Journal 1, p. 10

Math Boxes 1.9

1. Write the number that is 10 more.

42 __52__

57 __67__

2. Solve.

__2__ + 6 = 8

3. Write the amount.

Ⓝ Ⓝ Ⓟ Ⓟ Ⓓ

__22__ ¢

4. Draw the hands so the clock shows 4:45.

5. Circle the digit in the 100s place.

⑧ 4 9

6. Write these numbers in order. Start with the smallest number.

103   29   86

__29__ __86__ __103__

✦ Math Journal 1, p. 11

Ongoing Learning & Practice

✦ Going on a Number-Grid Hunt
(*Math Journal 1*, p. 10)

INDEPENDENT ACTIVITY 👤

Children draw shapes corresponding to missing numbers in the number grid on journal page 10.

Adjusting the Activity It may be easier for some children to complete this page by filling in the numbers on the grid. Children can write numbers directly on top of the shapes.

401		403	405	406	407	408	409	410
411	412	413		415		417		419	□
421	○		424		△		△		△
□	△		⏢	□	○	437		△	440
⏢	442	⏢	○		446		○	⏢
△		△		455		⏢	□	459	○
	462	○	□	⏢		□	△		470
□			474	△	476		○	□	⏢
⏢	□	483			□	⏢	488		○
491	○	⏢	△	○		497		△

✦ Math Boxes 1.9 (*Math Journal 1*, p. 11)

INDEPENDENT ACTIVITY 👤

Mixed Review This journal page provides opportunities for cumulative review or assessment of concepts and skills.

Options for Individualizing

◆ **ENRICHMENT** **Making Number-Grid Puzzle Pieces** (*Math Masters,* p. 15)

INDEPENDENT ACTIVITY 　　15–30 min

Children make number-grid puzzle pieces by cutting out grid pieces from *Math Masters,* page 15 and entering one or two numbers on each piece. You might want to suggest to children that their grid pieces have a minimum of five squares and can be in any shape.

These pieces can be taped or glued on half-sheets of paper and assembled into a class book. If the pages are laminated, the puzzles can be solved and erased many times.

◆ **RETEACHING** **Filling in Pieces of a Number Grid** (*Math Masters,* pp. 16 and 17)

INDEPENDENT ACTIVITY 　　15–30 min

Cut out and laminate the number-grid shapes from *Math Masters,* page 16. The shapes will fit over the number grid on *Math Masters,* page 17.

Tell children to place the T on the number grid so that it covers whole boxes. They can use a grease pencil or washable marker to fill in the covered numbers. Then they lift the T to check their responses.

Discuss the numbers and their placement, especially counts by 10s. This procedure can be repeated many times, using different shapes and placements on the number grid.

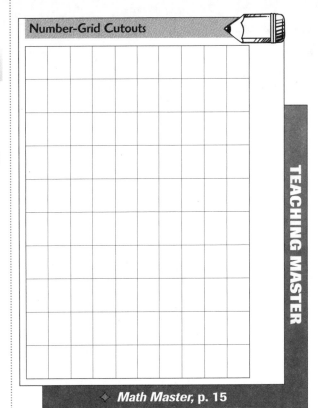

◆ *Math Master, p. 15*

11	12	13	14	15	16
21	22	23	24	25	26
31	32	33	34	35	36
41	42	43	44	45	46
51	52	53	54	55	56
61	62	63	64	65	66
71	72	73	74	75	76
81	82	83	84	85	86
91	92	93	94	95	96
101	102	103	104	105	106

One of the cutouts from *Math Masters,* page 16 placed over the number grid found on *Math Masters,* page 17

1.10 Equivalent Names for Numbers

OBJECTIVES To give equivalent names for numbers; and to review calculator use.

summaries	materials
1 Teaching the Lesson	
Children give equivalent names for people and numbers, review basic calculator functions, and skip count using their calculators. [Numeration] Children find equivalent names for numbers by solving *Broken Calculator* problems. [Numeration; Operations and Computation]	☐ *Math Journal 1*, p. 12 ☐ calculator ***See* Advance Preparation**
2 Ongoing Learning & Practice	
Children review grouping by 10s by playing the *Money Exchange Game*. [Numeration; Measurement and Reference Frames] Children practice and maintain skills through Math Boxes.	☐ *Math Journal 1*, p. 13 ☐ Teaching Masters (*Math Masters*, pp. 4–11 and 227) ☐ die; bills, tool-kit coins, or base-10 blocks
3 Options for Individualizing	
Enrichment Children explore counting patterns on the 100-grid. [Numeration] **Language Diversity** Children illustrate number equivalencies on a pan balance. [Numeration]	☐ Teaching Master (*Math Masters*, p. 18) ☐ calculator (optional) ☐ pan balance; 18 dice, dominoes, pennies, or other small identical objects ***See* Advance Preparation**

Additional Information

Advance Preparation Before beginning the lesson, familiarize yourself with your class's calculators. Every calculator has a "repeat" key. On most basic calculators, this is the $(=)$ key. Some calculators have an "operations" key that remembers and repeats operations.

For the optional Language Diversity activity in Part 3, set up a pan balance with a collection of identical objects.

Vocabulary • equivalent names

Getting Started

Mental Math and Reflexes

Have children name as many ways as they can to get 10 by adding two numbers. $1 + 9 = 10$, $8 + 2 = 10$, $4 + 6 = 10$, and so on. Record their suggestions on the board.

Math Message

Write the name of someone at home. What other names does this person have?

1 Teaching the Lesson

◆ Math Message Follow-Up

WHOLE-CLASS ACTIVITY

Ask a few volunteers to give several names for someone at home. For example, to most of her patients, Maya's mother is known as Dr. Singh. Her friends call her Roberta. People in her family call her Mom, Grandma, and Aunt Roberta. All are names for the same person.

◆ Reviewing Equivalent Names for Numbers

WHOLE-CLASS DISCUSSION

Point out that numbers can also be called by many different names. Direct children's attention to the addition problems from Mental Math and Reflexes that you recorded on the board.

Ask children to suggest subtraction names for the number 10, such as $12 - 2 = 10$. Record these names on the board.

Ask if anyone can think of ways to use words to name 10; for example, "ten" or "two less than a dozen."

Explain that names for the same number are called **equivalent names.**

 Adjusting the Activity If it was easy for children to collect names for 10, challenge them with greater numbers, such as 40.

◆ Reviewing Calculator Use

WHOLE-CLASS ACTIVITY

Many children will be familiar with calculators and can help those children who are not familiar with this tool. At this point, children should know how to do the following:

▷ Turn on the calculator.

▷ Enter numbers.

▷ Key in addition and subtraction expressions.

▷ Use the ⊜ key to display an answer.

▷ Clear the calculator.

◆ Skip Counting on the Calculator

WHOLE-CLASS ACTIVITY 👥👥👥👥

Using an overhead calculator, if possible, guide the children through the steps for counting up and down by any number. Have children perform each step on their own calculators. Adapt the following steps if necessary:

1. Always start by clearing the calculator. Press the ⓞⓝ/ⓒ key.

2. Tell the calculator what number to start with by entering the number. Enter ② in your calculator.

3. Tell the calculator to count—up or down—by pressing ⊕ for up or ⊖ for down. We will count up. Press ⊕ .

4. Tell the calculator what number to count by. Let's count by 2s. Enter ② .

5. Finally, tell the calculator to count by pressing ⊜ . Everyone count aloud while we press ⊜ repeatedly: 2, 4, 6, 8, ….

6. Stop.

Clear calculators and repeat the process, counting by a different number. Be sure to count both up and down by different numbers. For example, count up by 10s beginning with 40 and count down by 10s beginning with 100. Continue until children are comfortable with the procedure.

Adjusting the Activity Have children count down below zero so that negative numbers appear in the display. Do not expect children to understand or remember negative numbers at this time. Consider this activity to be an exposure to the concept that there are numbers below zero.

◆ Solving *Broken Calculator* Problems
(*Math Journal 1*, p. 12)

INDEPENDENT ACTIVITY

Ask children to pretend that the ⑨ key on their calculator is broken. How can they display the number 9 without using the "broken" key? Share and note on the board several ways of doing this. Encourage children to try using three or more numbers.

Broken Calculator

Example: Show 17. Broken key is ⑦. Show several ways:	**1.** Show 20. Broken key is ②. Show several ways:
11 + 6	10 + 10
20 − 3	30 − 10
8 + 8 + 1	7 + 7 + 7 − 1
2. Show 3. Broken key is ③. Show several ways:	**3.** Show 22. Broken key is ②. Show several ways:
1 + 1 + 1	19 + 3
5 − 2	30 − 8
10 − 7	11 + 11
4. Show 12. Broken key is ①. Show several ways:	**5.** Make up your own. Show _____. Broken key is _____. Show several ways:
4 + 4 + 4	Answers vary.
3 + 3 + 3 + 3	_____
6 + 6	_____
	_____

◆ *Math Journal 1*, p. 12

Try other *Broken Calculator* problems like the following:

▷ Show 2. The ② key is broken.

▷ Show 18. The ① and ⓪ keys are broken.

▷ Show 21. The ② key is broken.

Repeat the activity with other "broken" keys. If the children do well, make the problems more difficult.

Have children work alone or with partners to complete the problems on journal page 12.

ONGOING ASSESSMENT

There is an infinite number of correct responses at a variety of levels for the problems on this journal page.

For example, one child may show 17 as 9 + 8 or 18 − 1, while another may show 17 as 100 − 83. When assessing children's work on this page, note the level at which a child is performing. Also, encourage children to give answers appropriate to their abilities.

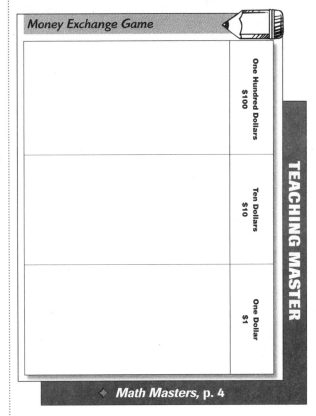

◆ *Math Masters, p. 4*

2 Ongoing Learning & Practice

◆ Playing the *Money Exchange Game*
(*Math Masters*, pp. 4–11 and 227)

PARTNER ACTIVITY

Children practice money skills by playing the *Money Exchange Game*. For detailed instructions, see Lesson 1.6.

◆ Math Boxes 1.10 (*Math Journal 1*, p. 13)

INDEPENDENT ACTIVITY

 Mixed Review This journal page provides opportunities for cumulative review or assessment of concepts and skills.

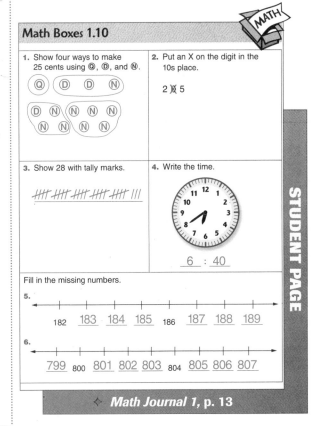

◆ *Math Journal 1, p. 13*

-9	-8	-7	-6	-5	-4	-3	-2	-1	0
1	2	3	④	5	⑥	7	⑧	9	10
11	⑫	13	14	15	⑯	17	⑱	19	⑳
21	22	23	㉔	25	26	27	㉘	29	㉚
31	㉜	33	34	35	㊱	37	38	39	㊵
41	㊷	43	㊹	45	46	47	㊽	49	50
51	㊺	53	㊺	55	㊻	57	58	59	⑥⓪
61	62	63	㊿	65	㊿	67	㊽	69	70
71	㉒	73	74	75	㊻	77	㊼	79	80
81	82	83	㊽	85	86	87	㊼	89	⑨⓪
91	㊒	93	94	95	㊻	97	98	99	⑩⓪

Count by 6s.

1. First, put your finger on the 0. Move it to the 1 as you count "1." Move it to the 2 as you count "2." Continue counting. When you reach 6, stop. Draw an X through the 6.

2. Put your finger on 6 and repeat the process. Move to 7 as you count "1." Move to 8 as you count "2," and so on. The second X you draw should be through the 12.

3. Continue until you reach the end of the grid.

Count by 4s.

Start again at 0. This time count by 4s. When you stop on a number, draw a circle around it. Look for patterns so that you can predict when you will stop next.

✦ *Math Masters, p. 18*

TEACHING MASTER

You may want to use straws, blocks, or pencils to demonstrate different ways to say the same number. For example: $4 + 3 = 5 + 2$.

3 Options for Individualizing

✦ ENRICHMENT Finding Counting Patterns on a Number Grid (*Math Masters*, p. 18)

INDEPENDENT ACTIVITY   5–15 min

Children count by 6s on a number grid and mark the numbers (6, 12, 18, …) with Xs. Make sure children understand the procedure: Put a finger on the 0, move it to the 1 and say "1"; continue counting; mark the 6; move to the 7 and start the count over; and so on.

Then children count by 4s, mark the numbers with Os, and look for patterns on the number grid. *Are there any numbers that are both circled and have an X drawn over them?* Yes; 12, 24, 36, 48, 60, 72, 84, and 96 Children can check their work by counting on the calculator.

✦ LANGUAGE DIVERSITY Illustrating Equivalencies Using a Pan Balance and Identical Objects

PARTNER ACTIVITY   15–30 min

This activity is good for children who do not yet understand the concept of equivalency.

Set up a pan balance. Mark or tape an = sign on the fulcrum.

Show a few ways of arranging 7 or any other number of identical objects on each of the two pans. Ask children to suggest additional arrangements. For each arrangement, write number models.

Vary the ways in which you express the situations. *For example:*

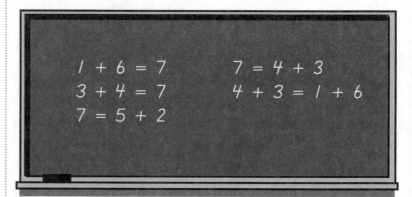

$$1 + 6 = 7 \qquad 7 = 4 + 3$$
$$3 + 4 = 7 \qquad 4 + 3 = 1 + 6$$
$$7 = 5 + 2$$

Repeat the process for other numbers.

1.11 Counting Patterns

OBJECTIVES To count on the calculator; and to look for patterns while counting.

summaries | materials

1 Teaching the Lesson

Children count by 10s. [Numeration]

Children count using a calculator and explore number patterns that result from counts. [Numeration; Patterns, Functions, and Algebra]

☐ *Math Journal 1*, p. 14
☐ calculator
☐ slate

2 Ongoing Learning & Practice

Children give equivalent names for numbers by solving *Broken Calculator* problems. [Numeration; Operations and Computation]

Children practice and maintain skills through Math Boxes.

☐ *Math Journal 1*, p. 15
☐ calculator

3 Options for Individualizing

Enrichment Children play *Pin the Number on the Number Grid* to strengthen their understanding of relationships on a number grid. [Patterns, Functions, and Algebra]

Language Diversity Children count rhythmically by 2s, 5s, and 10s. [Numeration]

☐ Class Number Grid Poster
☐ stick-on notes

Getting Started

Mental Math and Reflexes

Children use their slates to do problems like the following:

- Write 52. Circle the digit in the 10s place. Put an X on the digit in the 1s place.
- Write 120. Circle the digit in the 10s place. Put an X on the digit in the 1s place. Which digit is not marked?
- Write 209. Circle the digit in the 10s place. Put an X on the digit in the 1s place. Which digit has no marks on it?
- Write 143. Circle the 1. Put an X on the 3. What is the value of the digit that has no marks on it?

NOTE: Use numbers in the thousands if appropriate. Many classes will be able to do this.

Math Message

Count by 10s. Count as high as you can in 1 minute. Write the number you get to.

Counting with a Calculator

Clear the calculator.	(ON/C)
Enter the starting number.	[number]
Tell the calculator to count up or down.	(+) or (−)
Tell the calculator what number to count by.	[number]
Count by pressing the (=) key.	(=)

1. Count by 7s on your calculator. Write the numbers.

7, _14_, _21_, _28_, _35_, _42_, _49_

What number is added each time you press (=) ? _7_

2. Count by 6s on your calculator. Write the numbers.
Circle the 1s digit in each number.

6, ⑫, ⑱, ㉔, ㉚, ㊱, ㊷, ㊽, �554, ⑥0

What number is added each time you press (=) ? _6_

What pattern do you see in the 1s digits? _6, 2, 8, 4, 0_

3. Count by 4s on your calculator. Write the numbers.
Circle the 1s digit in each number.

4, ⑧, ⑫, ⑯, ⑳, ㉔, ㉘, ㉜, ㊱, ④0

What number is added each time you press (=) ? _4_

What pattern do you see in the 1s digits? _4, 8, 2, 6, 0_

Challenge

4. Jim counted on the calculator. He wrote these numbers: 3, 5, 7, 9, 11.

What keys did he press? ③ (+) ② (=) (=) (=) (=)

◇ Math Journal 1, p. 14

---

1 Teaching the Lesson

◆ Math Message Follow-Up

WHOLE-CLASS ACTIVITY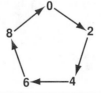

Count together by 10s up to 200.

◆ Counting with a Calculator
(*Math Journal 1,* p. 14)

WHOLE-CLASS ACTIVITY

Remind children that when they want to count using a calculator, they tell the calculator:

▷ to clear,

▷ to start with a certain number,

▷ to count up (+) or down (−),

▷ to count up or down by a certain number,

▷ to count by pressing (=) repeatedly.

Have children practice counting by 1s on their calculators.

Tell children that they are going to count by some unusual numbers. Have them turn to journal page 14. Point out the steps in the box at the top of the page. Give children a few minutes to do the first problem. Check to see that everyone understands what to do. Children then complete the page.

When most of the children have finished, briefly discuss the answers and any patterns they found.

Ask why you might choose not to use the calculator to count by 2s, 5s, or 10s. It's faster to do those counts without the calculator.

Adjusting the Activity Count by 2s to 24. Write the counts on the board and circle the 1s digits. The circled digits are 2, 4, 6, 8, 0, 2, 4, 6, 8, 0, 2, 4.

Now write the digits 0, 2, 4, 6, and 8 evenly spaced around a pentagon. (See art below.) Help children understand that the circled digits repeat the same pattern as the digits around the pentagon.

2 Ongoing Learning & Practice

✦ Solving *Broken Calculator* Problems

INDEPENDENT ACTIVITY

Pose *Broken Calculator* problems like those presented in Lesson 1.10 (*Math Journal 1,* page 12). If you wish, have children record their solutions on paper.

✦ Math Boxes 1.11 (*Math Journal 1,* p. 15)

INDEPENDENT ACTIVITY

Mixed Review This journal page provides opportunities for cumulative review or assessment of concepts and skills.

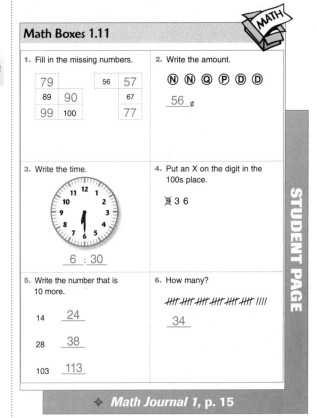

1. Fill in the missing numbers.

79		56	57
89	90		67
99	100		77

2. Write the amount.

Ⓝ Ⓝ Ⓠ Ⓟ Ⓓ Ⓓ

_56_ ¢

3. Write the time.

_6_ : _30_

4. Put an X on the digit in the 100s place.

✗ 3 6

5. Write the number that is 10 more.

14   _24_

28   _38_

103   _113_

6. How many?

H̶H̶T̶ H̶H̶T̶ H̶H̶T̶ H̶H̶T̶ H̶H̶T̶ H̶H̶T̶ IIII

_34_

✦ *Math Journal 1,* p. 15

---

3 Options for Individualizing

✦ ENRICHMENT Playing *Pin the Number on the Number Grid*

WHOLE-CLASS ACTIVITY   5–15 min

Ask the class to make some observations about the Class Number Grid Poster:

- Which numbers are in the top row?
- The bottom row?
- The middle?
- To the left?
- To the right?
- How many numbers are in each row?

A volunteer stands in front of the Class Number Grid Poster with eyes closed or wearing a blindfold. Write a number on a stick-on note. Tell the child the number to aim for, and hand him or her the note.

Going by sense of touch and what he or she knows about the placement of the numbers on the grid, the child tries to stick the number in the correct place. You may want to leave the notes children have placed on the grid, or remove the note after each try.

> NOTE: This is a challenging game in the beginning. Children get much better with practice.

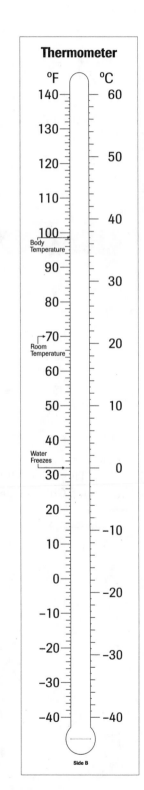

Thermometer

°F	
140	
130	
120	red
110	
100	
Body Temperature	
90	orange
80	
70	yellow
Room Temperature	
60	
50	green
40	
Water Freezes	
30	blue
20	
10	purple
0	
-10	
-20	white
-30	
-40	

Side A

Thermometer

°F	°C
140	60
130	
120	50
110	
100	40
Body Temperature	
90	30
80	
70	20
Room Temperature	
60	
50	10
40	
Water Freezes	0
30	
20	-10
10	
0	-20
-10	
-20	-30
-30	
-40	-40

Side B

Class Thermometers

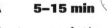

◆ LANGUAGE DIVERSITY Counting by 2s, 5s, and 10s

WHOLE-CLASS ACTIVITY 5–15 min

To practice counting by 2s, 5s, and 10s, try correlating rhythmic counting with movement. *For example:*

- 1, 2 (clap), 3, 4 (clap), …
- 1, 2, 3, 4, 5 (touch toes), 6, 7, 8, 9, 10 (touch toes), …
- 1, 2, 3, 4, 5, 6, 7, 8, 9, 10 (jumping jack), …

PLANNING AHEAD

Before beginning Lesson 1.13, assemble the Class Thermometer Poster so that the thermometer is full length. Note that one side of the thermometer includes only Fahrenheit temperatures, with the scale marked every 10 degrees. The other side has both Fahrenheit and Celsius scales marked at every degree.

Cut a long strip of red ribbon or crepe paper to represent the "mercury" in the thermometer tube. (The liquid is often called mercury, but may be something else.) Cut a slit in the thermometer bulb and pull the ribbon or crepe paper through the slit. Tape it at the top to hold it in place. Place a container beneath the poster to hold the excess ribbon or crepe paper. Cover the Celsius scale of the thermometer. (Celsius temperatures will be introduced in Unit 4.)

1.12 Relations (<, >, =) and Home Links

OBJECTIVES To compare numbers using the relation symbols <, >, and =; and to introduce Home Links.

summaries	materials

1 Teaching the Lesson

Children compare numbers by using words and by acting out pan-balance problems. [Numeration]

Children compare numbers by reading and writing number sentences that use the relation symbols =, <, and >.
[Numeration; Patterns, Functions, and Algebra]

- ☐ *Math Journal 1*, p. 16
- ☐ pan balance and 40 pennies or other small, identical objects (optional)
- ☐ slate

2 Ongoing Learning & Practice

Children review addition facts by playing *Addition Top-It*.
[Numeration; Operations and Computation]

Children practice and maintain skills through Math Boxes and Home Link activities.

- ☐ *Math Journal 1*, p. 17
- ☐ Home Link Masters (*Math Masters*, pp. 235 and 236)
- ☐ per partnership: 1 Everything Math Deck, if available; 1 set of double-9 dominoes; or 1 die or 3 dice (optional)

3 Options for Individualizing

Enrichment Children play *Digit Discovery* to practice place-value skills and to compare numbers. [Numeration]

Reteaching Children describe inequalities and equalities by using a pan balance to compare quantities. [Numeration]

- ☐ colored chalk (optional); number cards 0–9
- ☐ pan balance; 20 pennies or other identical objects

See **Advance Preparation**

Additional Information

Advance Preparation For the optional Enrichment activity in Part 3, use 4" by 6" index cards to make the three sets of number cards, 0 through 9 in each set. Each set of numbers can be written on a different-color card, or the numbers for each set can be written in a different color on white cards.

Vocabulary • **is equal to** • **is less than** • **is greater than**

Getting Started

Mental Math and Reflexes

Name pairs of numbers. Children write them on their slates and circle the larger or smaller number. Give problems like the following:

- Write 170 and 106. Circle the larger number.
- Write 200 and 189. Circle the smaller number.
- Write 115 and 107. Circle the smaller number.

Math Message

Write "is less than" or "is greater than" between each pair of numbers.

20 __>__ 12   40 __>__ 38

30 __<__ 35   70 __>__ 59

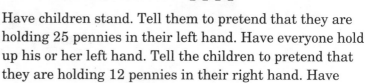

Adjusting the Activity Use an actual pan balance to demonstrate that 25 pennies are heavier than 12 pennies. Once children have seen several examples with the pan balance, pose similar problems for which they pretend to be a pan balance.

◆ Math Message Follow-Up

WHOLE-CLASS ACTIVITY

Have children stand. Tell them to pretend that they are holding 25 pennies in their left hand. Have everyone hold up his or her left hand. Tell the children to pretend that they are holding 12 pennies in their right hand. Have everyone hold up his or her right hand.

Which hand would be heavier? The hand with the 25 pennies Have children pretend they are pan balances and hold out their hands to show which hand would be lower. Ask why. The hand with 25 pennies would be lower, because 25 pennies are more than 12 pennies and the side with 25 pennies would be heavier.

Repeat the activity with 30 and 35 pennies. Encourage use of the language "30 is less than 35" and "35 is greater than 30."

◆ Reviewing Relations: Less Than (<), Greater Than (>), Equal To (=)

WHOLE-CLASS DISCUSSION

Write the following sentences on the board: "1 and 1 is the same as 2" and "1 plus 1 **is equal to** 2." Ask children which symbol can replace the words "is the same as" or "is equal to." = Erase these words and write = in their place. Ask which symbol can replace "and" or "plus" in these sentences. + Erase these words and put + in their place. Read the resulting sentences as, "1 and 1 is the same as 2," and "1 plus 1 is equal to 2," pointing to the number sentences on the board.

Write the following sentence on the board: "30 **is less than** 35." Remind children that symbols often replace words in mathematics. Ask if anyone knows which symbol can replace "is less than." If no one suggests it, show children the symbol "<." Erase "is less than" and replace the words with <.

Write "14 < 16" on the board. Ask a volunteer to read the number sentence. 14 is less than 16. Do several more examples like this.

Write "21 > 15" on the board. Ask a volunteer to tell what the symbol ">" means. "**Is greater than**," "is more than," "is larger than," or "is bigger than"

Explain that the open side of the symbols ">" and "<" is always next to the larger number. The vertex or point always points to the smaller number.

There are a number of strategies for remembering which is which.

▷ The "mouth" must be bigger to swallow the bigger number. (See the margin.)

▷ The "less" looks like the left-hand finger and thumb. (Less and left start with the same letter.) (See the margin.)

▷ The "meeting point" of the two lines always points to the smaller number.

▷ Draw dots on each open end of > or <, and draw one dot on the vertex or point. The number that is larger is on the side with 2 dots. The number that is smaller is on the side with 1 dot. (See the margin.)

▷ Draw two dots (:) next to the larger number and one dot next to the smaller number. Connect each of the two dots to the single dot, and the symbol will be correct. (See the margin.)

Write pairs of numbers on the board. *For example:*

15 $\underline{<}$ 25   40 $\underline{>}$ 34   20 $\underline{=}$ 20   102 $\underline{>}$ 27

Have volunteers come up and write the correct symbol between each pair of numbers.

◆ Practicing the Use of the Symbols <, >, and =
(*Math Journal 1,* p. 16)

WHOLE-CLASS ACTIVITY

Tell children pairs of numbers to write on their slates. Have them choose the symbol that goes between the numbers. Pose problems similar to those in the previous activity.

When children are ready, have them work alone or with a partner to complete journal page 16.

When most children have finished the page, discuss the answers.

ONGOING ASSESSMENT
If a child has difficulty with the coin problems, be sure to note whether the difficulty involves relation symbols or counting coin combinations.

3 ⦉ 5

5 ⦊ 3

Adjusting the Activity If children are comfortable with single numbers, challenge them with more complex problems; for example, 7 $\underline{>}$ 3 + 2; 4 + 1 $\underline{=}$ 5; 9 + 4 $\underline{>}$ 14 − 3

Using <, >, and =

3 < 5	5 > 3
3 is less than 5.	5 is greater than 3.

Write <, >, or =.

1. 61 $\underline{>}$ 26   2. 18 $\underline{<}$ 81   3. 107 $\underline{>}$ 57

4. 114 $\underline{=}$ 114   5. 299 $\underline{<}$ 302   6. 801 $\underline{>}$ 688

7. 15 $\underline{=}$ 7 + 8   8. 9 + 2 $\underline{>}$ 4 + 5   9. 5 + 6 $\underline{<}$ 8 + 4

10. Write the total amounts. Then write <, >, or =.

Example: Ⓓ Ⓝ Ⓝ Ⓟ Ⓟ = __22__¢ $\underline{<}$ __26__¢ = Ⓠ Ⓟ

a. Ⓝ Ⓝ Ⓓ Ⓟ = __21__¢ $\underline{<}$ __45__¢ = Ⓠ Ⓝ Ⓓ Ⓝ

b. Ⓝ Ⓓ Ⓟ Ⓠ = __41__¢ $\underline{<}$ __56__¢ = Ⓝ Ⓓ Ⓠ Ⓝ Ⓟ Ⓠ

c. Ⓓ Ⓓ Ⓠ Ⓓ = __55__¢ $\underline{>}$ __26__¢ = Ⓓ Ⓝ Ⓟ Ⓓ

STUDENT PAGE

◆ *Math Journal 1,* p. 16

STUDENT PAGE

1. Write 5 names for 15.

Sample answers:
$10 + 5$ $5 + 5 + 5$
$7 + 8$ $20 - 5$
$25 - 10$

2. Write the number.

〜〜〜 (tally marks) ~~~

_36_

3. Solve.

$$+ \boxed{5}$$

4. Fill in the blanks.

55, 60, _65_, _70_,
_75_, _80_, _85_

5. Write the amount.

Q N D N N P P

_52_ ¢

6. Draw the hands to show 9:00.

◆ *Math Journal 1, p. 17*

HOME LINK MASTER

Relations: <, >, =

Family Note

In *Second Grade Everyday Mathematics*, children "do mathematics." We expect that children will want to share their enthusiasm for the mathematics activities they do in school with their families. Your child will bring home assignments and activities to do as homework throughout the year. These assignments, called "Home Links," will be identified by the house at the top right corner of this page. The assignments will not take very much time to complete, but most of them involve interaction with an adult or an older child.

There are many reasons for including Home Links in the second grade program:

· The assignments encourage children to take *initiative* and *responsibility* for completing them. As you respond with encouragement and assistance, you help your child build independence and self-confidence.

· Home Links reinforce newly learned skills and concepts. They provide opportunities for children to think and practice at their own pace.

· These assignments are often designed to relate what is done in school to children's lives outside school. This helps tie mathematics to the real world, which is very important in the *Everyday Mathematics* program.

· The Home Links assignments will help you get a better idea of the mathematics your child is learning in school.

Generally, you can help by listening and responding to your child's requests and comments about mathematics. You also can help by linking numbers to real life, pointing out ways in which you use numbers (time, TV channels, page numbers, telephone numbers, bus routes, shopping lists, and so on). Extending the notion that "children who are read to, read," *Everyday Mathematics* supports the belief that children who have someone do math with them will learn mathematics. Playful counting and thinking games that are fun for both you and your child are very helpful for such learning.

*Please return the **second page** of this Home Link to school tomorrow.*

◆ *Math Masters, p. 235*

---

2 Ongoing Learning & Practice

◆ Playing *Addition Top-It*

PARTNER ACTIVITY

Partners continue to play the game as it was introduced in Lesson 1.4, or they play one of the following variations:

▷ Use double-9 dominoes instead of number cards.

▷ Draw 3 cards on each turn instead of 2.

▷ Roll a single die three times, or roll three separate dice, to generate three addends.

◆ Math Boxes 1.12 (*Math Journal 1,* p. 17)

INDEPENDENT ACTIVITY

Mixed Review This journal page provides opportunities for cumulative review or assessment of concepts and skills.

◆ Home Link 1.12 (*Math Masters,* pp. 235 and 236)

Home Connection Children compare numbers and write the symbols <, >, and =.

Distribute Home Link 1.12. Discuss the purpose of Home Links and children's responsibilities:

• Put your name, the date, and the time on your Home Link.

• Take home the correct Home Link.

• Discuss and complete the Home Link with someone at home—a parent, guardian, older brother or sister, other relative, caretaker, and so on.

• Return the completed Home Link to school the next school day. (Occasionally, Home Links take several days to complete.)

3 Options for Individualizing

◆ ENRICHMENT Playing *Digit Discovery*

SMALL-GROUP ACTIVITY 15–30 min

Use colored chalk, if available, to write the place-value names along the top of the board. For example, write "hundreds" in red, "tens" in blue, and "ones" in green. Children stand under these names and make a human place-value chart.

Mix and distribute the colored number cards so that each child has at least one. Give clues like the following to summon children to the board:

• I am the largest 3-digit number. Children with red 9, blue 9, and green 9 come to the board and stand under their colors, holding up their number cards.

• I am 10 less than the number up there now. Blue 9 sits down and is replaced by blue 8.

• I am 500 less than the number up there now. Red 9 sits down and is replaced by red 4.

If children do these problems easily, continue with more challenging ones. *For example:*

• I am 5 more than the number up there now. Blue 8 sits down and blue 9 returns. Green 9 sits down and is replaced by green 4.

Continue as time and interest allow.

Challenge children by asking them to make up the clues.

◆ RETEACHING Showing Equalities and Inequalities with a Pan Balance

SMALL-GROUP DISCUSSION 5–15 min

Use a pan balance and objects to demonstrate and help children verbalize *greater, less,* and *equal* relationships. For example, "The things on this side weigh more than the things on that side." "These objects weigh less than those objects." "These things weigh about the same."

Repeat with various quantities of identical objects.

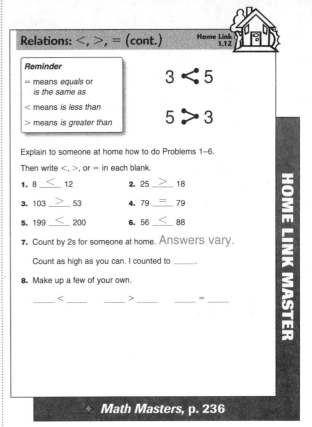

◆ *Math Masters,* p. 236

Relations: <, >, = (cont.)   Home Link 1.12

Reminder
= means *equals* or *is the same as*
< means *is less than*
> means *is greater than*

$3 < 5$

$5 > 3$

Explain to someone at home how to do Problems 1–6.
Then write <, >, or = in each blank.

1. 8 $\underline{<}$ 12   2. 25 $\underline{>}$ 18
3. 103 $\underline{>}$ 53   4. 79 $\underline{=}$ 79
5. 199 $\underline{<}$ 200   6. 56 $\underline{<}$ 88

7. Count by 2s for someone at home. Answers vary.
   Count as high as you can. I counted to _____.

8. Make up a few of your own.
   _____ < _____   _____ > _____   _____ = _____

HOME LINK MASTER

Playing *Digit Discovery* gives children practice with place-value skills and comparing numbers.

1.13
EXPLORATIONS

Exploring Temperatures, Base-10 Structures, and Dominoes

OBJECTIVES To read and display temperatures; to combine values of ones, tens, and hundreds using base-10 blocks; and to recognize addition facts on dominoes.

summaries	materials

1 Teaching the Lesson

Children are introduced to procedures and expectations for Explorations.

Exploration A: Children read and display temperatures on the Class Thermometer Poster. [Measurement and Reference Frames]

Exploration B: Children build structures from base-10 blocks and calculate the values represented by the structures. [Numeration; Operations and Computation]

Exploration C: Children sort dominoes according to the sums of the domino dots. [Numeration; Operations and Computation]

□ outdoor thermometer
□ Home Link 1.12

Exploration A: Per station:
□ Teaching Master (*Math Masters,* p. 19)
□ Class Thermometer Poster; quarter-sheets of paper

Exploration B: Per station:
□ Teaching Master (*Math Masters,* p. 20)
□ base-10 blocks (cubes, longs, flats)
□ quarter-sheets of paper

Exploration C: Per station:
□ Teaching Master (*Math Masters,* p. 21)
□ 1 set of the number cards 0–18 (from the Everything Math Deck, if available)
□ 1 or 2 sets of double-9 dominoes

See Advance Preparation

2 Ongoing Learning & Practice

Children play *Addition Top-It.* [Numeration; Operations and Computation]

Children practice and maintain skills through Math Boxes and Home Link activities.

□ *Math Journal 1,* p. 18
□ Home Link Master (*Math Masters,* p. 237)
□ four each of the number cards 0–10 (from the Everything Math Deck, if available) per partnership

3 Options for Individualizing

Extra Practice Children practice quick addition facts and compare temperatures. [multiple strands]

□ *Minute Math*®, pp. 10, 41, 97, and 136

Additional Information

Background Information For additional information on Explorations, see the *Teacher's Reference Manual.*

Advance Preparation You may want to create and display a poster of Rules for Explorations like the one shown on page 72. Decide how many stations you will need in order to accommodate your children in groups of 3, 4, or 5. You may want to:

• Set up two or three stations for each Exploration.

• Set up additional activities or games with which children are familiar. For example, *Addition Top-It* is suggested in this lesson. You will need an outdoor thermometer large enough so that children can easily see the level of the liquid. Cover the Celsius scale with masking tape.

Vocabulary • **temperature** • **thermometer** • **Fahrenheit** • **Explorations** • **base-10 blocks** • **cube** • **long** • **flat**

Getting Started

Mental Math and Reflexes

Have children name as many ways as they can to add two numbers to get 20.

Record responses on the board.

Math Message

Make a list of words to describe the weather.

Home Link 1.12 Follow-Up

Briefly go over the answers.

Ask volunteers to share some of the problems they made up.

---

1 Teaching the Lesson

◆ Math Message Follow-Up

WHOLE-CLASS ACTIVITY

Record children's responses on the board. Ask children which words describe **temperature.** Possible answers: hot, cold, warm, cool, freezing, boiling Circle the temperature words on the board.

Display an outdoor **thermometer.** Explain that an outdoor thermometer makes it possible to not only say that it's cold or hot outside, but also to say how cold or hot it is. For example, 6°F might be the temperature on a colder day and 89°F might be the temperature on a hotter day.

Have children look at the Class Thermometer Poster. Ask them to describe what they see. Sample answers: Numbers every 10 degrees; marks for degrees; the letter F at the top of the thermometer with the symbol "°" in front of it; arrows indicating body temperature, room temperature and the temperature at which water freezes; a red ribbon or strip of red crepe paper running next to the numbers of degrees

NOTE: You may want to explain that there is a second scale on many thermometers. It is called the Celsius temperature scale. The Celsius scale will be introduced in Unit 4.

Put your finger on the scale at 0. Move it up the scale while children count in unison the numbers of degrees by 10s: *0 degrees, 10 degrees, 20 degrees, …*

Repeat the activity with children counting the number of degrees by 2s.

Point out the numbers below 0 with the negative signs in front of them: −10, −20. These temperatures are read "10 degrees below zero," "20 degrees below zero," and so on.

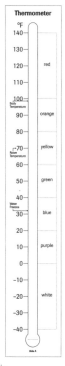

Class Thermometer Poster

Science Link

Point out that the letter F stands for **Fahrenheit,** which is the name of the physicist, Gabriel Daniel Fahrenheit, who developed this thermometer scale. A Fahrenheit thermometer measures temperature in *degrees Fahrenheit*. The symbol for degrees, "°," appears before the letter F and is read *degrees Fahrenheit*. Write 60°F on the board. Say, "This is read '60 degrees Fahrenheit.'"

Adjusting the Activity Tell children that these temperatures can also be read "negative 10 degrees," "negative 20 degrees," and so on. Point out that, on a number line, negative numbers are displayed to the left of 0.

Rules for Explorations

1. Cooperate with others.
2. Move about quietly.
3. Keep voices low.
4. Treat materials as tools, not as toys.
5. Straighten up when finished. Put materials back where they belong.

Temperature

Work in a group of 3 or 4 children.

Materials ❏ Class Thermometer Poster

❏ quarter-sheets of paper

Directions

Activity 1

1. Take turns. One person names a temperature. Another person shows that temperature on the Class Thermometer Poster.

2. Everyone in the group checks to see that the temperature is shown correctly.

3. Keep taking turns until each person has named a temperature and has shown a temperature on the Class Thermometer Poster.

Activity 2

1. Take turns showing a temperature on the Class Thermometer Poster. Everyone reads the thermometer and writes that temperature.

2. Everyone in the group compares the temperatures they wrote. Did everyone write the same temperature? Discuss any differences.

Follow-Up

Look at all of the temperatures that you recorded on your quarter-sheets of paper.

• Were some temperatures easier to read than others? Explain.

• Order the temperatures from coldest to hottest.

 Math Masters, p. 19

◆ Discussing Procedures and Expectations for Explorations

WHOLE-GROUP DISCUSSION

Review the expectations for small-group work from previous lessons. Talk about the purposes of and the management routines for **Explorations.** Model and explain the specific Exploration activities.

◆ Exploration A: Measuring Temperature
(*Math Masters,* p. 19)

SMALL-GROUP ACTIVITY

Have someone place the outdoor thermometer outside for a few minutes while you discuss the daily temperature routine.

Assign a child to be in charge of setting the temperature on the Class Thermometer Poster to show the outside temperature. Frequently rotate the job among the children in your class. You will need to supervise this routine in the beginning, but with experience, children will be able to complete the job independently.

On the Class Thermometer Poster, the red ribbon or crepe paper represents the mercury in a regular thermometer. At about the same time each day, a child should move the red ribbon on the Class Thermometer Poster to approximately match the temperature on the outdoor thermometer. Model how to do this and ask children to describe today's temperature reading. Encourage the use of such phrases as "between ___ and ___ degrees Fahrenheit," "almost ___ degrees Fahrenheit," and "about halfway between ___ and ___ degrees Fahrenheit."

Once children are comfortable setting a temperature on the Class Thermometer Poster, have them work as a group to complete *Math Masters,* page 19.

Adjusting the Activity Side 1 of the Class Thermometer Poster was used at the beginning of *First Grade Everyday Mathematics.* By Unit 4 of Grade 1, children began to set daily temperatures on Side 2 of the poster. If the children in your class have had limited exposure to thermometers, you may wish to use Side 1 to begin the daily temperature routine. Once children are accustomed to reading the thermometer and setting the temperature, switch over to Side 2.

✦ Exploration B: Calculating the Values of Base-10 Structures (*Math Masters,* p. 20)

SMALL-GROUP ACTIVITY

Introduce this Exploration to the whole class before children form small groups.

Show children a set of **base-10 blocks.** Hold up a **cube** and call it a *cube.* Explain that it represents one unit, or *one.* Hold up a **long** and call it a *long.* Ask:

- What numerical value might a long represent? 10 units, or 10

- How do you know? Sample answer: There are 10 units marked on it. It is 10 times as long as a cube.

Repeat with a hundreds **flat.**

Tell children that they will build structures with the base-10 blocks. Once children have built the structures, they can figure out how much each structure is worth by counting the number of cubes (1s), longs (10s), and flats (100s) that they used.

Explain to children that they will draw these structures and write their values on quarter-sheets of paper.

Children form small groups and proceed with the activity. If time permits, groups should arrange their written records in order from least to greatest value.

 Adjusting the Activity You may want to model some simple 2-dimensional structures on the overhead so that children can practice evaluating them.

✦ Exploration C: Sorting Dominoes (*Math Masters,* p. 21)

SMALL-GROUP ACTIVITY

Children work together in small groups to sort one or more sets of double-9 dominoes. Children first lay out the number cards from 0 through 18. They place each domino above the number card that shows the sum of the domino's dots. Each group makes a list of all the addition facts shown by the dominoes.

 Adjusting the Activity You might have children record the addition facts for only one number card.

Base-10 Structures

Work in a group of 3 or 4 children.

Materials ☐ base-10 blocks (cubes, longs, and flats)

☐ quarter-sheets of paper

Directions

1. Each person uses base-10 blocks to make a "building." The picture shows an example.

2. Each block has a value.

   The value of the cube is 1.
   The value of the long is 10.
   The value of the flat is 100.

•	=	1
I	=	10
☐	=	100

   What number does your building show? Use the symbols in the box above to help you.

3. Draw your building on a quarter-sheet of paper. Write the number with your drawing.

4. Have a friend help you check the number.

5. If there is time, make more buildings. Draw each building and record the number of each building.

Follow-Up

- Look at the numbers shown by your group's buildings.

- Order the numbers from smallest to largest.

✦ *Math Masters,* p. 20

TEACHING MASTER

Sorting Dominoes

Work in a group of 3 or 4 children.

Materials ☐ 1 or 2 sets of double-9 dominoes

☐ number cards 0–18 (from the Everything Math Deck, if available)

Directions

1. Lay down the number cards in order from 0 through 18.

2. Place each domino above the number card that shows the sum of the domino dots.

   5

3. List the addition facts shown by the dominoes on a sheet of paper. Before you begin, decide how your group will record the facts.

Follow-Up

- Look at the list of addition facts your group made.

- Try to think of a better way to record the facts.

- Talk about why you think the new way is better.

✦ *Math Masters,* p. 21

TEACHING MASTER

Math Boxes 1.13

1. Fill in the missing numbers.

92	93
	103
112	113

2. Use <, >, or =.

$7 + 8 \underline{=} 9 + 6$

$15 - 9 \underline{<} 24$

$8 + 8 \underline{>} 10 + 4$

3. Write 5 names for 18.

Sample answers:

$15 + 3 \quad 20 - 2$

$10 + 8 \quad 7 + 11$

$36 - 18$

4. Continue.

397, 398, 399, 400, 401, 402

5. Put a line under the digit in the ones place.

4 7 9

6. Continue. Circle the even numbers.

85, 90, 95, 100, 105, 110, 115

◆ *Math Journal, p. 18*

2 Ongoing Learning & Practice

◆ Playing *Addition Top-It*

PARTNER ACTIVITY

Children practice addition skills for numbers from 0 through 10 by playing *Addition Top-It*. For detailed instructions, see Lesson 1.4.

◆ Math Boxes 1.13 (*Math Journal 1,* p. 18)

INDEPENDENT ACTIVITY

 Mixed Review This journal page provides opportunities for cumulative review and assessment of concepts and skills.

◆ Home Link 1.13 (*Math Masters,* p. 237)

 Home Connection Children read Fahrenheit thermometers marked in 1-degree intervals.

Temperatures

Home Link 1.13

Family Note

In today's lesson, the class examined thermometers and practiced reading Fahrenheit temperatures. We began a daily routine of recording the outside temperature. If you have a nondigital thermometer at home (inside or outside), encourage your child to read the Fahrenheit temperatures to you. We will introduce Celsius temperatures in a later unit.

Please return this Home Link to school tomorrow.

1. Circle the thermometer that shows 30°F.

2. Circle the thermometer that shows 20°F.

3. Circle the thermometer that shows 12°F.

4. Circle the thermometer that shows 28°F.

◆ *Math Masters, p. 237*

3 Options for Individualizing

◆ EXTRA PRACTICE Minute Math

SMALL-GROUP ACTIVITY **5–15 min**

To offer children more experience with arithmetic facts and temperatures, see the following pages in *Minute Math:*

Basic Routines: p. 10

Operations: p. 41

Number Stories: pp. 97 and 136 (but work with Fahrenheit temperatures only)

1.14 Unit 1 Review and Assessment

OBJECTIVE To review and assess children's progress on the material covered in Unit 1.

1 Assess Progress

learning goals

1a **Developing Goal** Find values of coin and bill combinations. **(Lessons 1.2 and 1.6)**

1b **Developing Goal** Know "easy" addition facts (sums to 10). **(Lesson 1.2)**

1c **Developing Goal** Identify place value for ones, tens, and hundreds. **(Lesson 1.9)**

1d **Developing Goal** Complete number sequences; identify and use number patterns to solve problems. **(Lessons 1.1 and 1.8)**

1e **Developing Goal** Find equivalent names for numbers. **(Lessons 1.10 and 1.11)**

1f **Developing Goal** Compare numbers; write the symbol $<$, $>$, or $=$. **(Lesson 1.12)**

1g **Secure Goal** Count by 2s, 5s, and 10s. **(Lesson 1.11)**

1h **Secure Goal** Make tallies and give the total. **(Lesson 1.5)**

activities

1a
- ❑ Oral Assessment, Problem 5
- ❑ Slate Assessment, Problem 11
- ❑ Written Assessment, Problems 2 and 6

1b
- ❑ Slate Assessment, Problems 2, 8, and 9
- ❑ Written Assessment, Problem 4

1c
- ❑ Slate Assessment, Problems 4–6
- ❑ Written Assessment, Problem 3

1d
- ❑ Slate Assessment, Problem 1
- ❑ Written Assessment, Problem 5

1e
- ❑ Slate Assessment, Problem 3
- ❑ Written Assessment, Problem 7

1f
- ❑ Slate Assessment, Problem 7

1g
- ❑ Oral Assessment, Problems 1–4

1h
- ❑ Written Assessment, Problem 1

materials

- ❑ Home Link 1.13
- ❑ Assessment Master (*Math Masters*, p. 419)
- ❑ 1 set of tool-kit coins; demonstration clock; colored chalk
- ❑ overhead calculator (optional); grease pencil or washable marker; scissors
- ❑ calculator; number cards 0–9 (from the Everything Math Deck, if available)

2 Build Background for Unit 2

summaries

Children practice and maintain skills through Math Boxes and Home Link activities.

materials

- ❑ *Math Journal 1*, p. 19
- ❑ Home Link Masters (*Math Masters*, pp. 238–241)

Each **learning goal** listed above indicates a level of performance that might be expected at this point in the *Everyday Mathematics* K–6 curriculum. For a variety of reasons, the levels indicated may not accurately portray your class's performance.

Additional Information

Advance Preparation For *Digit Discovery* on page 78, you will need the number cards described in Lesson 1.12. (Use 4" by 6" index cards to make three sets of number cards, 0 through 9 in each set. Each set of numbers can be written on different-color cards, or the numbers for each set can be written in a different color on white cards.)

For additional information on assessment for Unit 1, see the *Assessment Handbook,* pages 40–42. For assessment checklists, see *Math Masters,* pages 448–449 and 485–488.

Getting Started

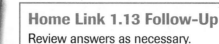

Math Message

My calculator is broken. The 0 and 1 keys do not work.

- *How can I show 10? Once I show 10, how can I show 50?*

Home Link 1.13 Follow-Up

Review answers as necessary.

Assess Progress

✦ Math Message Follow-Up

WHOLE-CLASS ACTIVITY

Have children share their solution strategies. Expect answers like the following:

▷ You can enter 5 and add 5 to get 10. Then you can add 49 and subtract 9.

▷ You can enter 8 and add 2 to get 10. Then you can add 42 and subtract 2.

▷ You can enter 32 and subtract 22 to get 10. Then you can add 35 and 5 more to get 50.

If time allows, have children try out several solutions using their calculators. If you have an overhead calculator, do the solution steps together.

✦ Oral and Slate Assessments

SMALL-GROUP ACTIVITY

Instead of doing the oral and slate activities with the whole class, you might want to work with small groups of children, one group at a time, over several days. While you do this, the rest of the class can work on the written review pages. It is not necessary to record every child's performance on every problem. Instead, you need only keep a record of children who are struggling. You can go back later and enter positive comments.

NOTE: Many of these assessment suggestions relate to learning goals that have been addressed in previous grades. Now is a good time to evaluate children's progress toward those goals.

If the suggested problems below are not appropriate for your class's level of performance, adjust the numbers in the problems—or adjust the problems themselves—to better assess your children's abilities.

Oral Assessment Suggestions

1. Count up by 2s beginning with 0, 10, 26, and 50.
   Goal 1g

2. Count up by 5s beginning with 0, 15, 45, and 70.
   Goal 1g

3. Count up by 10s beginning with 0, 40, and 60.
   Goal 1g

4. Do stop-and-start counts, beginning at 0, and counting by 10s. Stop at 40. Continue by 5s. Stop at 55. Continue by 1s to 58. **Goal 1g**

5. Have children show coin combinations for 9¢, 16¢, 21¢, and 32¢. **Goal 1a**

Slate Assessment Suggestions

1. Write the number that is one more than (or one less than) 15; 29; 72; 100. **Goal 1d**

2. Write the sum: $4 + 5 = ?$; $? = 2 + 8$; $7 + 5 = ?$; $? = 5 + 5$. **Goal 1b**

3. Write another name for the number 6; 12; 15; 20.
   Goal 1e

4. Write the number 41. Put an X through the digit in the ones place. **Goal 1c**

5. Write the number 125. Circle the digit in the hundreds place. Underline the digit in the ones place.
   Goal 1c

6. Write the number 708. Circle the digit in the tens place. **Goal 1c**

7. Write 15. Leave a space and write 18. Put the correct symbol between the numbers: $<$, $>$, or $=$. Do the same for 27 and 17; for 51 and 39. **Goal 1f**

Tell number stories like the following. Children record their answers on slates. If time allows, have children share strategies for how they figured out the answers. Encourage children to use manipulatives, drawings, doodles, or other strategies to solve the problems.

8. Flora wants to buy a hat. The hat costs $10. Flora has $7. How much more money does she need? **Goal 1b**

9. Bradley's family sleeps in a tent on their camping trip. The tent had 8 tent stakes to hold it up. The family lost 5 tent stakes. How many stakes do they have left? Do you think their tent will stay up?
   Goal 1b

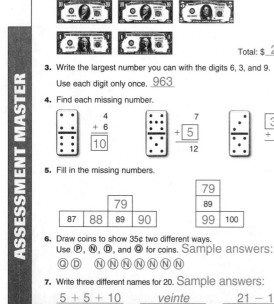

Unit 1 Checking Progress

1. Show 17 with tally marks. _|||| |||| |||| ||_

2. Write the amount.

Total: $ _27_

3. Write the largest number you can with the digits 6, 3, and 9.
   Use each digit only once. _963_

4. Find each missing number.

   4
   + 6
   [10]

   7
   +[5]
   12

   3
   +5
   8

5. Fill in the missing numbers.

		79	
87	88	89	90

79	
89	
99	100

6. Draw coins to show 35¢ two different ways.
   Use P, N, D, and Q for coins. Sample answers:
   Q D   N N N N N N N

7. Write three different names for 20. Sample answers:
   _5 + 5 + 10_   _veinte_   _21 − 1_

◆ *Math Masters*, p. 419

ASSESSMENT MASTER

10. Patrick won 2 guppies at the state fair. About 3 months later, Patrick noticed that his pair of guppies had given birth to 12 baby guppies. How many guppies did Patrick have altogether?

11. Gerard had a quarter. He needed another dime to buy his favorite candy bar. How much did the candy bar cost? **Goal 1a**

◆ Written Assessment (*Math Masters,* p. 419)

INDEPENDENT ACTIVITY

Read through the problems with the class. You may want to do examples with the class for some of the problems.

If appropriate, work through the problems together.

If your class can work independently, have children work alone or with a partner on this review page. Circulate and assist.

- Show 17 with tally marks. (Problem 1) **Goal 1h**
- Write the amount. (Problem 2) **Goal 1a**
- Write the largest number you can with the digits 6, 3, and 9. Use each digit only once. (Problem 3) **Goal 1c**
- Find each missing number. (Problem 4) **Goal 1b**
- Fill in the missing numbers. (Problem 5) **Goal 1d**
- Draw coins to show 35¢ two different ways. Use P, N, D, and Q for coins. (Problem 6) **Goal 1a**
- Write three different names for 20. (Problem 7) **Goal 1e**

◆ ALTERNATIVE ASSESSMENT OPTION
Play *Digit Discovery*

WHOLE-GROUP ACTIVITY

Use this game to assess children's understanding of place value. See Lesson 1.12 for instructions. Consider having children record the new numbers on a sheet of paper before the class acts out the problem. Collect the papers at the end of the game.

◆ ALTERNATIVE ASSESSMENT OPTION
Create Number-Grid Puzzles

INDEPENDENT ACTIVITY

Use this activity to assess children's ability to identify and use number-grid patterns. See Lesson 1.9 for instructions.

Portfolio Ideas

2 Build Background for Unit 2

◆ Math Boxes 1.14 (*Math Journal 1*, p. 19)

INDEPENDENT ACTIVITY 👤

Mixed Review This journal page provides opportunities for cumulative review or assessment of concepts and skills.

◆ Home Link 1.14: Unit 2 Family Letter
(*Math Masters*, pp. 238–241)

Home Connection This Home Link is a four-page newsletter that introduces parents and guardians to Unit 2's topics and terms. The letter also offers ideas for home-based mathematics activities that are supportive of classroom work.

STUDENT PAGE

1. Fill in names for 12.

_____ + _____ = 12

12 = _____ + _____

12 = _____ + _____

_____ + _____ = 12

Answers vary.

2. How much money?

$ 11 . 40

3. Play *Broken Calculator*.
Show 11. Broken key is 1.
Show 3 ways.

Sample answers:

8 + 3   7 + 4

20 − 9

4. Today is

_____ _____, _____.
(month)   (day)   (year)

This month has _____ days.

Answers vary.

5. Fill in the missing numbers.

	125	
134	135	136
144	145	146

6. Write the number that is 10 more.

97   107

197   207

297   307

◆ Math Journal 1, p. 19

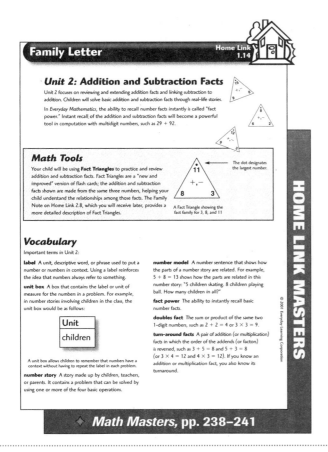

Family Letter   Home Link 1.14

Unit 2: Addition and Subtraction Facts

Unit 2 focuses on reviewing and extending addition facts and linking subtraction to addition. Children will solve basic addition and subtraction facts through real-life stories.

In *Everyday Mathematics*, the ability to recall number facts instantly is called "fact power." Instant recall of the addition and subtraction facts will become a powerful tool in computation with multidigit numbers, such as 29 + 92.

Math Tools

Your child will be using **Fact Triangles** to practice and review addition and subtraction facts. Fact Triangles are a "new and improved" version of flash cards; the addition and subtraction facts shown are made from the same three numbers, helping your child understand the relationships among those facts. The Family Note on Home Link 2.8, which you will receive later, provides a more detailed description of Fact Triangles.

The dot designates the largest number.

A Fact Triangle showing the fact family for 3, 8, and 11

Vocabulary

Important terms in Unit 2:

label A unit, descriptive word, or phrase used to put a number or numbers in context. Using a label reinforces the idea that numbers always refer to something.

unit box A box that contains the label or unit of measure for the numbers in a problem. For example, in number stories involving children in the class, the unit box would be as follows:

Unit
children

A unit box allows children to remember that numbers have a context without having to repeat the label in each problem.

number story A story made up by children, teachers, or parents. It contains a problem that can be solved by using one or more of the four basic operations.

number model A number sentence that shows how the parts of a number story are related. For example, 5 + 8 = 13 shows how the parts are related in this number story: "5 children skating. 8 children playing ball. How many children in all?"

fact power The ability to instantly recall basic number facts.

doubles fact The sum or product of the same two 1-digit numbers, such as 2 + 2 = 4 or 3 × 3 = 9.

turn-around facts A pair of addition (or multiplication) facts in which the order of the addends (or factors) is reversed, such as 3 + 5 = 8 and 5 + 3 = 8 (or 3 × 4 = 12 and 4 × 3 = 12). If you know an addition or multiplication fact, you also know its turnaround.

© 2001 Everyday Learning Corporation

HOME LINK MASTERS

◆ Math Masters, pp. 238–241

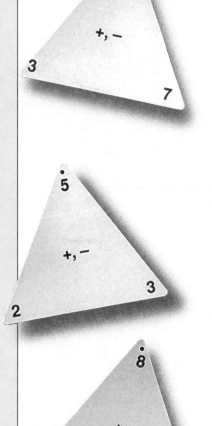

Unit 2
Addition and Subtraction Facts

Teachers know that children rarely master a new concept or skill from a single presentation. Understanding usually occurs after repeated exposures, with each experience building on previous ones. Children can "re-learn" forgotten ideas through reminders and by having interesting opportunities to reuse previously taught concepts.

Much of the material in Unit 2 serves to remind children of content covered in *First Grade Everyday Mathematics.* Routines are reviewed and extended. Frequent experiences with these routines should enable children to achieve mastery of most addition facts by the time they start Unit 4. Subtraction is linked to addition to help children develop facility with subtraction facts. Children also use their knowledge of the basic addition and subtraction facts to solve number stories involving real-life situations. Equivalent names for numbers, number sequences, and function tables provide additional practice with facts in problem-solving settings.

contents

UNIT

2

learning goals
in perspective

learning goals	links to the past	links to the future
2a **Developing Goal** Know "harder" subtraction facts. **(Lesson 2.13)**	Children were introduced to these subtraction facts in first grade.	Unit 6 provides focused practice with subtraction algorithms. *(Related Grade 2 lessons: 4.2, 4.4, 6.2, 6.4–6.6)*
2b **Developing/Secure Goal** Know "harder" addition facts. **(Lessons 2.4 and 2.5)**	Children worked on "easier" facts in first grade and in Unit 1. *(Related Grade 2 lessons: 1.2, 1.4, 1.7)*	Throughout second grade, children will practice addition facts through games and in a variety of problem-solving situations. *(Related Grade 2 lessons: 3.2, 3.7, 4.1, 4.6, 4.8, 4.9, 6.1, 6.4, 7.4)*
2c **Developing/Secure Goal** Know "easier" subtraction facts. **(Lessons 2.8 and 2.12)**	Children began learning basic subtraction facts in first grade.	Practice with subtraction facts is provided in relation to addition and through games and problem solving throughout the grades. *(Related Grade 2 lessons: 4.2, 4.4, 6.2, 6.4–6.6)*
2d **Developing/Secure Goal** Complete "What's My Rule?" tables. **(Lesson 2.11)**	Children were introduced to "What's My Rule?" in Kindergarten and began using the function machine diagram in first grade.	In third grade, "What's My Rule?" will be extended to include multiplication and division. *(Related Grade 2 lessons: 3.6, 5.1)*
2e **Developing/Secure Goal** Solve simple subtraction number stories. **(Lesson 2.6)**	Children began telling and solving number stories in Kindergarten, and continued throughout first grade.	Throughout the grades, children will continue to create and solve number stories. *(Related Grade 2 lessons: 4.1, 4.2, 6.2, 6.4, 6.11)*
2f **Secure Goal** Know "easier" addition facts. **(Lessons 2.2, 2.3, and 2.8)**	Children practiced +1, +0, doubles, and sums of ten addition facts during first grade, and reviewed addition facts in Unit 1. *(Related Grade 2 lessons: 1.4, 1.7)*	Addition will continue to be practiced through games and in a variety of problem-solving situations throughout second grade. *(Related Grade 2 lessons: 3.2, 3.7, 4.1, 4.6, 4.8, 4.9, 6.1, 6.4, 7.4)*
2g **Secure Goal** Construct fact families for addition and subtraction. **(Lessons 2.6 and 2.8)**	Fact families were introduced in first grade using Fact Triangles.	Fact Triangles will be used for basic fact review throughout second grade. Later on in second grade and in third grade, children will use Fact Triangles for multiplication and division fact families. *(Related Grade 2 lessons: 3.5, 3.9, 6.2, 6.6, 6.8)*
2h **Secure Goal** Complete simple Frames-and-Arrows diagrams. **(Lesson 2.10)**	The Frames-and-Arrows routine was introduced in first grade using one rule.	Frames and Arrows will be extended in second and third grades to incorporate more than one rule and to use a variety of concepts. *(Related Grade 2 lessons: 3.6, 5.1)*
2i **Secure Goal** Solve simple addition number stories. **(Lesson 2.1)**	Children began telling and solving number stories in Kindergarten and continued throughout first grade.	Throughout the grades, children will continue to create and solve number stories. *(Related Grade 2 lessons: 4.1, 4.2, 6.2, 6.4, 6.8)*
2j **Secure Goal** Find equivalent names for numbers. **(Lesson 2.9)**	Children began finding equivalent names for numbers in Kindergarten and made name-collection boxes in first grade. *(Related Grade 2 lesson: 1.10)*	Finding equivalent names for numbers is emphasized throughout the grades. *(Related Grade 2 lessons: 3.2, 3.4, 3.8, 5.3)*

assessment
ongoing • product • periodic

☑ Informal Assessment

Math Boxes These *Math Journal* pages provide opportunities for cumulative review or assessment of concepts and skills.

Ongoing Assessment: Kid Watching Use the Ongoing Assessment suggestions in the following lessons to make quick, on-the-spot observations about children's understanding of:
• Operations and Computation **(Lessons 2.3, 2.5, 2.6, 2.7, 2.9, and 2.10)**
• Measurement and Reference Frames **(Lesson 2.8)**

Portfolio Ideas Samples of children's work may be obtained from the following assignments:
• Making Up Addition Number Stories for a Bulletin Board or Book **(Lesson 2.1)**
• Creating and Solving Riddles **(Lesson 2.4)**
• Write and Solve Addition and Subtraction Number Stories **(Lesson 2.14)**

☑ Unit 2 Review and Assessment

Math Message Use the problem in Lesson 2.14 to assess children's progress toward the following learning goal: **Goal 2g**

Slate Assessments Use slate assessments during Lesson 2.14 to assess children's progress toward the following learning goals: **Goals 2a, 2b, 2c, 2e, 2f, 2g, 2i, and 2j**

Written Assessment Use a written review during Lesson 2.14 to assess children's progress toward the following learning goals: **Goals 2a, 2b, 2c, 2d, 2f, 2g, 2h, and 2j**

Performance/Group Assessment Use a small-group activity in Lesson 2.14 to assess children's progress toward the following learning goals:
Goals 2a, 2b, 2g, 2e, and 2i

assessment handbook

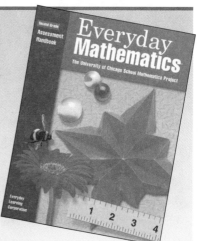

For more information on how to use different types of assessment in Unit 2, see the Assessment Overview on pages 43–45 in the *Assessment Handbook*. The following Assessment Masters can be found in the *Math Masters* book:

• Unit 2 Checking Progress, pp. 420 and 421
• Unit 2 Class Checklist, p. 450
• Unit 2 Individual Profile of Progress, p. 451
• Class Progress Indicator, p. 488
• Math Logs, pp. 493–495
• Self-Assessment Forms, pp. 496 and 497
• Interest Inventory, pp. 491 and 492

problemsolving

A process of modeling everyday situations using tools from mathematics

Encourage children to use a variety of strategies when attacking a given problem—and to explain those strategies. *Strategies children might use in this unit:*

- Identifying and using patterns
- Working backward
- Using pictures and models
- Using manipulatives
- Using number models

Four Problem-Solving REPRESENTATIONS

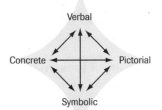

For more information about problem solving in *Everyday Mathematics,* see the *Teacher's Reference Manual,* pp. 197–208.

Lessons that teach *through* problem solving, not just *about* problem solving

Lesson	Activity	Lesson	Activity
2.1	Writing addition number stories	2.8	Identifying fact families on Fact Triangles
2.1	Solving number-grid puzzles	2.10	Determing a pattern in a number sequence and stating the rule
2.3	Reviewing the addition/subtraction facts table	2.11	Solving "What's My Rule?" problems
2.6	Using dominoes to generate related addition and subtraction facts	2.12	Counting back and counting up for subtraction

cross-curricularlinks

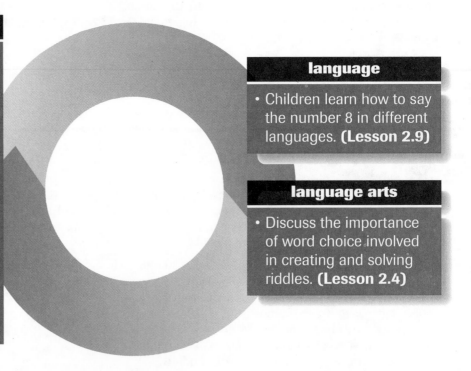

literature

- Read *Fish Eyes: A Book You Can Count On*, a book that focuses on $n + 1$ facts. **(Lesson 2.2)**

- Read *Two of Everything: A Chinese Folktale*, the story of a curious brass pot that doubles whatever is put into it. **(Lesson 2.3)**

- Read *Twelve Ways to Get Eleven*, a book that focuses on equivalent names for numbers. **(Lesson 2.9)**

language

- Children learn how to say the number 8 in different languages. **(Lesson 2.9)**

language arts

- Discuss the importance of word choice involved in creating and solving riddles. **(Lesson 2.4)**

meeting INDIVIDUAL needs

◆ RETEACHING

The following features provide additional instructional support:

Adjusting the Activity

- **Lesson 2.1, Parts 1, 2**
- **Lesson 2.4, Part 1**
- **Lesson 2.6, Part 1**
- **Lesson 2.8, Parts 1, 2**
- **Lesson 2.10, Part 1**
- **Lesson 2.12, Part 1**
- **Lesson 2.13, Part 1**

Options for Individualizing

- **Lesson 2.4** Using Counters and a Ten-Frame Card to Demonstrate the +9 Shortcut
- **Lesson 2.6** Using Dominoes to Generate Related Addition and Subtraction Facts
- **Lesson 2.8** Representing Part-Part-Whole Subtraction with Counters
- **Lesson 2.10** Counting on a Number Grid
- **Lesson 2.11** "What's My Rule?" Fishing
- **Lesson 2.13** Using a Ten-Frame to Develop −9 and −8 Shortcuts

◆ ENRICHMENT

The following features suggest enrichment and extension activities:

Adjusting the Activity

- **Lesson 2.2, Part 1**
- **Lesson 2.4, Part 1**
- **Lesson 2.5, Part 1**
- **Lesson 2.9, Part 1**
- **Lesson 2.10, Part 1**
- **Lesson 2.11, Part 1**

Options for Individualizing

- **Lesson 2.1** Making Up Addition Number Stories
- **Lesson 2.4** Creating and Solving Riddles
- **Lesson 2.5** Looking for Patterns
- **Lesson 2.10** Frames-and-Arrows Problems

◆ LANGUAGE DIVERSITY

The following features suggest ways to support children who are acquiring proficiency in English:

Adjusting the Activity

- **Lesson 2.6, Part 1**
- **Lesson 2.7, Part 1**
- **Lesson 2.12, Part 1**

Options for Individualizing

- **Lesson 2.3** Creating Visual Images for Doubles

◆ MULTIAGE CLASSROOM

The following chart lists related lessons from Grades 1 and 3 that can help you meet your instructional needs:

Grade 1	1.13 5.6–5.8	4.11 6.3–6.5	4.11 5.11 6.1	4.11 5.10 6.1	4.12 5.11 6.1	3.6 5.6 6.1	5.4 5.5	6.3 6.4	6.2 9.8	3.8 3.9	5.12 5.13 6.8	3.6 6.5 9.2	3.6 6.5 9.2
Grade 2	2.1	2.2	2.3	2.4	2.5	2.6	2.7	2.8	2.9	2.10	2.11	2.12	2.13
Grade 3	2.4–2.6	2.1 2.2	2.1 2.2	2.1 2.2	2.1 2.2	1.7	4.1 4.3 10.4	2.1	1.6 8.4		2.3	1.7 2.2 2.8	1.7 2.2 2.8

materials

lesson	📖 math masters pages	🧊 manipulative kit items	✂️ other items
2.1	Home Link Master, p. 242 Teaching Master, p. 22	slate demonstration clock	
2.2	Home Link Master, p. 243	slate number cards	calculator *Fish Eyes: A Book You Can Count On* (optional)
2.3	Home Link Master, p. 244 Teaching Masters, pp. 23–25	slate Class Facts Table ***See* Advance Preparation, p. 100**	calculator *Two of Everything: A Chinese Folktale*
2.4	Home Link Master, p. 245 Teaching Master, p. 26	slate Class Facts Table Class Number Grid Poster number cards	19 counters
2.5	Home Link Master, p. 246	slate 1 set of dominoes per partnership	envelope
2.6	Home Link Master, p. 247	1 set of dominoes per partnership	calculator
2.7	Home Link Master, p. 248 Teaching Master, p. 27	tape measure spring scale 1 six-sided die pan balance	10 pennies per group plastic bag objects weighing between .5 oz and 8 oz 6 quarter-sheets of paper 36 counters calculator ***See* Advance Preparation, p. 118**
2.8	Home Link Master, p. 250 transparency of Teaching Master, p. 28 (optional) ***See* Advance Preparation, p. 123**	slate pan balance (optional)	18 pennies or other counters per partnership
2.9	Home Link Master, p. 252	number cards	chart paper CD player or tape player CDs or tapes *Twelve Ways to Get Eleven* ***See* Advance Preparation, p. 128**
2.10	Home Link Master, p. 254 Teaching Master, p. 30 transparency of Teaching Master, p. 29 (optional) ***See* Advance Preparation, p. 133**	number cards Class Number Grid Poster	
2.11	Home Link Master, p. 256 transparency of Teaching Masters, pp. 31–32 ***See* Advance Preparation, p. 138**	slate	demonstration clock Fact Triangles
2.12	Home Link Master, p. 258	slate	counters (optional) Fact Triangles calculator
2.13	Home Link Master, p. 259 Teaching Masters, pp. 26 and 33 ***See* Advance Preparation, p. 147**	Class Number Grid Poster slate	Fact Triangles 18 counters
2.14	Home Link Masters, pp. 261–264 Teaching Master, p. 22 Assessment Masters, pp. 420–421	slate number cards	Fact Triangles

planning**tips**

Pacing

Pacing depends on a number of factors, such as children's individual needs and how long your school has been using *Everyday Mathematics*. At the beginning of Unit 2, review your Content by Strand Poster to help you set a monthly pace.

	← MOST CLASSROOMS →	
SEPTEMBER	OCTOBER	NOVEMBER

Using the Projects

Choose any of Projects 1 through 3 to introduce your class to the Projects during Unit 2. These Projects can also be used later in the year. In Project 1, your class will name fractional parts, practice following directions, and use paper-folding techniques to make paper boxes. Project 2 provides an opportunity for children to read thermometers and to observe and collect data on weather conditions. Project 3 is an introduction to the 12-year cycle of the Chinese calendar. The Projects can be found at the back of this book.

Home Communication

Share Home Links 2.1–2.13 with families to help them understand the content and procedures in this unit. At the end of the unit, use Home Link 2.14 to introduce Unit 3. Supplemental information can be found in the *Home Connection Handbook*.

NCTM Standards

Standard	1	2	3	4	5	6	7	8	9	10
Unit 2 Lessons	1–13	1–13	3, 5, 10, 12, 13	7, 8, 11	7, 12	1–13	1–13	1–13	1–13	1–13

Content Standards
1. Number and Operation
2. Patterns, Functions, and Algebra
3. Geometry and Spatial Sense
4. Measurement
5. Data Analysis, Statistics, and Probability

Process Standards
6. Problem Solving
7. Reasoning and Proof
8. Communication
9. Connections
10. Representations

PRACTICE *through* Games

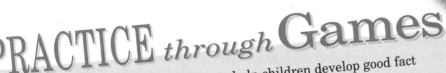

Everyday Mathematics uses games to help children develop good fact power and other math skills.

- Practice automaticity with *Beat the Calculator* **(Lessons 2.2, 2.3, 2.6, 2.7, and 2.12)**
- Practice basic facts in *Addition Top-It* **(Lessons 2.2, 2.5, and 2.6)**
- Practice addition and equivalent names for numbers in *Name That Number* **(Lessons 2.9 and 2.10)**

The notes below highlight the major content ideas presented in Unit 2. These notes may help you establish instructional priorities.

Addition Number Stories (Lesson 2.1 and following)

Throughout *Everyday Mathematics,* children are encouraged to make up and solve number stories. In Unit 2, these stories are used to show that numbers are usually used in context, which we indicate by using a label or a unit. Labels are recorded in a unit box—a device used to give context to number models and to sets of practice problems.

$$4 \text{ cups} + 3 \text{ cups} = 7 \text{ cups}$$

or

$$4 + 3 = 7$$

Unit
cups

Children use numbers in context. The unit box is a shortcut to assigning each number a label.

You should write number models on the board as your class solves number stories, but do not require children to write number models at this stage. Be aware of the types of addition and subtraction number stories, but do not teach children to categorize problems at this time. In Unit 2, our goal is to show children these different types of problems. More formal discussions through diagrams will take place in later units.

Most addition number stories that children make up will be of two types:

▷ *Parts-and-total,* in which two or more separate parts are known, and the total is to be found. *Example:* "Beth has 7 dollars. Joe has 6 dollars. How many dollars in all?"

▷ *Change-to-more,* in which there is a starting quantity. The starting quantity is increased, and the new quantity is to be found. *Example:* "Beth has 7 dollars. Joe gives her 6 dollars. How many dollars does Beth have now?"

Addition and Subtraction Facts (Lesson 2.2 and following)

In *Everyday Mathematics,* the ability to recall number facts instantly is called *fact power.* Instant recall is indeed a powerful tool, for it facilitates computation with multidigit numbers. Fact power is also essential in solving multistep problems.

Lessons 2.2 and 2.3 quickly review "easy" addition facts: 0-facts, 1-facts, and doubles—44 facts in all. This leaves 56 remaining facts. Because these 56 facts include all of the turn-around facts, like $2 + 3 = 5$ and $3 + 2 = 5$, there are really only 28 other facts that children need to learn. Lessons 2.4 and 2.5 develop strategies for remembering most of these facts, such as the plus-9 shortcut and the doubles-plus-1 and doubles-plus-2 strategies.

+,−	0	1	2	3	4	5	6	7	8	9
0	0	1	2	3	4	5	6	7	8	9
1	1	2	3	4	5	6	7	8	9	10
2	2	3	4	5	6	7	8	9	10	11
3	3	4	5	6	7	8	9	10	11	12
4	4	5	6	7	8	9	10	11	12	13
5	5	6	7	8	9	10	11	12	13	14
6	6	7	8	9	10	11	12	13	14	15
7	7	8	9	10	11	12	13	14	15	16
8	8	9	10	11	12	13	14	15	16	17
9	9	10	11	12	13	14	15	16	17	18

Zero-facts and double-facts are two of the shortcuts children learn to help them recall "easy" addition facts.

The inverse relationship of subtraction to addition forms the basis for the study of the subtraction facts. This relationship is first established by observing patterns on dominoes (Lesson 2.6) and then on Fact Triangle flashcards (Lesson 2.8). Children then use Fact Triangles to generate fact families, which are sets of related addition and subtraction facts (for example, $4 + 5 = 9$, $5 + 4 = 9$, $9 − 5 = 4$, and $9 − 4 = 5$).

Subtraction strategies for "harder" subtraction facts (subtracting 8 and 9 from a number, known algebraically as $n − 8$ and $n − 9$) are discussed in Lesson 2.13.

Since addition and subtraction facts are the main focus of this unit, it is suggested that you hold frequent oral drills. This gives children a chance to practice with the facts and provides you with one way to assess their progress.

Subtraction Number Stories (Lesson 2.6 and following)

Most subtraction number stories that children make up will be of two types:

▷ *Change-to-less,* in which there is a starting quantity. The quantity is decreased, and the new quantity is to be found. *Example:* "Bob has 10 model cars. He lost 3 of them. How many model cars does Bob have now?"

▷ *Comparison,* in which two separate quantities are compared by finding the difference (distance) between them. *Example:* "Bob has 10 model cars. Amit has 3 model cars. How many more model cars does Bob have?"

Again, you will want to expose children to these types of number stories, but do not ask children to categorize the stories by type at this time.

Children use a spring scale to find a set of objects whose combined weight is about 1 pound.

Exploring Weights, Scales, Equal Groups (Lesson 2.7)

Another essential part of the program, Explorations, is continued in Lesson 2.7. Explorations provide children with access to limited manipulative materials and, along with projects, provide group problem-solving activities.

Two Explorations in Lesson 2.7 offer experiences with a pan balance and a spring scale. By using the scale, children develop an awareness of the relationship between a pound and an ounce. Children use counters during the partner activity "Egg Nests" to develop the basic idea of multiplication.

Children use a pan balance to compare weights of different objects.

Frames and Arrows, "What's My Rule?," and Name-Collection Boxes (Lessons 2.9, 2.10, and 2.11)

Unit 2 extends other ideas introduced in *First Grade Everyday Mathematics:*

▷ *Frames-and-Arrows problems* provide experience with number sequences and their rules.

▷ *"What's My Rule?" problems* develop the concept of a function—a rule relating the numbers in a number pair.

Frames and Arrows

▷ *Name-collection boxes* stress that one number has many equivalent names. The fact that there are many ways to say the same number is a fundamental concept in mathematics.

Unit 2 Review and Assessment (Lesson 2.14)

Like every unit in *Second Grade Everyday Mathematics,* Unit 2 ends with a review and assessment lesson. This lesson includes a list of unit goals, as well as suggestions for oral and slate evaluation questions. Masters provide review items for children to complete in writing; each item is keyed to a unit goal.

5	
2 + 3	XXXXX
9 − 4	⧸⧸⧸⧸⧸
five	⬠

Name-collection box

Rule
+5

in	out
12	17
4	9
0	5
10	15
7	12
3	8

"What's My Rule?" table

For additional information on the following topics, see the *Teacher's Reference Manual:*

- addition and subtraction
- basic facts
- functions
- mathematical modeling
- number models and number sentences

- operations and use classes
- problem solving
- sequences
- weight and mass

2.1 Addition Number Stories

OBJECTIVES To make up, represent, and solve addition number stories.

summaries	materials

1 Teaching the Lesson

Children review the need for labels to put numbers in context, and make up and solve addition number stories. [Numeration; Operations and Computation; Patterns, Functions, and Algebra]

☐ *Math Journal 1*, p. 20

2 Ongoing Learning & Practice

Children complete number-grid puzzles. [Numeration; Patterns, Functions, and Algebra]

Children practice and maintain skills through Math Boxes and Home Link activities.

☐ *Math Journal 1*, pp. 21 and 22
☐ Home Link Master (*Math Masters*, p. 242)

3 Options for Individualizing

Enrichment Children make up addition number stories for a bulletin board or book. [Operations and Computation]

☐ Teaching Master (*Math Masters*, p. 22)

Additional Information

Vocabulary • addition number story • label • unit box • number model

---

Getting Started

Mental Math and Reflexes
Show the following times on the demonstration clock: 4:30, 7:45, 9:20, 8:50, 6:35.
Children record the times on their slates.

Math Message
5 children are skating.
8 children are playing ball.
How many children in all?

1 Teaching the Lesson

✦ Math Message Follow-Up

WHOLE-CLASS DISCUSSION

Ask children to share their strategies for answering the question. Children may count on their fingers, make tallies for 5 and 8 and count them, or add 5 and 8 mentally and announce the total.

Write "5 children + 8 children = 13 children" under the Math Message and say that this is one way to show an **addition number story.** Discuss the idea that numbers almost always occur in context and have a **label.** Labels can be the name of a thing (for example, books) or a measurement unit (for example, hours).

Talk about writing a label for the numbers in the story in a **unit box** so that you won't have to repeat the label. Using a unit box, the Math Message story can be shown this way: 5 + 8 = 13. Mention that 5 + 8 = 13 is called a **number model** for the story.

Unit
children

✦ Making Up and Solving Addition Number Stories

WHOLE-CLASS ACTIVITY

Ask children to make up addition number stories. Do the following for several stories:

1. Write the story on the board, or draw a picture to represent the story.

2. Draw an empty unit box under the story.

3. Have children write a label in the unit box and share how they would answer the question in the story.

4. Ask a volunteer to write a number model for the story.

Most of the stories children make up will probably belong in one of these two categories:

Parts-and-total
Two or more separate parts are known. Find the total.

Example: Beth has 7 dollars. Joe has 6 dollars. How many dollars do they have in all?

Change-to-more
Start with a number of things. Increase the number of things. Find how many things there are now.

Example: Beth has 7 dollars. Joe gives her 6 dollars. How many dollars does she have now?

NOTE: Children are not expected to categorize addition number stories as parts-and-total or change-to-more at this time. Later lessons will include practice with both types of addition number stories.

Addition Number Stories

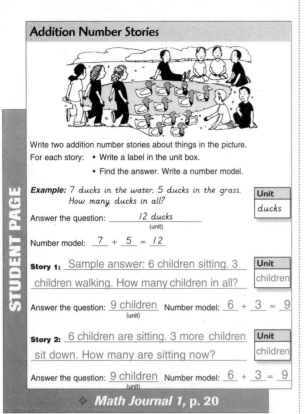

Write two addition number stories about things in the picture.

For each story: • Write a label in the unit box.
• Find the answer. Write a number model.

Example: *7 ducks in the water. 5 ducks in the grass. How many ducks in all?*

Unit
ducks

Answer the question: ____12 ducks____
(unit)

Number model: __7__ + __5__ = __12__

Story 1: Sample answer: 6 children sitting. 3 children walking. How many children in all?

Unit
children

Answer the question: __9 children__
(unit)
Number model: __6__ + __3__ = __9__

Story 2: 6 children are sitting. 3 more children sit down. How many are sitting now?

Unit
children

Answer the question: __9 children__
(unit)
Number model: __6__ + __3__ = __9__

✧ *Math Journal 1, p. 20*

Adjusting the Activity If children have difficulty writing number stories, suggest that they draw pictures instead.

Children can also represent objects with tallies. *Example:* ✝✝✝ / sitting. /// standing. How many in all?

Number-Grid Puzzles

Complete the number-grid puzzles.

		20			50	60

(number-grid puzzle, first grid: 11, 12, 14, 15, 17, 20; 22, 23, 25, 28; 32, 33, 34, 37, 39; 41, 43, 46, 50; 51, 52, 54, 55, 56, 58, 60)

(second grid: 332, 333, 335, 336, 338; 343, 345, 347, 349; 351, 353, 356, 357, 358, 360; 361, 362, 365, 367; 371, 373, 374, 375, 378, 380)

✧ *Math Journal 1, p. 21*

✦ Writing Addition Number Stories
(*Math Journal 1*, p. 20)

INDEPENDENT ACTIVITY

Children continue to make up and solve addition number stories by completing the journal page.

Examples

Parts-and-Total Stories

7 ducks are swimming. 5 ducks are on the grass. How many ducks are there in all? 12 ducks; $7 + 5 = 12$

6 children are sitting. 3 children are walking. How many children are there in all? 9 children; $6 + 3 = 9$

Change-to-More Stories

7 ducks are swimming. 5 ducks enter the pond. How many ducks are swimming now? 12 ducks; $7 + 5 = 12$

6 children are sitting. 3 children who were walking sit down. How many children are sitting now? 9 children; $6 + 3 = 9$

2 Ongoing Learning & Practice

✦ Completing Number-Grid Puzzles
(*Math Journal 1*, p. 21)

INDEPENDENT ACTIVITY

Number-grid puzzles were introduced in Lesson 1.9.

If children are able to complete the first grid but not the second, tell them to ignore the digits in the hundreds place for the numbers in the second grid. Guide children by saying the following:

• What number comes after 332?

• Ignore the hundreds. Which number comes after 32? (Write 33 in the next space on the grid.)

• Now remember the hundreds place and write 3 in front of the 33.

• The number that comes after 332 is 333.

Adjusting the Activity If children have difficulty filling in the number-grid puzzles, provide additional clues by filling in several of the blue cells. Children can also use their calculators to find 1 more, 1 less, 10 more, and 10 less.

◆ Math Boxes 2.1 (*Math Journal 1*, p. 22)

INDEPENDENT ACTIVITY

Mixed Review This journal page provides opportunities for cumulative review or assessment of concepts and skills.

◆ Home Link 2.1 (*Math Masters*, p. 242)

Home Connection Since the vocabulary in today's lesson consists of terms that will be used throughout the year, it is important to share their meanings with children's families. Home Link 2.1 suggests that children explain these terms to someone at home. The Unit 2 Family Letter explains the terms.

3 Options for Individualizing

◆ ENRICHMENT Making Up Addition Number Stories for a Bulletin Board or Book
(*Math Masters*, p. 22)

PARTNER ACTIVITY **15–30 min**

Encourage one child to tell another an addition number story. One partner records the story by drawing pictures, writing words, or doing both. Partners then reverse roles and repeat the activity. Collect the stories for a bulletin-board display or a classroom book. During the next few days, use some of these number stories as Mental Math and Reflexes and Extra Practice problems.

Portfolio Ideas

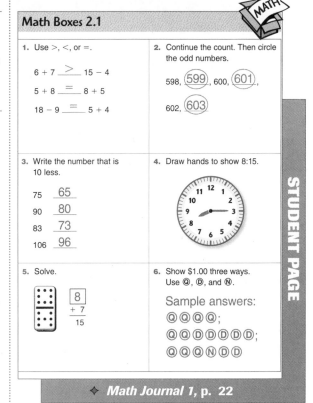

Math Journal 1, p. 22

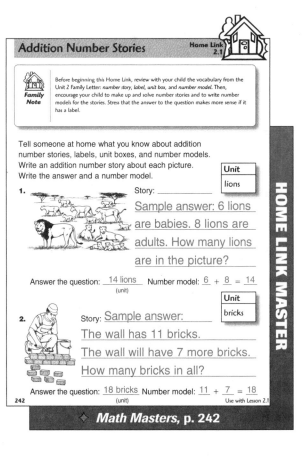

Math Masters, p. 242

2.2 Review "Easy" Addition Facts

OBJECTIVES To review +0 and +1 addition facts; and to practice addition facts in which one of the addends is 0, 1, 2, or 3.

summaries	**materials**
1 Teaching the Lesson	
Children make up addition stories, review the meaning of addition facts and the +0 and the +1 shortcuts, and review "easy" addition facts by playing *Beat the Calculator*. [Operations and Computation]	☐ *Math Journal 1*, p. 23 ☐ Home Link 2.1 ☐ slate ☐ 1 calculator for each child ☐ *Fish Eyes: A Book You Can Count On* (optional) ***See* Advance Preparation**
2 Ongoing Learning & Practice	
Children count to find distances on a number grid. [Numeration; Operations and Computation] Children practice and maintain skills through Math Boxes and Home Link activities.	☐ *Math Journal 1*, pp. 24 and 25 ☐ Home Link Master (*Math Masters*, p. 243)
3 Options for Individualizing	
Extra Practice Children practice addition facts by playing *Addition Top-It.* [Numeration; Operations and Computation]	☐ 0–9 number cards or Everything Math Deck, if available, per partnership

---

Additional Information

Advance Preparation For Part 1, mark the calculators with children's tool-kit numbers. As an additional way to review +1 facts, you may wish to obtain a copy of *Fish Eyes: A Book You Can Count On* by Lois Ehlert (Harcourt Brace, 1990).

Vocabulary • **addition fact** • **+0 facts** • **+1 facts** • **+0 shortcut** • **+1 shortcut** • **fact power**

Getting Started

Mental Math and Reflexes

Pose simple addition number stories. *Suggestion:*

• Jackson has 8 books. His grandmother gives him 3 more books. How many books does Jackson have now? 11 books

Math Message

Make up a story for the number model 11 = 8 + 3.

Sample answer: I had $8. I earned $3 more. Then I had $11 in all.

Home Link 2.1 Follow-Up

Have several children share their number stories with the class. Ask volunteers to solve the problems. During the next few days, you can use remaining number stories as Mental Math and Reflexes problems.

1 Teaching the Lesson

◆ Math Message Follow-Up

WHOLE-CLASS DISCUSSION

Write $11 = 8 + 3$ on the board and draw an empty unit box. Ask a few children to share their stories and to suggest labels to write in the unit box. Write one of these labels in the box. Say that it will be the label for all numbers in this lesson that are not otherwise labeled.

Review the meaning of "addition fact." Remind children that $11 = 8 + 3$ is an example of an **addition fact**—the sum of two 1-digit numbers. Write this fact on the board horizontally and vertically.

$$8 + 3 = 11 \qquad 11 = 8 + 3 \qquad \begin{array}{r} 8 \\ + 3 \\ \hline 11 \end{array}$$

Use all three forms, one as often as another.

◆ Reviewing +0 and +1 Shortcuts

WHOLE-CLASS DISCUSSION

Write some **+0 facts** and **+1 facts** on the board, without the sums. Use both horizontal and vertical forms, as shown in the margin.

Ask children to copy and complete the facts on their slates. See if they can find patterns for +0 facts and +1 facts. Discuss the **+0 shortcut** and the **+1 shortcut.**
If 0 is added to any number, or any number is added to 0, there is no change in the number.
If 1 is added to any number, or any number is added to 1, the result is the next larger number.

Write the following on the board: $87 + 0 = \underline{\quad}$.

After a volunteer has given the answer, ask someone else to check the answer on a calculator. Try several other +0 examples with 2-digit and 3-digit numbers—and with some very large numbers just for fun!

Follow the same routine with several +1 facts using 2-digit, 3-digit, and larger numbers.

Examples

$$5 + 0 = \underline{\quad}$$

$$0 + 8 = \underline{\quad} \qquad \begin{array}{r} 3 \\ + 1 \\ \hline \end{array} \qquad \begin{array}{r} 0 \\ + 6 \\ \hline \end{array}$$

$$\underline{\quad} = 1 + 9$$

◯ Literature Link

Fish Eyes: A Book You Can Count On by Lois Ehlert (Harcourt Brace, 1990) displays sets of 1 to 10 colorful fish. With each set, there is one additional black fish. Children are encouraged to include this fish as they count the fish on the page. For example, "5 spotted fish plus me (the black fish) makes 6." You can have children express a +1 fact for each set of fish. For example, $5 + 1 = 6$.

◆ Demonstrating *Beat the Calculator*
(*Math Journal 1*, p. 23)

WHOLE-CLASS ACTIVITY

Select 3 children to demonstrate how to play the game and to record their results.

1. Designate one child as the "Caller," a second child as the "Calculator," and the third as the "Brain."

Fact Power Table

$\dfrac{0}{+0}$ 0	$\dfrac{0}{+1}$ 1	$\dfrac{0}{+2}$ 2	$\dfrac{0}{+3}$ 3	$\dfrac{0}{+4}$ 4	$\dfrac{0}{+5}$ 5	$\dfrac{0}{+6}$ 6	$\dfrac{0}{+7}$ 7	$\dfrac{0}{+8}$ 8	$\dfrac{0}{+9}$ 9
$\dfrac{1}{+0}$ 1	$\dfrac{1}{+1}$ 2	$\dfrac{1}{+2}$ 3	$\dfrac{1}{+3}$ 4	$\dfrac{1}{+4}$ 5	$\dfrac{1}{+5}$ 6	$\dfrac{1}{+6}$ 7	$\dfrac{1}{+7}$ 8	$\dfrac{1}{+8}$ 9	$\dfrac{1}{+9}$ 10
$\dfrac{2}{+0}$ 2	$\dfrac{2}{+1}$ 3	$\dfrac{2}{+2}$ 4	$\dfrac{2}{+3}$ 5	$\dfrac{2}{+4}$ 6	$\dfrac{2}{+5}$ 7	$\dfrac{2}{+6}$ 8	$\dfrac{2}{+7}$ 9	$\dfrac{2}{+8}$ 10	$\dfrac{2}{+9}$ 11
$\dfrac{3}{+0}$ 3	$\dfrac{3}{+1}$ 4	$\dfrac{3}{+2}$ 5	$\dfrac{3}{+3}$ 6	$\dfrac{3}{+4}$ 7	$\dfrac{3}{+5}$ 8	$\dfrac{3}{+6}$ 9	$\dfrac{3}{+7}$ 10	$\dfrac{3}{+8}$ 11	$\dfrac{3}{+9}$ 12
$\dfrac{4}{+0}$ 4	$\dfrac{4}{+1}$ 5	$\dfrac{4}{+2}$ 6	$\dfrac{4}{+3}$ 7	$\dfrac{4}{+4}$ 8	$\dfrac{4}{+5}$ 9	$\dfrac{4}{+6}$ 10	$\dfrac{4}{+7}$ 11	$\dfrac{4}{+8}$ 12	$\dfrac{4}{+9}$ 13
$\dfrac{5}{+0}$ 5	$\dfrac{5}{+1}$ 6	$\dfrac{5}{+2}$ 7	$\dfrac{5}{+3}$ 8	$\dfrac{5}{+4}$ 9	$\dfrac{5}{+5}$ 10	$\dfrac{5}{+6}$ 11	$\dfrac{5}{+7}$ 12	$\dfrac{5}{+8}$ 13	$\dfrac{5}{+9}$ 14
$\dfrac{6}{+0}$ 6	$\dfrac{6}{+1}$ 7	$\dfrac{6}{+2}$ 8	$\dfrac{6}{+3}$ 9	$\dfrac{6}{+4}$ 10	$\dfrac{6}{+5}$ 11	$\dfrac{6}{+6}$ 12	$\dfrac{6}{+7}$ 13	$\dfrac{6}{+8}$ 14	$\dfrac{6}{+9}$ 15
$\dfrac{7}{+0}$ 7	$\dfrac{7}{+1}$ 8	$\dfrac{7}{+2}$ 9	$\dfrac{7}{+3}$ 10	$\dfrac{7}{+4}$ 11	$\dfrac{7}{+5}$ 12	$\dfrac{7}{+6}$ 13	$\dfrac{7}{+7}$ 14	$\dfrac{7}{+8}$ 15	$\dfrac{7}{+9}$ 16
$\dfrac{8}{+0}$ 8	$\dfrac{8}{+1}$ 9	$\dfrac{8}{+2}$ 10	$\dfrac{8}{+3}$ 11	$\dfrac{8}{+4}$ 12	$\dfrac{8}{+5}$ 13	$\dfrac{8}{+6}$ 14	$\dfrac{8}{+7}$ 15	$\dfrac{8}{+8}$ 16	$\dfrac{8}{+9}$ 17
$\dfrac{9}{+0}$ 9	$\dfrac{9}{+1}$ 10	$\dfrac{9}{+2}$ 11	$\dfrac{9}{+3}$ 12	$\dfrac{9}{+4}$ 13	$\dfrac{9}{+5}$ 14	$\dfrac{9}{+6}$ 15	$\dfrac{9}{+7}$ 16	$\dfrac{9}{+8}$ 17	$\dfrac{9}{+9}$ 18

✦ *Math Journal 1,* p. 23

▲ In this lesson, all fact problems should be selected from the unshaded area of the table.

Distances on a Number Grid

Example: *How many spaces do you move to go from 17 to 23 on the number grid?*

Solution: *Place a marker on 17. You move the marker 6 spaces before landing on 23.*

11	12	13	14	15	16	⟨17⟩	⟨18⟩	⟨19⟩	⟨20⟩
⟨21⟩	⟨22⟩	⟨23⟩	24	25	26	27	28	29	30

How many spaces from:

23 to 28? __5__	15 to 55? __40__	39 to 59? __20__
27 to 42? __15__	34 to 26? __8__	54 to 42? __12__
15 to 25? __10__	26 to 34? __8__	

1	2	3	4	5	6	7	8	9	10
11	12	13	14	15	16	17	18	19	20
21	22	23	24	25	26	27	28	29	30
31	32	33	34	35	36	37	38	39	40
41	42	43	44	45	46	47	48	49	50
51	52	53	54	55	56	57	58	59	60

✦ *Math Journal 1,* p. 24

2. The Caller selects a problem at random from the unshaded area of the Fact Power Table on journal page 23.

3. The Calculator solves the problem with a calculator while the Brain solves it without a calculator. The Caller decides who correctly answers the problem first.

If the Brain correctly beats the Calculator on a fact, the Caller makes a check mark in the box for the fact on the Brain's Fact Power Table.

Children trade roles every 10 turns or so.

◆ Playing *Beat the Calculator* (*Math Journal 1,* p. 23)

SMALL-GROUP ACTIVITY

Divide the class into groups of 3.

Circulate as children play; offer guidance when needed. It is important for children to understand the purpose of the game—to help one another develop fact power. Praise those who display a spirit of cooperation.

Adjusting the Activity If children can beat the calculator for many unshaded facts, have the Caller select fact problems from any part of the Fact Power Table.

If children are having difficulty, suggest that they count on mentally or by using their fingers when one of the addends is 1, 2, or 3. Start with the larger digit. *Examples:*

$9 + 2 = ?$ Think 9.   Say "10, 11."   The sum is 11.

$3 + 7 = ?$ Think 7.   Say "8, 9, 10."   The sum is 10.

◆ Stressing the Importance of "Fact Power"

WHOLE-CLASS DISCUSSION

Point out that the children who did not use calculators sometimes beat those who did use them. They were able to do so because they know those facts without having to take time to figure out the answers. Tell children that they will be reviewing shortcuts to help them beat the calculator, even on "harder" facts.

Explain that having **fact power** is similar to being a good reader. Reading is much easier and more enjoyable if one is able to recognize words immediately, without having to decipher them. The same is true of number facts: It is much easier to solve problems in mathematics if one knows the facts without having to figure them out.

Ongoing Learning & Practice

Finding Distances on a Number Grid
(*Math Journal 1*, p. 24)

INDEPENDENT ACTIVITY

Use the example problem to demonstrate how children should count moves ("spaces") in traveling from one number to another. Many children will find that it is easier to count spaces if they use a penny to act out the moves from the starting to the ending number.

Math Boxes 2.2 (*Math Journal 1*, p. 25)

INDEPENDENT ACTIVITY

Mixed Review This journal page provides opportunities for cumulative review or assessment of concepts and skills.

Home Link 2.2 (*Math Masters*, p. 243)

Home Connection Home Link 2.2 begins a maze practice routine that will be used several times. However, do not assign this Home Link as a maze problem. Simply tell children to answer all the problems on the page. (See Home Link 2.2 Follow-Up in Lesson 2.3.)

Options for Individualizing

EXTRA PRACTICE Playing *Addition Top-It*

PARTNER ACTIVITY   15–30 min

Addition Top-It was introduced in Lesson 1.4. Some children may prefer to practice addition facts with this game rather than *Beat the Calculator*.

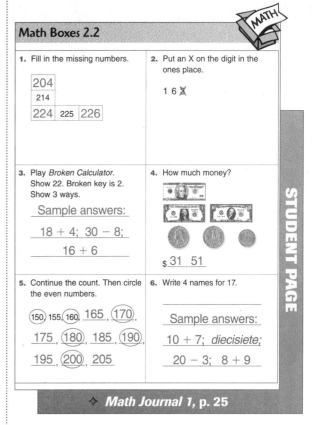

Math Boxes 2.2

1. Fill in the missing numbers.

| 204 |
| 214 |
| 224 | 225 | 226 |

2. Put an X on the digit in the ones place.

1 6 X̶

3. Play *Broken Calculator*. Show 22. Broken key is 2. Show 3 ways.

Sample answers:

18 + 4; 30 − 8;

16 + 6

4. How much money?

$ 31.51

5. Continue the count. Then circle the even numbers.

(150), 155, (160), 165, (170), 175, (180), 185, (190), 195, (200), 205

6. Write 4 names for 17.

Sample answers:

10 + 7; *diecisiete*;

20 − 3; 8 + 9

✦ *Math Journal 1*, p. 25

Addition Facts   Home Link 2.2

Family Note In class today, we continued working with addition stories. We reviewed shortcuts when adding 0 or 1 to a number. We also stressed the importance of memorizing the sum of two 1-digit numbers. Then we reinforced addition facts by playing a game called *Beat the Calculator*.

Please return this Home Link to school tomorrow.

Solve these addition fact problems.

	2	0	5	1	2	3	1	3	4	1
	+4	+0	+4	+4	+5	+2	+9	+6	+4	+1
	6	0	9	5	7	5	10	9	8	2
2	3	5	1	9	0	2	2	7	3	2
+0	+5	+1	+4	+2	+7	+3	+2	+2	+4	+8
2	8	6	5	11	7	5	4	9	7	10
6	1	5	0	4	0	1	4	5	4	3
+2	+6	+5	+6	+3	+5	+8	+6	+3	+0	+1
8	7	10	6	7	5	9	10	8	4	4
0	6	8	9	3	7	2	1	5	6	0
+8	+6	+2	+0	+3	+1	+6	+3	+2	+1	+4
8	12	10	9	6	8	8	4	7	7	4
2	2	6	6	0	4	6	0	5	1	2
+1	+9	+2	+4	+1	+2	+3	+2	+1	+2	+7
3	11	8	10	1	6	9	2	6	3	9
4	7	6	9	1	0	1	1	7	0	6
+5	+0	+2	+3	+5	+9	+7	+5	+3	+6	+5
9	7	8	12	6	9	8	6	10	6	11
9	8	6	8	1	6	3	0	3	3	
+1	+0	+2	+3	+0	+0	+3	+3	+8	+7	
10	8	8	11	1	6	6	3	11	10	

✦ *Math Masters*, p. 243

2.3 Doubles Facts

OBJECTIVE To review and practice the doubles facts.

summaries	materials
1 Teaching the Lesson	
Children write and practice doubles facts and "almost doubles" facts, and review using the Facts Table to identify +0 and doubles patterns. [Operations and Computation; Patterns, Functions, and Algebra]	☐ *Math Journal 1*, pp. 26 and 27 ☐ Home Link 2.2 ☐ Teaching Master (*Math Masters*, p. 23; optional) ☐ Teaching Master transparency (*Math Masters*, p. 24; optional) ☐ slate ☐ Class Facts Table ***See* Advance Preparation**
2 Ongoing Learning & Practice	
Children practice addition facts by playing *Beat the Calculator*. [Operations and Computation] Children practice and maintain skills through Math Boxes and Home Link activities.	☐ *Math Journal 1*, pp. 23 and 28 ☐ Home Link Master (*Math Masters*, p. 244) ☐ calculator
3 Options for Individualizing	
Language Diversity Children draw or color visual images of doubles facts. [Operations and Computation; Patterns, Functions, and Algebra] **Enrichment** Children identify and solve doubles facts problems found in literature. [Operations and Computation]	☐ Teaching Master (*Math Masters*, p. 25) ☐ *Two of Everything: A Chinese Folktale* ***See* Advance Preparation**

Additional Information

Advance Preparation For teaching activities in Part 1, you will need to prepare a large Class Facts Table like the one on journal page 26. Choose one of the following options:

▷ Draw it on the Class Data Pad, on a large piece of chart paper, or on posterboard.

▷ Tape together 4 copies of *Math Masters,* page 23 and fill in the facts.

▷ Make an overhead transparency of *Math Masters,* page 24.

Before beginning the lesson, draw a unit box on the board. Fill in the unit box with the label of your choice (or one supplied by children). Keep the unit box and label posted for all the numbers that are not labeled in this lesson.

For the optional Enrichment activity in Part 3, obtain the book *Two of Everything: A Chinese Folktale* by Lily Toy Hong (Albert Whitman & Company, 1993).

Vocabulary • **doubles facts** • **sum** • **Facts Table** • **row** • **column** • **diagonal**

Getting Started

Mental Math and Reflexes

Pose easy addition facts. Have children answer orally. *Suggestions:*

4 + 2 = ? 6	? = 2 + 8 10	3 + 6 = ? 9
? = 6 + 0 6	7 + 1 = ? 8	? = 1 + 4 5

Math Message

Write 2 + 2 = 4 and 5 + 5 = 10 on your slate. Write any other doubles facts that you know.

Home Link 2.2 Follow-Up

Briefly review the answers. Tell children that the mouse wants to find the cheese but can only go through boxes with a sum of 6. Ask children to draw the mouse's path. Tell them that the mouse can move up, down, left, right, or diagonally from box to box. When children have finished, ask a volunteer to display the page.

Some children might find the path more easily if they first color in each box that has the sum of 6.

---

1 Teaching the Lesson

◆ Math Message Follow-Up

WHOLE-CLASS DISCUSSION

Ask children to share their **doubles facts** as you write them on the board. Skip duplicates. Do not erase the board after finishing the follow-up. You will use these doubles facts for the *Reviewing the Doubles Facts* activity on page 102.

◆ Reviewing the Meaning of "Sum"

WHOLE-CLASS ACTIVITY

Remind children that the number obtained by adding two or more numbers is called their **sum.** Encourage them to use the word "sum" at every opportunity. For example, if a child says, "The answer to 8 + 8 is 16," you might say, "Yes. You are adding numbers, so the answer is called the sum." Another way to say it is, "The sum of 8 + 8 is 16."

◆ Reviewing the Facts Table
(*Math Journal 1*, p. 26; *Math Masters,* p. 23 or p. 24)

WHOLE-CLASS ACTIVITY

Use the Class **Facts Table** to review the meanings of **row, column,** and **diagonal.** As you explain these terms, have children follow along on the table on journal page 26. Then have children use the table to find the sums for several addition facts.

This is the Facts Table. Note that it is identical to *Math Masters,* page 24.

Facts Table

+,−	0	1	2	3	4	5	6	7	8	9
0	0	1	2	3	4	5	6	7	8	9
1	1	2	3	4	5	6	7	8	9	10
2	2	3	4	5	6	7	8	9	10	11
3	3	4	5	6	7	8	9	10	11	12
4	4	5	6	7	8	9	10	11	12	13
5	5	6	7	8	9	10	11	12	13	14
6	6	7	8	9	10	11	12	13	14	15
7	7	8	9	10	11	12	13	14	15	16
8	8	9	10	11	12	13	14	15	16	17
9	9	10	11	12	13	14	15	16	17	18

STUDENT PAGE

◆ *Math Journal 1*, p. 26

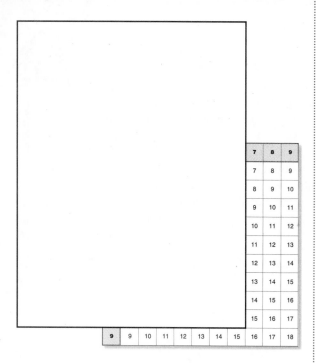

Paper used to highlight the 9-row and 7-column

NOTE: Some children may have difficulty locating the cell where a row and column intersect. Suggest that they use a blank sheet of paper to highlight the row and column of interest.

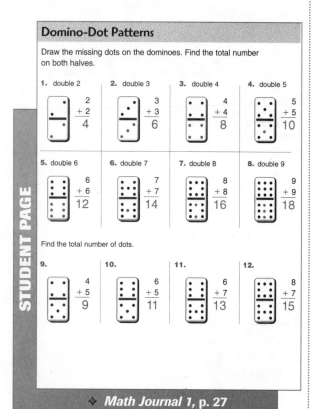

STUDENT PAGE

Domino-Dot Patterns

Draw the missing dots on the dominoes. Find the total number on both halves.

1. double 2

$\begin{array}{r} 2 \\ + 2 \\ \hline 4 \end{array}$

2. double 3

$\begin{array}{r} 3 \\ + 3 \\ \hline 6 \end{array}$

3. double 4

$\begin{array}{r} 4 \\ + 4 \\ \hline 8 \end{array}$

4. double 5

$\begin{array}{r} 5 \\ + 5 \\ \hline 10 \end{array}$

5. double 6

$\begin{array}{r} 6 \\ + 6 \\ \hline 12 \end{array}$

6. double 7

$\begin{array}{r} 7 \\ + 7 \\ \hline 14 \end{array}$

7. double 8

$\begin{array}{r} 8 \\ + 8 \\ \hline 16 \end{array}$

8. double 9

$\begin{array}{r} 9 \\ + 9 \\ \hline 18 \end{array}$

Find the total number of dots.

9.

$\begin{array}{r} 4 \\ + 5 \\ \hline 9 \end{array}$

10.

$\begin{array}{r} 6 \\ + 5 \\ \hline 11 \end{array}$

11.

$\begin{array}{r} 6 \\ + 7 \\ \hline 13 \end{array}$

12.

$\begin{array}{r} 8 \\ + 7 \\ \hline 15 \end{array}$

✦ *Math Journal 1,* p. 27

For example, to find 9 + 7, say:

- Find the 9-row. Go across the 9-row to the 7-column. The number that you see where the 9-row and the 7-column meet is 16. This tells you that 9 + 7 = 16. The sum is 16.

- Go across the 9-row until you find the number 16. Then look at the top of the column where you see the number 16. The number you see is 7. This means that 9 increased by 7 is 16.

By exploring patterns in the Facts Table, children will accelerate their mastery of facts.

Ask children to find the +0 facts in the Facts Table. The +0 facts appear in the top uncolored row and in the left uncolored column of the table. Have children use their pencils to lightly shade in the +0 facts. See whether they can identify the pattern for +0 facts in the table. Sample answer: The sums increase by 1 as you move across the row from left to right. The sums increase by 1 as you move down the column.

✦ Reviewing the Doubles Facts
(*Math Journal 1,* p. 26)

WHOLE-CLASS ACTIVITY

Use the Facts Table to verify the doubles facts that were shared by children and written on the board during the Math Message Follow-Up. Ask children to examine the table to find any doubles facts that they may have overlooked. Have them use pencils to lightly shade all of the doubles facts on the Facts Table. See if they can identify the pattern for doubles on the table. Doubles facts form a diagonal pattern from top left to bottom right. The sums increase by 2 as you move down diagonally.

✦ Practicing Doubles Facts and "Almost Doubles" Facts (*Math Journal 1,* p. 27)

INDEPENDENT ACTIVITY

Children practice doubles facts by exploring domino patterns. Problems 9 through 12 illustrate how knowing doubles facts can help with "almost doubles" facts. This is revisited in Lesson 2.5.

Example: For 4 + 5 = ?: Think 4 + 4, and 1 more. 8; 9

2 Ongoing Learning & Practice

◆ Playing *Beat the Calculator*
(*Math Journal 1*, p. 23)

SMALL-GROUP ACTIVITY

Children play *Beat the Calculator* to develop their recall of addition facts. They should record the facts for which they can beat the calculator by making a check mark in the box for that fact. The Caller should select problems at random from the white area of the Fact Power Table.

 ONGOING ASSESSMENT
Assess children's mastery of addition facts by playing *Beat the Calculator* frequently. Use journal page 23 as a record sheet. Children receive a check mark each time they beat the calculator. When they receive 3 check marks next to a particular fact, they can write the sum in that box to indicate that the fact has been mastered.

◆ Math Boxes 2.3 (*Math Journal 1*, p. 28)

INDEPENDENT ACTIVITY

Mixed Review This journal page provides opportunities for cumulative review or assessment of concepts and skills.

◆ Home Link 2.3 (*Math Masters*, p. 244)

Home Connection Children practice the doubles facts and use doubles facts to find the answers to "almost doubles" facts.

Math Boxes 2.3

1. Today is

_____ _____, _____
(month)   (day)   (year)

The date 1 week from today will be _____.

Answers vary.

2. Put a ✓ on the digit in the hundreds place.

✓2 7 3

3. Count back by 5s.

45, 40, _35_, _30_, 25, _20_, _15_, 10, _5_

Can you keep going?

0, _−5_, _−10_

4. Solve.

Unit

_0_ + 9 = 9

16 = _15_ + 1

_14_ = 14 + 0

18 = 1 + _17_

5. Kyra found 2 dimes and 3 nickels in her left pocket. She found 1 quarter and 2 pennies in her right pocket. How much money did she find?

_62¢_

6. Show tallies for 42.

̶H̶H̶T̶ ̶H̶H̶T̶ ̶H̶H̶T̶ ̶H̶H̶T̶ ̶H̶H̶T̶
̶H̶H̶T̶ ̶H̶H̶T̶ ̶H̶H̶T̶ //

◆ *Math Journal 1*, p. 28

Doubles Facts

Home Link 2.3

 Family Note

Today we worked with an Addition/Subtraction Facts Table and dominoes to practice with a special kind of addition problem called doubles facts. 3 + 3 = 6, 4 + 4 = 8, and 5 + 5 = 10 are examples of doubles facts. We also worked with almost-doubles facts, such as 3 + 4 = 7, 5 + 4 = 9, and 7 + 8 = 15. Review doubles facts and almost-doubles facts with your child.

Please return this Home Link to school tomorrow.

1. Write the sum for each doubles fact.

a. 2 + 2 = _4_   b. _10_ = 5 + 5   c. _0_ = 0 + 0

d.   7   e.   3   f.   8   g.   6
   + 7   + 3   + 8   + 6
   ‾‾‾‾   ‾‾‾   ‾‾‾‾   ‾‾‾‾
    14   6   16   12

h. 9 + 9 = _18_   i. _2_ = 1 + 1   j. _8_ = 4 + 4

2. Ask someone to give you doubles facts. You say the sums. Do this for about 10 minutes or until you know all the doubles facts.

3. Write each sum. Use doubles facts to help you.

a. 5 + 4 = _9_   b. 4 + 5 = _9_   c. _17_ = 9 + 8

d.   6   e.   2   f.   7   g.   6
   + 7   + 3   + 8   + 5
   ‾‾‾‾   ‾‾‾   ‾‾‾‾   ‾‾‾‾
    13   5   15   11

◆ *Math Masters*, p. 244

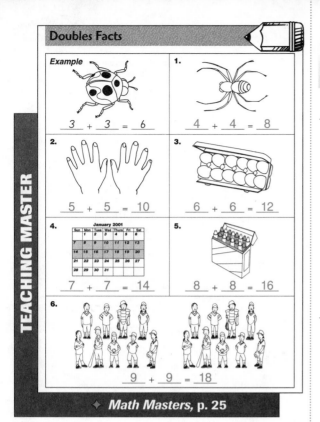

Doubles Facts

Example
$3 + 3 = 6$

1.
$4 + 4 = 8$

2.
$5 + 5 = 10$

3.
$6 + 6 = 12$

4.
January 2001
$7 + 7 = 14$

5.
$8 + 8 = 16$

6.
$9 + 9 = 18$

◆ *Math Masters, p. 25*

TEACHING MASTER

Options for Individualizing

◆ **LANGUAGE DIVERSITY** **Creating Visual Images for Doubles** (*Math Masters,* p. 25)

INDEPENDENT ACTIVITY   15–30 min

If children have difficulty with doubles facts, it may be helpful for them to draw a picture for each doubles fact or to color the pictures on *Math Masters,* page 25. They should write the corresponding doubles fact beneath each picture.

◆ **ENRICHMENT** **Finding Doubles in Literature**

SMALL-GROUP ACTIVITY   15–30 min

Literature Link Read the following book to groups of children, or have children read the book themselves.

Two of Everything: A Chinese Folktale

Summary: Doubles facts are illustrated in the story of a curious brass pot that doubles whatever is put into it.

Children can write a doubles fact for every item put into the pot.

2.4 Turn-Around Facts and the +9 Shortcut

OBJECTIVES To review the turn-around shortcut for addition; and to discover and practice a shortcut for addition facts that have 9 as an addend.

summaries	materials
1 Teaching the Lesson	
Children use the Facts Table and the Class Number Grid Poster to discuss turn-around facts and to discover the +9 shortcut. [Operations and Computation; Patterns, Functions, and Algebra]	☐ *Math Journal 1,* pp. 26 and 29 ☐ Home Link 2.3 ☐ Class Facts Table ☐ Class Number Grid Poster ***See* Advance Preparation**
2 Ongoing Learning & Practice	
Children practice doubles facts by solving a riddle. [Operations and Computation] Children practice and maintain skills through Math Boxes and Home Link activities.	☐ *Math Journal 1,* pp. 29 and 30 ☐ Home Link Master (*Math Masters,* p. 245)
3 Options for Individualizing	
Enrichment Children practice addition facts by creating and solving riddles. [Operations and Computation] **Reteaching** Children solve +9 addition facts by using a ten-frame card and counters. [Operations and Computation; Patterns, Functions, and Algebra]	☐ *Math Journal 1,* p. 29 ☐ Teaching Master (*Math Masters,* p. 26) ☐ 19 counters per child or partnership ☐ *Kids Are Punny: Jokes Sent by Kids to the Rosie O'Donnell Show* (optional) ☐ *Kids Are Punny 2: More Jokes Sent by Kids to the Rosie O'Donnell Show* (optional) ***See* Advance Preparation**

Additional Information

Advance Preparation To demonstrate the problems in Mental Math and Reflexes, you may wish to extend the Class Facts Table by adding a row and a column for 10.

Before beginning the lesson, draw a unit box on the board. Fill in the unit box with the label of your choice (or one supplied by children). Keep the unit box and label posted for all the numbers that are not labeled in this lesson.

Before beginning the optional Enrichment activity in Part 3, you may wish to obtain the books *Kids Are Punny: Jokes Sent by Kids to the Rosie O'Donnell Show* (Warner Books, 1997) and *Kids Are Punny 2: More Jokes Sent by Kids to the Rosie O'Donnell Show* (Warner Books, 1998). These books, as well as other riddle books, can be used as a source of riddles for children.

Vocabulary • **turn-around facts** • **+9 facts** • **+9 shortcut**
Vocabulary (teacher) • **commutative property of addition**

Getting Started

Math Message

Find the sums. Look for patterns.

1 + 6 = _7_   _8_ = 3 + 5   8 + 2 = _10_
6 + 1 = _7_   _8_ = 5 + 3   2 + 8 = _10_

Home Link 2.3 Follow-Up

Briefly review the answers. Ask children how they solved the "almost doubles" facts in Problem 3.

NOTE: Children who used *Everyday Mathematics* in first grade were introduced to the turn-around shortcut. The turn-around shortcut for addition is called the **commutative property of addition.** Do not require children to use this term.

 Adjusting the Activity To extend the activity, have children look at the Facts Table on journal page 26. The doubles facts form a diagonal. For each fact above the diagonal (such as 3 + 5 = 8), the turn-around fact (5 + 3 = 8) is below the diagonal, and vice versa.

1 Teaching the Lesson

✦ Math Message Follow-Up

WHOLE-CLASS DISCUSSION

Review the turn-around shortcut for addition facts illustrated in the Math Message. Ask children to share the patterns they observed.

Select a pair of **turn-around facts,** such as 3 + 5 = 8 and 5 + 3 = 8. Ask children to describe ways in which the facts are alike and different from each other. Sample answer: The facts are alike because they add the same numbers and have the same sum. The facts are different because the numbers are not added in the same order. Remind children that such facts are called turn-around facts. Ask: *Why is this a good name for such facts?* Sample answer: The order of the numbers being added (the addends) is reversed or "turned around."

Ask volunteers to give other examples of turn-around addition facts. Ask what the turn-around fact is for a doubles fact such as 3 + 3 = 6. A doubles fact and its turn-around fact are the same.

Discuss why knowing the turn-around shortcut can help children gain fact power. If you know an addition fact, then you also know its turn-around fact.

✦ Introducing the +9 Shortcut
(*Math Journal 1*, p. 26)

WHOLE-CLASS DISCUSSION

Ask children to use the Facts Table on journal page 26 to name facts that include 9 as one of the addends. Write these **+9 facts** on the board.

Use the Class Facts Table to help children notice that the +9 facts form patterns. If children have not already done so, point out the following:

- The +9 facts appear in the bottom row (the 9-row) and in the far right column (the 9-column) in the table.

- The digit in the ones place in the sum increases by 1 as you move across the 9-row from left to right and as you move down the 9-column.

- Beginning with the fact 1 + 9, the digit in the ones place in the sum is 1 less than the number added to 9. For example, 1 + 9 = 10. The digit 0 in the sum 10 is one less than the addend 1.

Have children use pencils to shade all of the +9 facts on the Facts Table in the journal.

See whether children can discover the +**9 shortcut.** It may help if you write pairs of related +9 and +10 combinations on the board. *For example:*

9 + 1 = 10	→	10 + 1 = 11
9 + 2 = 11	→	10 + 2 = 12
9 + 3 = 12	→	10 + 3 = 13
9 + 6 = 15	→	10 + 6 = 16
9 + 9 = 18	→	10 + 9 = 19

Help children describe the +9 shortcut in their own words. *For example:*

▷ You add 10 instead of 9 and then count back 1.

▷ Add 10, but go back to 1 less.

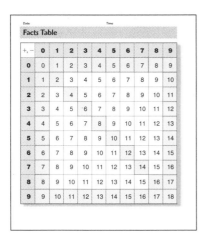

Facts Table

+,−	0	1	2	3	4	5	6	7	8	9
0	0	1	2	3	4	5	6	7	8	9
1	1	2	3	4	5	6	7	8	9	10
2	2	3	4	5	6	7	8	9	10	11
3	3	4	5	6	7	8	9	10	11	12
4	4	5	6	7	8	9	10	11	12	13
5	5	6	7	8	9	10	11	12	13	14
6	6	7	8	9	10	11	12	13	14	15
7	7	8	9	10	11	12	13	14	15	16
8	8	9	10	11	12	13	14	15	16	17
9	9	10	11	12	13	14	15	16	17	18

✦ *Math Journal 1*, p. 26

Adjusting the Activity If children are having difficulty describing the +9 shortcut, use the Class Number Grid Poster to demonstrate it: To find the sum of 9 and a number, locate that number on the number grid, move down to the next row (adding 10), and then move left 1 space (counting back by 1).

1	2	3	4	5	6	7	8	9	10
11	12	13	14	15	16	17	18	19	20

+9 shortcut

+9 Facts

Write the sums.

1. $\begin{array}{r} 3 \\ +9 \\ \hline 12 \end{array}$
2. $\begin{array}{r} 7 \\ +9 \\ \hline 16 \end{array}$
3. $\underline{14} = 9 + 5$
4. $\underline{11} = 2 + 9$
5. $\begin{array}{r} 9 \\ +4 \\ \hline 13 \end{array}$

6. $\begin{array}{r} 6 \\ +9 \\ \hline 15 \end{array}$
7. $\begin{array}{r} 9 \\ +8 \\ \hline 17 \end{array}$
8. $1 + 9 = \underline{10}$
9. $\underline{9} = 0 + 9$
10. $\begin{array}{r} 9 \\ +9 \\ \hline 18 \end{array}$

Write the missing numbers.

11. $9 + \underline{3} = 12$
12. $15 = 9 + \underline{6}$
13. $\underline{8} + 9 = 17$

14. $13 = \underline{4} + 9$
15. $16 = \underline{7} + 9$
16. $14 = 9 + \underline{5}$

Riddle Decoder

17. To solve the riddle, first write the sums. Then write the letter for each sum in the boxes.

Riddle: *What kind of dog has ticks?*

$\begin{array}{r} 9 \\ +9 \\ \hline 18 \end{array}$
$\begin{array}{r} 2 \\ +2 \\ \hline 4 \end{array}$
$\begin{array}{r} 8 \\ +8 \\ \hline 16 \end{array}$
$\begin{array}{r} 3 \\ +3 \\ \hline 6 \end{array}$
$\begin{array}{r} 6 \\ +6 \\ \hline 12 \end{array}$
$\begin{array}{r} 4 \\ +4 \\ \hline 8 \end{array}$
$\begin{array}{r} 7 \\ +7 \\ \hline 14 \end{array}$
$\begin{array}{r} 5 \\ +5 \\ \hline 10 \end{array}$

| W | A | T | C | H | D | O | G |

Sum	4	6	8	10	12	14	16	18
Letter	A	C	D	G	H	O	T	W

Math Journal 1, p. 29

Math Boxes 2.4

1. Write the sums.

   $7 + 0 = \underline{7}$ $\underline{8} = 7 + 1$

   $8 + 0 = \underline{8}$ $\underline{9} = 8 + 1$

   $9 + 0 = \underline{9}$ $\underline{10} = 9 + 1$

   $10 + 0 = \underline{10}$ $\underline{11} = 10 + 1$

2. Write 4 doubles facts that you know.

   Sample answers:

   $2 + 2 = 4$; $4 + 4 = 8$;

   $7 + 7 = 14$;

   $5 + 5 = 10$

3. Tonisha had 9 dominoes. She found 8 more. How many does she have now?

   $\underline{17}$ dominoes

4. Use a number grid. How many spaces from:

   17 to 26? $\underline{9}$

   49 to 28? $\underline{21}$

5. Draw hands to show 6:55.

6. Write the sums.

   Unit

   $5 + 7 = \underline{12}$

   $6 + 8 = \underline{14}$

   $\underline{15} = 9 + 6$ $6 + 7 = \underline{13}$

   $9 + 8 = \underline{17}$ $\underline{9} = 5 + 4$

Math Journal 1, p. 30

◆ Practicing +9 Facts (*Math Journal 1*, p. 29)

INDEPENDENT ACTIVITY

Assign Problems 1 through 16 at the top of the page. Briefly review the answers.

2 Ongoing Learning & Practice

◆ Practicing Doubles Facts (*Math Journal 1*, p. 29)

INDEPENDENT ACTIVITY

Children complete the "Riddle Decoder" at the bottom of the page. Make sure children understand that they are to write the letter for the sum in the box below the sum.

◆ Math Boxes 2.4 (*Math Journal 1*, p. 30)

INDEPENDENT ACTIVITY

 Mixed Review This journal page provides opportunities for cumulative review or assessment of concepts and skills.

◆ Home Link 2.4 (*Math Masters*, p. 245)

 Home Connection Children practice facts by writing sums and finding missing addends.

3 Options for Individualizing

◆ ENRICHMENT Creating and Solving Riddles (*Math Journal 1*, p. 29)

INDEPENDENT ACTIVITY   15–30 min

Return to the riddle activity at the bottom of the journal page. As a long-range project, ask children to bring in riddles with relatively short answers—answers up to 15 letters work well.

 Portfolio Ideas

Children create and share their own problems to solve the riddles. These riddles do not have to be limited to addition facts; riddles can be extended as children learn new skills.

To get children started, suggest a riddle of your own. For example, *What do ghosts chew?* boo boo gum You may wish to provide riddle books to help children create their own riddle problems.

You may want to compile the riddles into a "Class Riddle Book" or post them on a special bulletin board.

◆ RETEACHING Using Counters and a "Ten-Frame Card" to Demonstrate the +9 Shortcut (*Math Masters*, p. 26)

INDEPENDENT ACTIVITY   **15–30 min**

Each child needs a ten-frame card and 19 counters. To show 10 + 5, the child fills the ten-frame card with 10 counters and places 5 counters outside the frame. The child writes "10 + 5 = 15." For 9 + 5, the child takes one counter out of the frame and writes "9 + 5 = 14"; 9 + 5 is 1 less than 10 + 5. The activity can be repeated by placing a different number of counters (less than 10) outside of the frame each time.

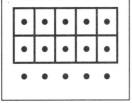   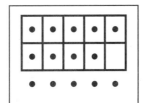

$$\begin{array}{r} 10 \\ + 5 \\ \hline 15 \end{array} \qquad \begin{array}{r} 9 \\ + 5 \\ \hline 14 \end{array}$$

PLANNING AHEAD

For the Explorations in Lesson 2.7, each small group of children will need objects weighing between $\frac{1}{2}$ ounce and 8 ounces. Objects include student tape measures ($\frac{1}{2}$ oz each), full pads of stick-on notes ($\frac{1}{2}$ oz each), 2-inch binder clips (1 oz each), calculators (2–4 oz each), decks of cards (3 oz each), large scissors (5 oz each), mugs (6 oz each), full pads of lined paper (7 oz each), and small paperback books (4–8 oz each).

Turn-Around, Doubles, and +9   Home Link 2.4

Family Note
It is important for children to have instant recall of addition facts. They use shortcuts to help them learn the facts. For example, *turn-around facts* are facts that have the same sum, but the numbers being added are reversed or turned around. *Doubles facts* are facts in which the same number is added. When solving +9 facts, children are encouraged to think of the easier +10 combinations and then subtract 1 from the sum.

Please return this Home Link to school tomorrow.

1. Write the sums. Tell someone at home what you know about turn-around facts.

   a. 6 + 1 = __7__   b. __11__ = 3 + 8   c. 5 + 2 = __7__

   d. 1 + 6 = __7__   e. __11__ = 8 + 3   f. 2 + 5 = __7__

2. Fill in the missing numbers. Tell someone at home what you know about doubles facts.

   a. __8__ + 8 = 16   b. 5 + __5__ = 10   c. 12 = __6__ + 6

   d. 6 = __3__ + 3   e. __7__ + 7 = 14   f. __9__ + 9 = 18

3. Write the sums. Tell someone what you know about +9 facts.

   a. 10 + 1 = __11__   b. __15__ = 5 + 10   c. 6 + 10 = __16__

   d. 1 + 9 = __10__   e. __14__ = 9 + 5   f. 6 + 9 = __15__

   g. 10 + 7 = __17__   h. __14__ = 4 + 10   i. 8 + 10 = __18__

   j. 7 + 9 = __16__   k. __13__ = 9 + 4   l. 8 + 9 = __17__

◆ *Math Masters*, p. 245

Ten-Frame Card

◆ *Math Masters*, p. 26

2.5 Addition Strategies That Use Doubles Facts

OBJECTIVE To explore and practice doubles-plus-1 and doubles-plus-2 facts.

	summaries	materials

1 Teaching the Lesson

Children identify and practice strategies for facts in which one addend is 1 or 2 more than the other addend. [Operations and Computation; Patterns, Functions, and Algebra]

☐ *Math Journal 1*, pp. 26 and 31
☐ Home Link 2.4
☐ slate

2 Ongoing Learning & Practice

Partners practice addition facts by playing a dominoes version of *Addition Top-It*. [Numeration; Operations and Computation]

Children cut out the first set of 18 Fact Triangles.

Children practice and maintain skills through Math Boxes and Home Link activities.

☐ *Math Journal 1*, p. 32 and Activity Sheets 1 and 2
☐ Home Link Master (*Math Masters*, p. 246)
☐ 1 set of dominoes per partnership
☐ scissors
☐ 1 envelope per child

3 Options for Individualizing

Enrichment Children work in small groups to identify and explain patterns in the Facts Table. [Operations and Computation; Patterns, Functions, and Algebra]

☐ *Math Journal 1*, p. 26

Additional Information

Advance Preparation Before beginning the lesson, draw a unit box on the board. Fill in the unit box with the label of your choice (or one supplied by children). Keep the unit box and label posted for all the numbers that are not labeled in this lesson.

Vocabulary • **doubles-plus-1 facts** • **doubles-plus-2 facts**

Getting Started

Mental Math and Reflexes

Pose +9 facts. Encourage children to think +10 and subtract 1.
Suggestions:

$2 + 9 = ?$ $4 + 9 = ?$ $9 + 5 = ?$
$? = 9 + 6$ $? = 7 + 9$ $8 + 9 = ?$

Math Message

Write all the doubles addition facts on a sheet of paper.

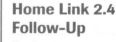

Home Link 2.4 Follow-Up

Review answers as necessary.

Teaching the Lesson

◆ Math Message Follow-Up
(*Math Journal 1*, p. 26)

WHOLE-CLASS DISCUSSION

Ask children to turn to the Facts Table on journal page 26. Help them as needed while they check their list of doubles facts against the table.

ONGOING ASSESSMENT
Use the Math Message to assess whether children know most or all of the doubles facts. Knowledge of doubles facts is important, as this lesson focuses on strategies that assume quick recall of these facts.

◆ Discussing Doubles-Plus-1 Facts

WHOLE-CLASS DISCUSSION

Doubles-plus-1 facts include those addition facts in which one addend is 1 more than the other addend (for example, $3 + 2$). Write some doubles-plus-1 facts on the board; leave out the sums. Use both horizontal and vertical forms. (See the margin.)

Ask children to copy and complete the facts on their slates. See whether any children mention a strategy that makes use of doubles. Discuss the doubles-plus-1 strategy. To add numbers where one addend is 1 more than the other, double the smaller number and then add 1.

◆ Discussing Doubles-Plus-2 Facts

WHOLE-CLASS DISCUSSION

Doubles-plus-2 facts are addition facts in which one addend is 2 more than the other addend (for example, $4 + 2$). Write some doubles-plus-2 facts on the board; leave out the sums. Use both horizontal and vertical forms. (See the margin.)

Ask children to copy and complete the facts on their slates. See whether any children mention a strategy that makes use of doubles. Discuss the doubles-plus-2 strategy. To add numbers where one addend is 2 more than the other, double the smaller number and then add 2.

Facts Table

+,–	0	1	2	3	4	5	6	7	8	9
0	0	1	2	3	4	5	6	7	8	9
1	1	2	3	4	5	6	7	8	9	10
2	2	3	4	5	6	7	8	9	10	11
3	3	4	5	6	7	8	9	10	11	12
4	4	5	6	7	8	9	10	11	12	13
5	5	6	7	8	9	10	11	12	13	14
6	6	7	8	9	10	11	12	13	14	15
7	7	8	9	10	11	12	13	14	15	16
8	8	9	10	11	12	13	14	15	16	17
9	9	10	11	12	13	14	15	16	17	18

◆ *Math Journal 1*, p. 26

$$4 + 5 = \underline{\hspace{1cm}}$$
$$\underline{\hspace{1cm}} = 9 + 8$$

$$\begin{array}{r} 7 \\ + 6 \\ \hline \end{array} \qquad \begin{array}{r} 5 \\ + 6 \\ \hline \end{array}$$

$$4 + 6 = \underline{\hspace{1cm}}$$
$$\underline{\hspace{1cm}} = 9 + 7$$

$$\begin{array}{r} 7 \\ + 5 \\ \hline \end{array} \qquad \begin{array}{r} 6 \\ + 8 \\ \hline \end{array}$$

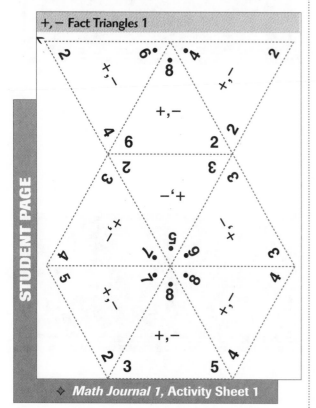

STUDENT PAGE

Addition Facts

If you know a double, you know the *1-more* and the *1-less* sums.

Reminder: If you know that 4 + 4 = 8, you know 4 + **5** = 9, and 4 + **3** = 7.

For Problems 1–10, find the sums.

1. $\underline{15} = 8 + 7$ 2. $3 + 4 = \underline{7}$ 3. $\underline{13} = 6 + 7$

4. $\begin{array}{r} 6 \\ +\,5 \\ \hline 11 \end{array}$ 5. $\begin{array}{r} 8 \\ +\,9 \\ \hline 17 \end{array}$ 6. $\begin{array}{r} 7 \\ +\,5 \\ \hline 12 \end{array}$ 7. $\begin{array}{r} 7 \\ +\,9 \\ \hline 16 \end{array}$

8. $5 + 8 = \underline{13}$ 9. $\underline{15} = 6 + 9$ 10. $8 + 6 = \underline{14}$

Try these.

11. $8 + 8 = 16$ 12. $12 + 12 = 24$ 13. $15 + 15 = 30$

$8 + 9 = \underline{17}$ $12 + 13 = \underline{25}$ $16 + 15 = \underline{31}$

$8 + 7 = \underline{15}$ $12 + 11 = \underline{23}$ $14 + 15 = \underline{29}$

14. Can you figure these out?

$14 + 12 = \underline{26}$ $15 + 13 = \underline{28}$

◆ *Math Journal 1,* p. 31

Adjusting the Activity You may want to extend the doubles strategies to facts in which the addends are separated by a value of 3 or more. For example, to calculate 8 + 5, solve the doubles fact 5 + 5 and then add 3.

+, − Fact Triangles 1

◆ *Math Journal 1,* **Activity Sheet 1**

Some children may discover that they can find the sum of a doubles-plus-2 fact by subtracting 1 from the larger addend and adding it to the smaller addend. For example, they might change 4 + 6 into the doubles fact 5 + 5.

◆ Practicing Addition Strategies That Use Doubles Facts (*Math Journal 1,* p. 31)

INDEPENDENT ACTIVITY

Children practice and extend the doubles-plus-1, doubles-plus-2, and doubles-plus-3 strategies.

2 Ongoing Learning & Practice

◆ Playing a Dominoes Version of *Addition Top-It*

PARTNER ACTIVITY

Have partners place dominoes facedown between them. Each player turns over a domino and calls out the sum of the dots on the two halves. The player with the higher sum wins and takes all the dominoes then in play.

The dominoes version is suggested in anticipation of Lesson 2.6, in which children use dominoes to construct subtraction facts. Children played a card version of *Addition Top-It* in Lesson 1.4.

◆ Cutting Out Fact Triangles (*Math Journal 1,* Activity Sheets 1 and 2)

INDEPENDENT ACTIVITY

Have children cut out the Fact Triangles from Activity Sheets 1 and 2. You might want to have them write their initials or draw a distinctive pattern on the back of each triangle. This will help children identify their individual sets.

Tell children to store the Fact Triangles in envelopes in their tool kits when they are not using them.

These Fact Triangles will be used in Lessons 2.8 and 2.11–2.13 as addition and subtraction flashcards. In Lesson 2.12, children will cut out a second set of Fact Triangles from Activity Sheets 3 and 4.

◆Math Boxes 2.5 (*Math Journal 1,* p. 32)

INDEPENDENT ACTIVITY

 Mixed Review This journal page provides opportunities for cumulative review or assessment of concepts and skills.

◆Home Link 2.5 (*Math Masters,* p. 246)

 Home Connection Children complete a page of addition facts and draw a path from the child to the ice cream cone by connecting sums of 9, 10, or 11.

Math Boxes 2.5

1. Write the turnaround for each fact.

$7 + 9 = 16$ $9 + 7 = 16$

$15 = 6 + 9$ $15 = 9 + 6$

$17 = 9 + 8$ $17 = 8 + 9$

2. Julie had 10 crayons. Rosa gave her 8 more crayons. How many crayons in all?

__18__ crayons

3. Write the numbers in order. Write the smallest number first.

56, 32, 75, 21

__21__, __32__, __56__, __75__

4. Fill in the missing numbers.

196	197
	207
217	218
227	228

5. Solve.

$\begin{array}{r} 7 \\ + \boxed{9} \\ \hline 16 \end{array}$

6. Write the number that is 10 more.

104   __114__

76   __86__

80   __90__

47   __57__

 Math Journal 1, p. 32

---

③ Options for Individualizing

◆ENRICHMENT Looking for Patterns in the Facts Table (*Math Journal 1,* p. 26)

SMALL-GROUP ACTIVITY 👥👥   30+ min 🕐

Divide the class into five or six groups. Ask each group to look for patterns in the Facts Table and to prepare a group report.

Once groups have had time to complete the task, bring the class together. Ask the spokesperson for each group to describe a pattern by using the Class Facts Table. Caution children to listen carefully and not to report a pattern that another group has already described. After each group has had its turn, ask if any groups have other patterns to report. *Possible patterns:*

▷ Each number is 1 less than the number to its right and 1 more than the number to its left.

▷ Each number is 1 less than the number below it. After the first row, each number is 1 more than the number above it.

▷ On the diagonal from top left to bottom right, the numbers increase by 2 as you move down the diagonal. On the diagonal from top right to bottom left, the numbers are the same.

Addition Facts Maze   Home Link 2.5

Family Note For homework, your child will review addition facts like the ones we have been working on in class. To help identify the path from the child to the ice cream cone, have your child circle the sums of 9, 10, and 11.

Please return this Home Link to school tomorrow.

Help the child find the ice cream. Answer all the problems. Then draw the child's path by connecting facts with sums of 9, 10, or 11. You can move up, down, left, or right as you move between boxes.

	2 +6 8	2 +5 7	1 +6 7	0 +8 8	5 +7 12	3 +9 12	7 +0 7	4 +4 8	1 +5 6	4 +3 7
2 +7 9	6 +5 11	1 +7 8	3 +5 8	6 +3 9	1 +8 9	8 +2 10	5 +3 8	2 +4 6	3 +3 6	8 +7 15
4 +4 8	5 +4 9	9 +3 12	0 +9 9	4 +6 10	7 +1 8	5 +5 10	8 +0 8	5 +9 14	6 +7 13	6 +1 7
6 +2 8	3 +8 11	7 +4 11	9 +2 11	5 +3 8	4 +4 8	2 +9 11	4 +8 12	4 +9 13	1 +1 2	5 +2 7
3 +4 7	6 +6 12	8 +4 12	7 +5 12	7 +0 7	6 +2 8	7 +3 10	3 +6 9	4 +7 11	6 +8 14	5 +6 11
8 +5 13	3 +6 9	4 +7 11	5 +2 7	1 +6 7	3 +5 8	6 +7 13	5 +7 12	8 +3 11	7 +7 14	9 +4 13
6 +1 7	8 +4 12	2 +6 8	7 +7 14	4 +2 6	1 +4 5	0 +7 7	3 +9 12	4 +5 9	6 +4 10	🍦

 Math Masters, p. 246

STUDENT PAGE

HOME LINK MASTER

2.6 Subtraction from Addition

OBJECTIVES To review the −0 and −1 shortcuts; and to identify the subtraction facts related to given addition facts.

summaries	materials
1 Teaching the Lesson	
Children make up and share number stories that are solved by subtraction, discover and practice the −0 and −1 shortcuts, and use dominoes to generate related addition and subtraction facts. [Operations and Computation]	☐ *Math Journal 1*, p. 33 ☐ Home Link 2.5 ☐ calculator ☐ 10 counters and 10 cubes (optional)
2 Ongoing Learning & Practice	
Partners practice addition facts by playing *Beat the Calculator* or a dominoes version of *Addition Top-It*. [Numeration; Operations and Computation] Children practice and maintain skills through Math Boxes and Home Link activities.	☐ *Math Journal 1*, p. 23 (optional); p. 34 ☐ Home Link Master (*Math Masters*, p. 247) ☐ 1 set of dominoes per partnership (optional) ☐ 1 calculator per group of 3 children (optional)
3 Options for Individualizing	
Reteaching Children use dominoes to generate related addition and subtraction facts. [Operations and Computation]	☐ 1 set of dominoes per partnership

Additional Information

Vocabulary • subtraction number story • −0 facts • −1 facts • −0 shortcut • −1 shortcut

Getting Started

Mental Math and Reflexes

Pose doubles-plus-1 and doubles-plus-2 facts. *Suggestions:*

6 + 7 = ? 13	? = 8 + 6 14
4 + 5 = ? 9	? = 4 + 6 10
8 + 9 = ? 17	? = 5 + 7 12
6 + 5 = ? 11	? = 7 + 9 16
8 + 7 = ? 15	? = 3 + 5 8

Math Message

Make up a story for the number model 10 − 3 = 7.

Home Link 2.5 Follow-Up

Check that children were able to find the correct path from the child to the ice cream cone.

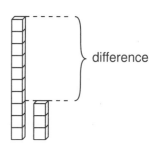

Teaching the Lesson

✦ Math Message Follow-Up

WHOLE-CLASS DISCUSSION

Write 10 − 3 = 7 on the board. Ask children to share their **subtraction number stories.** Draw an empty unit box. Have children suggest a label for each number story, and write it in the unit box.

Expect most of the children's number stories to be one of two types:

Change-to-less

Start with a number of things. Decrease the number of things. Find out the number of things after the number is decreased.

Example: Bob has 10 model cars. He loses 3 model cars. How many model cars does Bob have now? 7

Comparison

Two separate quantities are known. Compare them by finding the difference (distance) between them. Tell how many more or less.

Example: Bob has 10 model cars. Amit has 3 model cars. How many more model cars does Bob have? 7

✦ Discussing the −0 and the −1 Shortcuts

WHOLE-CLASS ACTIVITY

Write some **−0 facts** and **−1 facts** on the board; leave off the differences. Use both horizontal and vertical forms.

Examples

$$5 - 0 = \underline{\quad} \qquad \begin{matrix} 3 \\ -1 \\ \hline \end{matrix} \quad \underline{\quad} = 9 - 1 \qquad \begin{matrix} 9 \\ -0 \\ \hline \end{matrix} \quad \underline{\quad} = 8 - 0$$

Ask children to copy and complete the facts on their slates. See whether they can identify the **−0 shortcut** facts and the **−1 shortcut** facts. Discuss the pattern for each shortcut. If 0 is subtracted from any number, that number does not change. If 1 is subtracted from any number, the result is the next smaller number.

Adjusting the Activity Have children model change-to-less number stories by using counters to represent the number of things at the start. Children then cover the appropriate number of counters being removed. The remaining number of counters is the difference.

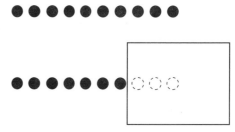

10 take away 3 is 7.

Children can also model comparison number stories by placing sets of connecting cubes side by side. The sets represent the numbers being compared. Children can determine the answer by visually comparing the two sets of cubes.

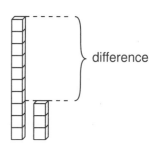

The difference between 10 and 3 is 7.

NOTE: *Change-to-less* (also called *take-away*) is the meaning of subtraction most often encountered in school work. The *comparison* meaning of subtraction (10 cars − 3 cars = 7 cars) does not involve take-away, because nothing is actually taken away; the two sets of cars are just being compared. Children are not expected to categorize subtraction stories as "change-to-less" or "comparison" at this time.

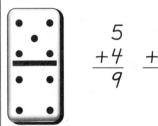

$$\begin{array}{r} 5 \\ +4 \\ \hline 9 \end{array} \quad \begin{array}{r} 4 \\ +5 \\ \hline 9 \end{array} \quad \begin{array}{r} 9 \\ -5 \\ \hline 4 \end{array} \quad \begin{array}{r} 9 \\ -4 \\ \hline 5 \end{array}$$

Adjusting the Activity Children who have difficulty recognizing the subtraction facts shown by a domino should erase or cover up one side of the domino. For example: Nine dots in all. Take away the 5 dots on one side by erasing them. Four dots remain. So $9 - 5 = 4$.

Domino Facts

For Problems 1–7, write 2 addition facts and 2 subtraction facts for each domino.

1.
$$\begin{array}{r} 4 \\ +2 \\ \hline 6 \end{array} \quad \begin{array}{r} 2 \\ +4 \\ \hline 6 \end{array} \quad \begin{array}{r} 6 \\ -2 \\ \hline 4 \end{array} \quad \begin{array}{r} 6 \\ -4 \\ \hline 2 \end{array}$$

2.
$$\begin{array}{r} 6 \\ +4 \\ \hline 10 \end{array} \quad \begin{array}{r} 4 \\ +6 \\ \hline 10 \end{array} \quad \begin{array}{r} 10 \\ -4 \\ \hline 6 \end{array} \quad \begin{array}{r} 10 \\ -6 \\ \hline 4 \end{array}$$

3.
$$\begin{array}{r} 5 \\ +7 \\ \hline 12 \end{array} \quad \begin{array}{r} 7 \\ +5 \\ \hline 12 \end{array} \quad \begin{array}{r} 12 \\ -7 \\ \hline 5 \end{array} \quad \begin{array}{r} 12 \\ -5 \\ \hline 7 \end{array}$$

4.
$$\begin{array}{r} 8 \\ +6 \\ \hline 14 \end{array} \quad \begin{array}{r} 6 \\ +8 \\ \hline 14 \end{array} \quad \begin{array}{r} 14 \\ -6 \\ \hline 8 \end{array} \quad \begin{array}{r} 14 \\ -8 \\ \hline 6 \end{array}$$

5.
$$\begin{array}{r} 3 \\ +8 \\ \hline 11 \end{array} \quad \begin{array}{r} 8 \\ +3 \\ \hline 11 \end{array} \quad \begin{array}{r} 11 \\ -8 \\ \hline 3 \end{array} \quad \begin{array}{r} 11 \\ -3 \\ \hline 8 \end{array}$$

6.
$$\begin{array}{r} 9 \\ +5 \\ \hline 14 \end{array} \quad \begin{array}{r} 5 \\ +9 \\ \hline 14 \end{array} \quad \begin{array}{r} 14 \\ -5 \\ \hline 9 \end{array} \quad \begin{array}{r} 14 \\ -9 \\ \hline 5 \end{array}$$

7.
$$\begin{array}{r} 9 \\ +0 \\ \hline 9 \end{array} \quad \begin{array}{r} 0 \\ +9 \\ \hline 9 \end{array} \quad \begin{array}{r} 9 \\ -0 \\ \hline 9 \end{array} \quad \begin{array}{r} 9 \\ -9 \\ \hline 0 \end{array}$$

8. Write one addition fact and one subtraction fact.
$$\begin{array}{r} 9 \\ +9 \\ \hline 18 \end{array} \quad \begin{array}{r} 18 \\ -9 \\ \hline 9 \end{array}$$

✦ *Math Journal 1, p. 33*

Write this problem on the board: $87 - 0 = \underline{\quad}$. After a volunteer has given the answer, ask someone else to check the answer on a calculator. Try several other examples with 2- and 3-digit numbers—and with some very large numbers, just for fun!

Follow the same procedure with several -1 examples. Use 2- and 3-digit numbers and some very large numbers.

◆ Using Dominoes to Generate Related Addition and Subtraction Facts

WHOLE-CLASS DISCUSSION

Draw a domino on the board. Help children discover a set of related facts shown by the domino. For example, for a domino with 5 dots on one half and 4 dots on the other, ask:

• What is the total number of dots shown? 9

• Which addition facts describe this domino? $5 + 4 = 9$ and $4 + 5 = 9$

Remind children about turn-around facts.

Write the numbers 5, 4, and 9 on the board. Then write the two addition facts just named: $5 + 4 = 9$ and $4 + 5 = 9$.

• Which subtraction facts can you write using the three numbers 5, 4, and 9? $9 - 5 = 4$ and $9 - 4 = 5$ Write these two subtraction facts on the board.

Continue with other domino examples in the same way.

◆ Practicing Domino Facts (*Math Journal 1,* p. 33)

INDEPENDENT ACTIVITY

Children write the addition and subtraction facts generated by each domino pattern on the journal page. The final problems include special features that may cause some children difficulty. The double-9 domino has only two related facts, not four: $9 + 9 = 18$ and $18 - 9 = 9$. The domino with 9 dots on the top and zero dots on the bottom may confuse children. Make sure children realize that the blank half of the domino stands for zero. The four related facts for this domino are $9 + 0 = 9$, $0 + 9 = 9$, $9 - 0 = 9$, and $9 - 9 = 0$.

ONGOING ASSESSMENT
In Part 1 of this lesson, children used dominoes to generate related addition and subtraction facts. Journal page 33 provides an opportunity to assess individual understanding of this concept.

Ongoing Learning & Practice

◆ **Practicing Addition Facts by Playing** *Beat the Calculator* **or** *Addition Top-It*
(*Math Journal 1,* p. 23)

PARTNER ACTIVITY

Children may practice addition facts by playing *Beat the Calculator.* They may also practice with a dominoes version of *Addition Top-It* (see page 112).

◆ **Math Boxes 2.6** (*Math Journal 1,* p. 34)

INDEPENDENT ACTIVITY

 Mixed Review This journal page provides opportunities for cumulative review or assessment of concepts and skills.

◆ **Home Link 2.6** (*Math Masters,* p. 247)

 Home Connection Children use dominoes to generate and solve related addition and subtraction facts. Children also practice doubles-plus-1 and doubles-plus-2 facts.

Options for Individualizing

◆ **RETEACHING Using Dominoes to Generate Related Addition and Subtraction Facts**

INDEPENDENT ACTIVITY   5–15 min

In Part 1 of this lesson, children used domino pictures to generate related addition and subtraction facts. Some children may benefit from spending extra time on this activity using actual dominoes.

PLANNING AHEAD

If children have not already cut out the Fact Triangles from Activity Sheets 1 and 2, have them do that soon. The Fact Triangles will be used in Lesson 2.8.

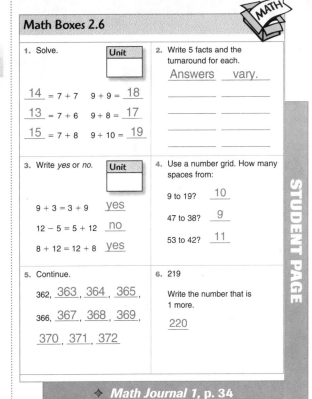

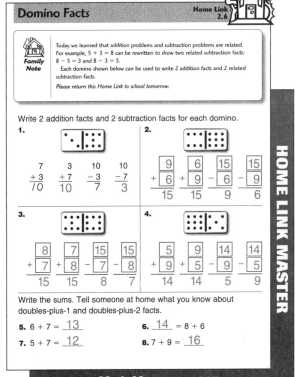

Lesson 2.6   **117**

2.7 EXPLORATIONS

Exploring Weights, Scales, Equal Groups

OBJECTIVES To use a pan balance and spring scale; to experience the ounce/pound relationship; and to find the total number of objects in equal groups.

summaries

materials

1 Teaching the Lesson

Exploration A: Children use a pan balance to compare weights of different objects. [Numeration; Measurement and Reference Frames]

Exploration B: Children use a spring scale to find a set of objects whose combined weight is about 1 pound. [Numeration; Measurement and Reference Frames]

Exploration C: Children develop readiness for multiplication by making equal groups of objects and finding the total. [Operations and Computation; Patterns, Functions, and Algebra]

☐ Home Link 2.6

Exploration A:
☐ tape measure; 10 pennies
  Per small group:
☐ *Math Journal 1,* p. 35
☐ pan balance
☐ objects weighing between $\frac{1}{2}$ oz and 8 oz

Exploration B: Per small group:
☐ *Math Journal 1,* p. 35
☐ spring scale
☐ plastic bag
☐ objects weighing between $\frac{1}{2}$ oz and 8 oz

Exploration C: Per partnership:
☐ Teaching Master (*Math Masters,* p. 27)
☐ 6 quarter-sheets of paper; 1 six-sided die
☐ 36 counters, such as pennies, cubes, or beans

***See* Advance Preparation**

2 Ongoing Learning & Practice

Children practice basic addition facts by playing *Beat the Calculator.* [Operations and Computation]

Children practice and maintain skills through Math Boxes and Home Link activities.

☐ *Math Journal 1,* pp. 23 and 36
☐ Home Link Masters (*Math Masters,* pp. 248 and 249)
☐ calculator

3 Options for Individualizing

Extra Practice Children name objects that measure time, weight, length, volume, and area. [Measurement and Reference Frames]

☐ *Minute Math®,* pp. 61 and 62

Additional Information

Advance Preparation Collect objects found in the classroom that weigh between $\frac{1}{2}$ ounce and 8 ounces. Objects found in many rooms include a student tape measure ($\frac{1}{2}$ oz), a full pad of stick-on notes ($\frac{1}{2}$ oz), a 2-inch binder clip (1 oz), a calculator (2 to 4 oz), a card deck (3 oz), a large pair of scissors (5 oz), a mug (6 oz), a full pad of lined paper (7 oz), and small paperback books (4 to 8 oz).

Vocabulary • ounce • pound • pan balance • heavier • lighter • in balance • spring scale

Getting Started

Mental Math and Reflexes

Say a number. Children write the doubles fact for the number. For example, say "12," and children write "6 + 6 = 12" on their slates. Repeat the activity with double +1 numbers.

Math Message

Which is heavier—1 ounce or 1 pound? 1 pound

Do you think your calculator weighs more than 1 pound or less than 1 pound? Less than 1 pound

Home Link 2.6 Follow-Up

Review answers as necessary.

1 Teaching the Lesson

◆ Math Message Follow-Up

WHOLE-CLASS DISCUSSION

Discuss children's answers. Say that **ounces** and **pounds** are different units of weight, just as inches and miles are different units of length. In the United States, short objects are measured in inches, and long distances are measured in miles. Light things are weighed in ounces, and heavy things are weighed in pounds.

◆ Demonstrating the Pan Balance

WHOLE-CLASS ACTIVITY

Place two objects of different weights in the pans on the **pan balance.** The pan with the **heavier** object will fall. The pan with the **lighter** object will rise. Point out that the balance does not have numbers on it like a bath scale.

Place a student tape measure in one pan. Slowly add pennies to the other pan until the pans are **in balance.** (A tape measure weighs about the same as 10 pennies.) Say that when the pans are equally balanced like this, the objects in the two pans have about the same weight.

◆ Demonstrating the Spring Scale

WHOLE-CLASS ACTIVITY

Show children the lines and numbers on the **spring scale.** Say that they are like the lines and numbers on a bath scale that let you read weight in pounds. A spring

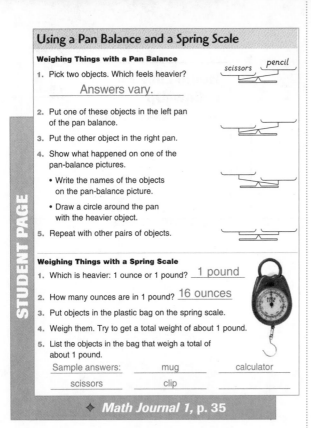

Using a Pan Balance and a Spring Scale

Weighing Things with a Pan Balance

1. Pick two objects. Which feels heavier?

   Answers vary.

2. Put one of these objects in the left pan of the pan balance.

3. Put the other object in the right pan.

4. Show what happened on one of the pan-balance pictures.

   • Write the names of the objects on the pan-balance picture.

   • Draw a circle around the pan with the heavier object.

5. Repeat with other pairs of objects.

Weighing Things with a Spring Scale

1. Which is heavier: 1 ounce or 1 pound? _1 pound_

2. How many ounces are in 1 pound? _16 ounces_

3. Put objects in the plastic bag on the spring scale.

4. Weigh them. Try to get a total weight of about 1 pound.

5. List the objects in the bag that weigh a total of about 1 pound.

   Sample answers: mug   calculator

   scissors   clip

✦ *Math Journal 1, p. 35*

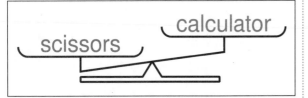

A pair of scissors weighs more than a calculator.

scale, however, is usually used with objects that weigh less than a pound. So the numbers on a spring scale represent ounces, not pounds.

Place an object that weighs more than 1 pound (for example, a book) in a plastic bag and hang the bag from the spring scale. The scale marker is pulled down to the bottom. This means that the object is too heavy for this scale because it weighs more than 1 pound.

Pull the hook on the spring scale down until the marker is at 16 ounces. Say that this is what a 1-pound weight would do. Say that ounces are lighter than pounds, and there are 16 ounces in a pound.

Hang a pair of scissors on the scale. This time the scale marker moves down part of the way, but not all the way to the bottom. Read the marker and tell the class how many ounces the pair of scissors weighs. Point out that the plastic bag is necessary for weighing objects that cannot be hung easily on the scale (like books).

✦ Exploration A: Using a Pan Balance
(*Math Journal 1*, p. 35)

SMALL-GROUP ACTIVITY

Help children understand the directions on the journal page. Two separate activities are recorded on this page: one using the pan balance and the other using the spring scale.

Children select two objects from the set of objects you have collected. They feel the objects and guess which is heavier. Then they use the pan balance to verify their guesses.

For each pair of objects compared, they should write the names of the objects on one of the pan-balance pictures to show what happened.

Example: To show that a pair of scissors weighs more than a calculator, children write "scissors" in the lower pan and "calculator" in the higher pan.

 Adjusting the Activity It might be helpful for some children to draw pictures of the objects on the pans rather than writing out the names of the objects.

To extend this activity, suggest that children place a light object in one pan and enough pennies in the other pan to put the pans in balance. Children can sketch this situation in the empty pan balances given on the journal page and record the object and number of pennies.

✦ Exploration B: Using a Spring Scale
(*Math Journal 1*, p. 35)

SMALL-GROUP ACTIVITY

Have children hang a plastic bag from the hook on the spring scale. The challenge is to fill the bag with different objects so that it weighs about 1 pound. Example: A 6 oz mug, a 4 oz calculator, a 5 oz pair of scissors, and a 1 oz binder clip weigh about 16 oz or 1 pound. Children record their work on the journal page.

✦ Exploration C: Making Equal Groups of Objects (*Math Masters*, p. 27)

PARTNER ACTIVITY

Partners follow instructions on *Math Masters*, page 27 to make "nests" that hold the same number of "eggs." This activity develops the basic concept of multiplication.

ONGOING ASSESSMENT
Observe how children answer the question "How many eggs are in all the nests?" Most will use repeated addition. For example, if there are 4 nests, with 3 eggs in each nest, they will answer $3 + 3 + 3 + 3 = 12$. Make note of children who think in terms of multiplication and answer $4 \times 3 = 12$ or 4 [3s] equals 12.

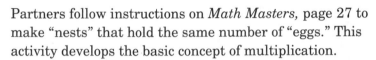

Ongoing Learning & Practice

✦ Playing *Beat the Calculator*
(*Math Journal 1*, p. 23)

SMALL-GROUP ACTIVITY

Children review calculator and addition skills by playing *Beat the Calculator*. For detailed instructions, see Lesson 2.2.

Egg Nests

Work with a partner.

Materials
- [ ] 1 six-sided die
- [ ] 1 sheet of plain paper
- [ ] 36 counters (for example, pennies, centimeter cubes, or dried beans)
- [ ] 6 quarter-sheets of paper

Directions

Pretend that the quarter-sheets of paper are birds' nests.

Pretend that the pennies, cubes, or beans are eggs.

1. Roll the die twice.
   - The first roll tells how many nests to use.
   - The second roll tells how many eggs to put in each nest.

2. Work together to set up the nests and eggs for the numbers you rolled. How many eggs are there in all of the nests?

3. Use your sheet of plain paper and draw a picture.
   - Show all the nests.
   - Show all the eggs in each nest.

4. Start again. Repeat Steps 1–3.

✦ *Math Masters*, p. 27

TEACHING MASTER

Fact Power Table

0 +0 0	0 +1 1	0 +2 2	0 +3 3	0 +4 4	0 +5 5	0 +6 6	0 +7 7	0 +8 8	0 +9 9
1 +0 1	1 +1 2	1 +2 3	1 +3 4	1 +4 5	1 +5 6	1 +6 7	1 +7 8	1 +8 9	1 +9 10
2 +0 2	2 +1 3	2 +2 4	2 +3 5	2 +4 6	2 +5 7	2 +6 8	2 +7 9	2 +8 10	2 +9 11
3 +0 3	3 +1 4	3 +2 5	3 +3 6	3 +4 7	3 +5 8	3 +6 9	3 +7 10	3 +8 11	3 +9 12
4 +0 4	4 +1 5	4 +2 6	4 +3 7	4 +4 8	4 +5 9	4 +6 10	4 +7 11	4 +8 12	4 +9 13
5 +0 5	5 +1 6	5 +2 7	5 +3 8	5 +4 9	5 +5 10	5 +6 11	5 +7 12	5 +8 13	5 +9 14
6 +0 6	6 +1 7	6 +2 8	6 +3 9	6 +4 10	6 +5 11	6 +6 12	6 +7 13	6 +8 14	6 +9 15
7 +0 7	7 +1 8	7 +2 9	7 +3 10	7 +4 11	7 +5 12	7 +6 13	7 +7 14	7 +8 15	7 +9 16
8 +0 8	8 +1 9	8 +2 10	8 +3 11	8 +4 12	8 +5 13	8 +6 14	8 +7 15	8 +8 16	8 +9 17
9 +0 9	9 +1 10	9 +2 11	9 +3 12	9 +4 13	9 +5 14	9 +6 15	9 +7 16	9 +8 17	9 +9 18

✦ *Math Journal 1*, p. 23

STUDENT PAGE

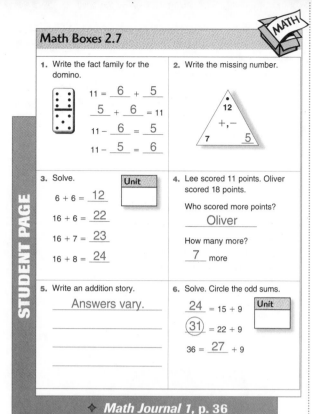

Math Boxes 2.7

1. Write the fact family for the domino.

$11 = \underline{6} + \underline{5}$

$\underline{5} + \underline{6} = 11$

$11 - \underline{6} = \underline{5}$

$11 - \underline{5} = \underline{6}$

2. Write the missing number.

12
+,−
7   5

3. Solve.

Unit

$6 + 6 = \underline{12}$

$16 + 6 = \underline{22}$

$16 + 7 = \underline{23}$

$16 + 8 = \underline{24}$

4. Lee scored 11 points. Oliver scored 18 points.

Who scored more points?

Oliver

How many more?

$\underline{7}$ more

5. Write an addition story.

Answers vary.

6. Solve. Circle the odd sums.

Unit

$\underline{24} = 15 + 9$

$(\underline{31}) = 22 + 9$

$36 = \underline{27} + 9$

♦ *Math Journal 1, p. 36*

STUDENT PAGE

♦ **Math Boxes 2.7** (*Math Journal 1*, p. 36)

INDEPENDENT ACTIVITY

Mixed Review This journal page provides opportunities for cumulative review or assessment of concepts and skills.

♦ **Home Link 2.7** (*Math Masters*, pp. 248 and 249)

Home Connection Children tell someone at home about how they used a pan balance and a spring scale. They compare the weights of objects and determine which objects in a group weigh less than 1 pound.

3 Options for Individualizing

♦ **EXTRA PRACTICE** **Minute Math**

SMALL-GROUP ACTIVITY **5–15 min**

To offer children more experience with time, weight, length, volume, and area, see the following pages in *Minute Math*:

Measurement: pp. 61 and 62

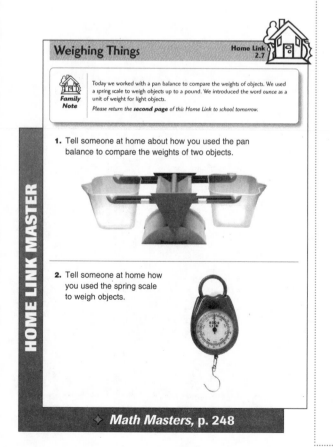

Weighing Things — Home Link 2.7

Family Note — Today we worked with a pan balance to compare the weights of objects. We used a spring scale to weigh objects up to a pound. We introduced the word *ounce* as a unit of weight for light objects.

*Please return the **second page** of this Home Link to school tomorrow.*

1. Tell someone at home about how you used the pan balance to compare the weights of two objects.

2. Tell someone at home how you used the spring scale to weigh objects.

♦ *Math Masters, p. 248*

HOME LINK MASTER

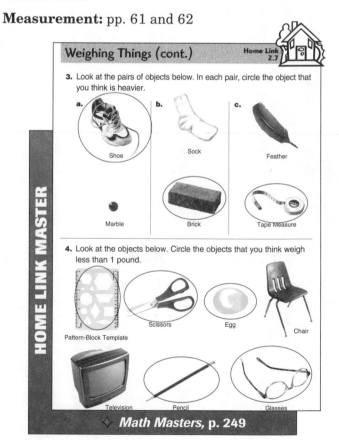

Weighing Things (cont.) — Home Link 2.7

3. Look at the pairs of objects below. In each pair, circle the object that you think is heavier.

a. Shoe / Marble   b. Sock / Brick   c. Feather / Tape Measure

4. Look at the objects below. Circle the objects that you think weigh less than 1 pound.

Pattern-Block Template   Scissors   Egg   Chair

Television   Pencil   Glasses

♦ *Math Masters, p. 249*

HOME LINK MASTER

2.8

Fact Families

OBJECTIVES To demonstrate the inverse relationship between addition and subtraction; and to practice addition and subtraction facts for sums up to and including 10.

summaries	materials
1 Teaching the Lesson	
Children identify the fact families shown on Fact Triangles, and practice the "easier" addition and subtraction facts by using Fact Triangles as flashcards. [Operations and Computation; Patterns, Functions, and Algebra]	☐ Fact Triangles cut from *Math Journal 1,* Activity Sheets 1 and 2 (see Lesson 2.5) ☐ Home Link 2.7 ☐ Teaching Master transparency (*Math Masters,* p. 28; optional) ☐ slate *See* **Advance Preparation**
2 Ongoing Learning & Practice	
Children represent weight comparisons by drawing pan-balance pictures. [Numeration; Measurement and Reference Frames] Children practice and maintain skills through Math Boxes and Home Link activities.	☐ *Math Journal 1,* pp. 37–39 ☐ Home Link Masters (*Math Masters,* pp. 250 and 251) ☐ pan balance (optional)
3 Options for Individualizing	
Reteaching Children represent part-part-whole subtraction by using counters. [Operations and Computation; Patterns, Functions, and Algebra]	☐ 18 pennies or other counters per partnership

Additional Information

Advance Preparation If children have not already cut out the Fact Triangles from Activity Sheets 1 and 2, they should do so before working on the Math Message.

For the *Discussing Fact Families* activity in Part 1, you may want to make an overhead transparency of *Math Masters,* page 28.

Vocabulary • **fact family** • **Fact Triangle**

Vocabulary (teacher) • **minuend**

Getting Started

Mental Math and Reflexes

Pose simple subtraction number story problems.
Suggestions:

• There are 8 boys on Team A and 12 boys on Team B.
  How many more boys are on Team B? 4 boys

• Jay had $20 and spent $7. What does Jay have now?
  $13

Math Message

*Take out your envelope of Fact Triangles. Write
your name, and write "Fact Triangles" on the envelope.*

Home Link 2.7 Follow-Up

Review answers as necessary.

Teaching the Lesson

◆ Math Message Follow-Up

WHOLE-CLASS DISCUSSION

Tell children to store the Fact Triangles in their tool kits
when they are not using them.

◆ Discussing Fact Families
(*Math Masters,* p. 28)

WHOLE-CLASS DISCUSSION

Draw a unit box on the board and let someone choose a
label for the day. Then display an overhead transparency
of *Math Masters,* page 28 or draw a large triangle on the
board. Write 6, 3, and 9 (with a large dot above the 9) in
the three corners. Ask children to describe ways in which
the three numbers are related.

Show children that the three numbers can be used to
make two addition facts (6 + 3 = 9 and 3 + 6 = 9) and
two subtraction facts (9 − 6 = 3 and 9 − 3 = 6). This
collection of facts is called a **fact family.** Point out that a
large dot is used to identify the sum for addition facts and
the first number (the **minuend**) for subtraction facts.

Ask someone to name three other numbers that are
related by addition. Write these numbers in the corners of
a triangle and have children write the fact family for the

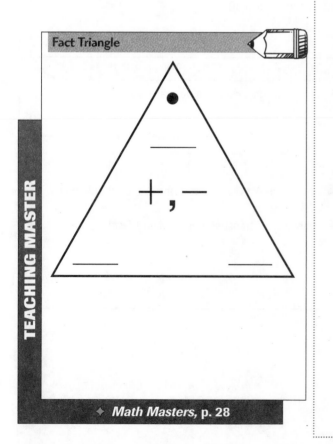

Fact Triangle

TEACHING MASTER

◆ *Math Masters, p. 28*

124 Unit 2 *Addition and Subtraction Facts*

numbers on their slates. Repeat with other triplets as needed.

- How many different facts are there in the fact family for a doubles fact? 2; for example, $4 + 4 = 8$ and $8 - 4 = 4$

- Do subtraction facts have turn-around facts? No; for example, $9 - 3 = 6$ but $3 - 9 = -6$

NOTE: Some teachers suggest having children write the fact families on the backs of the Fact Triangles. This could be an ongoing project, to be done a few at a time.

✦ Demonstrating the Use of +,− Fact Triangles

PARTNER ACTIVITY

Demonstrate the following flashcard procedure using an actual **Fact Triangle,** or the Fact Triangle on the transparency or board. Then have partners practice it.

1. One partner covers one corner of a Fact Triangle with a finger or thumb.

2. The covered number is part of an addition or subtraction fact. The other partner says the complete fact.

Two journal pages with 9 Fact Triangles on each page are provided in this unit (Activity Sheets 1 and 2). The full set of 36 addition/subtraction Fact Triangles (Activity Sheets 1–4) include all the facts except the 0-facts and the 1-facts. Encourage children to use the triangles at a pace that is comfortable for them. The first 18 triangles are used in this lesson and in Lessons 2.11–2.13; the remaining triangles are used in Lesson 2.13.

✦ Practicing with Fact Triangles

PARTNER ACTIVITY

Children continue the flashcard procedure described above. You may wish to have children write facts on their slates rather than saying them aloud. Circulate as children practice, offering guidance when needed.

 Adjusting the Activity When a child misses a fact, the partner should flash the other fact problems on the triangle and then return to the fact that was missed. For example, Sue can't answer $10 - 6$. Alex flashes $6 + 4$, then $10 - 4$, and finally $10 - 6$ a second time.

Use of the Fact Triangles will continually remind children that a good way to subtract is to ask, "How much do I *add*?" Each time a subtraction problem is posed, the child will receive two visual messages—a subtraction message and a related addition message.

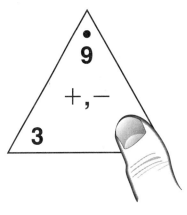

$9 - 3 = ?$ and $3 + ? = 9$

Pan-Balance Problems

Reminder: There are 16 ounces in 1 pound.

Some food items and their weights are shown below.

- Pretend you will put one or more items in each pan.
- Pick items that would make the balances tilt the way they are shown on journal page 39.
- Write the name of each item in the pan you put it in.
- Write the weight of each item below the pan you put it in.

Try to use a variety of food items.

Salad Dressing	Orange	Walnuts	Eggplant	Gummy Worms
1 ounce	8 ounces	3 ounces	15 ounces	4 ounces

Salt	Lemon	Flour	Banana	Potatoes
1 pound	6 ounces	2 pounds	6 ounces	5 pounds

Math Journal 1, p. 38

Example

Weight: __8 ounces__   Weight: __4 ounces__

On journal page 39, children make up and solve pan-balance problems.

Math Boxes 2.8

1. Match the items to the weights.

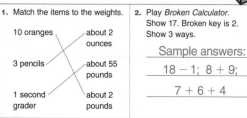

10 oranges — about 2 ounces

3 pencils — about 55 pounds

1 second grader — about 2 pounds

2. Play *Broken Calculator.*
Show 17. Broken key is 2.
Show 3 ways.

Sample answers:

__18 − 1; 8 + 9;__

__7 + 6 + 4__

3. 810

Write the number that is 1 more.

__811__

4. Write the sums.

Unit

10 + 10 = __20__

10 + 11 = __21__

10 + 12 = __22__

10 + 13 = __23__

5. Nate has 17 toy cars. Raul has 2 fewer toy cars than Nate. How many cars does Raul have?

__15__ cars

Write a number model.

__17 − 2 = 15 or 15 + 2 = 17__

6. Solve.

Unit

__20__ > 10 + 9

__16__ < 9 + 8

__2 + 2__ < 16 − 9

__13 − 2__ = 19 − 8

Sample answers

Math Journal 1, p. 37

Ongoing Learning & Practice

✦ Solving Pan-Balance Problems
(*Math Journal 1,* pp. 38 and 39)

INDEPENDENT ACTIVITY

Some food items and their weights are shown on journal page 38. Each problem on journal page 39 shows a pan balance tilted to the heavier side. Children imagine putting food items in the pans to make each balance tilt as shown. Work through a problem with children to be sure they understand what to do. The example from journal page 39 is shown in the margin.

Adjusting the Activity If children are having difficulty, select an item for one of the pans and record the item's name and weight on the child's journal page. The child must then, based on the position of the pans, decide whether to choose an item for the other pan that weighs more, less, or the same as the given item.

 ONGOING ASSESSMENT

In Lesson 2.7 children used a pan balance to compare weights of different objects. Use journal page 39 to assess whether or not they are able to transfer the work with the actual pan balance into a pictorial representation.

Note that working with a pan balance is still a developing skill. You may wish to provide children with an opportunity for practice by setting up a pan balance in an exploration center for children to use in their free time.

✦ Math Boxes 2.8 (*Math Journal 1,* p. 37)

INDEPENDENT ACTIVITY

 Mixed Review This journal page provides opportunities for cumulative review or assessment of concepts and skills.

◆ **Home Link 2.8** (*Math Masters,* pp. 250 and 251)

Home Connection Children show someone at home how they practice with Fact Triangles. The family note explains Fact Triangles in more detail and suggests regular use at home to complement fact work in class.

Fact Triangles

Fact Triangles are tools used to help build mental arithmetic skills. You might think of them as the *Everyday Mathematics* version of flash cards. Fact Triangles are more effective for helping children memorize facts, however, because of their emphasis on fact families. A **fact family** is a collection of related addition and subtraction facts that use the same 3 numbers. The fact family for the numbers 2, 4, and 6 consists of $2 + 4 = 6$, $4 + 2 = 6$, $6 - 4 = 2$, and $6 - 2 = 4$.

To use Fact Triangles to practice addition with your child, cover the number next to the large dot with your thumb.

Your child tells you the addition fact: $4 + 5 = 9$ or $5 + 4 = 9$.
To use Fact Triangles to practice subtraction, cover one of the numbers in the lower corners with your thumb.

Your child tells you the subtraction facts: $9 - 5 = 4$ and $9 - 4 = 5$.
If your child misses a fact, flash the other two fact problems on the card and then return to the fact that was missed.
Example: Sue can't answer $9 - 5$. Flash $4 + 5$, then $9 - 4$, and finally $9 - 5$ a second time.

Make this activity brief and fun. Spend about 10 minutes each night over the next few weeks or until your child masters all of the facts. The work that you do at home will help your child develop an instant recall of facts and will complement the work that we are doing at school.

◆ *Math Masters,* p. 250

NOTE: The second Home Link page (below) contains Fact Triangles that have been used in this lesson. With it, children have separate sets of Fact Triangles for their use at home and at school.

3 Options for Individualizing

◆ **RETEACHING** Representing Part-Part-Whole Subtraction with Counters

PARTNER ACTIVITY   5–15 min

When children use the Fact Triangles as flashcards, the covered number is the answer to either an addition or a subtraction fact. When the covered number is the answer to a subtraction fact, the child is looking at a part and the whole and must name the other part. Children who find this difficult may be helped by the following activity, which uses manipulatives to reinforce the part-part-whole subtraction concept.

1. Partners start with a known number of counters; for example, 12.

2. One child separates the counters into two piles or parts; for example, one pile of 7 and one pile of 5.

3. The same child then covers one of the two piles with a piece of paper.

4. The other child writes the subtraction fact; for example: 12 (*whole*) − 7 (*known part*) = 5 (*unknown part*). If necessary, the child may count the covered pile to check the answer.

5. The partners work together to write the three other facts in the fact family. $12 - 5 = 7$, $5 + 7 = 12$, $7 + 5 = 12$

The activity can be repeated with any number of counters in different combinations.

Fact Triangles (cont.)

Cut out the Fact Triangles. Show someone at home how you use them to practice adding and subtracting.

◆ *Math Masters,* p. 251

2.9 Name Collections

OBJECTIVE To review the concept that a number can be named in many ways.

summaries	materials

1 Teaching the Lesson

Children use name-collection boxes to write equivalent names for numbers, and children identify sums and differences that match a given number by playing *Name That Number*. [Numeration; Operations and Computation]

- ☐ *Math Journal 1*, p. 40
- ☐ Home Link 2.8
- ☐ 4 each of number cards 0–10 and 1 each of number cards 11–20, or Everything Math Deck, if available

***See* Advance Preparation**

2 Ongoing Learning & Practice

Children solve subtraction number stories. [Operations and Computation]

Children practice and maintain skills through Math Boxes and Home Link activities.

- ☐ *Math Journal 1*, pp. 41 and 42
- ☐ Home Link Masters (*Math Masters*, pp. 252 and 253)
- ☐ counters (optional)

3 Options for Individualizing

Extra Practice Children write equivalent names for numbers by playing *Musical Name-Collection Boxes*.
[Numeration; Operations and Computation]

Enrichment Children explore equivalent names found in literature. [Numeration]

- ☐ chart paper
- ☐ CD player or tape player
- ☐ CDs or tapes
- ☐ *Twelve Ways to Get Eleven*

***See* Advance Preparation**

Additional Information

Advance Preparation Before beginning the lesson, draw a unit box on the board. Fill in the unit box with the label of your choice (or one supplied by children). Keep the unit box and label posted for all the numbers that are not labeled in this lesson.

For the optional *Musical Name-Collection Boxes* activity in Part 3, you will need to draw four or five name-collection boxes on chart paper and post them around your classroom. You will also need a way to play music for this activity.

Before beginning the optional Enrichment activity in Part 3, obtain the book *Twelve Ways to Get Eleven* by Eve Merriam (Simon & Schuster, 1993).

Vocabulary • **name-collection box**

Mental Math and Reflexes

Do place-value exercises on slates. *For example:*

Write 506. Circle the digit in the 100s place. Put an X on the digit in the 1s place. Which digit is not marked? *The 0 in the 10s place*

Math Message

Write as many different names for the number 8 as you can.

Sample answers: 5 + 3, 9 − 1, 2 + 2 + 2 + 2

Home Link 2.8 Follow-Up

Ask children if they used the Fact Triangles to practice facts with someone at home. Remind children that the Fact Triangles can help them develop fact power, which makes it easier to solve problems.

---

1 Teaching the Lesson

◆ Math Message Follow-Up

WHOLE-CLASS DISCUSSION

Draw a box on the board like the one in the margin. Tell children that this is called an 8-box. It is a **name-collection box** for the number 8. Ask several volunteers to write names for the number 8 in the box.

If children limit the names for 8 to addition and subtraction expressions, ask them to think of ways to write 8 without using numbers. If necessary, suggest a few other possibilities, such as the following:

Examples

Tally marks: ⊥⊥⊥⊥ ///

Pictures or diagrams:

octagon   4-by-2 array

Roman numeral: VIII

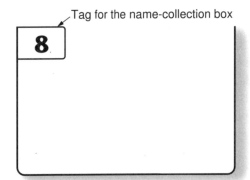

Tag for the name-collection box

8

Name-collection box

◯ Language Link

Word: eight

Ask: "Does anyone know how to say 'eight' in another language?" (acht *[German]*; ocho *[Spanish]*; roku *[Japanese]*; huit *[French]*; vocyem *[Russian]*)

NOTE: Roman numerals could be included in the name-collection box. Refer to the Enrichment activity in Lesson 1.1.

Sample

Mae's turn:

The number to be named is 6. The number 6 can be named "4 + 2," "8 − 2," or "10 − 4." Mae selects 4 + 2. She takes the 4, 2, and 6 cards. She replaces the 4 and 2 with the top two cards from the facedown deck and turns over the next card to replace the 6, as shown in Mike's turn below.

Mike's turn:

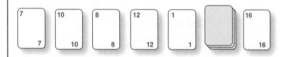

The number to be named is 16. Mike can't find two cards he can use to name 16. He turns over the next card from the facedown deck and places it on top of the 16. The next player tries to name the new target number.

A sample round for *Name That Number*

◆ Demonstrating *Name That Number*

PARTNER ACTIVITY

In *Name That Number,* children try to identify a sum or difference that names a given target number. The target numbers play the same role as numbers written on the tags of name-collection boxes.

Divide the class into groups of 2, 3, or 4. Explain the rules of *Name That Number.* Then have children play a game while you circulate and help groups that run into difficulty. Praise good group etiquette.

Materials: 4 each of number cards 0–10 and 1 each of number cards 11–20, or Everything Math Deck, if available

Number of Players: 2, 3, or 4

Rules

1. One player shuffles the cards and places the deck facedown.

2. A second player turns the top five cards faceup and places them in a row.

3. The second player then turns the next card faceup and places it next to the deck. This is the number to be named—the target number.

4. In turn, players try to name the target number by adding or subtracting the numbers on any two of the other faceup cards.

5. If a player names the target number with two cards, the player takes those two cards and the card for the target number. The player replaces the three cards with the top three cards from the facedown deck.

6. If a player cannot name the target number, the player turns over the top card from the facedown deck. This becomes the target number for the next player.

7. Play continues until all facedown cards have been turned over.

8. The player who has the most cards wins.

◆ Playing *Name That Number*

PARTNER ACTIVITY

Children continue playing the game. Teachers report that the game is popular and successful because children of all ability levels are able to participate.

Adjusting the Activity To extend the game, use any combination of two or more numbers and use both addition and subtraction. For example, Mike could have named 16 as $10 + 7 - 1$, or $10 + 12 - 7 + 1$, or $8 + 12 - 10 + 7 - 1$.

If children find the game difficult, increase the number of faceup cards.

ONGOING ASSESSMENT

For each round of play, have children record the number model that they used to name the target number. Use this record to assess children's progress in writing number models and identifying sums and differences that match a given number. It is expected that most children understand the concept of equivalent number names. However, children will display different levels of ability in the number models that they write to name the target number.

✦ Practicing with Name-Collection Boxes
(*Math Journal 1*, p. 40)

INDEPENDENT ACTIVITY

Children solve problems that involve name-collection boxes.

2 Ongoing Learning & Practice

✦ Solving Subtraction Number Stories
(*Math Journal 1*, p. 41)

INDEPENDENT ACTIVITY

Change-to-less and *comparison* subtraction number stories were covered previously in Lesson 2.6 and practiced in the Mental Math and Reflexes problems in Lesson 2.8.

ONGOING ASSESSMENT

Journal page 41 provides an opportunity to check individual student progress. Expect that the majority of children will be able to solve these simple subtraction number stories; some children may need to use a manipulative such as counters.

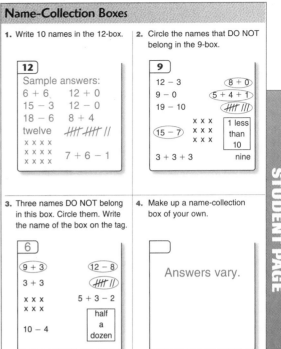

Name-Collection Boxes

1. Write 10 names in the 12-box.

12
Sample answers:
6 + 6   12 + 0
15 − 3   12 − 0
18 − 6   8 + 4
twelve   ⫽⫽⫽ ⫽⫽⫽ ⫽⫽
x x x x
x x x x   7 + 6 − 1
x x x x

2. Circle the names that DO NOT belong in the 9-box.

9
12 − 3   (8 + 0)
9 − 0   (5 + 4 + 1)
19 − 10   (⫽⫽⫽ ⫽⫽⫽)
(15 − 7)   x x x   1 less
           x x x   than
           x x x   10
3 + 3 + 3   nine

3. Three names DO NOT belong in this box. Circle them. Write the name of the box on the tag.

6
(9 + 3)   (12 − 8)
3 + 3   (⫽⫽⫽ ⫽⫽)
x x x   5 + 3 − 2
x x x
             half
10 − 4   a
             dozen

4. Make up a name-collection box of your own.

Answers vary.

Math Journal 1, p. 40

Subtraction Number Stories

Solve each problem.

1. Ross has $11. He buys a book for $6. How much money does he have left?

$ __5__

2. Martin has 7 markers. Jason has 4 markers. How many more markers does Martin have than Jason?

__3__ markers

3. There are 11 girls on Tina's softball team. There are 13 girls on Lisa's team. How many more girls are on Lisa's team than on Tina's?

__2__ girls

4. Lily has 10 flowers. She gives 4 flowers to her sister. How many flowers does she have left?

__6__ flowers

5. Emma has 8 chocolate cookies and 5 vanilla cookies. How many more chocolate cookies does she have than vanilla cookies?

__3__ chocolate cookies

6. Make up and solve your own subtraction story.

Sample answer: Mark had $20. He spent $9. How much money does he have left? $11

Math Journal 1, p. 41

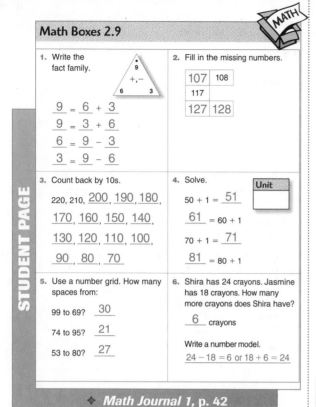

Math Boxes 2.9

STUDENT PAGE

1. Write the fact family.

9
+,−
6   3

$9 = 6 + 3$
$9 = 3 + 6$
$6 = 9 − 3$
$3 = 9 − 6$

2. Fill in the missing numbers.

107	108
117	
127	128

3. Count back by 10s.

220, 210, 200, 190, 180,
170, 160, 150, 140,
130, 120, 110, 100,
90, 80, 70

4. Solve.

Unit

$50 + 1 = 51$
$61 = 60 + 1$
$70 + 1 = 71$
$81 = 80 + 1$

5. Use a number grid. How many spaces from:

99 to 69?   30
74 to 95?   21
53 to 80?   27

6. Shira has 24 crayons. Jasmine has 18 crayons. How many more crayons does Shira have?

6 crayons

Write a number model.
$24 − 18 = 6$ or $18 + 6 = 24$

Math Journal 1, p. 42

PLANNING AHEAD

In preparation for tomorrow's class, make several copies of *Math Masters,* page 30 so that children can make up more Frames-and-Arrows problems if they wish.

HOME LINK MASTER

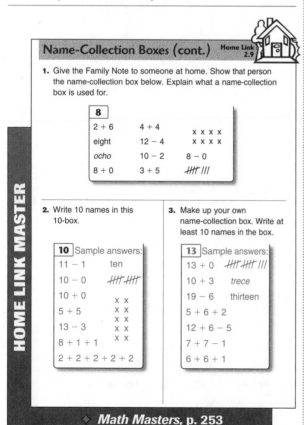

Name-Collection Boxes (cont.)   Home Link 2.9

1. Give the Family Note to someone at home. Show that person the name-collection box below. Explain what a name-collection box is used for.

8

2 + 6	4 + 4	x x x x
eight	12 − 4	x x x x
ocho	10 − 2	8 − 0
8 + 0	3 + 5	~~HHT~~ ///

2. Write 10 names in this 10-box.

10 Sample answers:
11 − 1   ten
10 − 0   ~~HHT HHT~~
10 + 0
5 + 5   x x
13 − 3   x x
            x x
8 + 1 + 1   x x
2 + 2 + 2 + 2 + 2

3. Make up your own name-collection box. Write at least 10 names in the box.

13 Sample answers:
13 + 0   ~~HHT HHT~~ ///
10 + 3   trece
19 − 6   thirteen
5 + 6 + 2
12 + 6 − 5
7 + 7 − 1
6 + 6 + 1

Math Masters, p. 253

◆ **Math Boxes 2.9** (*Math Journal 1,* p. 42)

INDEPENDENT ACTIVITY

 Mixed Review This journal page provides opportunities for cumulative review or assessment of concepts and skills.

◆ **Home Link 2.9** (*Math Masters,* pp. 252 and 253)

Home Connection Children solve a name-collection-box problem and then make up their own problem. The Family Note on the first page of Home Link 2.9 discusses name-collection boxes.

3 Options for Individualizing

◆ **EXTRA PRACTICE** Playing *Musical Name-Collection Boxes*

SMALL-GROUP ACTIVITY   **5–15 min**

Draw four or five name-collection boxes (with numbers on the tags) on chart paper and post them around the room. Play music while the children walk in a circle. Each child should be holding a crayon, pencil, or marker. When you stop the music, children find seats at the tables nearest to them. Give children several minutes to enter an expression or diagram in the nearest name-collection box for the number written on the tag. Children must enter a name that has not been used before. Continue playing and stopping the music. This can be a challenging task after several rounds.

◆ **ENRICHMENT** Exploring Equivalent Names in Literature

SMALL-GROUP ACTIVITY   **30+ min**

 Literature Link Read the following book to children, or have them read the book themselves.

Twelve Ways to Get Eleven

Summary: This book describes twelve ways to name the number 11; for example, 9 pine cones and 2 acorns or 6 peanuts and 5 popcorn kernels.

2.10 Frames-and-Arrows Routines

OBJECTIVES To use a given addition or subtraction rule to generate a number sequence; and to identify the rule for a given number sequence.

summaries

materials

1 Teaching the Lesson

Children review the Frames-and-Arrows notation and routine that were introduced in first grade, and use addition or subtraction rules to fill in frames, arrow rules, or both. [Operations and Computation; Patterns, Functions, and Algebra]

- ☐ *Math Journal 1*, p. 43
- ☐ Home Link 2.9
- ☐ Teaching Master transparency (*Math Masters*, p. 29; optional)

See **Advance Preparation**

2 Ongoing Learning & Practice

Children identify sums and differences that match a given number by playing *Name That Number*. [Numeration; Operations and Computation]

Children practice and maintain skills through Math Boxes and Home Link activities.

- ☐ *Math Journal 1*, p. 44
- ☐ Home Link Masters (*Math Masters*, pp. 254 and 255)
- ☐ number cards (see Lesson 2.9) or 1 Everything Math Deck, if available, per group

3 Options for Individualizing

Enrichment Children make up and solve Frames-and-Arrows problems. [Operations and Computation; Patterns, Functions, and Algebra]

Reteaching Children use a number grid to solve Frames-and-Arrows problems. [Operations and Computation; Patterns, Functions, and Algebra]

- ☐ Teaching Master (*Math Masters*, p. 30)
- ☐ number grid

Additional Information

Advance Preparation Before beginning the lesson, draw a unit box on the board. Fill in the unit box with the label of your choice (or the children's). Keep the unit box and label posted for all the numbers that are not labeled in this lesson. You may also want to make an overhead transparency of *Math Masters*, page 29 for the first Frames-and-Arrows activity in Part 1.

Vocabulary • **Frames-and-Arrows diagrams** • **frame** • **arrow** • **arrow rule**

Getting Started

Mental Math and Reflexes

Pose +9 facts. Encourage children to think +10 and subtract 1.
Suggestions:
5 + 9 = ? 14   ? = 9 + 7 16

Math Message

Which shape comes next? Draw it.

Home Link 2.9 Follow-Up

Ask volunteers to share the tag and one or two entries for the name-collection boxes that they created. Can other children suggest additional entries?

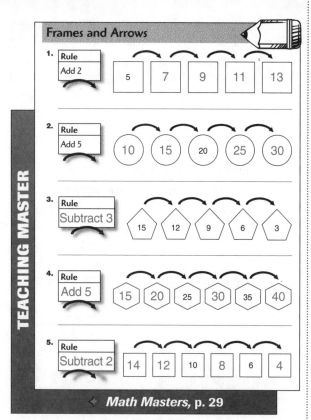

Frames and Arrows

1. Rule: Add 2

$\boxed{5}\ \boxed{7}\ \boxed{9}\ \boxed{11}\ \boxed{13}$

2. Rule: Add 5

10 15 20 25 30

3. Rule: Subtract 3

15 12 9 6 3

4. Rule: Add 5

15 20 25 30 35 40

5. Rule: Subtract 2

$\boxed{14}\ \boxed{12}\ \boxed{10}\ \boxed{8}\ \boxed{6}\ \boxed{4}$

Math Masters, p. 29

TEACHING MASTER

1 Teaching the Lesson

◆ Math Message Follow-Up

WHOLE-CLASS DISCUSSION

Briefly go over children's responses and ask them to share how they found the answers. Help them state a rule for each pattern. *For example:*

▷ In the first pattern, the dot moves clockwise from corner to corner. The next shape is $\boxed{\,{}^{\bullet}\,}$.

▷ The second pattern shows polygon shapes. Each shape has one more side than the preceding shape, so the shape following the pentagon has 6 sides (a hexagon). Ask children to name the shapes.

◆ Demonstrating Frames-and-Arrows Routines (*Math Masters*, p. 29)

WHOLE-CLASS DISCUSSION

Frames-and-Arrows diagrams consist of **frames,** or shapes, which are connected by **arrows** that show the path from one frame to the next. Each frame contains a number, and the numbers form a sequence. Each arrow represents a rule—the **arrow rule**—that determines which number goes in the next frame.

The Math Message problems and Frames-and-Arrows diagrams share a common feature. The problems and diagrams both use a rule to generate the pattern.

Use the Frames-and-Arrows diagram below as an example. Write the diagram on the board, or use an overhead transparency of *Math Masters,* page 29.

1.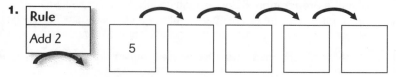

A possible Frames-and-Arrows diagram to put on the board.

Remind children that the squares are called frames and that the arrows stand for the rule that is written in the box. Ask children to use the rule "Add 2" to fill in the frames. Completed frames: 5, 7, 9, 11, 13

Do a few more examples. Use different addition and subtraction rules, and fill in the first frame with a number.

 Adjusting the Activity Frames-and-Arrows problems become progressively more complicated. Depending on the ability level of a child, move more slowly or quickly through example problems.

Continue with other examples, but leave the first frames empty so that children will have to work both forward and backward to fill in the empty frames. *For example:*

2.

Next, try examples in which the frames are filled in but the rule is missing. Ask children to identify the arrow rule. *For example:*

3.
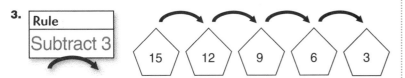

Write examples in which some of the frames are empty and the rule is missing. Ask children to find the rule and then fill in the missing frames. These problems are challenging: Children must first discover the rule and then work both forward and backward to fill in the frames.

4.

5.
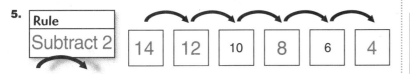

◆ Completing Frames-and-Arrows Diagrams
(*Math Journal 1*, p. 43)

PARTNER ACTIVITY

Have children fill in frames, arrow rules, or both. Circulate and offer help where needed.

Adjusting the Activity To extend this activity, ask children to name the figures used as frames on the journal page. Square, circle, pentagon, hexagon

If children are having difficulty, fill in some of the empty frames to provide additional clues.

Adjusting the Activity When children are asked to find a rule, encourage them to think in two steps.

Step 1: Decide which operation is being used. Are the numbers in the pattern getting larger or smaller?

Step 2: Once the operation has been determined, children can figure out which number is being added or subtracted. Suggest counting on or counting back (with the use of fingers to keep track, if necessary).

Math Journal 1, p. 43

STUDENT PAGE

1. Cross out names that do not belong.

12	
9 + 3	10 + 2	18 − 6

~~HHT HHT //~~   ⓓⓟⓟ

~~6 + 5~~   4 + 4 + 1

1 dozen   3 + 9

2. Write the fact family.

$$10 - 6 = 4$$
$$10 - 4 = 6$$
$$6 + 4 = 10$$
$$4 + 6 = 10$$

3. Continue.

230, 235, 240, 245, 250,
255, 260, 265, 270,
275, 280, 285, 290,
295, 300, 305

4. There are 10 houses on Jerry's block. There are 15 houses on Nancy's block. How many more houses are on Nancy's block?

5 houses

Write a number model.

15 − 10 = 5 or 10 + 5 = 15

5. 349 has:

3 hundreds

4 tens

9 ones

6. A pack of gum costs 25¢. Sean bought 3 packs. How much money did he spend?

75¢

✦ *Math Journal 1, p. 44*

Frames-and-Arrows Problems   Home Link 2.10

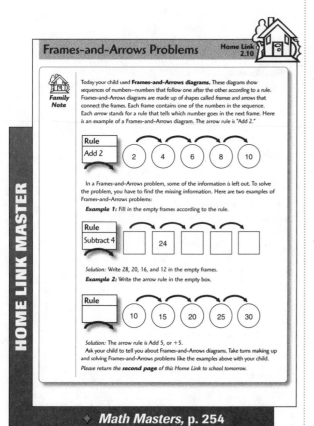

Family Note

Today your child used **Frames-and-Arrows diagrams**. These diagrams show sequences of numbers—numbers that follow one after the other according to a rule. Frames-and-Arrows diagrams are made up of shapes called *frames* and arrows that connect the frames. Each frame contains one of the numbers in the sequence. Each *arrow* stands for a rule that tells which number goes in the next frame. Here is an example of a Frames-and-Arrows diagram. The arrow rule is "Add 2."

Rule
Add 2

In a Frames-and-Arrows problem, some of the information is left out. To solve the problem, you have to find the missing information. Here are two examples of Frames-and-Arrows problems:

Example 1: Fill in the empty frames according to the rule.

Rule
Subtract 4

Solution: Write 28, 20, 16, and 12 in the empty frames.

Example 2: Write the arrow rule in the empty box.

Rule

Solution: The arrow rule is Add 5, or +5.

Ask your child to tell you about Frames-and-Arrows diagrams. Take turns making up and solving Frames-and-Arrows problems like the examples above with your child.

*Please return the **second page** of this Home Link to school tomorrow.*

✦ *Math Masters, p. 254*

Ongoing Learning & Practice

✦ Playing *Name That Number*

PARTNER ACTIVITY

This game was introduced in Lesson 2.9. To make the game more challenging, have children play a variation in which players may use two, three, four, or all five of the faceup cards to name the target number.

Example:

Use 2 cards: no solution
Use 3 cards: $7 + 8 + 1 = 16$
Use 4 cards: $10 + 12 + 1 - 7 = 16$
Use 5 cards: $12 - 10 + 8 + 7 - 1 = 16$

 ONGOING ASSESSMENT
For each round of play, have children record the number model that they used to name the target number. Use this record to assess children's progress in writing number models and identifying sums and differences that match a given number.

✦ Math Boxes 2.10 (*Math Journal 1, p. 44*)

INDEPENDENT ACTIVITY

Mixed Review This journal page provides opportunities for cumulative review or assessment of concepts and skills.

✦ Home Link 2.10 (*Math Masters, pp. 254 and 255*)

Home Connection Children complete Frames-and-Arrows problems. The Family Letter will help parents and guardians be more comfortable when assisting their children.

Options for Individualizing

◆ ENRICHMENT Making Up Frames-and-Arrows Problems (*Math Masters*, p. 30)

PARTNER ACTIVITY **5–15 min**

Children make up problems for their partners to solve. Encourage children to vary the types of problems they create.

◆ RETEACHING Counting on a Number Grid

PARTNER ACTIVITY **5–15 min**

Frames-and-Arrows problems involve counting patterns. Children having difficulty solving these problems may benefit from a review of counting patterns on a number grid. They can use a number grid to fill in frames or to determine a rule. *For example:*

▷ The rule is +10. The first frame is 0. Point to 0 on the number grid. Count up 10 steps. Note that the count ends on 10. Continue to count up, 10 more steps at a time. The counts end on 20, 30, and so on. Fill in the frames: 10, 20, 30, and so on.

▷ The rule is missing. The frames show 40, 35, 30, 25, 20. Point to 40 on the number grid. Count back 5 steps to 35, 5 more steps to 30, and so on. The rule is "subtract 5" or "−5."

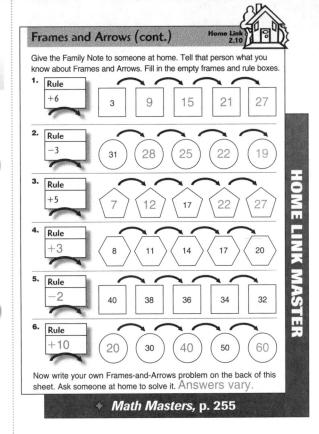

◆ *Math Masters*, p. 255

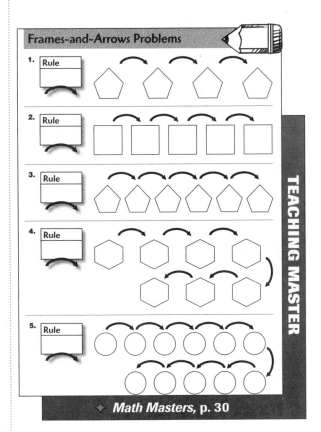

◆ *Math Masters*, p. 30

2.11

"What's My Rule?" Routines

OBJECTIVES To identify missing numbers in number pairs that are generated by a rule; and to determine the rule used to generate number pairs.

summaries	**materials**
1 Teaching the Lesson	
Children review the "What's My Rule?" routines and notation, use function machines to illustrate "What's My Rule?" tables, and solve "What's My Rule?" problems by determining missing numbers or rules. [Operations and Computation; Patterns, Functions, and Algebra]	☐ *Math Journal 1*, p. 45 ☐ Home Link 2.10 ☐ Teaching Master transparencies (*Math Masters*, pp. 31 and 32; optional) ***See* Advance Preparation**
2 Ongoing Learning & Practice	
Children practice addition and subtraction facts by using Fact Triangles as flashcards. [Operations and Computation; Patterns, Functions, and Algebra] Children practice and maintain skills through Math Boxes and Home Link activities.	☐ *Math Journal 1*, p. 46 ☐ Home Link Masters (*Math Masters*, pp. 256 and 257) ☐ envelope with Fact Triangles (from Lesson 2.5)
3 Options for Individualizing	
Reteaching Children identify rules by sorting attributes. [Patterns, Functions, and Algebra]	

Additional Information

Advance Preparation For additional information on "What's My Rule?" activities, see the *Teacher's Reference Manual*.

For the "What's My Rule" activities on pages 140 and 141 of Part 1, you may want to make overhead transparencies of *Math Masters*, pages 31 and 32.

Vocabulary • **"What's My Rule?"** • **function machine**

Getting Started

Mental Math and Reflexes

Show times on a demonstration clock while children record them on their slates. *Suggestions:* 5:30, 6:45, 8:20, 3:50, 2:35, 4:01, 1:46

Math Message

June is 3 years older than Kevin. If Kevin is 7 years old, how old is June?

Home Link 2.10 Follow-Up

Review the answers to the Frames-and-Arrows problems. If time allows, ask children to share with the class the problems that they created. Ask other volunteers to solve the problems.

Teaching the Lesson

✦ Math Message Follow-Up

WHOLE-CLASS DISCUSSION

Ask children to share their strategies for solving the problem. They may draw pictures, use tallies, or count on their fingers. Help children to summarize by writing a number model for the problem. $7 + 3 = 10$

✦ Establishing "What's My Rule?" Routines

WHOLE-CLASS DISCUSSION

The first through third grades **"What's My Rule?"** routines include number pairs displayed in a table of values. The numbers in each pair are related according to the same rule. The rule may be applied to *any* number in the left column (the "in" number) to generate the adjacent number in the right column (the "out" number). The table on the right shows a few pairs for the rule "add 3" or "+3."

Draw a unit box and table (as shown in the margin) on the board. Also draw an empty rule box beneath the table. Leave out the numbers and the label in the unit box for the time being.

Remind students about the Math Message problem. Then write the entries 7 and 10 in the table, write +3 in the rule box, and write "years" in the unit box. Explain that this is one way to show the information in the problem.

Continue to fill in the table as you ask questions like the following. As children give each answer, help them to summarize by writing a number model on the board.

- What if Kevin is 8 years old? How old is June then? 11 years old; $8 + 3 = 11$

- What if Kevin is 9 years old? June is 12 years old. $9 + 3 = 12$

- What if Kevin is 10 years old? June is 13 years old. $10 + 3 = 13$

Now write 15 in the first column and ask questions like the following:

- Which number goes in the second column? 18 How do you know? Because the number in the second column is always 3 more than the number in the first column

- Can anyone state a rule for finding June's age if you know Kevin's age? Add 3, or +3

in	out
0	3
1	4
2	5
3	6

A table of values for +3

Unit
years

Kevin	June
7	10
8	
9	
10	
15	

Rule
+3

Raissa	Joe
7	5
8	6
9	7
10	
15	

Rule

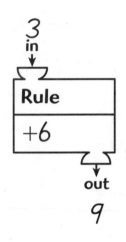

in	out
3	9

Copy the table with an empty rule box (as shown in the margin) on the board. Ask questions like the following:

- Who is younger, Raissa or Joe? Joe How many years younger? 2 years
- What's the rule for finding Joe's age if you know Raissa's age? Subtract 2 from Raissa's age, or −2. Write −2 in the rule box for Table 2.
- What if Raissa is 10 years old? How old is Joe then? 8 years old; 10 − 2 = 8
- What if Raissa is 15 years old? How old is Joe then? Joe is 13 years old. 15 − 2 = 13

◆ Using Function Machines to Illustrate "What's My Rule?" Tables
(*Math Masters*, pp. 31 and 32)

WHOLE-CLASS DISCUSSION

Draw the diagram and table shown in the margin on the board, or display an overhead transparency of *Math Masters*, page 31. Add "3," "+6," and "9," as shown in the margin.

Tell children that the diagram shows a **function machine.** The machine is set to follow a certain rule. Someone drops a number in the machine, the machine does something to the number according to the rule, and a new number comes out.

Draw various "What's My Rule?" tables on the board, or use an overhead transparency of *Math Masters*, page 32. Complete the tables with children. Use a function machine to illustrate the process.

Try to include each type of table shown below.

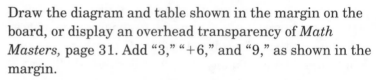

Rule +6		Rule ?		Rule +4		Rule −3	
in	out	in	out	in	out	in	out
3		6	2		6		4
5		10	6		16	12	
8		16	12		11		7
9		8	4		10	9	
We know: inputs, rule **Find:** outputs		**We know:** inputs, outputs **Find:** rule		**We know:** outputs, rule **Find:** inputs		**We know:** rule **Find:** missing data	

✦ Solving "What's My Rule?" Problems
(*Math Journal 1*, p. 45; and *Math Masters*, p. 32)

PARTNER ACTIVITY

Partners practice solving problems in which the rule is given and numbers must be determined and in which numbers are given and the rule must be determined. An overhead transparency of *Math Masters,* page 32 may be used as an aid in discussing children's answers.

2 Ongoing Learning & Practice

✦ Practicing with +,− Fact Triangles

PARTNER ACTIVITY

Partners practice addition and subtraction facts.

✦ Math Boxes 2.11 (*Math Journal 1*, p. 46)

INDEPENDENT ACTIVITY

Mixed Review This journal page provides opportunities for cumulative review or assessment of concepts and skills.

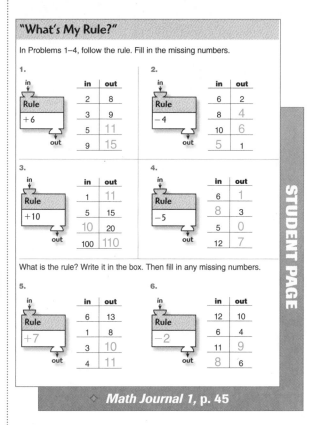

"What's My Rule?"

In Problems 1–4, follow the rule. Fill in the missing numbers.

What is the rule? Write it in the box. Then fill in any missing numbers.

Math Journal 1, p. 45

Adjusting the Activity If the "What's My Rule?" problems on journal page 45 are too easy, use *Math Masters,* page 32 to create more difficult problems tailored to the abilities of individual children.

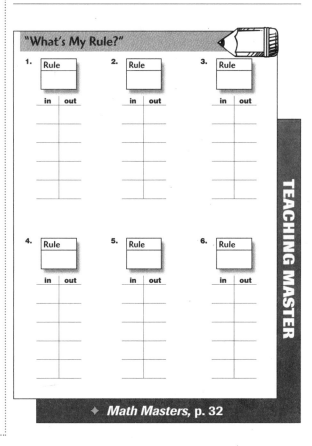

"What's My Rule?"

Math Masters, p. 32

Math Boxes 2.11

1. Solve.

$4 + 3 = \underline{7}$

$10 - 7 = \underline{3}$

$\begin{array}{r} 5 \\ + 4 \\ \hline 9 \end{array}$ $\begin{array}{r} 8 \\ - 3 \\ \hline 5 \end{array}$

2. Fill in the frames. Follow the arrow rule. **Rule +3**

3 6 9 12 18 15

3. Draw a rectangle around the digit in the tens place.

3 [4] 9

4 [0] 6

4. Fill in the tag on the name-collection box. Add 3 more names.

9

18 − 9   3 + 3 + 3

Answers vary, but each name should equal 9.

5. Complete the Fact Triangle and the fact family.

$12 = 9 + 3$

$3 + 9 = 12$

$12 - 3 = 9$

$3 = 12 - 9$

6. Match the items to the weights.

1 cat — 1 ounce

3 envelopes — 1 pound

1 book — 7 pounds

Math Journal 1, p. 46

Lesson 2.11   **141**

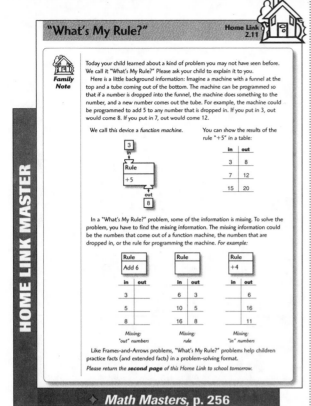

Math Masters, p. 256

Home Connection Children solve "What's My Rule?" problems. The Family Note explains the "What's My Rule?" routine.

3 Options for Individualizing

◆ RETEACHING "What's My Rule?" Fishing

WHOLE-CLASS ACTIVITY   5–15 min

If children are having difficulty with the "What's My Rule?" concept, you may wish to do the following attribute activity before working with number pairs.

With a group, "fish" for children using some obvious attribute. For example, fish out a few people wearing brown without explaining what you are fishing for. Ask: *What sort of fish am I going to catch next?* (or *"What's My Rule?"*). Let children guess until someone says, "People with brown on." Ask: *Who are the children not in my net?* All people without brown on Use a different attribute and play again. Use obvious things at first (wearing red shirts or sneakers, for example). Once the children understand the game, let one of them do the fishing.

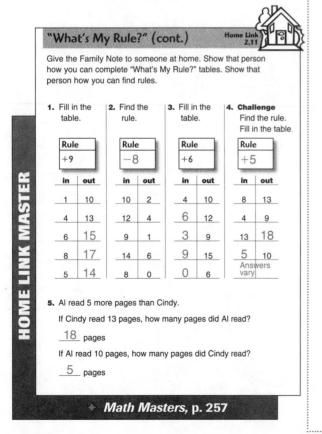

Math Masters, p. 257

2.12 Counting Strategies for Subtraction

OBJECTIVE To review, develop, and practice the counting-back and counting-up strategies for subtraction.

summaries	materials

1 Teaching the Lesson

Children share and solve subtraction number stories. [Operations and Computation; Patterns, Functions, and Algebra]

Children review and practice the counting-back and counting-up strategies for subtraction and practice "easier" subtraction facts by using Fact Triangles. [Operations and Computation; Patterns, Functions, and Algebra]

☐ counters (optional)
☐ Home Link 2.11
☐ envelope of Fact Triangles (from Lesson 2.5)
☐ slate

2 Ongoing Learning & Practice

Children practice "harder" addition facts by playing *Beat the Calculator*. [Operations and Computation]

Children cut out a second set of 18 Fact Triangles.

Children practice and maintain skills through Math Boxes and Home Link activities.

☐ *Math Journal 1*, pp. 23, 47, and Activity Sheets 3 and 4
☐ Home Link Master (*Math Masters*, p. 258)
☐ calculator
☐ scissors

3 Options for Individualizing

Extra Practice Children find the missing parts in sums and differences. [Operations and Computation]

☐ *Minute Math®*, p. 39

Additional Information
Vocabulary • difference

Getting Started

Mental Math and Reflexes

Would you weigh the following objects in ounces or pounds?

• a box of chalk ounces
• 10 student journals pounds
• chalkboard eraser ounces
• overhead projector pounds

Math Message
Make up a story for the number model 11 − 8 = 3.

Home Link 2.11 Follow-Up

Review answers with the class. For Problem 4, remind children to first use the in/out number pairs in the first two rows of the table to determine the rule. Then they can fill in the rest of the table.

1 Teaching the Lesson

◆ Math Message Follow-Up

WHOLE-CLASS DISCUSSION

Write "$11 - 8 = 3$" on the board and draw an empty unit box. Ask a few children to share their subtraction stories and to suggest labels to write in the unit box.

◆ Reviewing the Meaning of "Difference"

WHOLE-CLASS DISCUSSION

Remind children that the number obtained by subtracting one number from another is called the **difference.** Encourage them to use the word "difference" as much as possible. For example, if a child says, "The answer to $11 - 8$ is 3," you might say, "Yes. You are subtracting, so the answer is called the difference." Another way to say it is "The difference of $11 - 8$ is 3."

◆ Reviewing the Counting-Back Strategy for Subtraction

WHOLE-CLASS ACTIVITY

There are 100 different subtraction facts that may be posed using the Facts Table. Thirty of these facts are of the form $n - 1$, $n - 2$, or $n - 3$. Not all children will have achieved instant recall of these easier facts. The counting-back strategy shown in the examples below can enable these children to give answers quickly and achieve instant recall sooner.

Give several examples of counting back mentally. Use numbers in which the number being subtracted (subtrahend) is 1, 2, or 3. Count back, starting with the larger number (minuend).

Examples
$7 - 3 = ?$ Think 7.   Say "6, 5, 4." The answer (difference) is 4.
$37 - 2 = ?$ Think 37.   Say "36, 35." The answer (difference) is 35.

Pose similar problems, and ask children to write the answers on their slates.

 Adjusting the Activity Children can use counters to solve subtraction problems by counting back. For $7 - 3$, the child begins by placing 7 counters on the table. The child removes 3 counters one by one while counting back. The child then writes the number model, $7 - 3 = 4$. Repeat this activity for other facts in which 1, 2, or 3 is being subtracted.

◆ Reviewing the Counting-Up Strategy for Subtraction

WHOLE-CLASS ACTIVITY 👥👥👥👥

Forty of the subtraction facts on the Facts Table have differences of 0, 1, 2, or 3. Not all children will have instant recall of these easier facts. The counting-up strategy shown in the examples below can enable these children to give answers quickly and achieve instant recall sooner.

Give several examples of counting up mentally. Use subtraction problems that have a difference of 1, 2, or 3. Count up, starting with the smaller number (subtrahend).

Examples_____

$9 - 7 = ?$ Think 7.   Say "8 is 1, 9 is 2."
The answer (difference) is 2.
$15 - 12 = ?$ Think 12.   Say "13 is 1, 14 is 2, 15 is 3."
The answer (difference) is 3.

Counting up using fingers can be efficient. Children raise a new finger for each number that they count. The difference is the total number of fingers raised.

Examples_____

$9 - 7 = ?$ Think 7.   Say "8 ✋, 9 ✋."
The answer (difference) is 2.
$36 - 33 = ?$ Think 33.   Say "34 ✋, 35 ✋, 36 ✋."
The answer (difference) is 3.

Pose similar problems, and ask children to write the answers on their slates.

◆ Practicing with +,− Fact Triangles

PARTNER ACTIVITY

Children practice addition and subtraction facts.

The first set of Fact Triangles includes 18 individual Fact Triangles. All but 4 of these Fact Triangles include subtraction facts that may be answered by using the counting-up or counting-back strategies. With practice, children will rely less on strategies and more on memory as they begin to achieve instant recall of the facts.

🛡 **Adjusting the Activity** Children can use counters to solve subtraction problems by counting up. For $9 - 7$, a child begins by placing 9 counters on the table. The child touches 7 counters and counts up. "7, … 8, 9. I counted up 2, so the difference is 2. $9 - 7 = 2$." Repeat this activity for other facts for which the difference is 1, 2, or 3.

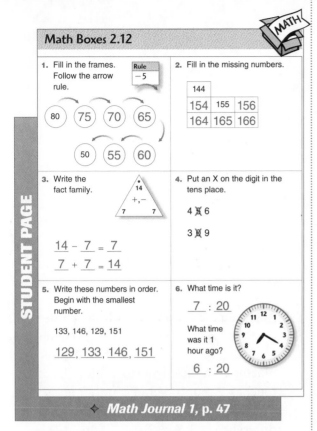

Math Boxes 2.12

1. Fill in the frames. Follow the arrow rule.

Rule
−5

80 75 70 65
50 55 60

2. Fill in the missing numbers.

144		
154	155	156
164	165	166

3. Write the fact family.

14
+,−
7   7

$14 - 7 = 7$

$7 + 7 = 14$

4. Put an X on the digit in the tens place.

4 X 6

3 X 9

5. Write these numbers in order. Begin with the smallest number.

133, 146, 129, 151

129, 133, 146, 151

6. What time is it?

7 : 20

What time was it 1 hour ago?

6 : 20

✦ *Math Journal 1, p. 47*

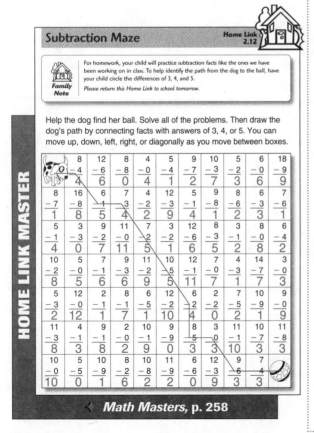

Subtraction Maze

Home Link
2.12

Family Note

For homework, your child will practice subtraction facts like the ones we have been working on in class. To help identify the path from the dog to the ball, have your child circle the differences of 3, 4, and 5.

Please return this Home Link to school tomorrow.

Help the dog find her ball. Solve all of the problems. Then draw the dog's path by connecting facts with answers of 3, 4, or 5. You can move up, down, left, right, or diagonally as you move between boxes.

< *Math Masters, p. 258*

---

2 Ongoing Learning & Practice

✦ Playing *Beat the Calculator*
(*Math Journal 1*, p. 23)

PARTNER ACTIVITY

The Caller should select problems at random from the gray area of the Fact Power Table. Problems from the gray area include the "hardest" addition facts.

✦ Cutting Out +,− Fact Triangles
(*Math Journal 1*, Activity Sheets 3 and 4)

INDEPENDENT ACTIVITY

Have children cut out the Fact Triangles from Activity Sheets 3 and 4 and place them in an envelope. These Fact Triangles will be used in Lesson 2.13.

NOTE: Children cut out the Fact Triangles from Activity Sheets 1 and 2 during Lesson 2.5.

✦ Math Boxes 2.12 (*Math Journal 1*, p. 47)

INDEPENDENT ACTIVITY

Mixed Review This journal page provides opportunities for cumulative review or assessment of concepts and skills.

✦ Home Link 2.12 (*Math Masters*, p. 258)

Home Connection Children solve subtraction facts and then trace a path through boxes with differences of 3, 4, or 5.

3 Options for Individualizing

✦ EXTRA PRACTICE Minute Math

SMALL-GROUP ACTIVITY   5–15 min

To offer children more experience with addition and subtraction problems, see the following page in *Minute Math:*

Operations: p. 39

2.13 Shortcuts for "Harder" Subtraction Facts

OBJECTIVE To discover and practice shortcuts for subtracting 9 or 8 from any number.

summaries	materials

1 Teaching the Lesson

Children make up and share subtraction stories, and children discover and practice the −9 and −8 shortcuts. [Operations and Computation; Patterns, Functions, and Algebra]

- ☐ *Math Journal 1*, p. 48
- ☐ Home Link 2.12
- ☐ Class Number Grid Poster (optional)
- ☐ slate

2 Ongoing Learning & Practice

Children practice addition and subtraction facts by using Fact Triangles as flashcards. [Operations and Computation; Patterns, Functions, and Algebra]

Children practice and maintain skills through Math Boxes and Home Link activities.

- ☐ envelopes with Fact Triangles (from Lessons 2.5 and 2.12)
- ☐ *Math Journal 1*, p. 49
- ☐ Home Link Masters (*Math Masters,* pp. 259 and 260)

See **Advance Preparation**

3 Options for Individualizing

Extra Practice Children use the "What's My Rule?" routine to practice −9 and −8 facts. [Operations and Computation; Patterns, Functions, and Algebra]

Reteaching Children use a ten-frame to develop the −9 and the −8 shortcuts. [Operations and Computation; Patterns, Functions, and Algebra]

- ☐ 18 counters per child
- ☐ Teaching Masters (*Math Masters,* pp. 26 and 33)

Additional Information

Advance Preparation Before beginning Part 2, children should cut out the Fact Triangles on Activity Sheets 3 and 4 if they have not already done so.

Vocabulary • −9 facts • −9 shortcut • −8 facts • −8 shortcut

Getting Started

Mental Math and Reflexes

Pose problems such as the following:

14 − 10 = ? 4	24 − 10 = ? 14
? − 10 = 5 15	? − 10 = 16 26

Solving a set of −10 problems will aid in the discovery of the −9 and −8 shortcuts later in this lesson.

Math Message

Make up a story for the number model
16 − 9 = 7.

Home Link 2.12 Follow-Up

Check that children were able to find the correct path through the maze.

1 Teaching the Lesson

◆ Math Message Follow-Up

WHOLE-CLASS DISCUSSION

Write 16 − 9 = 7 on the board and draw an empty unit box. Ask a few children to share their subtraction stories and to suggest labels to write in the unit box.

◆ Introducing a −9 Shortcut

WHOLE-CLASS DISCUSSION

Write some −**9 facts** and extended facts on the board; leave off the differences. Use both horizontal and vertical forms. (See the margin.)

Ask children to copy and complete the facts on their slates. See if they can discover a −**9 shortcut** for subtracting 9 from any number.

It may help if you write pairs of related −9 facts and −10 facts on the board.

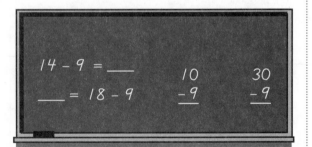

Ask children to describe the −9 shortcut in their own words. The following are good descriptions:

▷ You subtract 10 instead of 9, and then add on 1.

▷ Subtract 10, but make your answer 1 bigger.

 Adjusting the Activity If children have difficulty, demonstrate the −9 shortcut on the Class Number Grid Poster. Locate a number on the number grid. Subtract 10 by moving straight up to the row above. Then add 1 by moving right 1 square.

1	2	3	4	5	6	7→	8	9	10
11	12	13	14	15	16	(17)	18	19	20

✦ Introducing the −8 Shortcut

WHOLE-CLASS DISCUSSION

Write some −**8 facts** and extended facts on the board; leave off the differences. Use both horizontal and vertical forms. (See the margin.)

Use the same approach as you did with the −9 shortcut to help children discover a −**8 shortcut** for subtracting 8 from any number. Children might describe the shortcut in the following ways:

▷ You subtract 10 instead of 8, and then add on 2.

▷ Subtract 10, but make your answer 2 bigger.

✦ Practicing −9 and −8 Shortcuts
(*Math Journal 1*, p. 48)

INDEPENDENT ACTIVITY

Children practice shortcuts for subtracting 9 or 8 from any number.

Adjusting the Activity Some children may find it helpful to write the −10 fact next to each problem. For example, next to 17 − 9, write 17 − 10. Children find the answer to 17 − 10 and decide how that answer can be used to solve 17 − 9.

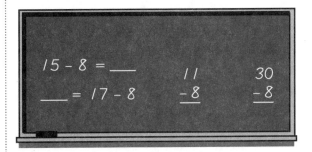

$15 - 8 = $ _____ 11 30
_____ $ = 17 - 8$ -8 -8

Subtract 9 or 8

1. Subtract. Use the −9 and −8 shortcuts.

  a. 13 − 9 = <u>4</u>   b. 14 − 8 = <u>6</u>   c. 16 − 9 = <u>7</u>

  d. <u>4</u> = 12 − 8   e. <u>8</u> = 17 − 9   f. 12 − 9 = <u>3</u>

  g. <u>5</u> = 13 − 8   h. 11 − 9 = <u>2</u>   i. <u>7</u> = 15 − 8

  j.   15   k.   17   l.   11
     <u>− 9</u>   <u>− 8</u>   <u>− 8</u>
     6   9   3

2. Find the differences.

> *Reminder:* To find 37 − 9, think 37 − 10 + 1.
> To find 37 − 8, think 37 − 10 + 2.

  a. 43 − 9 = <u>34</u>   b. 56 − 8 = <u>48</u>   c. 65 − 9 = <u>56</u>

  d. 37 − 8 = <u>29</u>   e. 45 − 9 = <u>36</u>   f. 53 − 8 = <u>45</u>

3. Solve.

  a. 4 = <u>13</u> − 9   b. 3 = <u>11</u> − 8

  c. 7 = <u>16</u> − 9   d. 6 = <u>14</u> − 8

✦ *Math Journal 1*, p. 48

STUDENT PAGE

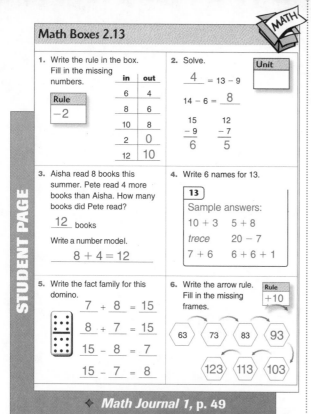

1. Write the rule in the box. Fill in the missing numbers.

Rule
−2

in	out
6	4
8	6
10	8
2	0
12	10

2. Solve.

Unit

$4 = 13 - 9$

$14 - 6 = 8$

$\begin{array}{r} 15 \\ -9 \\ \hline 6 \end{array}$ $\begin{array}{r} 12 \\ -7 \\ \hline 5 \end{array}$

3. Aisha read 8 books this summer. Pete read 4 more books than Aisha. How many books did Pete read?

12 books

Write a number model.

$8 + 4 = 12$

4. Write 6 names for 13.

13

Sample answers:

10 + 3	5 + 8
trece	20 − 7
7 + 6	6 + 6 + 1

5. Write the fact family for this domino.

$7 + 8 = 15$

$8 + 7 = 15$

$15 - 8 = 7$

$15 - 7 = 8$

6. Write the arrow rule. Fill in the missing frames.

Rule
+10

63 → 73 → 83 → 93

123 ← 113 ← 103

♦ *Math Journal 1, p. 49*

NOTE: The second Home Link page contains Fact Triangles that have been used in this lesson. With it, children have separate sets of Fact Triangles for their use at school and at home.

Ongoing Learning & Practice

♦ Practicing with +,− Fact Triangles

PARTNER ACTIVITY

Have children practice addition and subtraction facts by using Fact Triangles as flashcards. This procedure was first described in Lesson 2.8. If children have instant recall for most of the easier facts, ask them to remove the Fact Triangles that have sums that are less than 10. By doing this, children will focus on practicing the harder facts.

♦ Math Boxes 2.13 (*Math Journal 1,* p. 49)

INDEPENDENT ACTIVITY

Mixed Review This journal page provides opportunities for cumulative review or assessment of concepts and skills.

♦ Home Link 2.13 (*Math Masters,* pp. 259 and 260)

Home Connection Children solve addition and subtraction facts and then trace a path through boxes in which the answer is 6. The focus is on −9 and −8

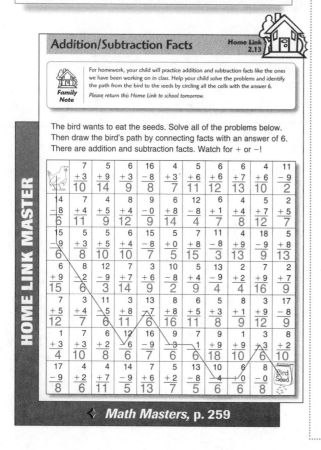

Addition/Subtraction Facts   Home Link 2.13

Family Note For homework, your child will practice addition and subtraction facts like the ones we have been working on in class. Help your child solve the problems and identify the path from the bird to the seeds by circling all the cells with the answer 6.

Please return this Home Link to school tomorrow.

The bird wants to eat the seeds. Solve all of the problems below. Then draw the bird's path by connecting facts with an answer of 6. There are addition and subtraction facts. Watch for + or −!

♦ *Math Masters, p. 259*

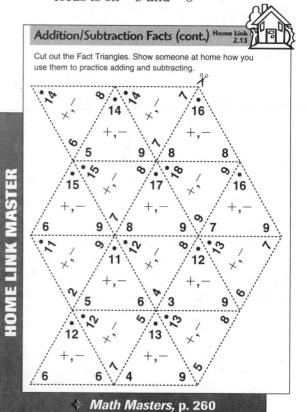

Addition/Subtraction Facts (cont.)   Home Link 2.13

Cut out the Fact Triangles. Show someone at home how you use them to practice adding and subtracting.

♦ *Math Masters, p. 260*

Options for Individualizing

◆ **EXTRA PRACTICE** Using the "What's My Rule?" Routine to Practice −9 and −8 Shortcuts (*Math Masters*, p. 33)

INDEPENDENT ACTIVITY   5–15 min

"What's My Rule?" was introduced in Lesson 2.11. *Math Masters,* page 33 provides an opportunity to use this routine to practice the −9 and −8 shortcuts.

◆ **RETEACHING** Using a Ten-Frame to Develop −9 and −8 Shortcuts (*Math Masters,* p. 26)

INDEPENDENT ACTIVITY   5–15 min

To find 15 − 9, a child places 9 counters on the ten-frame. Ask the child how many more counters are needed to show 15. Focus on the idea of *one more to get 10* and then the rest of the number.

The child may think:

▷ I'm starting with 9.

▷ How much to 10? 1

▷ How much more to 15? 5

▷ 1 + 5 = 6, so 15 − 9 = 6

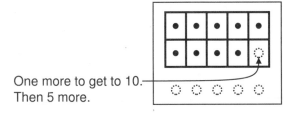

One more to get to 10.
Then 5 more.

Repeat for other differences, such as 12 − 9 and 18 − 9.

Use the same procedure for the −8 facts by showing 8 counters in the ten-frame. Focus on the idea of *two more to get 10* and then how many more to get to the starting number.

PLANNING AHEAD

To prepare for the activities in Lesson 3.1, organize a set of base-10 blocks for each partnership. Include 3 or 4 flats, 10 longs, and 10 cubes. Put the blocks into bags labeled with the children's tool-kit numbers. You will need a similar set for yourself. You may want to use base-10 blocks for the overhead projector.

"What's My Rule?" Problems

Write the rule for the table. Complete the table.

1. Rule: −10

in	out
44	34
26	16
78	68
82	72
64	54

2. Rule: −8

in	out
15	7
10	2
13	5
12	4
17	9

3. Rule: −9

in	out
18	9
13	4
16	7
15	6
14	5

Complete the table.

4. Rule: −9

in	out
37	28
83	74
71	62
62	53
96	87

5. Rule: −8

in	out
81	73
53	45
77	69
62	54
35	27

Write a rule of your own. Fill in the table.

6. Rule: ____

in	out
Answers vary.

◆ *Math Masters,* p. 33

TEACHING MASTER

Ten-Frame Card

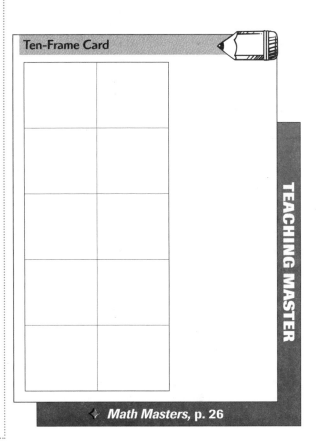

◆ *Math Masters,* p. 26

TEACHING MASTER

Unit 2 Review and Assessment

OBJECTIVE To review and assess children's progress on the material covered in Unit 2.

1 Assess Progress

learning goals

2a **Developing Goal** Know "harder" subtraction facts. **(Lesson 2.13)**

2b **Developing/Secure Goal** Know "harder" addition facts. **(Lessons 2.4 and 2.5)**

2c **Developing/Secure Goal** Know "easier" subtraction facts. **(Lessons 2.8 and 2.12)**

2d **Developing/Secure Goal** Complete "What's My Rule?" tables. **(Lesson 2.11)**

2e **Developing/Secure Goal** Solve simple subtraction number stories. **(Lesson 2.6)**

2f **Secure Goal** Know "easier" addition facts. **(Lessons 2.2, 2.3, and 2.8)**

2g **Secure Goal** Construct fact families for addition and subtraction. **(Lessons 2.6 and 2.8)**

2h **Secure Goal** Complete simple Frames-and-Arrows diagrams. **(Lesson 2.10)**

2i **Secure Goal** Solve simple addition number stories. **(Lesson 2.1)**

2j **Secure Goal** Find equivalent names for numbers. **(Lesson 2.9)**

activities

- Slate Assessment, Problems 10 and 11
- Written Assessment, Problem 8

- Slate Assessment, Problem 7
- Written Assessment, Problem 6

- Slate Assessment, Problem 9
- Written Assessment, Problem 7

- Written Assessment, Problem 4

- Slate Assessment, Problems 9, 10, and 11

- Slate Assessment, Problems 6 and 8
- Written Assessment, Problem 5

- Slate Assessment, Problem 2
- Written Assessment, Problem 1

- Written Assessment, Problem 3

- Slate Assessment, Problems 6, 7, and 8

- Slate Assessment, Problem 3; Written Assessment, Problem 2

materials

- ☐ Teaching Master (*Math Masters,* p. 22)
- ☐ Assessment Masters (*Math Masters,* pp. 420 and 421)
- ☐ Home Link 2.13
- ☐ slate; envelope of Fact Triangles; demonstration clock

2 Build Background for Unit 3

summaries

Children practice and maintain skills through Math Boxes and Home Link activities.

materials

- ☐ *Math Journal 1,* p. 50
- ☐ Home Link Masters (*Math Masters,* pp. 261–264)
- ☐ 2 envelopes of Fact Triangles (from Lessons 2.5 and 2.12)

Each **learning goal** listed above indicates a level of performance that might be expected at this point in the *Everyday Mathematics* K–6 curriculum. For a variety of reasons, the levels indicated may not accurately portray your class's performance.

Getting Started

Math Message

Explain how the numbers 9, 8, and 17 are related to one another.

Home Link 2.13 Follow-Up

Check to see that children were able to find the path through the maze. Ask children to explain how they solved some of the problems.

1 Assess Progress

◆ Math Message Follow-Up

WHOLE-CLASS DISCUSSION

Children's answers may provide insight into their thought processes regarding fact families. Ask children why $8 + 9 = 17$ and $9 + 8 = 17$ are called turn-around facts.

◆ Oral and Slate Assessments

WHOLE-CLASS ACTIVITY

If the suggested problems below are not appropriate for your class's level of performance, adjust the numbers in the problems—or adjust the problems themselves—to better assess your children's abilities.

Oral Assessment Suggestions

1. Count up by 2s, 5s, and 10s.

2. Count down by 2s, 5s, and 10s.

Slate Assessment Suggestions

1. Write the turn-around fact for $5 + 6 = 11$, $9 + 1 = 10$, and $8 + 5 = 13$.

2. Write two addition facts and two subtraction facts for the numbers 3, 5, and 8; for 7, 4, and 11; and for 7, 8, and 15. **Goal 2g**

3. Write another name for the number 12; for 17; for 30. **Goal 2j**

4. Record the time shown on the demonstration clock: 11:00, 7:45, 2:30, 4:15, 9:10, and 8:55.

> NOTE: Many of these assessment suggestions relate to learning goals that have been addressed in previous units. Now is a good time to evaluate children's progress toward these goals.

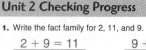
ASSESSMENT MASTER

1. Write the fact family for 2, 11, and 9.

$2 + 9 = 11$ $9 + 2 = 11$

$11 - 2 = 9$ $11 - 9 = 2$

2. Circle the names for 14.

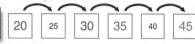

(9 + 5)   7 – 3   (12 + 2)   5 + 6   (8 + 6)

1 + 11   (7 + 7)   3 + 9   (18 – 4)

3. Fill in the empty frames.

| Rule +5 | 20 | 25 | 30 | 35 | 40 | 45 |

4. Find the rule and complete the table.

Rule +6

in	out
9	15
6	12
4	10
7	13
10	16
8	14

Math Masters, p. 420

---

5. Add.

a. 6 + 1 = __7__   **b.** 0 + 9 = __9__   **c.** __8__ = 2 + 6

d. 4
  +4
  ‾‾
   8

e. 3
  +5
  ‾‾
   8

6. Add.

a. 7 + 7 = __14__   **b.** 9 + 4 = __13__   **c.** __15__ = 6 + 9

d. 8
  +6
  ‾‾
  14

e. 5
  +7
  ‾‾
  12

7. Subtract.

a. 7 – 0 = __7__   **b.** __10__ = 11 – 1   **c.** 7 – 4 = __3__

d. 6
  –2
  ‾‾
   4

e. 9
  –5
  ‾‾
   4

8. Subtract.

a. 16 – 9 = __7__   **b.** 18 – 9 = __9__   **c.** __8__ = 14 – 6

d. 15
  – 8
  ‾‾
   7

e. 13
  – 5
  ‾‾
   8

Math Masters, p. 421

ASSESSMENT MASTER

---

5. Write *oz* or *lb* to indicate whether the following objects would be best measured in ounces or pounds: pencil oz, calculator oz, 4-month-old baby lb, magazine oz, case of soda pop lb.

Tell number stories like the following. Children record their answers on slates. If time allows, have children share strategies for how they figured out the answers. Encourage children to use manipulatives, drawings, or other strategies to solve the problems.

6. Two dogs are in the park. Five dogs enter the park. How many dogs are in the park now? 7 dogs **Goals 2f and 2i**

7. Marta has 4 stickers in her collection. Michelle has 7 stickers in her collection. How many stickers do the two girls have in all? 11 stickers **Goals 2b and 2i**

8. Dennis has 6 cupcakes. Maurice also has 6 cupcakes. How many cupcakes do the two boys have in all? 12 cupcakes **Goals 2f and 2i**

9. Jillian is 8 years old. Lara is 3 years old. How much older is Jillian than Lara? 5 years **Goals 2c and 2e**

10. Jack had 16 cherries. He ate 9 cherries during recess. How many cherries does he have left? 7 cherries **Goals 2a and 2e**

11. Andre had 15 pennies. He lost 7 pennies on his way to school. How many pennies does he have now? 8 pennies **Goals 2a and 2e**

✦ **Written Assessment**
(*Math Masters,* pp. 420 and 421)

INDEPENDENT ACTIVITY

Read through the problems with the class. You may want to do examples with the class for some of the problems.

If appropriate, work through the problems together, one at a time.

Circulate and assist as children work.

- Write the fact family for 2, 11, and 9. (Problem 1) **Goal 2g**

- Circle the names for 14. (Problem 2) **Goal 2j**

- Fill in the empty frames. (Problem 3) **Goal 2h**

- Find the rule and complete the table. (Problem 4) **Goal 2d**

- Add. (Problems 5 and 6) **Goals 2b and 2f**

- Subtract. (Problems 7 and 8) **Goals 2a and 2c**

ALTERNATIVE ASSESSMENT OPTION
Use +,− Fact Triangles

PARTNER ACTIVITY

Use the Fact Triangles to assess children's knowledge of addition and subtraction facts and fact families. Consider having children record facts that they still need to practice on a half-sheet of paper. Collect papers so that you can incorporate these facts into future Mental Math and Reflexes sessions.

ALTERNATIVE ASSESSMENT OPTION
Write and Solve Addition and Subtraction Number Stories (*Math Masters*, p. 22)

INDEPENDENT ACTIVITY

Use this activity to assess children's understanding of operations, number models, mental arithmetic, and mathematical language. Collect children's stories and assess whether or not the stories contain the following components: unit, picture, question, answer, and number model.

Portfolio Ideas

2 Build Background for Unit 3

Math Boxes 2.14 (*Math Journal 1*, p. 50)

INDEPENDENT ACTIVITY

Mixed Review This journal page provides opportunities for cumulative review or assessment of concepts and skills.

Home Link 2.14 (*Math Masters*, pp. 261–264)

Home Connection This Home Link is a four-page newsletter that introduces parents and guardians to Unit 3's topics and terms. The letter also offers ideas for home-based mathematics activities that are supportive of classroom work.

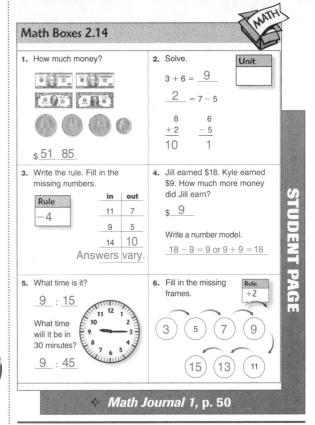

1. How much money?

$ 51 . 85

2. Solve.

Unit

$3 + 6 = 9$

$2 = 7 - 5$

$\begin{array}{c} 8 \\ +2 \\ \hline 10 \end{array}$ $\begin{array}{c} 6 \\ -5 \\ \hline 1 \end{array}$

3. Write the rule. Fill in the missing numbers.

Rule
−4

in	out
11	7
9	5
14	10

Answers vary.

4. Jill earned $18. Kyle earned $9. How much more money did Jill earn?

$ 9

Write a number model.

$18 − 9 = 9$ or $9 + 9 = 18$

5. What time is it?

9 : 15

What time will it be in 30 minutes?

9 : 45

6. Fill in the missing frames.

Rule
+2

3 5 7 9

15 13 11

Math Journal 1, p. 50

PLANNING AHEAD

To prepare for Lesson 3.1, organize a set of base-10 blocks for each partnership and for yourself. Include 3 or 4 flats, 10 longs, and 10 cubes. Put the blocks into bags labeled with the children's tool-kit numbers.

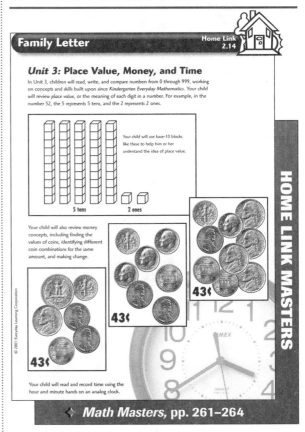

Family Letter

Home Link 2.14

Unit 3: Place Value, Money, and Time

In Unit 3, children will read, write, and compare numbers from 0 through 999, working on concepts and skills built upon since *Kindergarten Everyday Mathematics*. Your child will review *place value*, or the meaning of each digit in a number. For example, in the number 52, the 5 represents 5 tens, and the 2 represents 2 ones.

Your child will use base-10 blocks like these to help him or her understand the idea of place value.

5 tens   2 ones

Your child will also review money concepts, including finding the values of coins, identifying different coin combinations for the same amount, and making change.

43¢   43¢   43¢

Your child will read and record time using the hour and minute hands on an analog clock.

Math Masters, pp. 261–264

STUDENT PAGE

HOME LINK MASTERS

Unit **3**
Place Value,
Money, and Time

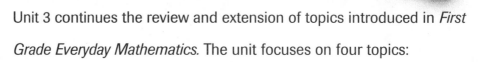

overview

Unit 3 continues the review and extension of topics introduced in *First Grade Everyday Mathematics.* The unit focuses on four topics:

- Numeration and place value
- Money
- Time
- Data collection and analysis

These concepts and skills are developed and expanded over time; few children will have mastered them as a result of their first-grade experiences. As usual, keep the activities lively and set a brisk pace. These topics will be brought up repeatedly in review exercises, in Mental Math and Reflexes, and in other opportunities throughout the school day.

contents

UNIT
3

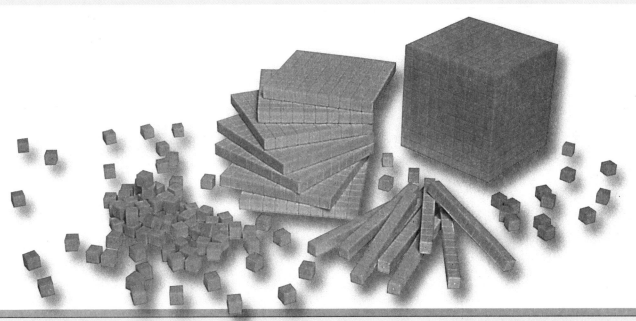

learning goals in perspective

learning goals	links to the past	links to the future
3a **Developing Goal** Solve Frames-and-Arrows problems having two rules. **(Lesson 3.6)**	The Frames-and-Arrows routine was introduced in first grade using one rule. *(Related Grade 2 lesson: 2.10)*	One-rule Frames and Arrows will continue to be used throughout second and third grades. Third grade children will use Frames and Arrows with 3-digit numbers and with multiplication and division. *(Related Grade 2 lesson: 5.1)*
3b **Developing Goal** Make change. **(Lessons 3.2, 3.7, and 3.8)**	Children were introduced to coins and bills in Kindergarten and counted combinations of coins in first grade. *(Related Grade 2 lessons: 1.2, 1.6)*	Children will continue to develop money-counting and change-making skills and strategies throughout second grade. *(Related Grade 2 lessons: 4.3, 4.6, 5.3)*
3c **Developing Goal** Know more difficult subtraction facts. **(Lesson 3.5)**	Children were introduced to these subtraction facts in first grade, and practiced them in Unit 2. *(Related Grade 2 lessons: 2.6, 2.8, 2.12, 2.13)*	Unit 6 provides focused practice with subtraction algorithms. *(Related Grade 2 lessons: 4.2, 4.4, 6.2, 6.4–6.6)*
3d **Developing/Secure Goal** Tell time to 5-minute intervals. **(Lessons 3.3 and 3.4)**	In first grade, children practiced telling time to the nearest half-hour and learned to use the minute hand.	Throughout second grade, children will practice telling time. Fractions of an hour and minutes before and after the hour will be introduced in third grade. *(Related Grade 2 lessons: 5.1, 12.2)*
3e **Secure Goal** Identify place value in 2-digit and 3-digit numbers. **(Lessons 3.1 and 3.4)**	In first grade, children were introduced to place value for 10s and 1s using base-10 blocks (longs and cubes). *(Related Grade 2 lesson: 1.9)*	Place-value concepts are used later to develop mental arithmetic strategies for adding and subtracting 2- and 3-digit numbers. *(Related Grade 2 lessons: 4.8, 6.5)*
3f **Secure Goal** Show ℗, ℕ, Ⓓ, and ⓠ for a given amount. **(Lesson 3.2)**	Children were introduced to coins and bills in Kindergarten and counted combinations of coins in first grade. *(Related Grade 2 lessons: 1.2, 1.6)*	Children will continue to develop money-counting and change-making skills and strategies throughout second grade. *(Related Grade 2 lessons: 4.3, 4.6, 5.3)*
3g **Secure Goal** Know all addition facts. **(Lesson 3.5)**	Children worked on "easier" facts in first grade and in Unit 1, and "harder" facts in Unit 2. *(Related Grade 2 lessons: 1.4, 2.1–2.5, 2.8)*	Throughout second grade, children will practice addition facts through games and in a variety of problem-solving situations. *(Related Grade 2 lessons: 4.1, 4.6, 4.8, 4.9, 6.1, 6.4, 7.3, 7.4)*
3h **Secure Goal** Know easy subtraction facts. **(Lesson 3.5)**	Children began learning basic subtraction facts in first grade, and practiced subtraction facts in Unit 2. *(Related Grade 2 lessons: 2.6, 2.8, 2.10–2.13)*	Practice with subtraction facts is provided in relation to addition and through games and problem solving throughout the grades. *(Related Grade 2 lessons: 4.2, 4.4, 6.2, 6.4–6.6)*

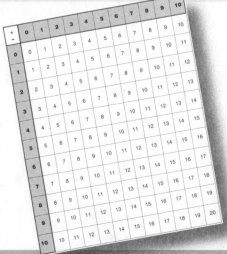

assessment
ongoing • product • periodic

✓ Informal Assessment

Math Boxes These *Math Journal* pages provide opportunities for cumulative review or assessment of concepts and skills.

Ongoing Assessment: Kid Watching Use the Ongoing Assessment suggestions in the following lessons to make quick, on-the-spot observations about children's understanding of:
- Numeration **(Lesson 3.2)**
- Patterns, Functions, and Algebra **(Lessons 3.3 and 3.5)**
- Measurement and Reference Frames **(Lesson 3.7)**
- Operations and Computation **(Lessons 3.5, 3.7, and 3.8)**

Portfolio Ideas Samples of children's work may be obtained from the following assignments:
- Making a Clock Booklet **(Lesson 3.4)**

✓ Unit 3 Review and Assessment

Math Message Use the question in Lesson 3.9 to assess children's progress toward the following learning goal: **Goal 3b**

Oral and Slate Assessments Use oral or slate assessments during Lesson 3.9 to assess children's progress toward the following learning goals: **Goals 3c, 3d, 3e, 3g, and 3h**

Written Assessment Use a written review during Lesson 3.9 to assess children's progress toward the following learning goals: **Goals 3a, 3b, 3d, and 3f**

assessment handbook

For more information on how to use different types of assessment in Unit 3, see the Assessment Overview on pages 46–49 in the *Assessment Handbook*. The following Assessment Masters can be found in the *Math Masters* book:

- Unit 3 Checking Progress, pp. 422 and 423
- Unit 3 Class Checklist, p. 452
- Unit 3 Individual Profile of Progress, p. 453
- Class Progress Indicator, p. 488
- Math Logs, pp. 493–495
- Self-Assessment Forms, pp. 496 and 497
- Interest Inventory, pp. 491 and 492
- Class Checklist: 1st Quarter, pp. 472 and 473
- Individual Profile of Progress: 1st Quarter, p. 474

problemsolving

A process of modeling everyday situations using tools from mathematics

Encourage children to use a variety of strategies when attacking a given problem—and to explain those strategies. *Strategies children might use in this unit:*

Four Problem-Solving REPRESENTATIONS

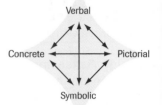

Verbal

Concrete ↔ Pictorial

Symbolic

- Acting out the problem
- Working backward
- Using manipulatives as models
- Using information to write a number story
- Making and using a graph
- Using information from a picture

Lessons that teach *through* problem solving, not just *about* problem solving

Lesson	Activity	Lesson	Activity
3.1	Solving magic square problems	3.5	Making a bar graph of pockets data
3.2	Buying and selling things with coins	3.6	Solving Frames-and-Arrows problems involving money
3.4	Writing a story about a time shown in the clock booklet	3.6	Read the "Brothers and Sisters" bar graph
3.4	Giving directions for duplicating shapes	3.8	Making purchases and making change using Fruit and Vegetables Stand and Vending Machine Posters

For more information about problem solving in *Everyday Mathematics,* see the *Teacher's Reference Manual,* pp. 197–208.

cross-curricularlinks

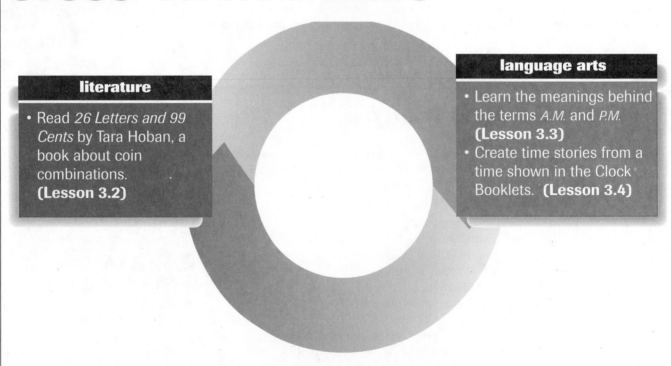

literature

- Read *26 Letters and 99 Cents* by Tara Hoban, a book about coin combinations. **(Lesson 3.2)**

language arts

- Learn the meanings behind the terms *A.M.* and *P.M.* **(Lesson 3.3)**
- Create time stories from a time shown in the Clock Booklets. **(Lesson 3.4)**

meeting INDIVIDUAL needs

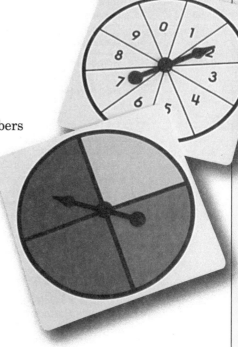

◆ RETEACHING

The following features provide additional instructional support:

Adjusting the Activity
- **Lesson 3.1, Parts 1, 2**
- **Lesson 3.6, Part 1**
- **Lesson 3.7, Part 1**

Options for Individualizing
- **Lesson 3.2** Making Different Coin Combinations for the Same Value
- **Lesson 3.2** Playing *Spinning for Money*
- **Lesson 3.7** Playing *Spinning for Money*

◆ ENRICHMENT

The following features suggest enrichment and extension activities:

Adjusting the Activity
- **Lesson 3.2, Parts 1, 2**
- **Lesson 3.4, Part 1**
- **Lesson 3.6, Part 1**
- **Lesson 3.7, Part 1**

Options for Individualizing
- **Lesson 3.1** Demonstrating 4-Digit Numbers with a Thousands Cube
- **Lesson 3.5** Comparing Pockets Data
- **Lesson 3.6** Making Up and Solving Frames-and-Arrows Problems Having Two Rules
- **Lesson 3.7** Solving a Coin Puzzle

◆ LANGUAGE DIVERSITY

The following features suggest ways to support children who are acquiring proficiency in English:

Adjusting the Activity
- **Lesson 3.5, Part 1**

Options for Individualizing
- **Lesson 3.7** Discussing the Meanings of the Word *Change*

◆ MULTIAGE CLASSROOM

The following chart lists related lessons from Grades 1 and 3 that can help you meet your instructional needs:

Grade 1	4.7 5.1 8.3	3.12 8.1 8.4	2.5 3.7 6.10	4.7 10.2	3.13 6.12 10.1	3.8 3.9	3.12 8.1 8.5	3.12 8.4 8.5
Grade 2	3.1	3.2	3.3	3.4	3.5	3.6	3.7	3.8
Grade 3	5.1– 5.7	1.9 9.5 9.7	1.12 11.8	5.6 9.3	1.5 5.12 10.7		1.9 9.5 9.7	1.10 9.5 9.7

materials

lesson	math masters pages	manipulative kit items	other items
3.1	Home Link Master, p. 265 Teaching Masters, pp. 34 and 35 **See Advance Preparation, p. 168**	base-10 blocks number cards 0–9	calculator
3.2	Home Link Master, p. 266 Teaching Masters, pp. 37 and 38 transparency of Teaching Master, p. 36 **See Advance Preparation, p. 173**	number cards 0–9	coins and bills paper clip *26 Letters and 99 Cents* by Tana Hoban **See Advance Preparation, p. 173**
3.3	Home Link Masters, pp. 267 and 268 Teaching Masters, pp. 39 and 40 **See Advance Preparation, p. 178**	slate (optional)	analog and digital clocks tool-kit clock demonstration clocks paper with time written in digital notation (1 per child) prize items
3.4	Home Link Master, p. 269 Teaching Masters, pp. 35 and 41–44 Teaching Masters, pp. 45, 46 or 47, 48, and 49 (optional) **See Advance Preparation, p. 183**	base-10 blocks number cards 0–9 clock-face stamp; stamp pad geoboard rubber bands	
3.5	Home Link Master, p. 270 Teaching Masters, pp. 50–52 transparency of Teaching Masters, pp. 51 and 52 **See Advance Preparation, p. 188**		+,– Fact Triangles per partnership
3.6	Home Link Master, p. 271 Teaching Masters, pp. 53–56 transparency of Teaching Masters, pp. 53–56 **See Advance Preparation, p. 193**		coins
3.7	Home Link Masters, pp. 272 and 273 Teaching Masters, pp. 37, 38, and 57	slate	coins; bills overhead coins (optional)
3.8	Home Link Master, p. 274 transparency of Teaching Masters, pp. 58 (optional) **See Advance Preparation, p. 202**	slate 2 dice per group	coins; bills items to use for a bank picture dictionaries
3.9	Home Link Masters, pp. 275–278 Assessment Masters, pp. 422 and 423	2 six-sided dice slate base-10 blocks	clock booklets from Lesson 3.4 coins; bills demonstration clock item to use as a bank stick-on notes +,– Fact Triangles with sums greater than 10

planningtips

Pacing

Pacing depends on a number of factors, such as children's individual needs and how long your school has been using *Everyday Mathematics*. At the beginning of Unit 3, review your Content by Strand Poster to help you set a monthly pace.

SEPTEMBER	OCTOBER	NOVEMBER

←—MOST CLASSROOMS—→

Using the Projects

Use Project 4, Dates on Pennies, during or after Unit 3. This Project provides an opportunity for your children to gain experience with 4-digit numbers in the form of notation for years (1998, 1999, and so on) and to tally, graph, and compare data. The Projects can be found at the back of this book.

Home Communication

Share Home Links 3.1–3.8 with families to help them understand the content and procedures in this unit. At the end of the unit, use Home Link 3.9 to introduce Unit 4. Supplemental information can be found in the *Home Connection Handbook*.

NCTM Standards

Standard	1	2	3	4	5	6	7	8	9	10
Unit 3 Lessons	1, 2, 4–8	1–7	4	2–4, 7, 8	5, 6	1–8	1–8	1–8	1–8	1–8

Content Standards
1 Number and Operation
2 Patterns, Functions, and Algebra
3 Geometry and Spatial Sense
4 Measurement
5 Data Analysis, Statistics, and Probability

Process Standards
6 Problem Solving
7 Reasoning and Proof
8 Communication
9 Connections
10 Representations

PRACTICE *through* Games

Everyday Mathematics uses games to help children develop good fact power and other math skills.
- Make the largest number and compare in the *Digit Game* **(Lesson 3.2)**
- Count and exchange coins in *Spinning for Money* **(Lessons 3.2 and 3.7)**
- Practice telling time in *Prize Time* **(Lesson 3.3)**
- Find complements of 100 in *Dollar Rummy* **(Lesson 3.4)**
- Practice money exchange in *Making Change* **(Lessons 3.8 and 3.9)**

unit 3 content highlights

The notes below highlight the major content ideas presented in Unit 3. These notes may help you establish instructional priorities.

Numeration and Place Value (Lesson 3.1)

In *Kindergarten* and *First Grade Everyday Mathematics*, children had a great deal of experience with place value through free play and exploration with base-10 blocks. Most children will also be familiar with recording whole numbers on paper and slates, entering numbers into a calculator, and representing numbers with number cards.

This lesson allows you to assess how children are able to translate among spoken numbers, written numbers, displays of base-10 blocks, and numbers displayed on a Place-Value Mat. This lesson also provides opportunities for you to assess whether children can tell how many ones, tens, and hundreds are in a given number, and whether they can write numbers if given the number of ones, tens, and hundreds.

Keep in mind the importance of identifying the unit for different contexts. For example, if "cent" is given as the unit, then "dime" represents 10 cents and "dollar" represents 100 cents. If children understand the concept of unit, they will have no trouble grasping the relationship between whole numbers and decimals that they will encounter later in *Everyday Mathematics:* If "dollar" is the unit, then "dime" represents $\frac{1}{10}$, or 0.1, and "penny" represents $\frac{1}{100}$, or 0.01.

Continue to remind children that numbers are used to describe something that is identified by a label or a unit. In each of the place-value drills, have children choose a unit as a context for the numbers.

Children practice place value by naming the hundreds, tens, and ones for numbers in a calculator display.

I bought a melon slice, two apples and a pear with half a dollar. Is my number story true?

A child's number story based on the Fruit and Vegetables Stand Poster.

Money (Lessons 3.2, 3.7, and 3.8)

The lessons on money serve as a vehicle for adding and subtracting 2-digit numbers using manipulatives (coins). These activities prepare children for the focus on mental arithmetic in Unit 4. Actual or play money (at least 10 pennies, 6 nickels, 6 dimes, 4 quarters, and two $1 bills per child) is used in several lessons. Therefore, you may want to have children keep a set of coins and bills in their tool kits or in a classroom bank for the duration of the unit. If children store the coins in their tool kits, be sure they use a container such as an empty film canister or a resealable plastic bag.

Two posters form the basis for number stories about money: a Fruit and Vegetables Stand Poster (Lesson 3.2) and a Milk and Juice Vending Machine Poster (Lesson 3.8). As usual, partners make up and solve many problems and record just a few of them in their journals.

Children practice money skills by playing the roles of a customer paying for an item and a clerk giving the customer the appropriate change. Children also play the *Making Change* game beginning in Lesson 3.8.

Telling Time (Lesson 3.3)

Since it takes many experiences over an extended period to develop time-telling skills, it would be unrealistic to expect mastery at this point. The objective of the lessons in this unit is to give children experiences in reading and recording time on analog clocks and to assess how often children need to practice these skills over the next few weeks. Children will benefit greatly from brief but regular activities like the following:

▷ Ask children to read the time on the classroom clock.

▷ Say an approximate time. Ask children to show the time on their tool-kit clocks.

▷ Once your classroom schedule has become familiar to children, ask them to say and write the times that they need to be at certain activities, such as recess or lunch. About where will the hour hand be at that time? About where will the minute hand be?

Repeat such activities often during the school year.

Children may know several equivalent names for the same time—7:15, quarter after 7, 15 minutes after 7, and so on. Encourage children to use the different terms shown in the margin.

> 7:15
> 15 minutes after 7
> quarter after 7
> A little past 7 o'clock
> 15 past 7

Different ways to describe the same time

Explorations: Numbers, Time, and Geoboards (Lesson 3.4)

This lesson contains three activities designed as Explorations. (See "Explorations" in the Managing the Curriculum section of the Management Guide, which is located in the *Teacher's Reference Manual*.)

In the first Exploration, children develop place-value concepts by using base-10 blocks to show 2- and 3-digit numbers in different ways (for example, 26 as 2 tens and 6 ones, 1 ten and 16 ones, or as 26 ones).

In the second Exploration, children make clock-face booklets showing analog and digital times. These booklets can be saved and used later to practice time-telling skills.

In the third Exploration, children make, describe, and compare shapes on a geoboard. Because one goal of this Exploration is to encourage children to communicate clearly about mathematics, children do these activities working with a partner and in small groups.

The game *Dollar Rummy* is also introduced. This game strengthens counting and calculating skills as children find complements of 100.

Data Day: Pockets (Lesson 3.5)

Children count their pockets, tally their results, identify the middle value in their data, and represent their data by making a bar graph.

Date		Time

Pockets Data Table

Count the pockets of children in your class. Sample answers:

Pockets	Children	
	Tallies	Number
0		0
1		0
2	//	2
3	//	2
4	///	3
5	////	4
6	///	3
7	////	4
8	//	2
9	/	1
10		0
11		0
12		0
13 or more		0

66 (sixty-six)   Use with Lesson 3.5.

If there is an even number of values in a set of data, there is no single middle value; you and the children can decide how to handle this. The mathematical term for this middle value is *median*. In everyday life, people often refer to this as the "average." In mathematics and statistics, however, "average" usually refers to the "arithmetic average" (also called the "mean"), which is obtained by adding the numbers in the data set and dividing the sum by the number of data entries. The median usually gives an equally valid indication of what is "typical" and is usually much easier to obtain.

The data in this activity do not lend themselves to finding an arithmetic average. In other activities involving data, however, some second graders might enjoy using their calculators to find the arithmetic average and comparing it to the median.

Frames and Arrows with Two Rules (Lesson 3.6)

Frames-and-Arrows puzzles are extended to number sequences with two rules. (See "Frames-and-Arrows Diagrams" in the Managing the Curriculum section of the Management Guide and section 9.4 of the Patterns, Sequences, Functions, and Algebra Essay in the *Teacher's Reference Manual*.)

Review and Assessment (Lesson 3.9)

Like every unit in *Second Grade Everyday Mathematics*, Unit 3 ends with a review and assessment lesson. There is a list of unit goals, as well as suggestions for oral and slate evaluation questions. A master provides review items for children to complete; each item is keyed to a unit goal.

You can assess children's understanding of money concepts by observing them as they play *Making Change* and act out the roles of customers and clerks. You can review and assess children's time-telling skills by frequently asking them to write or say the time shown on your classroom clock.

If you are planning a quarterly assessment for Units 1–3, you may want to refer to the *Assessment Handbook*. The quarterly learning goals Class Checklist and Individual Profile of Progress checklist (*Math Masters*, pages 470–472) are useful tools for keeping track of children's progress.

For additional information on the following topics, see the
Teacher's Reference Manual:

- data collection, organization, and analysis
- Frames and Arrows

- money
- numeration and place value
- time

3.1

Numeration and Place Value

OBJECTIVE To review place value in 2-digit and 3-digit numbers.

summaries	materials

1 Teaching the Lesson

Children are introduced to base-10 blocks and a simple way to draw them; match number cards on a Place-Value Mat to numbers represented by base-10 blocks; place base-10 blocks on a Place-Value Mat to represent given numbers; model 2- and 3-digit numbers with one or two zeros; and translate among spoken numbers, written numbers, displays of base-10 blocks, number cards, and calculator displays.
[Numeration]

- ☐ *Math Journal 1,* p. 51
- ☐ Teaching Master transparency (*Math Masters,* p. 34; optional)
- ☐ Teaching Master (*Math Masters,* p. 35)
- ☐ base-10 blocks: 10 flats, 30 longs, and 30 cubes
- ☐ number cards labeled 0–9 per partnership (from the Everything Math Deck, if available)
- ☐ calculator

***See* Advance Preparation**

2 Ongoing Learning & Practice

Children practice addition facts by completing magic squares.
[Operations and Computation; Patterns, Functions, and Algebra]

Children practice and maintain skills through Math Boxes and Home Link activities.

- ☐ *Math Journal 1,* pp. 52 and 53
- ☐ Home Link Master (*Math Masters,* p. 265)

3 Options for Individualizing

Enrichment Children model and display 4-digit numbers using a thousands cube. [Numeration]

- ☐ base-10 blocks: 1 big cube, 10 flats, 30 longs, and 30 cm cubes

Additional Information

Advance Preparation You should plan to spend at least two days on this lesson.

For Part 1, you and each partnership will need a set of base-10 blocks (3 or 4 flats, 10 longs, and 10 cubes in bags labeled with children's tool-kit numbers). You may want to borrow additional flats from another classroom. You may want to use base-10 blocks for the overhead projector.

For Part 1, decide how you will display a Place-Value Mat. One way is to make an overhead transparency of *Math Masters,* page 34. You can also draw a Place-Value Mat on the board using semipermanent chalk. To do this, thoroughly wet a section of the board. Draw the mat. Wait for the area to dry *completely.* You will be able to write or draw on the mat and erase a number of times without losing the outline of the mat. To remove the drawing of the mat, wash the board with water.

Vocabulary • base-10 blocks • cube • long • flat • base-10 system

Getting Started

Mental Math and Reflexes

Pose number stories that involve "harder" addition and subtraction facts. *Suggestions:*

- Cleo read 8 pages of her book last night and 6 pages this morning. How many pages did she read in all? 14 pages
- Austin brought 17 cupcakes to school for his birthday. He gave 8 to his classmates. How many cupcakes does he have left? 9 cupcakes

Math Message

52 = __5__ tens and __2__ ones

25 = __2__ tens and __5__ ones

1 Teaching the Lesson

◆ Math Message Follow-Up

WHOLE-CLASS ACTIVITY

Briefly discuss children's responses. Ask children to explain how they decided which digit names the tens and which digit names the ones. These numbers will be revisited later in the lesson.

◆ Exploring a Simple Way to Draw Base-10 Blocks

WHOLE-CLASS DISCUSSION

Hold up a cube, a long, and a flat. Say, *These are called* **base-10 blocks.** Hold up a **cube.** Say, *This is a base-10 cube. It represents one.* Then hold up a **long** and say, *This is a long. It represents ten.* Last, hold up a **flat** and say, *This is a flat. It represents one hundred.* Display the blocks on the overhead projector.

Remind children that our system for writing numbers is called the **base-10 system,** because it is based on grouping things by tens. Explain that base-10 blocks are useful for understanding numbers and solving problems. Show children the pictures in the margin as a quick and easy way to draw base-10 blocks.

Drawing pictures may be more convenient than using the actual blocks, and pictures are often useful for explaining and recording solutions.

Base-10 blocks

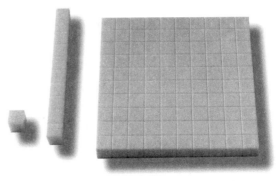

cube   long   flat

cube   long   flat

Adjusting the Activity If children are having difficulty showing the correct base-10 blocks, write the numbers on a Place-Value Mat that you have drawn on the board or use an overhead transparency of *Math Masters*, page 34.

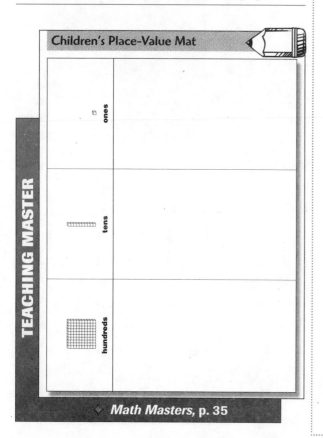

Children's Place-Value Mat

ones

tens

hundreds

TEACHING MASTER

Math Masters, p. 35

✦ Matching Numbers and Displays of Base-10 Blocks
(*Math Masters*, pp. 34 and 35)

WHOLE-CLASS ACTIVITY

Give each child or partnership a set of number cards (0–9) and a Place-Value Mat. Display 3 flats, 5 longs, and 2 cubes on a Place-Value Mat. (See Advance Preparation.) Ask children to show the number 352 by putting cards on their Place-Value Mats. Children show 352 by putting the card for 3 in the hundreds place, the card for 5 in the tens place, and the card for 2 in the ones place. Ask:

• How many hundreds are in this number? 3

• How many tens? 5

• How many ones? 2

Then ask children to read the number in unison. Three hundred fifty-two

Repeat with other 2- and 3-digit numbers, including the numbers 52 and 25 from the Math Message. Ask children to explain what the digits 5 and 2 mean in each number. Display the place-value blocks at random without the mat. By doing this, children will have to sort the blocks mentally into ones, tens, and hundreds.

Then reverse the procedure. Write a 2- or 3-digit number on the board and ask children to show the number by placing base-10 blocks on their Place-Value Mats. Repeat with several other 2- or 3-digit numbers.

Now, repeat the previous procedures using numbers with zero in the tens or ones place. For example, display 3 flats and 4 cubes and ask children to use digit cards to show the number on their Place-Value Mats. Some children may put no digit card in the tens column; others will put a zero. Point out that not including the zero can cause problems when there is no Place-Value Mat.

Write 34 and 304 on the board and ask which number matches the base-10 blocks. 304 Ask which digit in 304 shows that there are no longs. The zero

Repeat the process for other numbers with zeros. Have children use number cards to show numbers for base-10 blocks and also have them display base-10 blocks for numbers written on the board or on an overhead.

If anyone asks, explain that leading zeros are usually skipped; for example, we usually write 57, not 057.

✦ Saying, Writing, Displaying, and Describing Numbers

WHOLE-CLASS ACTIVITY

Continue with a series of translations among spoken numbers, written numbers, base-10 blocks, number cards, and calculator displays. *For example:*

▷ Write 749 on the board. Say, *Read the number on the board.*

▷ Ask, *In 567, which number is in the ones place?* 7 *The tens place?* 6 *The hundreds place?* 5

▷ Say, *Show the number 508 with base-10 blocks.*

▷ Say, *Use cards to show the number with 4 in the ones place, 0 in the tens place, and 8 in the hundreds place.* 804

✦ Doing Place-Value Exercises
(*Math Journal 1*, p. 51)

INDEPENDENT ACTIVITY

After children have completed the journal page, review the answers with them. For Problem 3, make sure that children have written 305 and not 530, 503, or 350. Ask a volunteer to explain the answer to Problem 5. Have other children explain why they agree or disagree with the answer. Make sure that children are able to correctly identify each of the base-10 materials in the pictures.

2 Ongoing Learning & Practice

✦ Completing Magic Squares
(*Math Journal 1*, p. 52)

INDEPENDENT ACTIVITY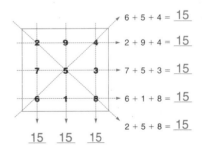

Children practice addition facts in a problem-solving format.

> **Adjusting the Activity** If some children are having difficulty, have the class work on this page in groups of 3 or 4. Include an advanced child in each group.

Place Value

Write the number for each group of base-10 blocks.

1. _545_

2. _403_

3. Write a number with …

5 in the ones place
3 in the hundreds place
0 in the tens place _305_

4. 960

How many hundreds? _9_
How many tens? _6_
How many ones? _0_

5. Amelia wrote 24 to describe the number shown by these base-10 blocks:

Is Amelia right? Explain your answer.

Sample answer: No, Amelia is not right because the base-10 blocks show 2 hundreds and 4 ones. The blocks represent the number 204, not 24.

✦ *Math Journal 1*, p. 51

Magic Squares

1. Add the numbers in each row. Add the numbers in each column. Add the numbers on each diagonal.

Are the sums all the same? Yes, they are.

$6 + 5 + 4 = $ _15_
$2 + 9 + 4 = $ _15_
$7 + 5 + 3 = $ _15_
$6 + 1 + 8 = $ _15_
$2 + 5 + 8 = $ _15_

2	9	4
7	5	3
6	1	8

_15_ _15_ _15_

2. The sum of each row, column, and diagonal must be 15. Find the missing numbers. Write them in the blank boxes.

2	7	6
9	5	1
4	3	8

8	1	6
3	5	7
4	9	2

✦ *Math Journal 1*, p. 52

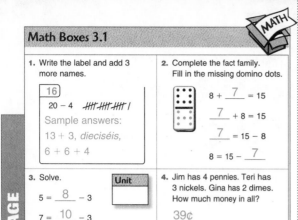

Math Boxes 3.1

1. Write the label and add 3 more names.

16

20 − 4   ̶H̶H̶T̶ ̶H̶H̶T̶ ̶H̶H̶T̶ /

Sample answers:

13 + 3, *dieciséis*,

6 + 6 + 4

2. Complete the fact family. Fill in the missing domino dots.

8 + __7__ = 15

__7__ + 8 = 15

__7__ = 15 − 8

8 = 15 − __7__

3. Solve.

Unit

5 = __8__ − 3

7 = __10__ − 3

6 = __9__ − 3

4. Jim has 4 pennies. Teri has 3 nickels. Gina has 2 dimes. How much money in all?

39¢

5. Fill in the missing rule and numbers.

Rule	in	out
−10	48	38
	37	27
	73	63
	114	104

6. Circle the number models that are true.

(9 + 7 = 7 + 9)

8 − 5 = 5 − 8

(6 + 5 = 5 + 6)

♦ *Math Journal 1, p. 53*

STUDENT PAGE

HOME LINK MASTER

Place Value

Home Link 3.1

Family Note

All numbers are made up of digits. The value of a digit depends on its place in the number. In the number 704, the digit 7 means 7 hundreds, the digit 0 means 0 tens, and the digit 4 means 4 ones. This idea is called **place value.**

Your child has been using base-10 blocks to help him or her understand the idea of place value. Base-10 blocks are shown in Problems 1a and 1b below. A "cube" (with each side 1 unit long) represents 1. A "long" (a rod that is 10 units long) represents 10. And a "flat" (a square with each side 10 units long) represents 100.

Please return this Home Link to school tomorrow.

1. Which number do the base-10 blocks show?

a.

374

b.

507

2. Write a number with 7 in the hundreds place, 0 in the ones place, and 4 in the tens place.

740

3. Write a number with 3 in the tens place, 6 in the ones place, and 9 in the hundreds place.

936

4. In 806, how many hundreds? __8__

How many tens? __0__

How many ones? __6__

5. In 231, how many hundreds? __2__

How many tens? __3__

How many ones? __1__

♦ *Math Masters, p. 265*

♦ Math Boxes 3.1 (*Math Journal 1,* p. 53)

INDEPENDENT ACTIVITY

Mixed Review This journal page provides opportunities for cumulative review or assessment of concepts and skills.

♦ Home Link 3.1 (*Math Masters,* p. 265)

Home Connection Children continue their work with base-10 blocks and Place-Value Mats as they complete place-value exercises similar to those on journal page 51.

3 Options for Individualizing

♦ ENRICHMENT Demonstrating 4-Digit Numbers with a Thousands Cube

SMALL-GROUP ACTIVITY 5–15 min

Extend place-value activities to thousands by introducing the "big cube." Ask:

• What does one side of the cube look like? A flat

• How many flats are in the big cube? 10

• Which number does the big cube stand for?
  10 one-hundreds or 1,000

Repeat the earlier activities using 4-digit numbers less than 2,000. Include numbers with zero in one or more places.

PLANNING AHEAD

Before beginning Lesson 3.2, make an overhead transparency of *Math Masters,* page 36, the Fruit and Vegetables Stand Poster.

3.2 Using Coins to Buy Things

OBJECTIVES To review coin values and exchanges among coins; and to find coin combinations needed to pay for items.

summaries	**materials**

1 Teaching the Lesson

Children determine the total value of a set of coins and bills; review the values of coins and bills and the exchanges among them; and name coin combinations to make purchases and make change while buying and selling items. [Numeration; Measurement and Reference Frames]

☐ *Math Journal 1*, pp. 54 and 55

☐ Home Link 3.1

☐ Teaching Master transparency (*Math Masters*, p. 36)

☐ coins and bills: 10 pennies, 6 nickels, 6 dimes, 4 quarters, and two $1 bills

***See* Advance Preparation**

2 Ongoing Learning & Practice

Children practice forming and comparing numbers by playing the *Digit Game*. [Numeration]

Children practice and maintain skills through Math Boxes and Home Link activities.

☐ *Math Journal 1*, pp. 56 and 57

☐ Home Link Master (*Math Masters*, p. 266)

☐ number cards labeled 0–9 (from the Everything Math Deck, if available)

3 Options for Individualizing

Reteaching Children read about and make different coin combinations using the fewest number of coins possible. [Measurement and Reference Frames]

Reteaching Children practice coin and bill exchanges by playing *Spinning for Money*. [Numeration; Measurement and Reference Frames]

☐ Teaching Masters (*Math Masters*, pp. 37 and 38)

☐ *26 Letters and 99 Cents*

☐ large paper clip

☐ coins and bills per partnership or group: 7 pennies, 5 nickels, 5 dimes, 4 quarters, and one $1 bill

***See* Advance Preparation**

Additional Information

Advance Preparation For the *Paying For Things* activity in Part 1, create an overhead transparency of *Math Masters*, page 36.

For the first optional Reteaching activity in Part 3, you may want to obtain the book *26 Letters and 99 Cents* by Tana Hoban (Greenwillow Books, 1987).

For the second optional Reteaching activity in Part 3, each child will need to construct a Money-Game Spinner from *Math Masters*, page 37. Instructions are found on *Math Masters*, page 38.

Vocabulary • nickel • penny • dime • quarter • $1 bill

Getting Started

Mental Math and Reflexes

Count by 5s, 10s, and 25s.
- Begin at 5. Count by 5s to 100.
- Begin at 30. Count by 10s to 150.
- Begin at 25. Count by 25s to 200.

If children have difficulty, allow them to use coins as they count.

Math Message
Take 10 *, 6* Ⓝ *, 6* Ⓓ *, 4* Ⓠ *, and 2* 🔲 *.*
How much money is that?

Home Link 3.1 Follow-Up
Review answers as necessary.

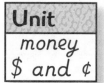

Unit
money
$ and ¢

NOTE: Although the focus of this lesson is not on money notation, such as 25¢ or $0.25; or $1, $1.00, or 100¢, be sure to use these different notations during this lesson.

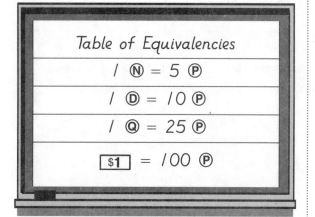

Table of Equivalencies

1 Ⓝ	= 5 Ⓟ
1 Ⓓ	= 10 Ⓟ
1 Ⓠ	= 25 Ⓟ
🔲	= 100 Ⓟ

Children may find it helpful to refer to this Table of Equivalencies during the remainder of the lesson.

1 Teaching the Lesson

✦ Math Message Follow-Up

WHOLE-CLASS DISCUSSION

Ask children to share the strategies they used to find the total amount ($4.00).

One approach is to count the monetary units in order from greatest to least. The dollar bills are $2.00. Count on the four quarters to reach $3.00. Count by 10s from $3.00 for the six dimes to reach $3.60. Then count by 5s from $3.60 for the six nickels to reach $3.90. Finally, count by 1s from $3.90 for the ten pennies for a total of $4.00.

✦ Reviewing the Exchanges for Coins and $1 Bills

WHOLE-CLASS DISCUSSION

On the board, draw a unit box as shown in the margin. Have children respond in unison to questions about the coins and the $1 bill.

Hold up a **nickel.** Ask, *What is this called? How much is it worth? How much are two nickels worth?* Repeat with a **penny, dime, quarter,** and **$1 bill.**

Hold up a penny and a nickel. Ask, *How many pennies would you trade for a nickel?* 5 pennies Hold up the appropriate pairs of coins or bills as you ask questions like the following:

- How many pennies would you trade for a dime? For a quarter? For one dollar? For two dollars?

- How many nickels would you trade for a dime? For a quarter? For a dollar?

- How many dimes would you trade for a dollar?

◆ Paying for Things with Coins
(*Math Masters*, p. 36)

WHOLE-CLASS ACTIVITY 👥👥👥

Display an overhead transparency of the Fruit and Vegetables Stand Poster on *Math Masters*, page 36. (Note that the poster is also found on journal page 54.) Ask children to count out the coins they would use to pay for one pear. Partners check each other's coin combinations.

Ask volunteers to share with the class the coin combinations they used. List their responses on the board.

Ⓟ Ⓟ Ⓟ Ⓟ Ⓟ   Ⓓ Ⓟ   Ⓝ Ⓟ   Ⓝ Ⓟ Ⓟ

Ⓟ Ⓟ Ⓟ Ⓟ Ⓟ   Ⓟ   Ⓝ Ⓟ   Ⓟ Ⓟ Ⓟ

Ⓟ Ⓟ Ⓟ   Ⓟ   Ⓟ   Ⓟ Ⓟ Ⓟ

Possible coin combinations for 13¢

Ask children if there are any other ways they could have paid for the pear. Sample response: Pay for the pear with 1 dime and 1 nickel and receive 2 pennies as change.

Repeat the activity with other items until children are ready to work independently.

◆ Taking Turns Buying and Selling
(*Math Journal 1*, pp. 54 and 55)

PARTNER ACTIVITY 👥

Partners take turns being customer and clerk at the Fruit and Vegetables Stand. The customer points to an item and pays the exact amount with coins. The clerk checks that the customer has paid the correct amount. Children record four of these transactions in their journals; they show two possible combinations for each transaction.

When the activity is over, ask children to share some of their answers from journal page 55. Finally, ask children to divide up the money and return it to their tool kits or to the classroom bank.

 Adjusting the Activity Making change is covered in Lessons 3.7 and 3.8. However, some children may be ready to make change now. Ask them to draw coins that could be given to the cashier that show an amount greater than the price of the item. Then have them draw the change that they would receive.

Fruit and Vegetables Stand Poster

Pear 13¢ Orange 18¢ Green Pepper 24¢
Melon Slice 30¢ Plum 6¢ Banana 9¢
Apple 12¢ Tomato 20¢ Onion 7¢
Lettuce 45¢ Corn 15¢ Cabbage 40¢

◆ *Math Journal 1*, p. 54

✓ **ONGOING ASSESSMENT**
As children work, note the following:
· Do they begin counting coins with the coins of greatest value?
· Can children skip count with nickels and dimes?

Buying Fruit and Vegetables

Select the fruit and vegetables from journal page 54 that you would like to buy. Write the name of each item. Then draw the coins you could use to pay for each item. Write Ⓟ, Ⓝ, Ⓓ, or Ⓠ.
For Problems 3 and 4, write the total amount of money that you would spend. Sample answers:

I bought (Draw coins)	I paid (Draw coins)	I paid (Draw coins another way)
Example one *orange*	Ⓓ Ⓝ Ⓟ Ⓟ Ⓟ	Ⓝ Ⓝ Ⓟ Ⓟ Ⓟ Ⓟ Ⓟ Ⓟ Ⓟ Ⓟ
1. one melon slice	Ⓠ Ⓝ	Ⓓ Ⓓ Ⓝ Ⓟ Ⓟ Ⓟ Ⓟ Ⓟ
2. one head of lettuce	Ⓠ Ⓝ Ⓝ Ⓝ Ⓝ	Ⓓ Ⓓ Ⓓ Ⓓ Ⓝ
3. one apple and one plum	Ⓝ Ⓝ Ⓟ Ⓟ Ⓝ Ⓟ	Ⓓ Ⓟ Ⓟ Ⓟ Ⓟ Ⓟ Ⓟ Ⓟ Ⓟ Total: 18¢
4. one ear of corn, one banana, and one green pepper	Ⓠ Ⓓ Ⓓ Ⓟ Ⓟ Ⓟ	Ⓓ Ⓓ Ⓓ Ⓓ Ⓝ Ⓟ Ⓟ Ⓟ Total: 48¢

◆ *Math Journal 1*, p. 55

STUDENT PAGE

The *Digit Game*

Materials ☐ 4 cards each of numbers 0–9
(from the Everything Math Deck, if available)

Players 2

Directions

1. Shuffle the deck. Place it facedown between the players.

2. Each player draws 2 cards from the deck and uses them to make the largest number possible.

3. The player who makes the larger number takes all of the cards.

4. The game is over when all of the cards have been used.

5. The player with more cards wins.

Other Ways to Play

A. Players draw 3 cards instead of 2 cards each time. Each player makes the largest 3-digit number possible.

B. Players try to make the smallest number possible each time. The person who makes the greatest number takes all of the cards. The player with fewer cards at the end wins.

Math Journal 1, p. 56

Math Boxes 3.2

1. Jerry scored 9 points. Lisa scored 7 points. How many points did they score in all?

   <u>16</u> points

   Write a number model.

   <u>9 + 7 = 16</u>

2. 132 has …

   <u>1</u> hundreds

   <u>3</u> tens

   <u>2</u> ones

3. How many in all?

   <u>148</u>

4. How much money?

   Ⓠ Ⓠ Ⓠ Ⓓ Ⓟ Ⓟ

   <u>87¢</u>

5. Fill in the frames.

   Rule +7

   7 14 21 28 42 35

6. Write >, <, or =.

   4 dimes <u><</u> 50¢

   3 quarters <u>=</u> 75¢

   $1.00 <u><</u> 11 dimes

Math Journal 1, p. 57

---

2 Ongoing Learning & Practice

✦ Playing the *Digit Game* (*Math Journal 1*, p. 56)

PARTNER ACTIVITY

Explain the rules of the *Digit Game,* which are found on the journal page. Play several demonstration hands with the class.

Partners play with a set of number cards 0–9, 4 cards for each number. The deck is shuffled and placed facedown between the partners. Each player draws 2 cards from the deck and uses the cards to make the largest number possible. The player who makes the larger number takes all of the cards. Play continues in this way. The game is over when all of the cards have been used. The partner with more cards wins.

Have partners play several rounds of the game.

Adjusting the Activity Challenge children to choose three nonzero cards from the deck and use the cards to make up as many 3-digit numbers as they can. Encourage children to share their strategies.

It is possible to make six 3-digit numbers out of three different nonzero digits. For example, the following six numbers can be made with 1, 4, and 9: 149, 194, 419, 491, 914, and 941.

✦ Math Boxes 3.2 (*Math Journal 1*, p. 57)

INDEPENDENT ACTIVITY

Mixed Review This journal page provides opportunities for cumulative review or assessment of concepts and skills.

♦ Home Link 3.2 (*Math Masters*, p. 266)

Home Connection Children use store advertisements to find items that cost less than $2.00. They draw coins and bills to show two ways to pay for each item.

How Much Does It Cost? Home Link 3.2

Family Note In this activity, your child looks through advertisements, selects items that cost less than $2.00, and shows how to pay for those items in more than one way. For example, your child could pay for an item that costs 79¢ by drawing 3 quarters and 4 pennies or by drawing 7 dimes and 9 pennies. If you do not have advertisements showing prices, make up some items and prices for your child.
Please return this Home Link to school tomorrow.

Look at newspaper or magazine advertisements. Find items that cost less than $2.00. Write the name and price of each item.

Show someone at home how you would pay for these items with coins and a $1 bill. Write Ⓟ, Ⓝ, Ⓓ, Ⓠ, and ⬚$1. Try to show amounts in more than one way. Answers vary.

1. I would buy _____. It costs _____.

   This is one way I would pay: _____

   This is another way: _____

2. I would buy _____. It costs _____.

   This is one way I would pay: _____

   This is another way: _____

3. I would buy _____. It costs _____.

   This is one way I would pay: _____

   This is another way: _____

♦ *Math Masters*, p. 266

HOME LINK MASTER

3 Options for Individualizing

♦ RETEACHING Making Different Coin Combinations for the Same Value

SMALL-GROUP ACTIVITY   15–30 min

 Literature Link The book *26 Letters and 99 Cents* by Tana Hoban (Greenwillow Books, 1987) shows photographs of coins representing the numbers 1 to 30, 35, 40, 45, 50, 60, 70, 80, 90, and 99. Sometimes more than one combination is shown, but often the least possible number of coins is shown. This book could provide practice with representing the same value in different ways.

♦ RETEACHING Playing *Spinning for Money* (*Math Masters*, pp. 37 and 38)

SMALL-GROUP ACTIVITY   15–30 min

Players put pennies, nickels, dimes, quarters, and $1 bills into a "bank." They then take turns spinning the Money-Game Spinner and taking the coins shown by the spinner from the bank. Whenever possible, players exchange coins for a single coin or bill of the same value. The first player to exchange for a $1 bill wins.

PLANNING AHEAD

For the next lesson, you will need a demonstration clock with an hour hand only, and each child will need a tool-kit clock. You can make the clock face out of *Math Masters*, page 39, or you can draw a clock face on the board with semipermanent chalk. Write children's tool-kit numbers on their clocks.

NOTE: Ask children to write their names on the backs of their Money-Game Spinners. Collect the spinners for reuse in Lessons 3.7 and 10.1.

Spinning for Money (cont.)

Materials
- ❑ Money-Game Spinner (*Math Masters*, p. 37)
- ❑ pencil
- ❑ large paper clip
- ❑ 7 pennies, 5 nickels, 5 dimes, 4 quarters, and one $1 bill for each player

Players 2, 3, or 4

Directions

1. Each player puts 7 pennies, 5 nickels, 5 dimes, 4 quarters, and one $1 bill into a "bank."

2. Players take turns spinning the Money-Game Spinner and taking the coins shown by the spinner from the bank.

3. Whenever possible, players exchange coins for a single coin or bill of the same value. For example, a player could exchange 5 pennies for a nickel or 2 dimes and 1 nickel for a quarter.

4. The first player to exchange for a $1 bill wins.

Use a large paper clip and pencil to make a spinner.

♦ *Math Masters*, p. 38

TEACHING MASTER

3.3 Telling Time

OBJECTIVES To tell time; and to write time in digital-clock notation.

summaries	materials

1 Teaching the Lesson

Children review the functions of the clock hands, use clocks to tell and show time, and practice writing and telling time. [Measurement and Reference Frames]

- ☐ *Math Journal 1*, p. 58
- ☐ Home Link 3.2
- ☐ Teaching Master (*Math Masters*, p. 39; optional)
- ☐ hour-hand-only demonstration clock
- ☐ a variety of analog and digital clocks
- ☐ tool-kit clock or clock made from Teaching Master (*Math Masters*, p. 40; optional)
- ☐ demonstration clock with both minute and hour hands
- ☐ slate (optional)

See Advance Preparation

2 Ongoing Learning & Practice

Children solve Frames-and-Arrows problems about money. [Numeration; Patterns, Functions, and Algebra]

Children practice and maintain skills through Math Boxes and Home Link activities.

- ☐ *Math Journal 1*, pp. 59 and 60
- ☐ Home Link Masters (*Math Masters*, pp. 267 and 268)

See Advance Preparation

3 Options for Individualizing

Extra Practice Children practice telling time by playing *Prize Time*. [Measurement and Reference Frames]

- ☐ 1 small piece of paper per child with a time written in digital notation
- ☐ prize items, such as small candies or stickers

Additional Information

Advance Preparation For the Math Message, each child will need a small tool-kit clock. If you prefer, clocks can be made from *Math Masters*, page 40, preferably copied onto stiff paper. Each child will need *Math Masters*, page 40, scissors, red and green markers, and a paper fastener. Children fill in the 5-minute numbers around the clock face and then cut out the face. They color, cut out, and attach a minute hand and an hour hand.

For Part 1, prepare a demonstration clock with an hour hand only. You can make it with *Math Masters*, page 40 and a paper fastener, or you can draw a clock face on the board with semipermanent chalk.

For Part 2, children will need a clock to do Home Link 3.3. They can take home the clock they made in this lesson, or you may want to send home *Math Masters*, page 40, which provides instructions for making a clock.

Vocabulary • **minute hand** • **hour hand** • **clock face** • **analog clock** • **digital clock**

Getting Started

Mental Math and Reflexes

Say a number and have children record tally marks for that number on their slates. *Suggestions:*

3, 5, 8, 10, 15, 18

Make tally marks for a number on the board. Have children count the marks and write the number on their slates.

Math Message

Find the clock with your tool-kit number on it.
Set the hands to show the time when school starts.

OR

Take a copy of Math Masters, *page 40.*

Home Link 3.2 Follow-Up

Ask several children to name the price of an item and the coin combination they chose to pay for it. Ask other children in the class to suggest other coin combinations for each item.

1 Teaching the Lesson

✦ Math Message Follow-Up

WHOLE-CLASS DISCUSSION

If you chose to have children make paper clocks from *Math Masters*, page 40, have them do so now.

Ask children to set the hands to show the time when school starts. Ask several children to display their clocks, and check several of them.

✦ Discussing the Functions of Clock Hands

WHOLE-CLASS DISCUSSION

Use a demonstration clock to review the functions of the hands of a clock:

▷ The shorter (hour) hand shows the hour of the day. It takes 1 hour to move from 1 to 2, from 2 to 3, and so on. The hand moves completely around the clock face in 12 hours.

▷ The longer (minute) hand shows minutes after or before the hour. It takes 1 minute to move from one mark to the next on the clock face and 5 minutes to move from 1 to 2, from 2 to 3, and so on.

NOTE: You may want to display examples of analog and digital clocks for children to examine.

Language Arts Link

Explain that A.M. means "before the middle of the day." It is an abbreviation for *ante meridiem*. Similarly, P.M. means "after the middle of the day." It is an abbreviation for *post meridiem*.

Set the hands on the demonstration clock so that they show 9 o'clock. Slowly move the **minute hand** around the clock face, and ask children to observe the movement of the **hour hand** as you do so. Ask questions like the following:

* Which hand do you think is more important—the hour hand or the minute hand?
* Could you estimate the time if your clock had only a minute hand? no What if it had only an hour hand? yes

Tell children that a clock with an hour hand, a minute hand, and numbers and marks around the **clock face** is called an **analog clock.** A clock that shows the hour and minutes with digits, separated by a colon, is called a **digital clock.**

◆ Estimating Time with an Hour Hand Only (*Math Masters*, pp. 39 or 40)

WHOLE-CLASS ACTIVITY

Use the demonstration clock with an hour hand only, or draw a clock face on the board or on an overhead transparency. Move or draw the hour hand to various positions and ask children to tell the time shown. Remind them to use estimation language: *about ____ o'clock; just before (after) ____ o'clock; between ____ and ____ o'clock.* Remind children that telling time is always an estimate— by the time you say the time, it is a little later!

If clocks are made from *Math Masters,* page 40, have children put the two hands on their clock together, and pretend that the clock has only an hour hand.

Partners take turns. One partner moves the two hands together to a certain position; the other estimates the time shown. Or partners ask each other to show the times when daily activities, such as going to lunch, take place.

◆ Estimating Time with the Hour Hand and the Minute Hand (*Math Masters*, p. 40)

WHOLE-CLASS DISCUSSION

The minute hand makes it possible to tell time more precisely—to the nearest minute. In everyday situations, however, people are often less precise, giving the time to the nearest 5 minutes or quarter-hour: "about three-twenty," "almost quarter to six." With repeated experience over the next few weeks, children will develop the ability to estimate time to the nearest 5-minute increment.

TEACHING MASTER

5-Minute Clock

* Color the hour hand red, and color the minute hand green.
* Cut out the clock face and hands.
* Punch a hole through the center of the clock face and through the Xs on the hands. Fasten the hands to the clock face with a brad.

◆ *Math Masters, p. 40*

Start the discussion by reviewing the movement of the minute hand on the demonstration clock. Remind children that the distance between consecutive pairs of numbers on the clock face represents 5 minutes. Have them count by 5s in unison as you point to the numbers on the clock face.

Show several times on the demonstration clock, and have children estimate what time it is. Record the times on the board using digital notation (hour:minute): about 9:00; about 3:30; and so on. Discuss the notation used to record the time: "It looks like the display of a digital clock: The hour of the day is first, then a colon, and then the minutes after the hour." Say an approximate time, such as "about 3:30," and write it on the board for children to show on their tool-kit clocks.

◆ Telling and Writing Time
(*Math Journal 1*, p. 58)

PARTNER ACTIVITY

Partners take turns. One child sets the hands on a tool-kit clock; the other tells the time and records it on a piece of paper or a slate. Then they reverse the procedure. One child says a time and writes it on a piece of paper or a slate; the other sets the hands on the tool-kit clock. Circulate and offer help as needed.

Each child then completes the clock exercises on journal page 58.

2 Ongoing Learning & Practice

◆ Solving Frames-and-Arrows Problems
(*Math Journal 1*, p. 59)

INDEPENDENT ACTIVITY

Children solve Frames-and-Arrows problems about money.

ONGOING ASSESSMENT

Lesson 2.10 introduced Frames-and-Arrows problems with one rule. Use journal page 59 to assess children's proficiency with one-rule problems. You may want to make up additional problems with one rule to provide extra practice.

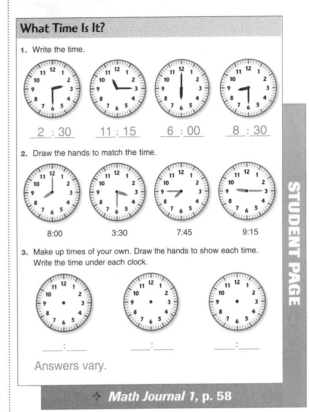

✦ *Math Journal 1*, p. 58

NOTE: Often during the next few weeks, ask children to tell about what time it is by looking at the classroom clock. Hold occasional practice sessions during which you say a time for children to show on their tool-kit clocks.

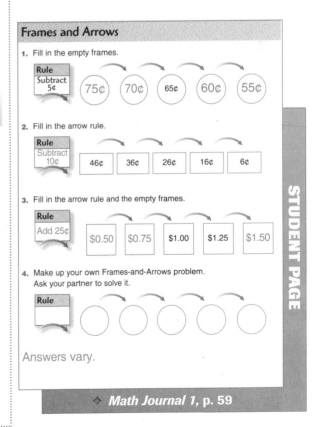

✦ *Math Journal 1*, p. 59

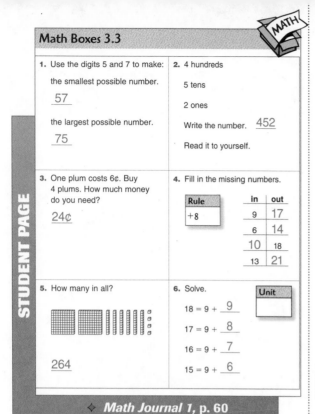

Math Boxes 3.3

1. Use the digits 5 and 7 to make:

   the smallest possible number.

   <u>57</u>

   the largest possible number.

   <u>75</u>

2. 4 hundreds

   5 tens

   2 ones

   Write the number. <u>452</u>

   Read it to yourself.

3. One plum costs 6¢. Buy 4 plums. How much money do you need?

   <u>24¢</u>

4. Fill in the missing numbers.

Rule		in	out
+8		9	17
		6	14
		10	18
		13	21

5. How many in all?

   264

6. Solve.

Unit

   18 = 9 + <u>9</u>

   17 = 9 + <u>8</u>

   16 = 9 + <u>7</u>

   15 = 9 + <u>6</u>

◆ *Math Journal 1, p. 60*

◆ **Math Boxes 3.3** (*Math Journal 1*, p. 60)

INDEPENDENT ACTIVITY

Mixed Review This journal page provides opportunities for cumulative review or assessment of concepts and skills.

◆ **Home Link 3.3** (*Math Masters,* pp. 267 and 268)

Home Connection Children use a clock to discuss time with someone at home. They can take home the clock made in this lesson or a copy of *Math Masters,* page 40 and make a paper-plate clock.

3 Options for Individualizing

◆ **EXTRA PRACTICE** Playing *Prize Time*

WHOLE-CLASS ACTIVITY **15–30 min**

Write a time (X:XX) on a piece of paper for each child. Children present the papers to you when their times arrive on the clock. If correct, they receive a small prize. Ask others in the class to verify the times.

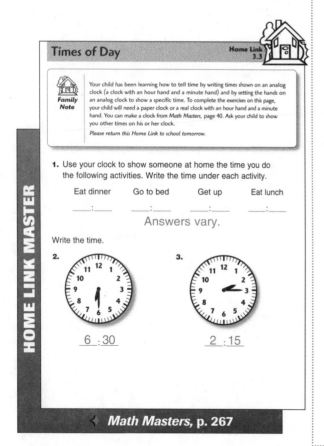

Times of Day   Home Link 3.3

Family Note Your child has been learning how to tell time by writing times shown on an analog clock (a clock with an hour hand and a minute hand) and by setting the hands on an analog clock to show a specific time. To complete the exercises on this page, your child will need a paper clock or a real clock with an hour hand and a minute hand. You can make a clock from *Math Masters*, page 40. Ask your child to show you other times on his or her clock.

Please return this Home Link to school tomorrow.

1. Use your clock to show someone at home the time you do the following activities. Write the time under each activity.

   Eat dinner   Go to bed   Get up   Eat lunch

   ___:___   ___:___   ___:___   ___:___

   Answers vary.

Write the time.

2.   <u>6</u>:<u>30</u>

3.   <u>2</u>:<u>15</u>

◆ *Math Masters, p. 267*

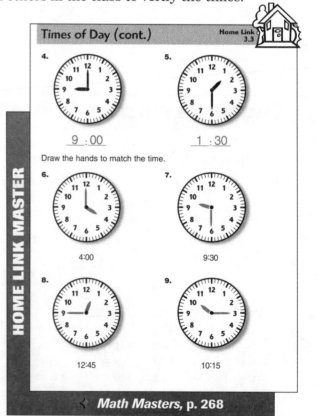

Times of Day (cont.)   Home Link 3.3

4.   <u>9</u>:<u>00</u>

5.   <u>1</u>:<u>30</u>

Draw the hands to match the time.

6.   4:00

7.   9:30

8.   12:45

9.   10:15

◆ *Math Masters, p. 268*

3.4
EXPLORATIONS

Exploring Numbers, Time, and Geoboards

OBJECTIVES To represent and rename numbers with base-10 blocks; to review writing and telling time; and to make, describe, and compare shapes on a geoboard.

summaries	materials

1 Teaching the Lesson

	□ Home Link 3.3
Exploration A: Children use base-10 blocks to show 2- and 3-digit numbers in different ways. [Numeration]	**Exploration A:** Per partnership: □ *Math Journal 1*, p. 61 □ Teaching Masters (*Math Masters*, pp. 35, 41, and 42) □ base-10 blocks: 9 longs and 30 cubes; 9 flats (optional) □ number cards labeled 0–9 (from the Everything Math Deck, if available)
Exploration B: Children practice writing and telling time by making clock-face booklets. [Measurement and Reference Frames]	**Exploration B:** Per partnership: □ Teaching Masters (*Math Masters*, pp. 43 and 44) □ at least 2 sheets of plain paper □ scissors; stapler □ clock-face rubber stamp and stamp pad
Exploration C: Children make, describe, and compare shapes on a geoboard. [Geometry]	**Exploration C:** □ geoboard and several rubber bands for each student Per group: □ *Math Journal 1*, p. 62 □ Teaching Masters (*Math Masters*, p. 45; and pp. 46 or 47, optional)

2 Ongoing Learning & Practice

	□ *Math Journal 1*, pp. 63 and 64
Children determine complements of 100 by playing *Dollar Rummy*. [Numeration; Operations and Computation]	□ Teaching Masters (*Math Masters*, p. 48; and p. 49, optional)
Children practice and maintain skills through Math Boxes and Home Link activities.	□ Home Link Master (*Math Masters*, p. 269) □ scissors *See* **Advance Preparation**

3 Options for Individualizing

Extra Practice Children practice working with digits, shapes, and time. [Numeration; Operations and Computation]	□ *Minute Math®*, pp. 33, 36, 53, 60, 71, and 73

Additional Information

Advance Preparation Before playing *Dollar Rummy* in Part 2, children will need to cut up *Math Masters*, page 48 to make cards. If children are ready for a more challenging version of the game, they should make cards from *Math Masters*, page 49 as well. If possible, copy these masters onto stiff paper. You may want to have children store them in plastic bags or other containers for future play.

Getting Started

Mental Math and Reflexes

Ask children to record on their slates the 100-complement of a number you say. If you say 90, children should write 10. Record the number model on the board: $90 + 10 = 100$. Give multiples of 10 and 25. Challenge children with multiples of 5.

Math Message

The picture below shows one way to draw 36.

||| ......

On your slates, draw at least two other ways to show 36.

Home Link 3.3 Follow-Up

Review the answers. Ask children to report the times when they go to bed in the evening and get up in the morning.

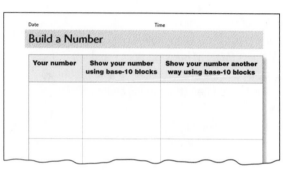

Math Journal 1, page 61

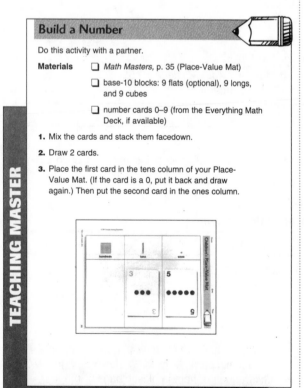

---

1 Teaching the Lesson

◆ Math Message Follow-Up

WHOLE CLASS ACTIVITY

Ask children to share their solutions. For example, 36 can also be shown as follows:

◆ Exploration A: Building and Renaming Numbers
(*Math Journal 1,* p. 61; *Math Masters,* pp. 35, 41, and 42)

PARTNER ACTIVITY

Partners follow instructions on *Math Masters,* pages 41 and 42 to build a 2-digit number by drawing cards from the deck of number cards. To make the activity more challenging, children can draw three cards and build 3-digit numbers.

NOTE: This activity provides important practice for work with the partial-sums algorithm in Unit 4 and with trade-first subtraction in Unit 6.

✦ Exploration B: Making a Clock Booklet
(*Math Masters*, pp. 43 and 44)

PARTNER ACTIVITY 👥

Partners follow instructions on *Math Masters*, pages 43 and 44 to make a booklet showing different times.

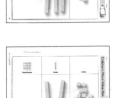
Portfolio Ideas

Children make clock booklets by following instructions on *Math Masters*, pages 43 and 44.

Language Arts Link Children can work together to make up a story about a time shown in their booklets. They should write their stories on a separate piece of paper. You may wish to have children share their stories with the rest of the class or post the stories on a bulletin board.

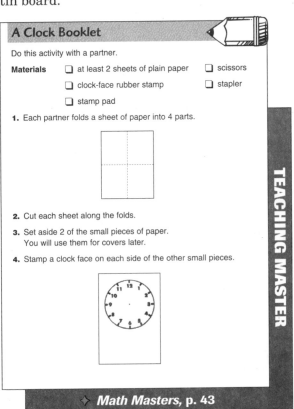

A Clock Booklet

Do this activity with a partner.

Materials
- ☐ at least 2 sheets of plain paper
- ☐ clock-face rubber stamp
- ☐ stamp pad
- ☐ scissors
- ☐ stapler

1. Each partner folds a sheet of paper into 4 parts.

2. Cut each sheet along the folds.

3. Set aside 2 of the small pieces of paper. You will use them for covers later.

4. Stamp a clock face on each side of the other small pieces.

✦ *Math Masters, p. 43*

TEACHING MASTER

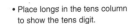

Build a Number (cont.)

4. Build the number.
- Place longs in the tens column to show the tens digit.
- Place cubes in the ones column to show the ones digit.

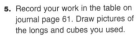

5. Record your work in the table on journal page 61. Draw pictures of the longs and cubes you used.

6. Use the Place-Value Mat and blocks to build the same number in a different way. Draw the longs and cubes you used.

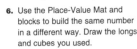

7. Build 3 or 4 more numbers in the same way. Record your numbers and draw pictures to show the two ways you built each number.

Challenge

Draw 3 cards instead of 2. Put 1 card in each column of the Place-Value Mat. Draw flats, longs, and cubes on journal page 61 to show your number.

Build the same number in a different way. Draw the blocks you used.

✦ *Math Masters, p. 42*

TEACHING MASTER

Adjusting the Activity If children are proficient at telling time to the hour, half-hour, and quarter-hour, encourage them to put times in their booklets to the nearest 5 minutes or even to the nearest minute.

A Clock Booklet (cont.)

5. For each clock face:
- Think of a time. Help each other draw the hour and minute hands to show that time.
- Write the time as you would see it on a digital clock.

6. Stack the pieces. Put a piece without a clock face on the top. Put the other piece without a clock face at the bottom.
- Staple the left side of the pieces together to make a book.
- Write a title and your names on the front cover.

Follow-Up Activities

You and your partner can use your book to do these activities:

- Take turns. One partner covers the digital time on a page. The other partner tells what time is shown on the clock face.

- Work together to make up a story about one or more of the times shown in your booklet. Write your story on another piece of paper.

✦ *Math Masters, p. 44*

TEACHING MASTER

Geoboard Shapes

Materials per child ☐ geoboard
                         ☐ rubber bands

Number of children 1, 2, 3, or 4

Do this activity on your own:

1. Make at least 4 shapes, designs, or pictures on your geoboard. Make things like a house, a boat, or a car.

2. Record your favorites on the geoboard dot paper on journal page 62.

Do this activity with a partner:

1. Make an easy shape on a geoboard. Make sure your partner can't see it.

2. Tell—but don't show—your partner how to make the shape.

3. Your partner makes the shape on another geoboard.

4. Compare the two shapes. How are they alike? How are they different? Did you give good directions?

5. Repeat the activity. This time your partner makes the shape first.

Do this activity in a small group:

1. Agree on a shape that everyone will make. Describe the shape in words, but don't draw it.

2. Everyone in your group makes the shape on his or her own geoboard.

3. Compare results. How are your shapes the same? How are they different?

◆ *Math Masters, p. 45*

TEACHING MASTER

 Adjusting the Activity To make the game more challenging, add the cards from *Math Masters*, page 49 to the deck. These cards have multiples of 5.

STUDENT PAGE

Dollar Rummy

Materials
  ☐ *Dollar Rummy* cards (*Math Masters*, p. 48)
  ☐ scissors to cut out cards
  ☐ cards from *Math Masters*, p. 49 for a harder game

Players 2

Directions

1. Deal 2 *Dollar Rummy* cards to each player.

2. Put the rest of the deck facedown between the players.

3. Take turns. When it's your turn, take the top card from the deck. Lay it faceup on the table.

4. Look for two cards that add up to $1.00. Use any cards that are in your hand or faceup on the table.

5. If you find two cards that add up to $1.00, lay these two cards facedown in front of you.

6. When you can't find any more cards that add up to $1.00, it is the other player's turn.

7. The game ends when all of the cards have been used or when neither player can make a $1.00 pair.

8. The winner is the player with more $1.00 pairs.

◇ *Math Journal 1, p. 63*

◆ **Exploration C: Making and Comparing Shapes on a Geoboard**
(*Math Journal 1*, p. 62; *Math Masters*, pp. 45–47)

SMALL-GROUP ACTIVITY

Children record shapes, designs, or pictures on journal page 62, which is geoboard dot paper. Note that designs, pictures, and shapes drawn will vary. *Math Masters,* pages 46 and 47 can also be used to provide additional geoboard dot paper.

Children will make a number of geoboard shapes. They will work independently, with partners, and in small groups (see *Math Masters,* page 45). As they work in partnerships, guide children to give very clear directions so that partners are able to duplicate the original shapes.

NOTE: Identifying likenesses and differences of shapes will prepare children for geometry in Unit 5. In that unit, children will compare 2- and 3-dimensional shapes.

---

2 Ongoing Learning & Practice

◆ **Practicing Complements of 100 by Playing** *Dollar Rummy*
(*Math Journal 1*, p. 63;
Math Masters, pp. 48 and 49)

PARTNER ACTIVITY

Explain the rules of *Dollar Rummy,* which are found on journal page 63. Using game cards cut from *Math Masters*, page 48, play several demonstration rounds of the game before children begin to play with partners.

Beginning play in *Dollar Rummy*

Continuing play

◆ **Math Boxes 3.4** (*Math Journal 1*, p. 64)

INDEPENDENT ACTIVITY

Mixed Review This journal page provides opportunities for cumulative review or assessment of concepts and skills.

◆ **Home Link 3.4** (*Math Masters*, p. 269)

Home Connection Children draw simple pictures of base-10 blocks to complete "What's My Rule?" tables.

3 Options for Individualizing

◆ **EXTRA PRACTICE** Minute Math

SMALL-GROUP ACTIVITY   5–15 min

To offer children more experience with digits, shapes, and time, see the following pages in *Minute Math:*

Counting: pp. 33 and 36

Geometry: pp. 53 and 60

Measurement: pp. 71 and 73

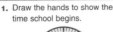

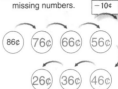

Math Boxes 3.4

1. Draw the hands to show the time school begins.

Sample answer

2. Fill in the missing numbers.   Rule −10¢

86¢ 76¢ 66¢ 56¢

26¢ 36¢ 46¢

3. Write A.M. or P.M. on the lines.

7:00 A.M. Wake up.

7:30 A.M. Eat breakfast.

3:45 P.M. Start homework.

6:00 P.M. Eat dinner.

4. An apple costs 12¢ and a banana costs 9¢. Show the coins needed to buy both.

Sample answer:

Ⓓ Ⓓ Ⓟ

5. Use the digits 8 and 9 to make:

the smallest number possible.

89

the largest number possible.

98

6. Fill in the sum on the Fact Triangle. Write the fact family.

13
+,−
8   5

8 + 5 = 13
5 + 8 = 13
13 − 8 = 5
13 − 5 = 8

◆ *Math Journal 1, p. 64*

STUDENT PAGE

"What's My Rule?" with Blocks   Home Link 3.4

Family Note Your child will complete the tables on this page by drawing tens and ones for 2-digit numbers. More than one picture can be drawn for a number. For example, to show 26, your child might draw 2 tens and 6 ones, 1 ten and 16 ones, or 26 ones. The symbol | stands for 10, and the symbol • stands for 1.

Please return this Home Link to school tomorrow.

1. Draw simple pictures of base-10 blocks to complete the table. Sample answers: Rule Add 12

In	Out	Out in a Different Way
•••	|......	:::::......
|	||..	|:::... ....
||....	|||......	||:::::.:....
||.......	|||........	||:::::.:::.

2. Write the rule. Then complete the table. Sample answers: Rule Add 16

In	Out	Out in a Different Way
||||...	|||||........	||||:::::.:::.
|.......	||:::....	|:::::.:::::
||||.	|||||......	||||:::::.::.
......	|:........	||.

◆ *Math Masters, p. 269*

HOME LINK MASTER

Lesson 3.4 **187**

3.5 Data Day: Pockets

OBJECTIVES To gather data by counting, enter the data in a table, and draw a bar graph of the data; and to identify the middle value (median) in a data set.

summaries	materials
1 Teaching the Lesson	
Children count the number of pockets on their clothes and compare the greatest and least number of pockets. Children tally the class pocket data and make a bar graph using those data. Children also identify the middle value (median) in the pockets data by displaying the data in order. [Numeration; Data and Chance]	□ *Math Journal 1*, pp. 66 and 67 □ Home Link 3.4 □ Teaching Masters (*Math Masters*, pp. 50–52) □ Teaching Master transparencies (*Math Masters*, pp. 51 and 52) □ cubes (optional) ***See* Advance Preparation**
2 Ongoing Learning & Practice	
Children practice the "harder" addition and subtraction facts using Fact Triangles. [Operations and Computation] Children practice and maintain skills through Math Boxes and Home Link activities.	□ *Math Journal 1*, p. 65 □ Home Link Master (*Math Masters*, p. 270) □ +,− Fact Triangles per partnership (triangles with sums greater than 10)
3 Options for Individualizing	
Enrichment Children compare their class's pocket data to data from other classes and prepare a summary of their findings. [Numeration; Data and Chance]	□ *Math Journal 1*, pp. 66 and 67

Additional Information

Advance Preparation For the Math Message, you will need to make one copy of *Math Masters,* page 50 for every 2 children. Cut the copies apart and place the slips of paper near the Math Message. If your school requires a uniform, modify the *Finding the Middle Number of Pockets* activity in Part 1 to include the number of pencils, pens, or other objects children can tally. You will also need to create overhead transparencies of *Math Masters,* pages 51 and 52 for the last two pockets data activities.

Vocabulary • **predict** • **middle number** • **bar graph**

Vocabulary (teacher) • **median** • **mode**

Getting Started

Mental Math and Reflexes

Pose −9 and −8 subtraction facts. *Suggestions:*

$13 − 9 = ?$ $17 − 9 = ?$ $? = 15 − 8$ $14 − 8 = ?$ $13 − 8 = ?$ $? = 14 − 9$

NOTE: If children are having difficulty doing these exercises, remind them to think of "helper" 10-facts. For example, $13 − 10 = 3$, so $13 − 9 = 4$.

Math Message

Take one of the small pieces of paper labeled Counting Pockets. Do what it says.

Home Link 3.4 Follow-Up

Have volunteers share the combinations of base-10 blocks that they used to represent numbers in the "What's My Rule?" table. If children are having difficulty, demonstrate how to find one of the missing table entries by using actual base-10 blocks.

1 Teaching the Lesson

✦ Math Message Follow-Up
(*Math Masters,* p. 50)

WHOLE-CLASS ACTIVITY

Ask children to tell you how many pockets they have on their clothes. Ask children with the greatest and fewest number of pockets to stand. Ask: *How many more pockets would* (child's name with least number of pockets) *need in order to have as many pockets as* (child's name with the greatest number of pockets)?

Give children a few moments to find the answer. Ask children to explain their strategies. Since the question was designed to encourage counting up, be sure to discuss this strategy for finding differences. For example, "The fewest number of pockets is 2. The greatest is 8. Count up from 2: 3 is 1 more, 4 is 2 more, …, 8 is 6 more."

You may also want to discuss number models that fit this situation, such as $2 + 6 = 8$ and $8 - 2 = 6$.

✦ Finding the Middle Number of Pockets

WHOLE-CLASS ACTIVITY

Ask children to pretend that a new child is joining the class. Ask them to **predict** how many pockets the new child will have.

Have children report their predictions and how they made them. Expect answers to be rather informal—"I think 5 pockets, because I have 5 pockets and I hope the new child will be like me." Some children may base their predictions on a **middle number** of pockets—"The fewest

Adjusting the Activity

If children are having difficulty, model the counting-up situation with cubes.

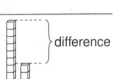

If you have 2, you need 6 more to get to 8.

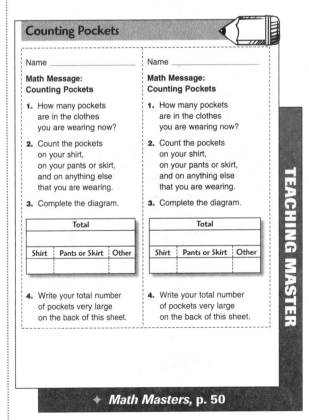

Counting Pockets

| Name _____ | Name _____ |

Math Message: Counting Pockets

1. How many pockets are in the clothes you are wearing now?

2. Count the pockets on your shirt, on your pants or skirt, and on anything else that you are wearing.

3. Complete the diagram.

Total		
Shirt	Pants or Skirt	Other

4. Write your total number of pockets very large on the back of this sheet.

Math Message: Counting Pockets

1. How many pockets are in the clothes you are wearing now?

2. Count the pockets on your shirt, on your pants or skirt, and on anything else that you are wearing.

3. Complete the diagram.

Total		
Shirt	Pants or Skirt	Other

4. Write your total number of pockets very large on the back of this sheet.

✦ *Math Masters,* p. 50

TEACHING MASTER

number of pockets is 2 and the greatest is 8. I think the new child might have 5, because 5 is in the middle of 2 and 8."

Use this idea to motivate children to find the middle number of pockets. Help children see that the middle number would be a good prediction for the new child. Then use the following procedure to find the middle, or **median,** number of pockets:

Step 1. Ask children with the most and fewest numbers of pockets to come to the front of the room and stand on opposite sides. They should face the class holding their Math Message slips so that their total numbers of pockets can be easily seen.

Step 2. Ask the remaining children to come to the front, one by one, and to place themselves in order between the children already in line. Remind them to hold up their Math Message slips as they join the line. Children with the same number of pockets should stand next to one another, but it doesn't matter in which order they stand.

Step 3. When all children are in line, check that they are in the correct order.

Step 4. Ask the two children on the ends of the line to take two big steps forward. Then ask the two children on the ends of the remaining line to step forward.

Step 5. Continue asking pairs of children on the ends to step forward until only one or two children are left. If one child is left, then the middle number of pockets is that child's number. If two children are left, the middle number of pockets is halfway between their numbers, but you can use any number between them that makes sense.

Ask some of the following questions to stimulate discussion:

• Is the middle number of pockets a good prediction for the new child?

• Would you be surprised if the new child had more or fewer pockets than the middle number?

• Would it help if we knew whether the new child was a boy or a girl?

• How do you think the greatest and fewest number of pockets would change if our school had uniforms? How do you think the middle number might change?

Children find the median number of pockets.

✦ Tallying the Pockets Data
(*Math Journal 1*, p. 66; *Math Masters*, p. 51)

WHOLE-CLASS ACTIVITY

Ask children one by one to tell how many pockets they have. Tally these numbers on an overhead transparency of *Math Masters*, page 51. At the same time, have children tally them on journal page 66.

Once you have counted the tallies, have children complete the Number column and then spend a few minutes talking about the table. Ask such questions as:

• How many children have 5 pockets? (Repeat for other numbers of pockets.)

• What is the most common number of pockets?

• What does this number mean? (Point to a number in the Number column.)

NOTE: The most common number in a data set is called the **mode.** There may be more than one mode in a data set. The mode will be discussed later in *Everyday Mathematics.*

✦ Making a Bar Graph of the Pockets Data
(*Math Journal 1*, p. 67; *Math Masters*, p. 52)

INDEPENDENT ACTIVITY

After you have discussed the table, have children use the journal page to make a **bar graph** of the data. Use an overhead transparency of *Math Masters*, page 52 to demonstrate. Because some children may confuse the numbers for pockets with the numbers for children, you may want to model the whole graph.

When children have finished their graphs, lead a discussion. Ask such questions as:

• Which bar is the tallest? What does that bar mean? What does the shortest bar tell you?

• Why are the bars taller near the middle of the graph and shorter near the ends?

• Pretend that you are going to count the pockets that people at a beach have on their clothes. How many pockets do you think people would have? How would the graph look different?

Pockets Data Table

Count the pockets of children in your class. Sample answers:

Pockets	Children	
	Tallies	Number
0		0
1		0
2	//	2
3	//	2
4	///	3
5	////	4
6	///	3
7	////	4
8	//	2
9	/	1
10		0
11		0
12		0
13 or more		0

Math Journal 1, p. 66

▲ Teachers may also find this table on *Math Masters*, page 51.

▼ Teachers may also find this graph on *Math Masters*, page 52.

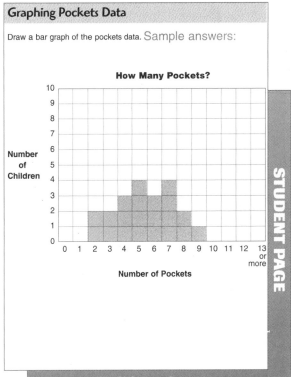

Math Journal 1, p. 67

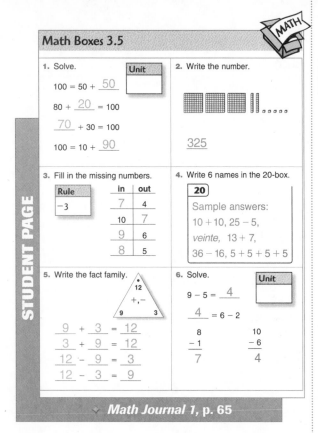

Math Boxes 3.5

1. Solve.

Unit

$100 = 50 + \underline{50}$

$80 + \underline{20} = 100$

$\underline{70} + 30 = 100$

$100 = 10 + \underline{90}$

2. Write the number.

$\underline{325}$

3. Fill in the missing numbers.

Rule	in	out
-3	7	4
	10	7
	9	6
	8	5

4. Write 6 names in the 20-box.

20

Sample answers:

$10 + 10$, $25 - 5$,

veinte, $13 + 7$,

$36 - 16$, $5 + 5 + 5 + 5$

5. Write the fact family.

$\underline{9} + \underline{3} = \underline{12}$

$\underline{3} + \underline{9} = \underline{12}$

$\underline{12} - \underline{9} = \underline{3}$

$\underline{12} - \underline{3} = \underline{9}$

6. Solve.

Unit

$9 - 5 = \underline{4}$

$\underline{4} = 6 - 2$

$\begin{array}{r} 8 \\ -1 \\ \hline 7 \end{array}$ $\begin{array}{r} 10 \\ -6 \\ \hline 4 \end{array}$

Math Journal 1, p. 65

Pockets Bar Graph

Home Link 3.5

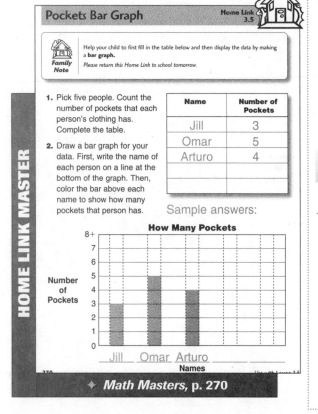

Family Note Help your child to first fill in the table below and then display the data by making a **bar graph**.

Please return this Home Link to school tomorrow.

1. Pick five people. Count the number of pockets that each person's clothing has. Complete the table.

2. Draw a bar graph for your data. First, write the name of each person on a line at the bottom of the graph. Then, color the bar above each name to show how many pockets that person has.

Name	Number of Pockets
Jill	3
Omar	5
Arturo	4

Sample answers:

How Many Pockets

Number of Pockets

Jill Omar Arturo

Names

Math Masters, p. 270

Ongoing Learning & Practice

◆ Practicing with +,− Fact Triangles

PARTNER ACTIVITY

Have children work in pairs to practice addition and subtraction facts using their Fact Triangles. Because practice should focus on the "harder" facts, remove the Fact Triangles whose sums are less than 10.

ONGOING ASSESSMENT

As they practice, ask children to sort the Fact Triangles into two piles—facts they can recall quickly and facts that need more practice. Have them write those that need practice. Writing the facts gives children practice and gives you a list for later Mental Math and Reflexes exercises.

◆ Math Boxes 3.5 (*Math Journal 1,* p. 65)

INDEPENDENT ACTIVITY

Mixed Review This journal page provides opportunities for cumulative review or assessment of concepts and skills.

◆ Home Link 3.5 (*Math Masters,* p. 270)

Home Connection Children count pockets of five people at home and make a bar graph using their data.

Options for Individualizing

◆ ENRICHMENT Comparing Pockets Data
(*Math Journal 1,* pp. 66 and 67)

SMALL-GROUP ACTIVITY   **30+ min**

Many schools have more than one second grade class. Some children may be interested in comparing their class's pocket data to those of another class. Arrange for groups of children in different classes to use one another's journals to compare tally charts and bar graphs (pages 66 and 67).

Have groups write a brief summary to share with the class.

3.6 Frames and Arrows Having Two Rules

OBJECTIVE To solve Frames-and-Arrows problems having two rules.

summaries	materials

1 Teaching the Lesson

Children make up and solve Frames-and-Arrows problems about coins and use coins to solve Frames-and-Arrows problems having two rules. [Patterns, Functions, and Algebra; Operations and Computation]

- ☐ *Math Journal 1,* pp. 68 and 69
- ☐ Home Link 3.5
- ☐ Teaching Masters (*Math Masters,* pp. 53–55; p. 56, optional)
- ☐ Teaching Masters transparencies (*Math Masters,* pp. 53–56)
- ☐ coins per child: 5 quarters, 5 dimes, 5 nickels, and 5 pennies

***See* Advance Preparation**

2 Ongoing Learning & Practice

Children practice reading a bar graph. [Data and Chance]

Children practice and maintain skills through Math Boxes and Home Link activities.

- ☐ *Math Journal 1,* pp. 70 and 71
- ☐ Home Link Master (*Math Masters,* p. 271)

3 Options for Individualizing

Enrichment Children make up and solve Frames-and-Arrows problems having two rules. [Patterns, Functions, and Algebra; Operations and Computation]

- ☐ Teaching Master (*Math Masters,* p. 56)

Additional Information

Advance Preparation For the Math Message, make one copy of *Math Masters,* page 53 for every two children. Cut the copies apart and place them near the Math Message.

For the Part 1 activities, decide how you will display Frames-and-Arrows diagrams:

- Make overhead transparencies of *Math Masters,* pages 53–56.
- Draw a two-rule Frames-and-Arrows diagram on the board with semipermanent chalk. Erase the rules and numbers for each new problem.
- Draw and erase Frames-and-Arrows diagrams on the board as needed.

Getting Started

Mental Math and Reflexes

Pose comparison number stories, which practice -9 and -8 subtraction facts or $+9$ and $+8$ addition facts, depending on which number model a child uses. For example, $4 + 8 = 12$ or $12 - 4 = 8$. *Suggestions:*

- Jenna has $4. Martina has $12. How many more dollars does Jenna need in order to have the same amount of money as Martina? $8

- Jackson has 14 sports magazines in his collection. Theo has 9. How many more magazines does Theo need in order to have the same number of magazines as Jackson? 5 magazines

Math Message

Here is a Frames-and-Arrows problem that uses nickels:

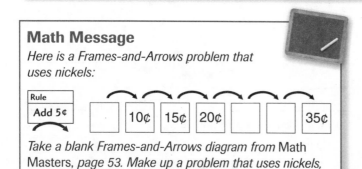

Take a blank Frames-and-Arrows diagram from Math Masters, *page 53. Make up a problem that uses nickels, dimes, or quarters. Hand in your problem.*

Home Link 3.5 Follow-Up

You may want to have children work in small groups. Have groups compare their bar graphs by asking questions like the following:

- What is the greatest number of pockets shown by any graph? The smallest number?

- Use all of your group's graphs. What is the total number of people who had zero pockets? 1 pocket? (Continue with other numbers.)

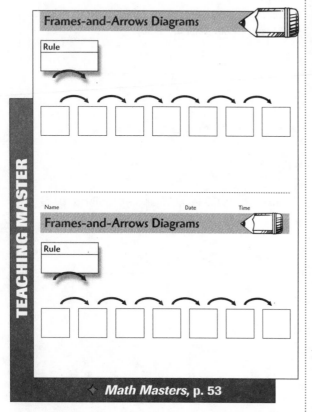

Math Masters, p. 53

1 Teaching the Lesson

◆ Math Message Follow-Up
(*Math Masters,* p. 53)

WHOLE-CLASS ACTIVITY

Choose two of the children's Frames-and-Arrows problems. Review filling in frames and finding a missing rule. Share solution strategies with the class on an overhead transparency of *Math Masters,* page 53 or on the board. Make sure that everyone understands these one-rule Frames-and-Arrows diagrams.

◆ Frames-and-Arrows Diagrams Having Two Rules (*Math Masters,* pp. 54–56)

WHOLE-CLASS ACTIVITY

Display the example on *Math Masters,* page 54. Ask what is different about this Frames-and-Arrows diagram from Frames-and-Arrows diagrams that children have seen before. Sample answer: There are two kinds of arrows, one dashed and one solid. Explain that the two kinds of arrows stand for two different rules.

Have children act out the example with you. Start with a dime as indicated in the first frame; add a nickel (solid-arrow rule) to get the result shown in the second frame; add a dime (dashed-arrow rule) to get the result shown in the third frame; and so on.

Repeat the procedure with the other problems on *Math Masters,* pages 54 and 55. Use the blank diagrams on *Math Masters,* page 56 to make up more problems as necessary.

Adjusting the Activity In Problems 4 and 5, children find one of the rules and complete the frames. To find the rule, children should use coins to act out the pattern. Children can then fill in the empty frames.

If needed, focus on Problems 1–3. With additional practice on journal pages and in Math Boxes throughout the year, children will be better prepared for problems like 4 and 5.

To extend the activity, point out to children that the rules in the Frames-and-Arrows problems alternate between solid (Rule 1) and dashed (Rule 2) arrows. Challenge children to solve problems having more complicated rule patterns, such as Rule 1, Rule 2, Rule 2, Rule 1, Rule 2, Rule 2, Rule 1.

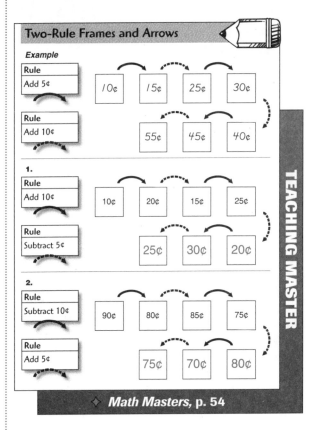

◇ *Math Masters,* p. 54

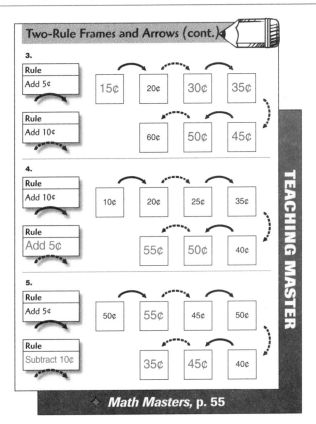

◇ *Math Masters,* p. 55

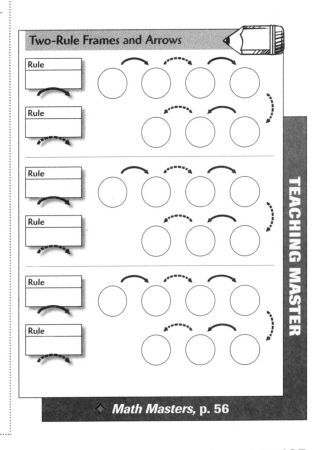

◇ *Math Masters,* p. 56

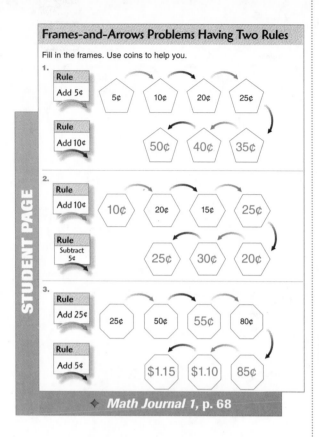

Frames-and-Arrows Problems Having Two Rules

Fill in the frames. Use coins to help you.

1.

Rule: Add 5¢
Rule: Add 10¢

5¢ → 10¢ → 20¢ → 25¢
50¢ ← 40¢ ← 35¢

2.

Rule: Add 10¢
Rule: Subtract 5¢

10¢ → 20¢ → 15¢ → 25¢
25¢ ← 30¢ ← 20¢

3.

Rule: Add 25¢
Rule: Add 5¢

25¢ → 50¢ → 55¢ → 80¢
$1.15 ← $1.10 ← 85¢

♦ Math Journal 1, p. 68

Math Journal 1, pp. 68 and 69

♦ Solving Frames-and-Arrows Problems
(*Math Journal 1,* pp. 68 and 69)

INDEPENDENT ACTIVITY

Children solve Frames-and-Arrows problems and use coins to help them. Encourage children to check each problem after they have completed it by applying the rules to the completed frames. For example, to check Problem 2, children begin with their answer of 10¢. The color rule is *Add 10¢.* The second frame is 20¢. Does $10¢ + 10¢ = 20¢$? Yes, so the answer is correct.

2 Ongoing Learning & Practice

♦ Reading a Bar Graph
(*Math Journal 1,* p. 70)

INDEPENDENT ACTIVITY

Children answer questions about a bar graph. Make sure that they understand the difference between the two sets of numbers on the graph—one set names the number of

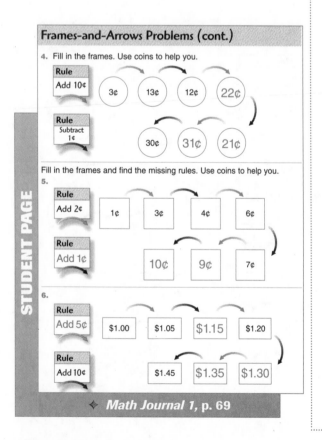

Frames-and-Arrows Problems (cont.)

4. Fill in the frames. Use coins to help you.

Rule: Add 10¢
Rule: Subtract 1¢

3¢ → 13¢ → 12¢ → 22¢
30¢ ← 31¢ ← 21¢

Fill in the frames and find the missing rules. Use coins to help you.

5.

Rule: Add 2¢
Rule: Add 1¢

1¢ → 3¢ → 4¢ → 6¢
10¢ ← 9¢ ← 7¢

6.

Rule: Add 5¢
Rule: Add 10¢

$1.00 → $1.05 → $1.15 → $1.20
$1.45 ← $1.35 ← $1.30

♦ Math Journal 1, p. 69

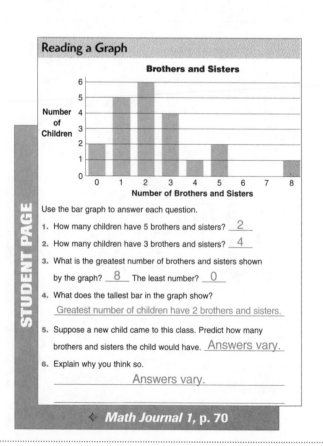

Reading a Graph

Brothers and Sisters

Use the bar graph to answer each question.

1. How many children have 5 brothers and sisters? __2__

2. How many children have 3 brothers and sisters? __4__

3. What is the greatest number of brothers and sisters shown by the graph? __8__ The least number? __0__

4. What does the tallest bar in the graph show?
   Greatest number of children have 2 brothers and sisters.

5. Suppose a new child came to this class. Predict how many brothers and sisters the child would have. Answers vary.

6. Explain why you think so.
   Answers vary.

♦ Math Journal 1, p. 70

brothers and sisters children have, and the other set is used to tell how many children have a certain number of brothers and sisters.

✦ Math Boxes 3.6 (*Math Journal 1, p. 71*)

INDEPENDENT ACTIVITY

Mixed Review This journal page provides opportunities for cumulative review or assessment of concepts and skills.

✦ Home Link 3.6 (*Math Masters, p. 271*)

Home Connection Children use coins to solve Frames-and-Arrows problems having two rules.

3 Options for Individualizing

✦ ENRICHMENT Making Up and Solving Frames-and-Arrows Problems Having Two Rules (*Math Masters, p. 56*)

PARTNER ACTIVITY 　　　　15–30 min

This is the first lesson in which children work with Frames-and-Arrows problems having two rules. Expect that the majority of children *will not* be able to make up problems on their own until they have had additional practice solving two-rule problems on journal pages and in Math Boxes.

However, a few children in your class may be up to the challenge. If so, have them use *Math Masters,* page 56 to create problems. After children have created problems, have them trade papers with a partner and solve their partner's problems.

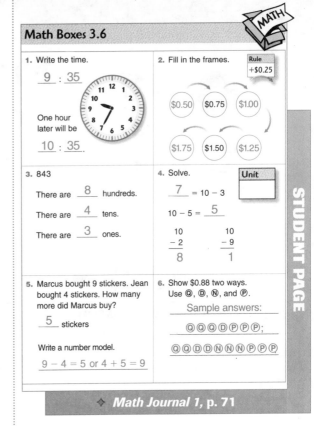

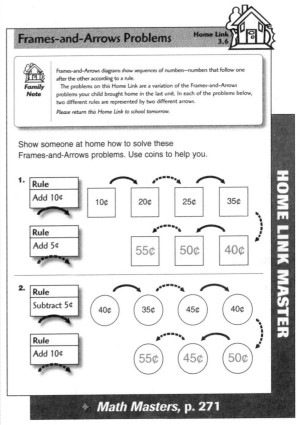

3.7 Making Change by Counting Up

OBJECTIVE To make change by counting up from the cost of an item to the amount tendered.

summaries	materials

1 Teaching the Lesson

Children identify the coins that can be used to make a purchase; make change by counting up from the cost of an item to the amount tendered; and practice making change by acting out the roles of a customer and a clerk. [Numeration; Measurement and Reference Frames]

- ☐ *Math Journal 1,* pp. 54 and 72
- ☐ Home Link 3.6
- ☐ coins per partnership: 10 pennies, 10 nickels, 5 dimes, 3 quarters, and one $1 dollar bill
- ☐ overhead coins in the quantities given above (optional)
- ☐ slate

2 Ongoing Learning & Practice

Children solve Frames-and-Arrows problems having two rules. [Patterns, Functions, and Algebra; Operations and Computation]

Children practice and maintain skills through Math Boxes and Home Link activities.

- ☐ *Math Journal 1,* pp. 73 and 74
- ☐ Home Link Masters (*Math Masters,* pp. 272 and 273)

3 Options for Individualizing

Reteaching Children practice coin and bill exchanges by playing *Spinning for Money.* [Numeration; Measurement and Reference Frames]

Enrichment Children solve a coin puzzle. [Numeration; Measurement and Reference Frames]

- ☐ Teaching Masters (*Math Masters,* pp. 38 and 57)
- ☐ Money-Game Spinner made from Teaching Master (*Math Masters,* p. 37)
- ☐ coins and bills per player: 7 pennies, 5 nickels, 5 dimes, 4 quarters, and one $1 bill

Additional Information
Vocabulary • make change by counting up

Getting Started

Mental Math and Reflexes

Count by 5s, 10s, and 25s.
Suggestions:
- Begin at 50. Count by 5s to 100.
- Begin at 25. Count by 10s to 105.
- Begin at 100. Count by 25s to 300.

Math Message

You buy a toy that costs 48¢. Which coins would you use to pay for it? Draw the coins on your slate. Use Ⓟ, Ⓝ, Ⓓ, or Ⓠ.

Home Link 3.6 Follow-Up

Ask volunteers to demonstrate how they found the numbers that belong in the empty frames for each problem. If children have difficulty, show them how to use coins to determine the missing numbers.

Teaching the Lesson

◆ Math Message Follow-Up

WHOLE-CLASS ACTIVITY 👥👥👥

Ask several children to share their solutions. *How can you find the fewest number of coins that would be needed to buy the toy?* Sample answer: I start with the coin of the highest value, a quarter. I can use 1 quarter. Then I count on from 25¢ with the next-highest-value coin. I can use 2 dimes, so I count 25¢, 35¢, 45¢. I cannot use any nickels. So I count on from 45¢ with pennies: 45¢, 46¢, 47¢, 48¢. The fewest number of coins that I would need to buy the toy is 6: 1 quarter, 2 dimes, and 3 pennies. Explain to children that any group of coins that has a value of 48¢ is a correct solution.

◆ Demonstrating How to Make Change by Counting Up (*Math Journal 1*, p. 54)

WHOLE-CLASS ACTIVITY 👥👥👥

Have children turn to the Fruit and Vegetables Stand Poster in their journals. Then pose this problem: *I buy an orange. I give the clerk 2 dimes. How much change will the clerk give me back?*

Show how to **make change by counting up.**

1. Start with the cost of the item—18¢.

2. Count up to the amount of money used to pay for the item—20¢. Say "19, 20" while putting down 2 pennies.

3. Record the transaction on the board as follows:

I bought:	I paid:	My change was:
an orange for 18¢	Ⓓ Ⓓ	Ⓟ Ⓟ

4. Repeat this routine with several other examples.

Point out that the same transaction can involve different coin combinations. In the sample problem above, a child could have paid for the orange with a quarter. The change would have been 1 nickel and 2 pennies, or 7 pennies.

Partners take turns being the Customer and the Clerk. The Customer selects an item and gives the Clerk coins to pay for the item. The Clerk counts out the change. Encourage children to make change using the fewest possible number of coins. Have children share several

---

Fruit and Vegetables Stand Poster

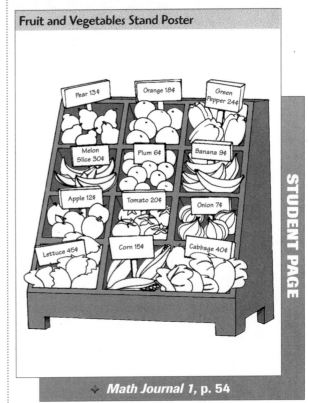

✦ *Math Journal 1*, p. 54

ONGOING ASSESSMENT

Most children should be able to use coins to pay for an item. For more practice, use the Fruit and Vegetables Stand Poster on journal page 54. Keep the pace brisk.

Shopping at the Fruit and Vegetables Stand

Price per Item					
pear	13¢	melon slice	30¢	lettuce	45¢
orange	18¢	apple	12¢	green pepper	24¢
banana	9¢	tomato	20¢	corn	15¢
plum	6¢	onion	7¢	cabbage	40¢

Complete the table. Answers vary.

I bought	I paid (Draw coins or $1 bill)	I got in change
_____		_____ ¢
_____		_____ ¢
_____		_____ ¢

Challenge　　　　　　　　　　　Answers vary.

Buy 2 items. How much change from $1.00 will you get?

I bought	I paid	I got in change
_____ and _____	$1	_____ ¢

✦ *Math Journal 1*, p. 72

Frames-and-Arrows Problems Having Two Rules

Fill in the frames. Use coins to help you.

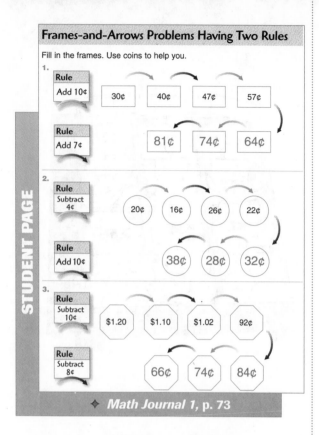

1.

| Rule | | | | |
| Add 10¢ | 30¢ | 40¢ | 47¢ | 57¢ |

| Rule | | | | |
| Add 7¢ | 81¢ | 74¢ | 64¢ | |

2.

| Rule | | | | |
| Subtract 4¢ | 20¢ | 16¢ | 26¢ | 22¢ |

| Rule | | | | |
| Add 10¢ | 38¢ | 28¢ | 32¢ | |

3.

| Rule | | | | |
| Subtract 10¢ | $1.20 | $1.10 | $1.02 | 92¢ |

| Rule | | | | |
| Subtract 8¢ | 66¢ | 74¢ | 84¢ | |

◆ Math Journal 1, p. 73

Math Boxes 3.7

1. Solve.

Unit

Answers vary.

$15 > 8 + \underline{}$

$6 + 7 < 6 + \underline{}$

$17 = 9 + \underline{8}$

2. How much money?

$ 21.45

3. Draw hands on the clock to show 6:15.

4. Fill in the missing numbers.

Rule Add 1 hour	in	out
	6:00	7:00
	12:30	1:30
	2:15	3:15
	12:45	1:45

5. Write the fact family.

$9 + 9 = 18$

$18 - 9 = 9$

6.

+5   −1

3   8   7   12

20   15   16   11

◆ Math Journal 1, p. 74

---

transactions with the class and record them in the table on the board.

 Adjusting the Activity If needed, present examples where the Clerk uses 4 pennies or fewer for the change. Then move on to making change with nickels, dimes, and quarters.

To extend the activity, guide children to write number models for transactions: If you pay for a 13¢ pear with two dimes, you could use the number model $13¢ + 7¢ = 20¢$ to show counting up to make the change. 13¢ is the cost, 20¢ is the amount used to pay, and 7¢ is the amount of change.

◆ Acting as Customer or Clerk
(*Math Journal 1*, p. 72)

PARTNER ACTIVITY

Partners continue the shopping activity. They take turns being the Customer and the Clerk. Children record a few of their transactions in their journals, using the notation Ⓟ, Ⓝ, Ⓓ, Ⓠ, and $1.

2 Ongoing Learning & Practice

◆ Solving Frames-and-Arrows Problems Having Two Rules (*Math Journal 1*, p. 73)

INDEPENDENT ACTIVITY

Children solve Frames-and-Arrows problems involving two rules. If children are having difficulty, encourage them to act out the problems with coins.

◆ Math Boxes 3.7 (*Math Journal 1*, p. 74)

INDEPENDENT ACTIVITY

Mixed Review This journal page provides opportunities for cumulative review or assessment of concepts and skills.

◆ Home Link 3.7 (*Math Masters*, pp. 272 and 273)

Home Connection With small items from home, children have a pretend garage sale. They "price" each item under $1; they "buy" each item with a $1 bill.

Options for Individualizing

◆ RETEACHING Playing *Spinning for Money*
(*Math Masters*, pp. 37 and 38)

SMALL-GROUP ACTIVITY   **15–30 min**

Children practice money-counting and money-exchange skills by playing *Spinning for Money*. For detailed instructions, see Lesson 3.2.

◆ ENRICHMENT Solving a Coin Puzzle
(*Math Masters*, p. 57)

INDEPENDENT ACTIVITY   **5–15 min**

Pose the example: *I have two coins. Together they are worth 30¢. One is not a nickel. What are the coins?* A quarter and a nickel. One of the coins is not a nickel, but the other coin is a nickel.

Change at a Garage Sale
Home Link 3.7

Family Note

Encourage your child to make change by counting up. Using real coins and dollar bills will make this activity easier. *For example:*
- Start with the cost of an item—65 cents.
- Count up to the money given—$1.00.

One way to make change: Put down a nickel and say "70." Then put down 3 dimes and say "80, 90, 1 dollar." *Another way:* Put down 3 dimes and say "75, 85, 95." Then put down 5 pennies and say "96, 97, 98, 99, 1 dollar."

Please return this Home Link to school tomorrow.

Pretend you are having a garage sale. Do the following:
- Find small items in your home to "sell."
- Give each item a price less than $1.00. Give each item a different price.
- Pretend that customers pay for each item with a $1 bill.
- Show someone at home how you would make change by counting up. Use Ⓟ, Ⓝ, Ⓓ, and Ⓠ.
- Show another way you could make change for the same item.

Example

The customer buys ___a pen___ for ___65¢___.

One way I can make change: ⓃⒹⒹⒹ

Another way I can make change: ⒹⒹⒹⓅⓅⓅⓅⓅ

◇ *Math Masters*, p. 272

Coin Puzzles

Use the clues to solve the coin puzzles.

Example

Clue 1: I have two coins.

Clue 2: Together they are worth 30¢.

Clue 3: One is not a nickel.

Coin Puzzle: What are the coins? *A quarter and a nickel*

1. **Clue 1:** I have 46¢.

   Clue 2: I have 7 coins.

   Coin Puzzle: Which coins do I have? Three dimes, three nickels, and one penny

2. **Clue 1:** I have 49¢ in one pocket.

   Clue 2: I have 16¢ in another pocket.

   Clue 3: When I put all my coins on the table, I count 10 pennies.

   Clue 4: None of the coins is a nickel.

   Coin Puzzle: What are the coins? One quarter, three dimes, and ten pennies

3. **Clue 1:** I have 5 coins.

   Clue 2: I have a total of 46¢.

   Clue 3: Three coins are not nickels.

   Coin Puzzle: Which coins do I have? One quarter, one dime, two nickels, and one penny

◆ *Math Masters*, p. 57

Change at a Garage Sale (cont.)
Home Link 3.7

1. The customer buys _____ for _____.

   One way I can make change: _____

   Another way I can make change: _____

2. The customer buys _____ for _____.

   One way I can make change: _____

   Another way I can make change: _____

3. The customer buys _____ for _____.

   One way I can make change: _____

   Another way I can make change: _____

4. The customer buys _____ for _____.

   One way I can make change: _____

   Another way I can make change: _____

5. The customer buys _____ for _____.

   One way I can make change: _____

   Another way I can make change: _____

   Answers vary.

◇ *Math Masters*, p. 273

Coin Exchanges

3.8

OBJECTIVE To solve multistep problems for amounts under $1.00; and to practice making change using nickels, dimes, and quarters.

summaries	materials

1 Teaching the Lesson

Children identify the coins and bills that can be used to make a purchase under $1.00, and they practice making change with nickels, dimes, and quarters by pretending to buy items from a milk and juice vending machine. [Numeration; Measurement and Reference Frames]

- ☐ *Math Journal 1,* pp. 76 and 77
- ☐ Home Link 3.7
- ☐ Teaching Master transparency (*Math Masters,* p. 58; optional)
- ☐ slate
- ☐ coins per child (optional): 10 pennies, 10 nickels, 5 dimes, 3 quarters, and one $1 bill

***See* Advance Preparation**

2 Ongoing Learning & Practice

Children play *Making Change* to identify coins equal to a given value and to practice making change. [Numeration; Measurement and Reference Frames]

Children practice and maintain skills through Math Boxes and Home Link activities.

- ☐ *Math Journal 1,* pp. 75 and 78
- ☐ Home Link Master (*Math Masters,* p. 274)
- ☐ money amounts per child: 2 nickels, 2 dimes, 2 quarters, and one $1 bill
- ☐ 2 dice per group
- ☐ item to use as a bank, such as a cup, small box, or piece of paper

3 Options for Individualizing

Language Diversity Children explore meanings of the word *change.*

Extra Practice Children continue their work with money. [Measurement and Reference Frames]

- ☐ picture dictionaries
- ☐ *Minute Math®,* pp. 22, 35, 67, 69, and 70

Additional Information

Advance Preparation For the Math Message Follow-Up in Part 1, you may want to create an overhead transparency of *Math Masters,* page 58.

Vocabulary • exact change light

Getting Started

Mental Math and Reflexes

Show how you could pay for each item. Draw Ⓝ, Ⓓ, or Ⓠ on your slate.

- An apple that costs 55¢
- A bottle of juice that costs 75¢
- A package of gum that costs 35¢

Math Message

Turn to page 76 in your journal. Do you know what this machine is called? Do you know how it works? Be ready to discuss this machine.

Home Link 3.7 Follow-Up

Ask volunteers to name an item they "sold," the price of the item, and how they made change. You may want to have children demonstrate their transactions using coins.

---

1 Teaching the Lesson

◆ Math Message Follow-Up
(*Math Journal 1*, p. 76; *Math Masters*, p. 58)

WHOLE-CLASS ACTIVITY

Display an overhead transparency of the Milk and Juice Vending Machine Poster (*Math Masters*, page 58), or have children turn to journal page 76. Ask:

- What is this machine? How does it work?

- Which coins or bills can you use in the machine? Nickels, dimes, quarters, and dollar bills

- Can you buy something if you don't have the exact amount? Yes, unless the "exact change" light is on. What does the **exact change light** mean? If it is on, the machine won't return change if the buyer puts in more money than an item costs.

Review the concept of making change: The buyer pays with coins or bills that add up to more than the cost of the item. The vending machine gives back the money owed (the difference).

◆ *Math Masters, p. 58*

Buying from a Vending Machine

1. The exact change light is on. You want to buy a carton of orange juice. Which coins will you put in? Draw Ⓝ, Ⓓ, and Ⓠ to show the coins.

   Sample answer: Ⓠ Ⓠ Ⓓ Ⓝ

2. The exact change light is off. You want to buy a carton of 2% milk. You don't have the exact change. Which coins or bills will you put in? Draw coins or a $1 bill.

   Sample answers: Put in a $1 bill; the change is 65¢. Put in 2 quarters; the change is 15¢. Put in 4 dimes; the change is 5¢

   How much change will you get? Answers vary.

◆ *Math Journal 1, p. 76*

◆ **Buying Items with Exact Change Only**
(*Math Journal 1,* p. 76)

WHOLE-CLASS ACTIVITY

Ask children to pretend that the exact change light is on and that they want to buy a can of grape juice. On their slates, have them draw the coins they would use. Sample answers: 1 quarter and 2 dimes, 4 dimes and 1 nickel, or 9 nickels Have children share their coin combinations as you list them on the board. Repeat the question for other items from the vending machine as necessary.

◆ **Buying Items without Exact Change**
(*Math Journal 1,* p. 76)

WHOLE-CLASS ACTIVITY

Ask children what happens when the exact change light is off. The buyer can put in more money than the cost of an item, and the machine will give change.

Ask children to pretend that they want to buy a carton of orange juice. Have them suggest various coin combinations they might use to pay with exact change.

Next, ask children to pretend that they don't have the exact change to buy the juice. Have them use their slates to draw the coins and bills they might put into the machine. Then they should draw the change that the machine would give back and write the amount. (See below.) Sample answers: Pay with $1 and receive 35¢ change; pay with 3 quarters and receive 1 dime change; or pay with 7 dimes and receive 1 nickel change.

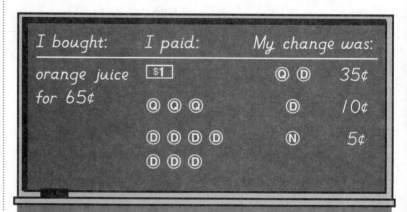

Have children share responses. Repeat the question for other items as necessary.

✦ Making Vending-Machine Purchases
(*Math Journal 1*, pp. 76 and 77)

PARTNER ACTIVITY

In Problems 1 and 3, the exact change light is on; in Problems 2 and 4, it is off.

In Problems 3 and 4, have children work with a partner. Partners take turns buying items from the vending machine and checking each other's work. The first two transactions in each problem are specified on the journal page; other transactions are of children's own choosing.

 Adjusting the Activity If children are having difficulty, encourage them to use coins to model the problems.

ONGOING ASSESSMENT
Problems 1 and 2 summarize the concepts covered in the whole-class portion of the lesson. Use the problems to assess children's understanding on an individual basis.

Buying from a Vending Machine (cont.)

3. The exact change light is on.

You buy:	Draw the coins you put in.
chocolate milk	Sample answers: 1 Ⓠ, 1 Ⓓ, and 1 Ⓝ; 4 Ⓓ; or 8 Ⓝ
yogurt drink	Sample answers: 2 Ⓠ and 2 Ⓓ; 7 Ⓓ; or 5 Ⓓ and 4 Ⓝ
Item chosen will vary.	Coin combinations will vary but should equal the price of the chosen item.

4. The exact change light is off.

You buy:	Draw the coins or the $1 bill you put in.	What is your change?
orange juice	Ⓠ Ⓠ Ⓠ	10 ¢
chocolate milk	$1	60 ¢
Answers vary.		____ ¢
Answers vary.		____ ¢
Answers vary.		____ ¢

✦ *Math Journal 1*, p. 77

---

2 Ongoing Learning & Practice

✦ Playing *Making Change* (*Math Journal 1*, p. 78)

SMALL-GROUP ACTIVITY

Explain the rules and play a demonstration game. Then divide the class into groups of 2 or 3 players each, and have children play the game.

Making Change

Materials
- ☐ 2 nickels, 2 dimes, 2 quarters, and one $1 bill for each player
- ☐ 2 six-sided dice
- ☐ a cup, a small box, or a piece of paper to use as a bank

Players 2 or 3

Directions

1. Each player starts the game with 2 nickels, 2 dimes, 2 quarters, and one $1 bill. Players take turns rolling the dice and finding the total number of dots that are faceup.

2. Players use the chart to find out how much money they must put in the bank. (There is no money in the bank at the beginning of the game.)

Making Change **Chart**

Total for Dice Roll	2	3	4	5	6	7	8	9	10	11	12
Amount to Pay the Bank	10¢	15¢	20¢	25¢	30¢	35¢	40¢	45¢	50¢	55¢	60¢

3. Players use their coins to pay the amount to the bank. Players can get change from the bank.

4. The winner is the first player who doesn't have enough money left to pay the bank.

✦ *Math Journal 1*, p. 78

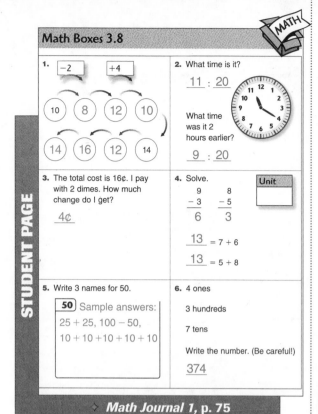

1.

-2   +4

10   8   12   10

14   16   12   14

2. What time is it?

11 : 20

What time was it 2 hours earlier?

9 : 20

3. The total cost is 16¢. I pay with 2 dimes. How much change do I get?

4¢

4. Solve.

Unit

$$\begin{array}{r} 9 \\ -3 \\ \hline 6 \end{array} \qquad \begin{array}{r} 8 \\ -5 \\ \hline 3 \end{array}$$

$$\underline{13} = 7 + 6$$

$$\underline{13} = 5 + 8$$

5. Write 3 names for 50.

50 Sample answers:
25 + 25, 100 − 50,
10 + 10 + 10 + 10 + 10

6. 4 ones

3 hundreds

7 tens

Write the number. (Be careful!)

374

◆ *Math Journal 1,* p. 75

◆ Math Boxes 3.8 (*Math Journal 1,* p. 75)

INDEPENDENT ACTIVITY

Mixed Review This journal page provides opportunities for cumulative review or assessment of concepts and skills.

◆ Home Link 3.8 (*Math Masters,* p. 274)

Home Connection Children determine the amount of change they would receive when more than the required amount was paid.

3 Options for Individualizing

◆ LANGUAGE DIVERSITY Discussing the Meanings of the Word *Change*

SMALL-GROUP DISCUSSION 15–30 min

In English, the word *change* has many meanings. *Change,* when used as a verb, may mean *to exchange, to alter,* or *to transfer.* When *change* is used as a noun, it can refer to *money, an alteration,* or *a substitution.*

You may want to share a few meanings with your children from picture dictionaries.

◆ EXTRA PRACTICE Minute Math

SMALL-GROUP ACTIVITY 30+ min

To offer children more experience working with money, see the following pages in *Minute Math:*

Basic Routines: p. 22

Counting: p. 35

Measurement: pp. 67, 69, and 70

PLANNING AHEAD

Before doing the third Alternative Assessment activity in Lesson 3.9, place stick-on notes over the digital times in the clock booklets that children made in Lesson 3.4.

Counting up to Make Change   Home Link 3.8

Family Note Help your child identify the amount of change that he or she would receive by "counting up" from the price of the item to the amount of money that was used to pay for the item. It may be helpful to act out the problems with your child using real coins and bills.

Please return this Home Link to school tomorrow.

Complete the table.

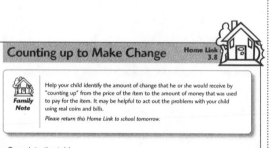

I buy:	It costs:	I pay with:	My change is:
a bag of potato chips	70¢	Q Q Q	5 ¢
a box of crayons	65¢	$1	35 ¢
a pen	59¢	Q Q Q	16 ¢
an apple	45¢	D D D D D	5 ¢
a notebook	73¢	Q Q D D N	2 ¢
a ruler	48¢	$1	52 ¢
Answers vary.			¢
Answers vary.			¢

◆ *Math Masters,* p. 274

3.9 Unit 3 Review and Assessment

OBJECTIVE To review and assess children's progress on the material covered in Unit 3.

1 Assess Progress

learning goals	activities
3a **Developing Goal** Solve Frames-and-Arrows problems having two rules. **(Lesson 3.6)**	❑ Written Assessment, Problems 2 and 3
3b **Developing Goal** Make change. **(Lessons 3.2, 3.7, and 3.8)**	❑ Written Assessment, Problems 4 and 5
3c **Developing Goal** Know more difficult subtraction facts. **(Lesson 3.5)**	❑ Slate Assessment, Problem 9
3d **Developing/Secure Goal** Tell time to 5-minute intervals. **(Lessons 3.3 and 3.4)**	❑ Slate Assessment, Problem 4 ❑ Written Assessment, Problems 6–9
3e **Secure Goal** Identify place value in 2-digit and 3-digit numbers. **(Lessons 3.1 and 3.4)**	❑ Oral Assessment ❑ Slate Assessment, Problems 1–3
3f **Secure Goal** Show Ⓟ, Ⓝ, Ⓓ, and Ⓠ for a given amount. **(Lesson 3.2)**	❑ Written Assessment, Problem 1
3g **Secure Goal** Know all addition facts. **(Lesson 3.5)**	❑ Slate Assessment, Problem 7
3h **Secure Goal** Know easy subtraction facts. **(Lesson 3.5)**	❑ Slate Assessment, Problem 8

materials

- ❑ *Math Journal 1,* p. 78
- ❑ Home Link 3.8
- ❑ Assessment Masters (*Math Masters,* pp. 422 and 423)

- ❑ base-10 blocks: 9 flats, 9 longs, and 9 cubes
- ❑ demonstration clock
- ❑ money amounts per child: 2 nickels, 2 dimes, 2 quarters, and one $1 bill
- ❑ +,− Fact Triangles with sums greater than 10

- ❑ 2 six-sided dice
- ❑ item to use as a bank, such as a cup, small box, or piece of paper
- ❑ stick-on notes
- ❑ clock booklets from Lesson 3.4
- ❑ slate

2 Build Background for Unit 4

summaries

Children practice and maintain skills through Math Boxes and Home Link activities.

materials

- ❑ *Math Journal 1,* p. 79
- ❑ Home Link Masters (*Math Masters,* pp. 275–278)

Each **learning goal** listed above indicates a level of performance that might be expected at this point in the *Everyday Mathematics* K–6 curriculum. For a variety of reasons, the levels indicated may not accurately portray your class's performance.

Getting Started

Math Message

Time to Reflect *Have you ever heard adults ask for change? Whom did they ask? What did they need the change for? Be ready to discuss.* **Goal 3b**

Home Link 3.8 Follow-Up

Review the amount of change for each purchase. Ask children to name combinations of coins that would represent each amount. Some children may want to share with the class the items from the last two rows, which they made up themselves.

1 Assess Progress

◆ Math Message Follow-Up

WHOLE-CLASS ACTIVITY

In this unit, children have discussed change in terms of the money given back when a customer overpays for an item purchased. Use the Math Message question to determine whether children recognize that change can also be seen in terms of an exchange.

Example: A person has 5 dimes, but the parking meter accepts only quarters. He asks a friend for 2 quarters in exchange for the 5 dimes.

◆ Oral and Slate Assessments

SMALL-GROUP ACTIVITY

If the following list of suggested problems is not appropriate for your class's level of performance, adjust the numbers in the problems or adjust the problems themselves to better assess your children's abilities.

NOTE: Many of these assessment suggestions relate to learning goals that have been addressed in previous units. Now is a good time to evaluate children's progress toward those goals.

Oral Assessment Suggestions

Write 2- and 3-digit numbers on the board. Have children read the numbers aloud. If children are ready, extend the activity to 4-digit numbers. Goal 3e

Slate Assessment Suggestions

1. Display sets of base-10 blocks—flats, longs, and cubes. Include some sets with no longs and/or no cubes. Children write the numbers shown. Goal 3e

2. Write 2- and 3-digit numbers on the board. Children write the digits in the hundreds, tens, and ones places. Goal 3e

3. Say 2- and 3-digit numbers. Children write them. Goal 3e

4. Set times on the demonstration clock, such as 11:05, 6:45, 2:55, 1:15, 9:10, and 8:35. Children record the times. Goal 3d

5. Write sets of numbers on the board, such as 4, 7, 9, 11, 15 9; and 1, 4, 7, 11, 12 7. Children identify the middle value for each set.

6. Say a number. Children record the 100-complement of that number. Begin with multiples of 10 and multiples of 25. Extend to multiples of 5 if children are ready.

7. Pose addition facts, such as:

    5 + 9 = ? 14   ? = 3 + 7 10
    8 + 6 = ? 14   ? = 6 + 6 12
    4 + 5 = ? 9   ? = 8 + 1 9
    9 + 2 = ? 11   ? = 9 + 7 16

    Goal 3g

8. Pose easy subtraction facts, such as:

    10 − 6 = ? 4   ? = 7 − 5 2
    7 − 3 = ? 4   ? = 10 − 7 3
    9 − 4 = ? 5   ? = 9 − 2 7
    8 − 5 = ? 3   ? = 8 − 4 4

    Goal 3h

9. Pose more difficult subtraction facts, such as:

    11 − 9 = ? 2   ? = 12 − 6 6
    16 − 7 = ? 9   ? = 18 − 9 9
    13 − 5 = ? 8   ? = 14 − 8 6
    17 − 8 = ? 9   ? = 15 − 6 9

    Goal 3c

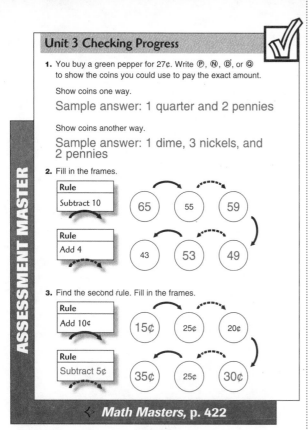

Unit 3 Checking Progress

1. You buy a green pepper for 27¢. Write Ⓟ, Ⓝ, Ⓓ, or Ⓠ to show the coins you could use to pay the exact amount.

Show coins one way.
Sample answer: 1 quarter and 2 pennies

Show coins another way.
Sample answer: 1 dime, 3 nickels, and 2 pennies

2. Fill in the frames.

Rule | Subtract 10
65 55 59

Rule | Add 4
43 53 49

3. Find the second rule. Fill in the frames.

Rule | Add 10¢
15¢ 25¢ 20¢

Rule | Subtract 5¢
35¢ 25¢ 30¢

Math Masters, p. 422

ASSESSMENT MASTER

Unit 3 Checking Progress (cont.)

4. You buy carrot juice for 60¢. You put 3 quarters in the vending machine. How much change should you receive? __15¢__

5. You buy a head of lettuce for 68¢. You pay with a $1 bill. How much change should you receive? __32¢__

6. Draw the hands to show 5:15.

7. Draw the hands to show 9:05.

8. Write the time.
__3__ : __20__

9. Write the time.
__7__ : __50__

Math Masters, p. 423

ASSESSMENT MASTER

◆ **Written Assessment**
(*Math Masters*, pp. 422 and 423)

WHOLE-CLASS ACTIVITY 👥👥👥

Read through the problems with the class. You may want to do examples with the class for some of the problems.

If appropriate, work through problems together. Wait for children to complete a problem before reading the next one.

If your class can work independently, have children work alone or with a partner on this review page. Circulate and assist.

• You buy a green pepper for 27¢. Write ⓅⓃⒹ, or Ⓠ to show the coins you could use to pay the exact amount. Show coins in one way. Show coins in another way. (Problem 1) **Goal 3f**

• Fill in the frames. (Problem 2) **Goal 3a**

• Find the second rule. Fill in the frames. (Problem 3) **Goal 3a**

• You buy carrot juice for 60¢. You put 3 quarters in the vending machine. How much change should you receive? (Problem 4) **Goal 3b**

• You buy a head of lettuce for 68¢. You pay with a $1 bill. How much change should you receive? (Problem 5) **Goal 3b**

• Draw the hands to show 5:15. (Problem 6) **Goal 3d**

• Draw the hands to show 9:05. (Problem 7) **Goal 3d**

• Write the time. (Problems 8 and 9) **Goal 3d**

◆ **ALTERNATIVE ASSESSMENT OPTION**
Use Addition/Subtraction Fact Triangles

INDEPENDENT ACTIVITY

Use Fact Triangles to assess children's knowledge of "harder" addition and subtraction facts and fact families. Consider having children record facts that they still need to practice on a half-sheet of paper. Incorporate these facts into Mental Math and Reflexes sessions.

◆ **ALTERNATIVE ASSESSMENT OPTION**
Play *Making Change* (*Math Journal 1*, p. 78)

INDEPENDENT ACTIVITY

Use this game to assess children's ability to make change. Consider having children record their transactions on a sheet of paper divided into three columns labeled

Amount of Money I Owe the Bank, Amount of Money I Put in the Bank, My Change. Collect papers to assess how children progress. See journal page 78 for game directions.

✦ ALTERNATIVE ASSESSMENT OPTION
Use Clock Booklets

INDEPENDENT ACTIVITY

Use the clock booklets that children made in Lesson 3.4 to assess children's time-telling skills. Use stick-on notes to cover each of the digital notations in the booklets. Ask children to look at the clock face on each page and to record the corresponding time in digital notation. Collect the booklets to assess children's progress.

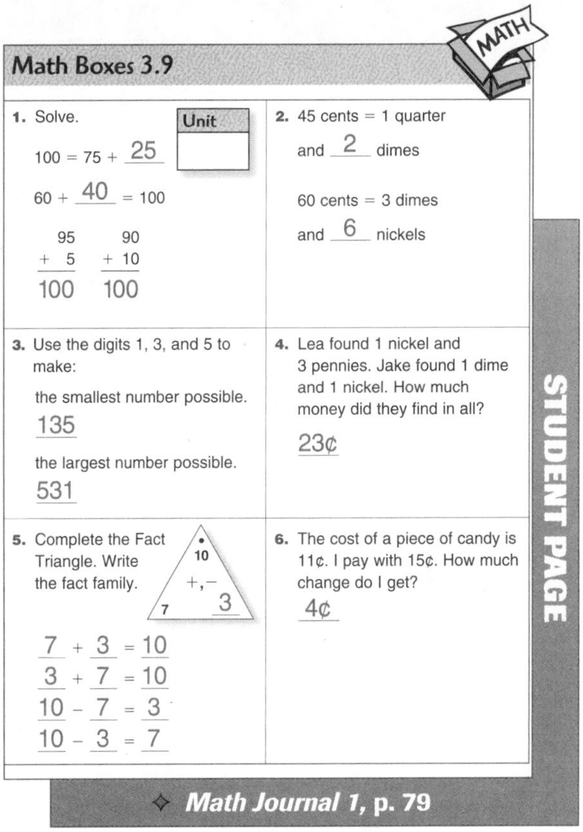

2 Build Background for Unit 4

✦ Math Boxes 3.9 (*Math Journal 1*, p. 79)

INDEPENDENT ACTIVITY

Mixed Review This journal page provides opportunities for cumulative review or assessment of concepts and skills.

✦ Home Link 3.9 (*Math Masters*, pp. 275–278)

Home Connection This Home Link is a four-page newsletter that introduces parents and guardians to Unit 4's topics and terms. The letter also offers ideas for home-based mathematics activities that are supportive of classroom work.

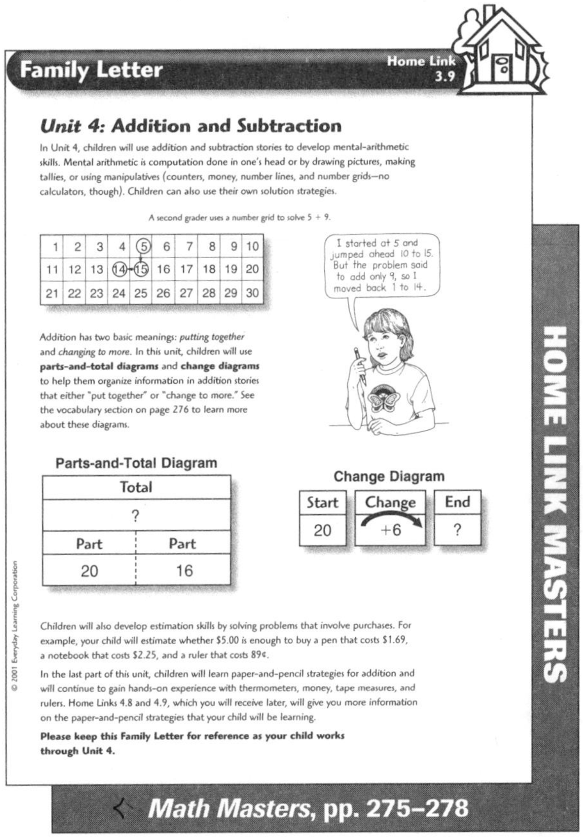

PLANNING AHEAD

In Lesson 4.1, a change diagram will need to be displayed. You might want to draw the diagram on the board with semipermanent chalk. To do so, wet the area where you will draw. Draw the diagram while the board is wet. Wait for it to dry completely. You will be able to erase a number of times without losing the foundation drawing. To remove the drawing completely, wash it with water.

Math Boxes 3.9

1. Solve.

| Unit |
| |

100 = 75 + __25__

60 + __40__ = 100

95	90
+ 5	+ 10
100	100

2. 45 cents = 1 quarter
and __2__ dimes

60 cents = 3 dimes
and __6__ nickels

3. Use the digits 1, 3, and 5 to make:

the smallest number possible.
__135__

the largest number possible.
__531__

4. Lea found 1 nickel and 3 pennies. Jake found 1 dime and 1 nickel. How much money did they find in all?

__23¢__

5. Complete the Fact Triangle. Write the fact family.

(triangle: 10 at top, +,− center, 7 and 3 at bottom)

__7__ + __3__ = __10__
__3__ + __7__ = __10__
__10__ − __7__ = __3__
__10__ − __3__ = __7__

6. The cost of a piece of candy is 11¢. I pay with 15¢. How much change do I get?

__4¢__

✦ *Math Journal 1, p. 79*

Family Letter

Home Link 3.9

Unit 4: Addition and Subtraction

In Unit 4, children will use addition and subtraction stories to develop mental-arithmetic skills. Mental arithmetic is computation done in one's head or by drawing pictures, making tallies, or using manipulatives (counters, money, number lines, and number grids—no calculators, though). Children can also use their own solution strategies.

A second grader uses a number grid to solve 5 + 9.

1	2	3	4	⑤	6	7	8	9	10
11	12	13	⑭–⑮	16	17	18	19	20
21	22	23	24	25	26	27	28	29	30

I started at 5 and jumped ahead 10 to 15. But the problem said to add only 9, so I moved back 1 to 14.

Addition has two basic meanings: *putting together* and *changing to more.* In this unit, children will use **parts-and-total diagrams** and **change diagrams** to help them organize information in addition stories that either "put together" or "change to more." See the vocabulary section on page 276 to learn more about these diagrams.

Parts-and-Total Diagram

Total	
?	
Part	Part
20	16

Change Diagram

Start	Change	End
20	+6	?

Children will also develop estimation skills by solving problems that involve purchases. For example, your child will estimate whether $5.00 is enough to buy a pen that costs $1.69, a notebook that costs $2.25, and a ruler that costs 89¢.

In the last part of this unit, children will learn paper-and-pencil strategies for addition and will continue to gain hands-on experience with thermometers, money, tape measures, and rulers. Home Links 4.8 and 4.9, which you will receive later, will give you more information on the paper-and-pencil strategies that your child will be learning.

Please keep this Family Letter for reference as your child works through Unit 4.

‹ *Math Masters, pp. 275–278*

Unit **4**
Addition and Subtraction

overview

In Unit 4, addition and subtraction number stories are used as a vehicle for developing mental arithmetic skills. The unit ends with work on pencil-and-paper addition strategies.

Mental arithmetic, as defined in *Everyday Mathematics,* does not require all computations to be done in one's head. Children may draw pictures and use other concrete aids such as number lines and grids, if necessary—but not calculators. What is most important is that children devise their own solution strategies. They should be encouraged to experiment with various approaches to solving computational problems.

Sharing solutions is important. By putting their thoughts into words, children are given the opportunity to evaluate their own work. By trying to understand other people's strategies, children strengthen their understanding of the processes involved and obtain valuable input for refining their own strategies.

contents

UNIT

4

learning goals
in perspective

learning goals	links to the past	links to the future
4a **Developing Goal** Devise and use strategies for finding sums of 2-digit numbers. **(Lessons 4.1 and 4.6–4.9)**	In Kindergarten and first grade, children found ways to add smaller numbers. In earlier units of second grade, children worked with single-digit addition. *(Related Grade 2 lessons: 1.4, 1.13, 2.1–2.5, 2.10)*	In Unit 6, children will work with three or more addends. In third grade, they will add larger numbers. *(Related Grade 2 lessons: 6.1, 6.4, 7.2, 7.4, 11.1)*
4b **Developing Goal** Devise and use strategies for finding differences of 2-digit numbers. **(Lesson 4.4)**	In Kindergarten and first grade, children found ways to subtract smaller numbers. In earlier units of second grade, children worked with single-digit subtraction. *(Related Grade 2 lessons: 2.6, 2.8, 2.10–2.13)*	In Unit 6, children will solve comparison number stories and learn the trade-first subtraction algorithm. In third grade they will subtract larger numbers. *(Related Grade 2 lessons: 6.2, 6.4, 6.6, 7.3, 11.2)*
4c **Developing Goal** Estimate approximate costs and sums. **(Lessons 4.5 and 4.8)**	Children begin to work with estimates in first grade by estimating how many pattern blocks will fill an area and by estimating the lengths of objects.	Estimation and mental arithmetic are found throughout *Everyday Mathematics.* In Unit 10, children will do some further work with estimating costs. *(Related Grade 2 lessons: 10.5, 10.6)*
4d **Developing Goal** Read °F on a thermometer. **(Lessons 4.3 and 4.4)**	In both Kindergarten and first grade children recorded daily temperatures and became familiar with the Celsius and Fahrenheit scales.	Beyond second grade, children will use temperature as a context for exploring negative numbers.
4e **Secure Goal** Add and subtract multiples of 10. **(Lessons 4.1–4.3 and 4.6–4.9)**	Children began counting by 10s in Kindergarten. Previous experiences with number grids will also contribute to success with this goal. *(Related Grade 2 lessons: 1.4, 1.6, 1.8, 1.9, 1.11, 1.13, 2.1–2.6, 3.1, 3.4)*	In Unit 7, children will use counting patterns to help with mental arithmetic. *(Related Grade 2 lessons: 6.5, 7.1–7.4)*

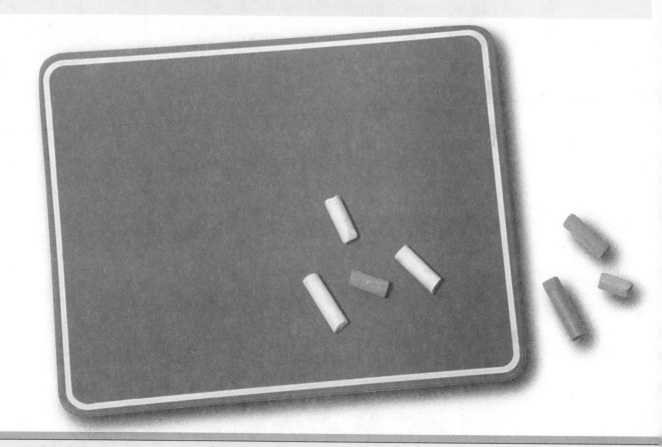

assessment
ongoing • product • periodic

☑ Informal Assessment

Math Boxes These *Math Journal* pages provide opportunities for cumulative review or assessment of concepts and skills.

Ongoing Assessment: Kid Watching Use the Ongoing Assessment suggestions in the following lessons to make quick, on-the-spot observations about children's understanding of:
• Operations and Computation **(Lessons 4.1, 4.6, 4.8, and 4.9)**
• Measurement and Reference Frames **(Lesson 4.3)**

Portfolio Ideas Samples of children's work may be obtained from the following assignments:
• Making Coin-Stamp Booklets **(Lesson 4.3)**
• Exploring Pattern-Block Designs **(Lesson 4.9)**

☑ Unit 4 Review and Assessment

Math Message Use the question in Lesson 4.10 to assess children's progress toward the following learning goal: **Goal 4d**

Slate Assessments Use the slate assessments during Lesson 4.10 to assess children's progress toward the following learning goals: **Goals 4a, 4b, 4c, and 4e**

Written Assessment Use a written review during Lesson 4.10 to assess children's progress toward the following learning goals: **Goals 4a, 4b, and 4d**

Performance/Group Assessment Use a small-group activity in Lesson 4.10 to assess children's progress toward the following learning goal: **Goal 4a**

assessmenthandbook

For more information on how to use different types of assessment in Unit 4, see the Assessment Overview on pages 50–52 in the *Assessment Handbook*. The following Assessment Masters can be found in the *Math Masters* book:

• Unit 4 Checking Progress, pp. 424 and 425
• Unit 4 Class Checklist, p. 454
• Unit 4 Individual Profile of Progress, p. 455
• Class Progress Indicator, p. 488
• Math Logs, pp. 493–495
• Self-Assessment Forms, pp. 496 and 497
• Interest Inventory, pp. 491 and 492

problemsolving

A process of modeling everyday situations using tools from mathematics

Encourage children to use a variety of strategies when attacking a given problem—and to explain those strategies. *Strategies children might use in this unit:*

- Using a diagram
- Using information from a table or picture
- Writing a number model
- Using estimation
- Acting out the problem

Four Problem-Solving
REPRESENTATIONS

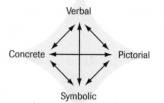

Verbal

Concrete — Pictorial

Symbolic

Lessons that teach *through* problem solving, not just *about* problem solving

Lesson	Activity	Lesson	Activity
4.1	Solving change-to-more problems involving fish weights	4.5	Estimating to solve money problems
4.2	Solving parts-and-total problems about buying items at a snack bar	4.6	Solving problems involving shopping and making change
4.4	Solving problems involving temperature changes	4.9	Making pattern-block designs to see that there are many ways to solve a problem

For more information about problem solving in *Everyday Mathematics,* see the *Teacher's Reference Manual,* pp. 197–208.

cross-curricularlinks

science

- Review the Fahrenheit scale and introduce the Celsius scale. Children then use thermometers to learn how to measure degrees in Fahrenheit and Celsius.
(Lesson 4.3)

literature

- Read *26 Letters and 99 Cents* to encourage children to use different ways of showing the same value.
(Lesson 4.3)

- Read *A Cloak for the Dreamer,* a book about shapes and tiling.
(Lesson 4.7)

meeting
INDIVIDUAL needs

◆ RETEACHING

The following features provide additional instructional support:

Adjusting the Activity

- **Lesson 4.1, Part 1**
- **Lesson 4.3, Part 1**
- **Lesson 4.4, Part 1**
- **Lesson 4.5, Part 1**
- **Lesson 4.6, Part 1**
- **Lesson 4.7, Part 1**
- **Lesson 4.8, Part 1**

Options for Individualizing

- **Lesson 4.1** Finding Distances on a Number Grid
- **Lesson 4.2** Playing *Two-Fisted Penny Addition*
- **Lesson 4.2** Using Coins to Act Out Solutions
- **Lesson 4.5** Mnemonic Devices for < and >
- **Lesson 4.6** Adding Multiples of 10
- **Lesson 4.8** Reviewing Place-Value Concepts

◆ ENRICHMENT

The following features suggest enrichment and extension activities:

Adjusting the Activity

- **Lesson 4.2, Part 1**
- **Lesson 4.3, Part 1**
- **Lesson 4.5, Part 1**
- **Lesson 4.6, Part 1**
- **Lesson 4.7, Part 1**
- **Lesson 4.8, Part 1**
- **Lesson 4.9, Part 1**

Options for Individualizing

- **Lesson 4.4** Identifying Situations as Change to More or Change to Less
- **Lesson 4.5** Using Estimation to Compare Sums of Weights
- **Lesson 4.9** Exploring Pattern-Block Designs

◆ LANGUAGE DIVERSITY

The following feature suggests ways to support children who are acquiring proficiency in English:

Adjusting the Activity

- **Lesson 4.3, Part 1**

Options for Individualizing

- **Lesson 4.7** Demonstrating Inch and Centimeter Scales

◆ MULTIAGE CLASSROOM

The following chart lists related lessons from Grades 1 and 3 that can help you meet your instructional needs:

Grade 1	2.11 5.6 9.4	1.13 5.9	1.12 7.2 10.6	1.12 4.1 10.6	8.4 10.3 10.4	8.1– 8.5 10.3	4.2– 4.7 7.1	2.11 9.2 9.4	5.8 9.2
Grade 2	4.1	4.2	4.3	4.4	4.5	4.6	4.7	4.8	4.9
Grade 3	1.10 2.5 2.9	1.10 2.4 2.9	6.4– 6.6 11.9	11.9	1.10 7.7 9.5	1.10 7.7 9.5	3.1– 3.7	2.7 2.9 5.5	2.7 2.9 5.5

materials

lesson	math masters pages	manipulative kit items	other items
4.1	Home Link Masters, pp. 279 and 280 Teaching Master, p. 60 transparency of Teaching Master, p. 59 *See* **Advance Preparation, p. 224**	pan balance (optional)	2 paper towels; water (optional) penny or other small object
4.2	Home Link Masters, pp. 281 and 282 Teaching Masters, pp. 61 and 62; and p. 63 (optional) transparency of Teaching Master, p. 61 *See* **Advance Preparation, p. 230**		calculator; paper clips coins
4.3	Home Link Master, p. 283 Teaching Masters, pp. 62–65 *See* **Advance Preparation, p. 235**	stamp pad rubber stamps of coins slate attribute blocks Class Thermometer Poster	paper clips calculator thermometer cups of hot and cold water *See* **Advance Preparation, p. 235**
4.4	Home Link Masters, pp. 284 and 285 Teaching Master, p. 66	Class Thermometer Poster slate	index card or ruler (optional)
4.5	Home Link Master, p. 286 transparency of Home Link Masters, pp. 284 and 285 (optional) *See* **Advance Preparation, p. 247**		
4.6	Home Link Master, p. 287 Teaching Masters, pp. 61, 62, and 67 *See* **Advance Preparation, p. 252**	base-10 blocks	bills and coins paper clip calculator
4.7	Home Link Master, p. 288 Teaching Masters, pp. 61 and 68–70 *See* **Advance Preparation, p. 257**	pattern blocks Pattern-Block Template number cards slate attribute blocks tape measure; yardstick	bills and coins (optional) calculator ruler marked in cm and in. objects with lengths of 1 cm poster showing in. and cm *A Cloak for the Dreamer* by Aileen Friedman
4.8	Home Link Masters, pp. 289 and 290 Teaching Masters, pp. 35 and 71	base-10 blocks number cards	
4.9	Home Link Master, p. 291 Teaching Masters, pp. 72 and 73	pattern blocks Pattern-Block Template base-10 blocks overhead base-10 blocks (optional)	
4.10	Home Link Masters, pp. 292–295 Teaching Masters, pp. 62, 63, and 67 Assessment Masters, pp. 424 and 425	slate	calculator paper clip bills (optional)

planning tips

Pacing

Pacing depends on a number of factors, such as children's individual needs and how long your school has been using *Everyday Mathematics*. At the beginning of Unit 4, review your Content by Strand Poster to help you set a monthly pace.

OCTOBER	NOVEMBER	DECEMBER

← MOST CLASSROOMS →

Using the Projects

Use Project 5 during Unit 4, Unit 6, or Unit 8 to experiment with paper folding, creating snowflakes that represent real 6-sided water crystals. The Projects can be found at the back of this book.

Home Communication

Share Home Links 4.1–4.9 with families to help them understand the content and procedures in this unit. At the end of the unit, use Home Link 4.10 to introduce Unit 5. Supplemental information can be found in the *Home Connection Handbook*.

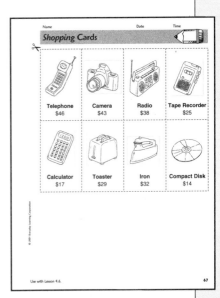

NCTM Standards

Standard	1	2	3	4	5	6	7	8	9	10
Unit 4 Lessons	1, 2, 4–6, 8, 9	1, 2, 4, 8	3, 7	2–7		1–9	1–9	1–9	1–9	1–9

Content Standards
1   Number and Operation
2   Patterns, Functions, and Algebra
3   Geometry and Spatial Sense
4   Measurement
5   Data Analysis, Statistics, and Probability

Process Standards
6   Problem Solving
7   Reasoning and Proof
8   Communication
9   Connections
10   Representations

PRACTICE through Games

Everyday Mathematics uses games to help children develop good fact power and other math skills.

- Practice addition of 2-digit or other size numbers in *Addition Spin* **(Lessons 4.2, 4.3, 4.6, and 4.10)**
- Practice combining parts to obtain a whole in *Two-Fisted Penny Addition* **(Lessons 4.2)**

The notes below highlight the major content ideas presented in Unit 4. These notes may help you establish instructional priorities.

Mental Arithmetic (Lesson 4.1 and following)

The following routine for developing mental arithmetic skills is introduced in Lesson 4.1 with the help of a poster that displays the lengths and weights of fish (*Math Journal 1,* page 80).

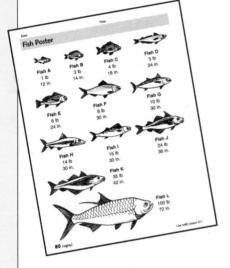

Solving Number Stories

1. Children make up problems for the class to solve.

2. With a partner or individually, children devise solution strategies to solve the problems.

3. Children share their strategies. As children discuss these strategies, record them on the board by writing a label in the unit box, drawing the appropriate addition or subtraction diagram (see below), and writing a number model.

It is suggested that you follow these steps throughout the unit.

Encourage children to write number models. Some exercises will require them to do so.

Addition has two basic meanings: putting together and changing to more. Change stories are discussed in Lessons 4.1 and 4.4. In Lessons 4.2 and 4.6, the focus is on parts-and-total stories, in which two or more parts are put together (added) to find a total.

Two diagrams are introduced for organizing the information in number stories—the **change diagram** and the **parts-and-total diagram.** Children are not expected to draw the diagrams themselves, but children should be able to fill in the diagrams that are provided in the journal.

In a change number story there is a starting quantity. This quantity is increased (or decreased), so that the ending quantity is more (or less) than the starting quantity. Lesson 4.1 focuses on change-to-more number stories, in which the starting quantity is increased. Change-to-less number stories are discussed in Lesson 4.4.

Example: Change-to-more number story

Sara had $40. She earned $20 more mowing lawns. How much money did she have then?

The starting quantity and the change are known. The end quantity is to be found.

The change diagram in the margin displays the information in this story.

$

Unit box

Start	Change	End
40	+20	?

Change diagram

In a parts-and-total number story, two or more quantities (parts) are combined to form a total quantity.

Example: Parts-and-total number story

Twelve fourth graders and 23 third graders are on a bus. How many children in all are on the bus?

The parts are known. The total is to be found.

The parts-and-total diagram in the margin displays the information in this story.

Once the known quantities and a question mark for the unknown quantity are entered in a diagram, it becomes easy to write a number model and to decide which operation is needed to solve the problem.

Don't expect children to be experts at adding and subtracting 2-digit numbers. It is less important that they solve a great many problems than it is for them to think their way through each problem and share their strategies. There will be many opportunities throughout the year to refine mental arithmetic skills.

To practice addition of multidigit numbers, children can play different versions of *Addition Spin*. These games may be played over and over, and customized to your class's level of proficiency.

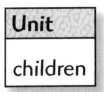

Unit
children

Total	
?	
Part	**Part**
12	23

Real-Life Themes (Lesson 4.3 and following)

In addition to the work with fish weights, children solve many problems that involve purchases: food in a snack bar, school supplies, and so on.

Science Link Temperature is a major theme of this unit. The Fahrenheit scale is reviewed, and the Celsius scale is introduced. Children read temperatures shown on a thermometer. They also solve a variety of problems involving temperature changes.

You may want to give children some additional background information on thermometers.

▷ The invention of the thermometer is usually credited to Galileo Galilei (1564–1642).

▷ German physicist Daniel Gabriel Fahrenheit (1686–1736) invented several accurate thermometers containing mercury and alcohol. He developed the Fahrenheit temperature scale between 1700 and 1730.

The Class Thermometer shows Fahrenheit and Celsius scales.

▷ The Celsius scale was invented in 1742 by Swedish astronomer Anders Celsius (1701–1744). At first he designated 0 degrees as the boiling point of water and 100 degrees as the freezing point of water. Later the scale was reversed. The scale was called *centigrade* until officially renamed for Celsius in 1948.

▷ Temperature scales are made by choosing a cold point and a hot point, and then making an equal number of gradations between them.

▷ Pure water freezes at 32 degrees Fahrenheit, but 0 degrees Fahrenheit has a special significance as well—it is the freezing point of a specific mixture of salt and water.

▷ Fahrenheit made a mistake when he invented his temperature scale. He wanted 100 degrees to be the normal body temperature. He mistakenly used the body temperature of a cow instead of a human. A cow's normal body temperature is about 100°F. A human's normal body temperature is slightly less, about 98.6°F.

Pencil-and-Paper Addition Strategies (Lessons 4.8 and 4.9)

Children are encouraged to develop their own strategies for addition. Children's strategies usually are of three major types:

▷ counting on

▷ combining groups (ones, tens, etc.) separately

▷ adjusting and compensating

Examples of these three methods are illustrated in Lesson 4.8.

The partial-sums addition algorithm is the topic of Lesson 4.8. The initial demonstration utilizes base-10 blocks, followed by the pencil-and-paper method.

Example: 45 + 22

1. Add the tens. 4 tens + 2 tens = 6 tens, or 60. Write 60 below the line.

2. Add the ones. 5 ones + 2 ones = 7 ones, or 7. Write 7 below 60.

3. Add the partial sums. Draw a second line beneath the 60 and 7. Write 67 beneath this line.

$$
\begin{array}{r}
45 \\
+\ 22 \\
\hline
60 \\
+\ \ 7 \\
\hline
67
\end{array}
$$

Explorations: Temperature, Money, and Shapes (Lesson 4.3)

In Lesson 4.3, Exploration A provides hands-on experience with thermometers. In Exploration B, children reinforce their knowledge of money by making booklets that show sets of coins and their values. In Exploration C, children sort attribute blocks by shape, color, and size.

Explorations: Length, Area, and Attributes (Lesson 4.7)

In Lesson 4.7, Explorations D and E provide hands-on measuring experiences using tape measures and different objects to tile surfaces. In Exploration F, children sort attribute blocks according to a rule.

Review and Assessment (Lesson 4.10)

Besides assessing children's progress on the unit goals, which focus on addition, subtraction, and temperature, this lesson provides an opportunity to check children's estimation and time-telling skills.

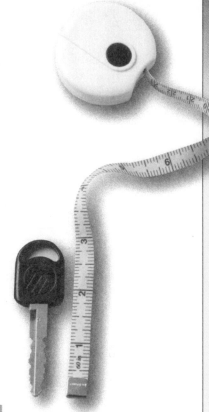

Use a tape measure to measure length.

For **additional information** on the following topics, see the *Teacher's Reference Manual:*

- addition and subtraction
- algorithm invention
- area
- computational algorithms
- groups and partnerships
- length
- mathematical modeling
- mental arithmetic
- money
- number models and number sentences
- number stories
- problem representations
- standard and alternative algorithms
- teaching problem solving
- temperature

4.1 Change-to-More Number Stories

OBJECTIVE To solve change-to-more number stories.

summaries	materials

1 Teaching the Lesson

Children are introduced to the change diagram for recording known and missing information in change-to-more number stories. They then solve change-to-more number stories, displaying the information in change diagrams. [Operations and Computation]

- □ *Math Journal 1*, pp. 80–82
- □ Teaching Master transparency (*Math Masters*, p. 59; optional)
- □ 2 paper towels; pan balance; water (optional)

***See* Advance Preparation**

2 Ongoing Learning & Practice

Children find distances (jumps) between numbers on a number line. [Patterns, Functions, and Algebra]

Children practice and maintain skills through Math Boxes and Home Link activities.

- □ *Math Journal 1*, pp. 83 and 84
- □ Home Link Masters (*Math Masters*, pp. 279 and 280)
- □ penny or other small object

3 Options for Individualizing

Reteaching Children find distances between numbers on a number grid. [Patterns, Functions, and Algebra]

Extra Practice Children add and subtract using multiples of 10. [Operations and Computation; Patterns, Functions, and Algebra]

- □ Teaching Master (*Math Masters*, p. 60)
- □ penny or other small object
- □ *Minute Math®*, pp. 24 and 42

Additional Information

Background Information Read about the change diagram on page 225 of this book.

Advance Preparation Before you begin this lesson, decide how you will display a change diagram:

▷ Make an overhead transparency of *Math Masters,* page 59.

▷ Draw a change diagram on the board with semipermanent chalk. (See Planning Ahead on page 211.)

▷ Draw and erase change diagrams on the board as needed.

Vocabulary • change-to-more number story • change diagram • mental arithmetic

---

Getting Started

Mental Math and Reflexes

Pose problems, such as the following:

30 + 40 = ? 70	? = 50 − 30 20	20 + 60 = ? 80	80 − 70 = ? 10
20 + 8 = ? 28	96 − 6 = ? 90	? = 45 − 20 25	87 − 40 = ? 47

Math Message

*Which weighs more—
a dry paper towel or a wet paper
towel? Why?*

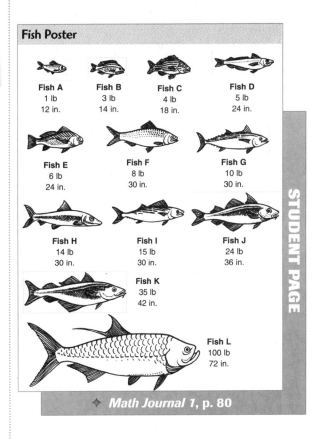

Fish Poster

Fish A
1 lb
12 in.

Fish B
3 lb
14 in.

Fish C
4 lb
18 in.

Fish D
5 lb
24 in.

Fish E
6 lb
24 in.

Fish F
8 lb
30 in.

Fish G
10 lb
30 in.

Fish H
14 lb
30 in.

Fish I
15 lb
30 in.

Fish J
24 lb
36 in.

Fish K
35 lb
42 in.

Fish L
100 lb
72 in.

◆ *Math Journal 1, p. 80*

1 Teaching the Lesson

◆ Math Message Follow-Up

WHOLE-CLASS ACTIVITY

The weight of the paper towel increases, or changes to more, when it absorbs liquid. You may wish to do the following demonstration with the class. Fold or wad two paper towels of the same size, and place one on each side of a pan balance. The pans will be in balance. Then soak one of the towels in water, wring it out, and put it back in the empty pan. Ask children to explain how they know which towel is heavier. Sample answer: The wet towel is heavier because that pan is lower.

◆ Introducing the Change Diagram
(*Math Journal 1,* p. 80)

WHOLE-CLASS DISCUSSION

In a change number story, there is a starting quantity. This quantity is increased (or decreased) so that the ending quantity is more (or less) than the starting quantity. The focus in this lesson is on change-to-more number stories, in which the starting quantity is increased. Change-to-less number stories will be discussed in Lesson 4.4.

Have children turn to the Fish Poster on journal page 80. Make up a **change-to-more number story** based on the Fish Poster. *For example:*

▷ Fish K weighs 35 pounds. It swallows Fish D, which weighs 5 pounds. How much does Fish K weigh now?

Draw a unit box with the label "pounds." Display a **change diagram** (see Planning Ahead on page 211) and discuss it as you fill in the numbers. Ask such questions as the following:

• Which label goes in the unit box? pounds

• Do we know Fish K's weight before it swallowed Fish D? Yes, 35 pounds

Unit

pounds

Start | Change | End

$$35 + 5 = 40$$

NOTE: Children are not expected to draw change diagrams at this time. They are, however, expected to use a given change diagram to record the known information and identify the missing information with a question mark.

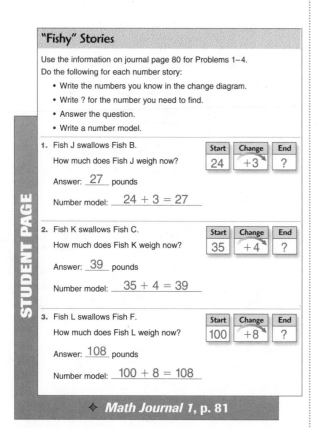

Write 35 in the Start box.

• What change occurred? Fish K gained 5 pounds. Is this a change to more or to less? To more

Write +5 in the Change box. Then write ? in the End box.

• How do we find Fish K's weight after it has swallowed Fish D? Add 35 + 5. What is Fish K's final weight? 40 pounds

• What number model can we write for this number story? 35 + 5 = 40

Together with the children, make up other change-to-more number stories using the Fish Poster. Emphasize stories for which Start and Change are known and End is to be found. But include some stories for which Start or Change is not known and must be found. *Examples:*

▷ Fish J swallowed another fish. Fish J now weighs 29 pounds. How much does the fish weigh that Fish J swallowed? 24 + ? = 29; 5 pounds Which fish did Fish J swallow? Fish D

▷ A fish that swallowed Fish A now weighs 36 pounds. How much did the fish weigh before it swallowed Fish A? ? + 1 = 36; 35 pounds

Model children's solutions on the board by doing the following:

Step 1

Fill in a change diagram for each problem. Write in the numbers that are known, and write a ? for the number that is to be found.

Step 2

Describe each solution using children's language and procedures as much as possible.

Step 3

Write a number model that summarizes the problem.

◆ **Solving Change-to-More Number Stories**
(*Math Journal 1,* pp. 81 and 82)

PARTNER ACTIVITY 👥

Partners complete the problems on journal pages 81 and 82. Circulate and offer help where needed. Check that children are recording the known information in the correct boxes in the change diagram, writing ? for the unknown number, and writing a number model. Encourage children to use **mental arithmetic** to obtain answers.

Adjusting the Activity If children are having difficulty filling in the change diagrams in Problems 1–4 on journal pages 81 and 82, suggest that they record the weight of each fish above its name in the problem. Having information directly on the journal page may make it easier for children to fill in the change diagram.

Bring the class together and have partners share their solution strategies.

✓ **ONGOING ASSESSMENT**
· Do children use efficient mental arithmetic strategies? Can they explain their strategies?
· Do children work well with their partners? Do they accept ideas suggested by their partners? Can they tell you something they learned from their partners?

NOTE: Lesson commentaries often suggest that children share solution strategies, and sometimes possible strategies are described. This does not mean, however, that children must be comfortable with every strategy. Children having difficulty solving a problem will benefit from hearing the strategies that others have used. Assist those children in choosing a strategy that will work best for them.

Ongoing Learning & Practice

✦Finding Distances on a Number Line
(*Math Journal 1*, p. 83)

INDEPENDENT ACTIVITY

Use the example problem to demonstrate how children should count moves (jumps) in traveling from one number to another. Many children will find that it is easier to count moves if they use a penny or another small object to act out the jumps from the starting number to the ending number.

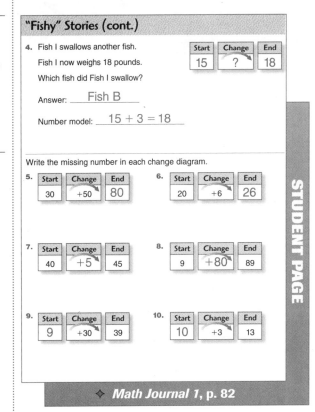

✦ *Math Journal 1*, p. 82

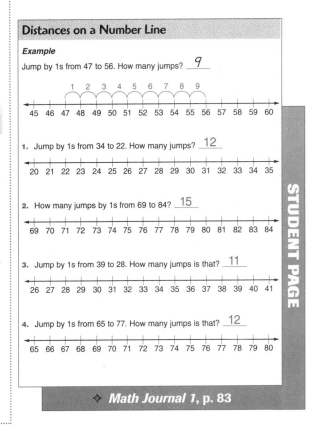

✦ *Math Journal 1*, p. 83

Math Boxes 4.1

1. Solve.

Unit

$70 + \underline{30} = 100$

$100 = 20 + 30 + \underline{50}$

$\underline{100} = 50 + 40 + 10$

$100 = \underline{30} + 10 + 60$

2. Write the number. Be careful!

5 ones

6 hundreds

3 tens

$\underline{635}$

3. The cost is 18¢. I pay with a quarter. How much change do I get?

$\underline{7¢}$

4. Solve.

Unit

$18 = 8 + \underline{10}$

$17 = 8 + \underline{9}$

$16 = 8 + \underline{8}$

$15 = 8 + \underline{7}$

5. Use the digits 3, 1, and 5.

Write the smallest possible number. $\underline{135}$

Write the largest possible number. $\underline{531}$

6. Fill in the missing numbers.

88	89	
98	99	100
108	109	110

◆ *Math Journal 1, p. 84*

STUDENT PAGE

INDEPENDENT ACTIVITY

Mixed Review This journal page provides opportunities for cumulative review or assessment of concepts and skills.

◆ Home Link 4.1 (*Math Masters,* pp. 279 and 280)

Home Connection Children solve change-to-more number stories. They fill in a change diagram and write a number model for each problem. Children also solve problems in which they:

- add and subtract multiples of 10.
- add a 1-digit number to a multiple of 10.
- subtract a 1-digit number from a 2-digit number where the answer is a multiple of 10.

Change Number Stories

Home Link 4.1

Family Note

Your child has learned about a device called a "change diagram," and it is shown in the example below. Diagrams like this can help your child organize the information in a problem. When the information is organized, it is easier to decide which operation $(+, -, \times, \div)$ to use to solve the problem. Change diagrams are used to represent problems in which a starting quantity is increased or decreased. For the number stories on this Home Link, the starting quantity is always increased.

*Please return the **second page** of this Home Link to school tomorrow.*

Do the following for each number story on the next page:

- Write the numbers you know in the change diagram.
- Write ? for the number you need to find.
- Answer the question.
- Write a number model.

Example: Twenty-five children are riding on a bus.
At the next stop, 5 more children get on.
How many children are on the bus now?

Start	Change	End
25	+5	?

The starting number of children has been increased.

Answer: There are 30 children on the bus now.

Possible number model: 25 + 5 = 30

HOME LINK MASTER

◆ *Math Masters, p. 279*

Change Number Stories (cont.)

Home Link 4.1

1. Becky ate 11 grapes. Later in the day she ate 7 more grapes. How many grapes did she eat in all? $\underline{18}$ grapes

Start	Change	End
11	+7	?

Number model:

$11 + 7 = 18$

2. Bob has 30 baseball cards. He buys 8 more. How many baseball cards does Bob have now? $\underline{38}$ cards

Start	Change	End
30	+8	?

Number model:

$30 + 8 = 38$

3. A large fish weighs 42 pounds. A small fish weighs 10 pounds. The large fish swallows the small fish. How much does the large fish weigh now? $\underline{52}$ pounds

Start	Change	End
42	+10	?

Number model:

$42 + 10 = 52$

Add or subtract.

4. $20 + 7 = \underline{27}$

5. $\underline{80} = 40 + 40$

6. $3 + 80 = \underline{83}$

7. $30 - 20 = \underline{10}$

8. $47 - 30 = \underline{17}$

9. $50 + 20 = \underline{70}$

10. $\underline{30} = 90 - 60$

11. $86 - 20 = \underline{66}$

12. $\underline{80} = 83 - 3$

HOME LINK MASTER

◆ *Math Masters, p. 280*

Options for Individualizing

◆ RETEACHING Finding Distances on a Number Grid (*Math Masters,* p. 60)

INDEPENDENT ACTIVITY   **5–15 min**

Many children will find that it is easier to find distances on a number grid if they use a penny or another small object to act out the spaces moved from the starting number to the ending number. Some children will count every space moved from the starting number to the ending number. Encourage children to find the distances between numbers by moving vertically among the rows counting by 10s and moving horizontally counting by 1s.

51	52	53	54	55	56	57	58	59	60
61	62	63	64	65	66	67	68	69	70
71	72	73	74	75	76	77	78	79	80
81	82	83	84	85	86	87	88	89	90
91	92	93	94	95	96	97	98	99	100
101	102	103	104	105	106	107	108	109	110

Using a number grid to find the distance from 52 to 77

◆ EXTRA PRACTICE Minute Math

SMALL-GROUP ACTIVITY   **5–15 min**

To offer children more experience adding and subtracting with multiples of 10, see the following pages in *Minute Math:*

Basic Routines: p. 24

Operations: p. 42

PLANNING AHEAD

You may wish to obtain a copy of the book *26 Letters and 99 Cents* by Tana Hoban (Greenwillow Books, 1987). This book can be used as an additional resource for Exploration B of Lesson 4.3.

Distances on a Number Grid

Use the number grid below. Find the distance from the first number to the second. Start at the first number and count the number of spaces moved to reach the second number.

1. 53 and 58 __5__   2. 64 and 56 __8__
3. 69 and 99 __30__   4. 83 and 63 __20__
5. 77 and 92 __15__   6. 93 and 71 __22__
7. 84 and 104 __20__   8. 106 and 88 __18__
9. 94 and 99 __5__   10. 85 and 76 __9__
11. 58 and 108 __50__   12. 107 and 57 __50__
13. 61 and 78 __17__   14. 72 and 53 __19__
15. 52 and 100 __48__   16. 100 and 78 __22__

51	52	53	54	55	56	57	58	59	60
61	62	63	64	65	66	67	68	69	70
71	72	73	74	75	76	77	78	79	80
81	82	83	84	85	86	87	88	89	90
91	92	93	94	95	96	97	98	99	100
101	102	103	104	105	106	107	108	109	110

◆ *Math Masters,* p. 60

TEACHING MASTER

4.2 Parts-and-Total Number Stories

OBJECTIVE To solve parts-and-total number stories.

summaries

materials

1 Teaching the Lesson

Children are introduced to the parts-and-total diagram for recording known and missing information in number stories that involve combining quantities (parts) to find a total. Children solve parts-and-total number stories, displaying information in parts-and-total diagrams. [Operations and Computation]

- ☐ *Math Journal 1*, p. 85
- ☐ Home Link 4.1
- ☐ Teaching Master transparency (*Math Masters*, p. 61; optional)

See **Advance Preparation**

2 Ongoing Learning & Practice

Children practice adding numbers that are multiples of 5 by playing the *Addition Spin* game. [Operations and Computation]

Children practice and maintain skills through Math Boxes and Home Link activities.

- ☐ *Math Journal 1*, pp. 86 and 87
- ☐ Home Link Master (*Math Masters*, pp. 281 and 282)
- ☐ Teaching Masters (*Math Masters*, p. 62 per partnership; and p. 63, optional)
- ☐ per partnership: calculator and paper clip

3 Options for Individualizing

Reteaching Children combine parts to obtain a total by playing *Two-Fisted Penny Addition*. [Numeration; Operations and Computation]

Reteaching Children act out solutions to number stories by using coins and parts-and-total diagrams. [Operations and Computation; Measurement and Reference Frames]

- ☐ *Math Journal 1*, p. 85
- ☐ Teaching Master (*Math Masters*, p. 61)
- ☐ 10 pennies
- ☐ coins per partnership: 10 nickels and 10 dimes

Additional Information

Background Information Read more about parts-and-total number stories on page 231 of this book.

Advance Preparation Before beginning this lesson, decide how you will display a parts-and-total diagram:

▷ Make an overhead transparency of *Math Masters*, page 61.

▷ Draw a parts-and-total diagram on the board with semipermanent chalk. (Read about semipermanent chalk on page 211.)

▷ Draw and erase parts-and-total diagrams on the board as needed.

For the problems in Mental Math and Reflexes, you might have children use nickels and dimes to show the various amounts.

Vocabulary • **parts-and-total diagram** • **parts-and-total number story**

Getting Started

Mental Math and Reflexes

Children use nickels and dimes to show various amounts. They share their solutions with the class. Instead of actual coins, children can use the symbols Ⓓ and Ⓝ. *Examples:*

▷ 20¢ ⒹⒹ, ⒹⓃⓃ, or ⓃⓃⓃⓃ

▷ 40¢ Sample answers: ⒹⒹⒹⒹ or ⒹⒹⒹⓃⓃ

Other suggestions: 15¢, 60¢, 30¢, or 65¢

You may want to challenge children to combine two amounts into a single pile of coins. They should then say or write the total.

Math Message

What is the total number of dots? 17

A hot dog costs 45¢. An orange costs 25¢. What is the total cost?

Home Link 4.1 Follow-Up

Review answers as necessary.

---

1 Teaching the Lesson

✦ Math Message Follow-Up

WHOLE-CLASS ACTIVITY

Draw a unit box with the label dots. Display a **parts-and-total diagram.** (See Advance Preparation.) Write 8 and 9 in the two boxes labeled Part. Write 17 in the box labeled Total.

Tell children that the diagram is a convenient way to describe the domino in the Math Message. The boxes labeled Part show the number of dots on each part of the domino; the box labeled Total shows the total number of dots on the domino.

Erase the label in the unit box and the numbers in the parts-and-total diagram. Write the label ¢ in the unit box. Discuss why the diagram is a good one to use for the **parts-and-total number story** in the Math Message about the cost of a hot dog and an orange. The cost of a hot dog is one part of the total cost, and the cost of an orange is the other part. Write 45 and 25 in the two Part boxes. The total cost is to be found; write ? in the Total box.

Ask children to share solution strategies for finding the total cost. Since children have solved similar problems in Unit 3 by using coins, they should be ready to use more abstract techniques. *For example:*

• Count up from the larger addend by using the values of dimes and nickels. *45¢, 55¢, 65¢, 70¢*

Unit
dots

Total	
17	
Part	**Part**
8	9

A parts-and-total diagram for the domino in the Math Message

Total	
?	
Part	**Part**
45	25

A parts-and-total diagram for the hot dog and orange problem in the Math Message

Parts-and-Total Number Stories

Lucy's Snack Bar Menu

Sandwiches		Drinks		Desserts	
Hamburger	65¢	Juice	45¢	Apple	15¢
Hot dog	45¢	Milk	35¢	Orange	25¢
Cheese	40¢	Soft drink	40¢	Banana	10¢
Peanut butter and jelly	35¢	Water	25¢	Cherry pie	40¢

For Problems 1–4, you are buying two items. Use the diagrams to record both the cost of each item and the total cost.

1. a cheese sandwich and milk

Total	
75¢	
Part	Part
40¢	35¢

2. juice and a slice of pie

Total	
85¢	
Part	Part
45¢	40¢

3. a hot dog and an apple

Total	
60¢	
Part	Part
45¢	15¢

4. a hamburger and juice

Total	
$1.10	
Part	Part
65¢	45¢

5. Jean buys milk and an orange. The cost is 60¢.

Jean gives the cashier 3 quarters.

How much change does she get? 15¢

✧ *Math Journal 1*, p. 85

NOTE: Children are not expected to draw parts-and-total diagrams at this time. They are expected, however, to record the known and missing information for a problem in a given parts-and-total diagram.

Addition Spin

Materials ☐ paper clip ☐ pencil
☐ *Math Masters*, p. 62
☐ calculator
☐ 2 sheets of paper

1. Players take turns being the "Spinner" and the "Checker."

2. The Spinner uses a pencil and a paper clip to make a spinner on *Math Masters*, page 62.

3. The Spinner spins the paper clip.

4. The Spinner writes the number that the paper clip points to. If the spinner points to more than one number, the Spinner writes the smaller number.

5. The Spinner spins a second time and writes the new number.

6. The Spinner adds the two numbers and writes the sum. The Checker checks the sum of the two numbers by using a calculator.

7. If the sum is correct, the Spinner circles it. If the sum is incorrect, the Spinner corrects it but does not circle it.

8. Players switch roles. The new Spinner spins the paper clip and writes the numbers and their sum on another sheet of paper. The new Checker checks the sum.

9. Players stop after they have each played 5 turns. Each player uses a calculator to find the sum of his or her circled scores.

10. The player with the higher total wins.

✧ *Math Journal 1*, p. 86

- Think of 45¢ as 4 dimes and 1 nickel. Think of 25¢ as 2 dimes and 1 nickel. Add the dimes, and then add the nickels. Then find the total cost. 4 dimes + 2 dimes = 6 dimes; 1 nickel + 1 nickel = 2 nickels; 6 dimes + 2 nickels = 70¢

◆ Finding the Cost of Two or More Items
(*Math Journal 1*, p. 85)

WHOLE-CLASS ACTIVITY

Working together as a class, make up and solve several number stories like Problem 1 on the journal page. Display and use parts-and-total diagrams.

Working alone or with a partner, children find the costs of the items in Problem 1 on the journal page. Go over the answers and have children share solution strategies. Draw parts-and-total diagrams as children share their solutions. From the discussion, you should be able to determine how much help they will need to complete the rest of the journal page.

Adjusting the Activity Challenge children with the following questions:

- What is the total cost of all of the items on the snack bar menu? $4.20 Use a calculator to check the total.

- Josh has $1.00. He buys a hot dog and milk. What can he buy for dessert? An apple or a banana

- Choose a sandwich, a drink, and a dessert for yourself. How much will they cost? Write a number model. Answers vary.

2 Ongoing Learning & Practice

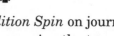

◆ Playing *Addition Spin*
(*Math Journal 1*, p. 86;
Math Masters, pp. 62 and 63)

PARTNER ACTIVITY

Explain the rules of *Addition Spin* on journal page 86. Play a demonstration game using the top spinner on *Math Masters*, page 62. Then divide the class into partnerships and have the children play.

To extend the game, players spin 3 times and add 3 numbers for each turn.

NOTE: *Addition Spin* can be played throughout the year, using a variety of numbers and operations. The game played by using the top spinner on *Math Masters*, page 62 focuses on addition of numbers that are multiples of 5. Blank *Addition Spin* mats have been provided on *Math Masters*, page 63 so that you can customize the game for your class as the year progresses.

◆ Math Boxes 4.2 (*Math Journal 1*, p. 87)

INDEPENDENT ACTIVITY

 Mixed Review This journal page provides opportunities for cumulative review or assessment of concepts and skills.

◆ Home Link 4.2 (*Math Masters*, pp. 281 and 282)

 Home Connection Children solve parts-and-total number stories. They fill in a parts-and-total diagram and write a number model for each problem.

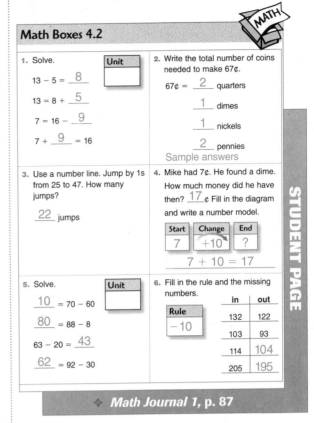

1. Solve.

Unit

$13 - 5 = $ ___8___

$13 = 8 + $ ___5___

$7 = 16 - $ ___9___

$7 + $ ___9___ $= 16$

2. Write the total number of coins needed to make 67¢.

67¢ = ___2___ quarters

___1___ dimes

___1___ nickels

___2___ pennies

Sample answers

3. Use a number line. Jump by 1s from 25 to 47. How many jumps?

___22___ jumps

4. Mike had 7¢. He found a dime. How much money did he have then? ___17___ ¢ Fill in the diagram and write a number model.

Start	Change	End
7	+10	?

$7 + 10 = 17$

5. Solve.

Unit

___10___ $= 70 - 60$

___80___ $= 88 - 8$

$63 - 20 = $ ___43___

___62___ $= 92 - 30$

6. Fill in the rule and the missing numbers.

Rule	in	out
−10	132	122
	103	93
	114	104
	205	195

◆ *Math Journal 1*, p. 87

STUDENT PAGE

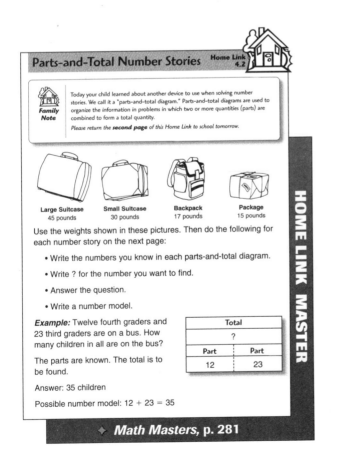

Parts-and-Total Number Stories Home Link 4.2

Family Note Today your child learned about another device to use when solving number stories. We call it a "parts-and-total diagram." Parts-and-total diagrams are used to organize the information in problems in which two or more quantities (parts) are combined to form a total quantity.

*Please return the **second page** of this Home Link to school tomorrow.*

Large Suitcase 45 pounds **Small Suitcase** 30 pounds **Backpack** 17 pounds **Package** 15 pounds

Use the weights shown in these pictures. Then do the following for each number story on the next page:

- Write the numbers you know in each parts-and-total diagram.
- Write ? for the number you want to find.
- Answer the question.
- Write a number model.

Example: Twelve fourth graders and 23 third graders are on a bus. How many children in all are on the bus?

The parts are known. The total is to be found.

Total	
?	
Part	Part
12	23

Answer: 35 children

Possible number model: 12 + 23 = 35

HOME LINK MASTER

◆ *Math Masters*, p. 281

Number Stories (cont.) Home Link 4.2

1. You wear the backpack and carry the small suitcase. How many pounds do you carry in all? ___47___ pounds

Total	
?	
Part	Part
17	30

Number model:

___17 + 30 = 47___

2. You carry the large suitcase and the small suitcase. How many pounds do you carry in all? ___75___ pounds

Total	
?	
Part	Part
45	30

Number model:

___45 + 30 = 75___

3. You carry the package and the large suitcase. How many pounds do you carry in all? ___60___ pounds

Total	
?	
Part	Part
15	45

Number model:

___15 + 45 = 60___

4. You wear the backpack and carry both of the suitcases. How many pounds do you carry in all? ___92___ pounds

Total		
?		
Part	Part	Part
17	45	30

Number model:

___17 + 45 + 30 = 92___

HOME LINK MASTER

◆ *Math Masters*, p. 282

TEACHING MASTER

Total

Part	Part

Math Masters, p. 61

Total
?

Part	Part

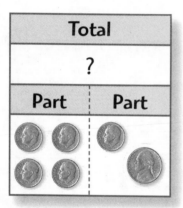

Using coins to act out a snacks purchase

PLANNING AHEAD

At the end of the lesson, collect unused copies of:

▷ *Math Masters,* page 61 to use in Lesson 4.6.

▷ *Math Masters,* page 63 to use in Lesson 4.3 and later lessons.

---

3 Options for Individualizing

◆ RETEACHING Playing *Two-Fisted Penny Addition*

SMALL-GROUP ACTIVITY 5–15 min

Some children may benefit from doing parts-and-total activities with simple numbers and manipulatives.

Each child counts out 10 pennies and divides the pennies between his or her two hands. Call on several children to describe the number of pennies they have. For example: *My left hand has 3 pennies and my right hand has 7 pennies. The total number of pennies in both hands is 10.*

You can record the information in a parts-and-total diagram.

Continue to play as necessary, varying the total numbers of pennies.

◆ RETEACHING Using Coins to Act Out Solutions
(*Math Journal 1,* p. 85; *Math Masters,* p. 61)

PARTNER ACTIVITY 15–30 min

Children use coins with *Math Masters,* page 61 to act out solutions.

Example

Find the total cost for a cheese sandwich (40¢) and an apple (15¢).

Suggest that children think of the diagram on *Math Masters,* page 61 as a lunch tray. The Part compartments of the tray hold coins for each item they buy. The Total compartment is used to place the coins for the total cost of the items bought.

You write 40¢ and 15¢ in the Part boxes and ? in the Total box. Children place coins that total 40¢ and 15¢ in the two Part boxes.

Children then combine the coins in the two Part boxes, slide these to the Total box, and count coins to establish that the total cost is 55¢. You record this in the Total box.

4.3 Exploring Temperature, Money, and Shapes

EXPLORATIONS

OBJECTIVES To read temperatures on a thermometer; to determine the total value of a group of coins; and to develop readiness for classifying geometric shapes.

summaries	materials

1 Teaching the Lesson

Children are introduced to the Celsius scale and learn how to find equivalent Fahrenheit and Celsius temperatures.

Exploration A: Children use a thermometer to measure the temperature of the classroom, hot water, and ice water; children choose the more sensible temperature for a given situation. [Measurement and Reference Frames]

Exploration B: Children make coin booklets showing groups of coins and the total value in dollars-and-cents notation.
[Measurement and Reference Frames; Operations and Computation]

Exploration C: Children develop readiness for classifying geometric shapes by sorting attribute blocks by size, color, and shape. [Geometry]

□ Home Link 4.2

Exploration A:
□ *Math Journal 1*, p. 88
□ Class Thermometer Poster
   Per group of 3 or 4 children:
□ cups of hot tap water and ice water
□ thermometer, preferably showing both °F and °C scales

Exploration B: Per partnership:
□ Teaching Master (*Math Masters*, p. 64)
□ rubber stamps of coins; stamp pad
□ scissors; stapler; slate; 2 sheets of paper
□ *26 Letters and 99 Cents* (optional)

Exploration C: Per group:
□ Teaching Masters (*Math Masters*, p. 65)
□ set of attribute blocks; sheets of paper

***See* Advance Preparation**

2 Ongoing Learning & Practice

Children practice adding 2-digit numbers by playing *Addition Spin*. [Operations and Computation]

Children practice and maintain skills through Math Boxes and Home Link activities.

□ *Math Journal 1*, pp. 86 and 89
   Per partnership:
□ Home Link Master (*Math Masters*, p. 283)
□ Teaching Master (*Math Masters*, p. 62; and p. 63, optional)
□ paper clip, calculator

3 Options for Individualizing

Extra Practice Children identify and discuss the different shapes of road signs. [Geometry]

□ *Minute Math®*, p. 55

Additional Information

Advance Preparation Plan to spend most of your time with children working on Exploration A. Note that if you covered the Celsius scale on the Class Thermometer Poster in Lesson 1.13, uncover it. For Exploration B, you may want to obtain the book *26 Letters and 99 Cents* by Tana Hoban (Greenwillow Books, 1987). For Explorations B and C, you may want to place copies of *Math Masters*, pages 64 and 65 at workstations.

Vocabulary • degrees Fahrenheit (°F) • degrees Celsius (°C) • thermometer • degree marks

Getting Started

Math Message

Why are there two sets of marks and numbers on our Class Thermometer Poster?

Home Link 4.2 Follow-Up

Review answers as necessary.

---

1 Teaching the Lesson

◆ Math Message Follow-Up

WHOLE-CLASS DISCUSSION

Point out that there are two different scales that are most often used to measure temperature. Temperatures in weather reports in the United States are usually given in **degrees Fahrenheit (°F).** Temperatures used in science are almost always given in **degrees Celsius (°C).** Celsius temperature readings are also becoming more common in everyday life in the United States.

◆ Translating between Fahrenheit and Celsius Temperatures

WHOLE-CLASS DISCUSSION

Science Link Begin with the benchmark temperatures indicated on the Class Thermometer Poster. For example, set the "mercury" in the **thermometer** at the room temperature line.

What is room temperature on the Fahrenheit side of the thermometer? 70 degrees On the Celsius side? About 20 degrees Point out that there are **degree marks** on each scale at every degree. Extend questions to other temperatures. *For example:*

▷ Set the mercury at 90 degrees on the Fahrenheit side. Ask what the equivalent temperature is on the Celsius side. About 32 degrees Celsius

▷ Set the mercury at 10 degrees on the Celsius side. Ask what the equivalent temperature is on the Fahrenheit side. 50 degrees Fahrenheit

✦ Exploration A: Measuring Temperatures
(*Math Journal 1*, p. 88)

SMALL-GROUP ACTIVITY 🏃🏃🏃🏃

If the thermometer you are using has only a single scale
(°F or °C), tell children to find and record this reading.
They can then use the Class Thermometer Poster or the
thermometer pictures on the journal page to translate any
temperature to the other scale.

When children take temperature readings of hot water or
ice water, they should leave the thermometer in the water
for about 30 seconds, remove it, and read the temperature
promptly.

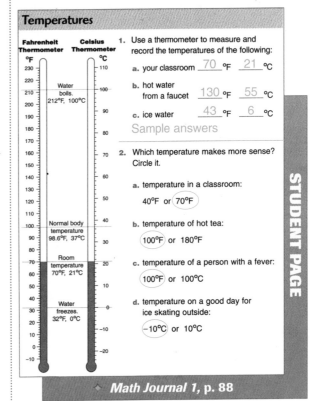

Math Journal 1, p. 88

The Class Thermometer Poster displaying room temperature

ONGOING ASSESSMENT
Watch for children who have trouble reading the
actual thermometer because it is much smaller
than the thermometer pictured on the poster.
Lesson 4.4 will focus on developing skills for
reading a thermometer. For now, work closely
with children to help them interpret their
thermometer readings.

Coin-Stamp Booklets

Work with a partner.

Materials
- coin stamps
- stamp pad
- stapler
- scissors
- sheets of plain paper
- slate

1. Each partner folds a sheet of paper into 4 parts.

2. Cut the sheet along the folds.

3. Put aside 2 pieces of paper. Use them later for a book cover.

4. Stamp a group of coins on one side of each of the other six pieces of paper.

5. Write the total value of the coins on the other side of the paper. Use a dollar sign and a decimal point: $0.00. Check your partner's work.

6. Stack the pieces. Put the sides with the coins faceup.
   - Put 1 blank piece of paper on top of the stack.
   - Put the other blank piece at the bottom.
   - Staple the pieces together to make a small book.
   - Write your names on the cover of the book.

Follow-Up

- Take turns. One partner counts the value of the coins on a page and writes the total value on a slate. The other partner checks that the value is correct.

- Work together. Make up a story about the coins on a page and write it on a piece of paper.

◆ *Math Masters, p. 64*

TEACHING MASTER

A coin-stamp booklet

◆ Exploration B: Making Coin-Stamp Booklets
(*Math Masters,* p. 64)

PARTNER ACTIVITY 👥

Partners follow instructions on the master page to make a booklet showing different groups of coins and their values.

Portfolio Ideas

1. First each partner folds a sheet of paper into fourths and cuts along the fold lines. They set aside 2 quarter-sheets to use as covers.

2. Next, each partner uses the coin stamps to stamp a group of coins on one side of each quarter-sheet.

3. Each partner writes the total value of the group of coins on the other side of the sheet using dollars-and-cents notation ($0.00).

4. Partners check each other's work.

5. When all of the amounts are correct, partners stack the pages with the coins facing up, add the blank sheets as covers, and staple the pages together to make a booklet.

6. Partners write their names on the cover of their booklets.

Partners use the new booklets to practice determining the value of a group of coins. One partner counts the coin values and writes the total on a slate; the other partner checks the answer. Partners take turns with each role.

⬇ Adjusting the Activity Challenge children to find the total value of all of the coins stamped in a booklet. Have partners check each other's answers.

⭕ **Literature Link** The book *26 Letters and 99 Cents* by Tana Hoban (Greenwillow Books, 1987) shows photographs of coins representing the numbers 1 through 30, 35, 40, 45, 50, 60, 70, 80, 90, and 99. Sometimes more than one combination is shown, but often the least possible number of coins is shown. This book can be used to encourage children to explore different ways of showing the same value.

✦ Exploration C: Sorting Attribute Blocks
(*Math Masters*, p. 65)

SMALL-GROUP ACTIVITY

Group members work together to sort the set of attribute blocks in three different ways:

▷ by color

▷ by size

▷ by shape

For each sort, they organize the blocks belonging to the sort, trace the blocks onto paper to make a record, and label the sort.

Adjusting the Activity You may want to help some children by preparing the sorting sheets for them. For example, provide children with sheets of paper labeled "red," "blue," and "yellow." You can provide a model by tracing and coloring one or two blocks that fit the rule on each sheet. For example, on the "red" sheet, trace and color a small red triangle and a large red circle.

Attribute Sorts

Work in a small group.

Materials ☐ set of attribute blocks
☐ paper for recording

1. Work together to sort the blocks by *color*.
   • One way to do the sorting is to use a different sheet of paper for each color. Label each sheet with a different color.
   • Record how you sorted the blocks. On each sheet, write words or draw pictures to show which blocks belong with that color.

2. Sort the blocks again. Sort them by *size*.
   • Remember to label each sheet with a different size.
   • Record how you sorted the blocks by writing words or drawing pictures.

3. Sort the blocks once more. This time sort them by *shape*.
   • Did you label each sheet with a different shape?
   • Did you make a record of your work?

Math Masters, p. 65

---

2 Ongoing Learning & Practice

✦ Playing *Addition Spin*
(*Math Journal 1*, p. 86; *Math Masters*, p. 62 or 63)

PARTNER ACTIVITY

This game was introduced in Lesson 4.2. In that lesson, children used the top spinner on *Math Masters*, page 62, which is numbered with multiples of 5. Children could use the bottom spinner on this page to give them practice adding other 2-digit numbers. If you prefer, create your own spinner by using a blank spinner on *Math Masters*, page 63.

Addition Spin

Materials ☐ paper clip ☐ pencil
☐ *Math Masters*, p. 62
☐ calculator
☐ 2 sheets of paper

1. Players take turns being the "Spinner" and the "Checker."

2. The Spinner uses a pencil and a paper clip to make a spinner on *Math Masters*, page 62.

3. The Spinner spins the paper clip.

4. The Spinner writes the number that the paper clip points to. If the spinner points to more than one number, the Spinner writes the smaller number.

5. The Spinner spins a second time and writes the new number.

6. The Spinner adds the two numbers and writes the sum. The Checker checks the sum of the two numbers by using a calculator.

7. If the sum is correct, the Spinner circles it. If the sum is incorrect, the Spinner corrects it but does not circle it.

8. Players switch roles. The new Spinner spins the paper clip and writes the numbers and their sum on another sheet of paper. The new Checker checks the sum.

9. Players stop after they have each played 5 turns. Each player uses a calculator to find the sum of his or her circled scores.

10. The player with the higher total wins.

✦ *Math Journal 1*, p. 86

Math Boxes 4.3

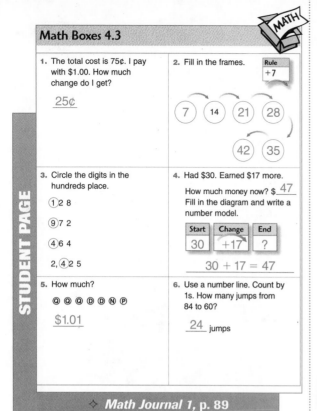

1. The total cost is 75¢. I pay with $1.00. How much change do I get?

_25¢_

2. Fill in the frames.

Rule
+7

7   14   21   28
            42   35

3. Circle the digits in the hundreds place.

①2 8
⑨7 2
④6 4
2,④2 5

4. Had $30. Earned $17 more.

How much money now? $ _47_
Fill in the diagram and write a number model.

Start	Change	End
30	+17	?

30 + 17 = 47

5. How much?

Ⓠ Ⓠ Ⓠ Ⓓ Ⓝ Ⓟ

$1.01

6. Use a number line. Count by 1s. How many jumps from 84 to 60?

_24_ jumps

◆ Math Boxes 4.3 (_Math Journal 1_, p. 89)

INDEPENDENT ACTIVITY

Mixed Review This journal page provides opportunities for cumulative review or assessment of concepts and skills.

◆ Home Link 4.3 (_Math Masters_, p. 283)

Home Connection Children practice reading thermometers to identify which of two thermometers shows a specific temperature.

3 Options for Individualizing

◆ EXTRA PRACTICE Minute Math

SMALL-GROUP ACTIVITY **5–15 min**

To offer children more experience with identifying and sorting shapes, see the following page in _Minute Math_:

Geometry: p. 55

Reading a Thermometer

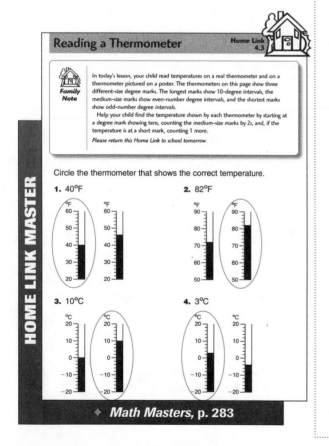

Home Link 4.3

Family Note

In today's lesson, your child read temperatures on a real thermometer and on a thermometer pictured on a poster. The thermometers on this page show three different-size degree marks. The longest marks show 10-degree intervals, the medium-size marks show even-number degree intervals, and the shortest marks show odd-number degree intervals.

Help your child find the temperature shown by each thermometer by starting at a degree mark showing tens, counting the medium-size marks by 2s, and, if the temperature is at a short mark, counting 1 more.

Please return this Home Link to school tomorrow.

Circle the thermometer that shows the correct temperature.

1. 40°F

2. 82°F

3. 10°C

4. 3°C

4.4 Temperature Changes

OBJECTIVES To read and show temperatures; and to solve number stories about temperature changes.

summaries	materials

1 Teaching the Lesson

Children review thermometers, compare Fahrenheit and Celsius scales, and solve "How much warmer (colder)?" problems. Children solve temperature-change problems, including change-to-less, using change diagrams.
[Measurement and Reference Frames; Operations and Computation]

Children read and show temperatures on thermometers.
[Measurement and Reference Frames]

☐ *Math Journal 1*, pp. 88, 90, and 91

☐ Home Link 4.3

☐ Teaching Master transparency (*Math Masters*, p. 59; optional)

☐ Class Thermometer Poster

☐ index card or ruler (optional)

☐ slate

***See* Advanced Preparation**

2 Ongoing Learning & Practice

Children solve and make up parts-and-total number stories.
[Operations and Computation]

Children practice and maintain skills through Math Boxes and Home Link activities.

☐ *Math Journal 1*, pp. 92 and 93

☐ Home Link Masters (*Math Masters*, pp. 284 and 285)

3 Options for Individualizing

Enrichment Children identify situations as change to more or change to less. [Operations and Computation]

Extra Practice Children solve problems involving outdoor temperatures. [Measurement and Reference Frames; Operations and Computation]

☐ Teaching Master (*Math Masters*, p. 66)

☐ *Minute Math*®, p. 97

Additional Information

Advance Preparation Before beginning this lesson, decide how you will display change diagrams. (See Advance Preparation on page 224.)

Vocabulary • **thermometer** • **degrees Fahrenheit (°F)** • **degrees Celsius (°C)** • **degree marks**

Getting Started

Mental Math and Reflexes

Children practice counting by 10s and 2s from a multiple of 10. Counting by 2s is a useful skill for reading temperatures on a thermometer with a scale having 2-degree intervals.

The class counts orally in unison:

- by 10s from 0 to 100.
- by 10s from 100 back to 0.
- by 2s from 0 to 20.
- by 2s from 20 back to 10.
- by 2s from 60 to 70.
- by 2s from 60 back to 50.

Math Message

At what temperature does water freeze (turn to ice)? 32°F or 0°C

Home Link 4.3 Follow-Up

Ask volunteers to explain how they determined which thermometer showed the correct temperature. Ask children to tell the temperature that is shown on the thermometer that was not circled.

1 Teaching the Lesson

◆ Math Message Follow-Up
(*Math Journal 1*, p. 88)

WHOLE-CLASS ACTIVITY

Ask the class to look at the Class Thermometer Poster and the thermometers on journal page 88. Discuss the fact that a thermometer shows how hot or cold something is (relative to the number scale on that thermometer). Cover the following points:

▷ The narrow glass tube on a **thermometer** contains a liquid that expands when the temperature gets warmer. This causes the liquid to rise in the tube. The warmer the temperature, the higher the liquid rises.

▷ In the United States, everyday temperatures, such as those in weather reports and recipes, are usually given in **degrees Fahrenheit (°F)**. In science, temperatures are almost always given in **degrees Celsius (°C).** Celsius temperature readings are also becoming common in everyday life.

Compare the Fahrenheit and Celsius thermometers.

▷ Each multiple of 10 degrees is written as a number.

▷ Between the multiples of 10 degrees, the longer **degree marks** are spaced at 2-degree intervals; for example, at 72, 74, 76, and 78 degrees.

▷ The shorter degree marks indicate 1-degree intervals.

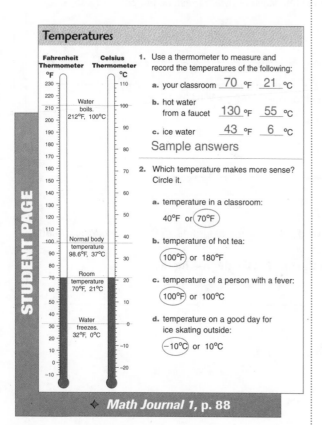

STUDENT PAGE

Temperatures

Fahrenheit Thermometer °F	Celsius Thermometer °C

1. Use a thermometer to measure and record the temperatures of the following:

   a. your classroom __70__ °F __21__ °C

   b. hot water from a faucet __130__ °F __55__ °C

   c. ice water __43__ °F __6__ °C

   Sample answers

2. Which temperature makes more sense? Circle it.

   a. temperature in a classroom:
      40°F or (70°F)

   b. temperature of hot tea:
      (100°F) or 180°F

   c. temperature of a person with a fever:
      (100°F) or 100°C

   d. temperature on a good day for ice skating outside:
      (−10°C) or 10°C

Water boils. 212°F, 100°C

Normal body temperature 98.6°F, 37°C

Room temperature 70°F, 21°C

Water freezes. 32°F, 0°C

◆ *Math Journal 1, p. 88*

Ask:

- On which thermometer are the distances between degree marks greater? Celsius

- At what Fahrenheit temperature does water freeze? 32°F

- At what Celsius temperature does water freeze? 0°C

✦ Solving "How Much Warmer (Colder)?" Problems

WHOLE-CLASS ACTIVITY 👥👥

Display a change diagram, and draw a unit box labeled degrees Fahrenheit (°F).

Using temperatures that are multiples of 5 or 10, pose several temperature change problems like those below. Have children write the answers on their slates.

- It was 50°F at 9 o'clock in the morning, and 70°F at noon. Did it get warmer or colder? warmer

- By how many degrees? 20°F

Have children share their solution strategies while you write the information in the change diagram you displayed. Write:

1. 50 in the Start box.

2. 70 in the End box.

3. ? in the Change box.

Most children should be able to identify the change as 20 degrees. Be sure that they also identify the change as change to more. For example, children might say "the temperature goes up" or "it gets warmer." Write +20 in the Change box.

- It was 40°F at 6 o'clock. By 10 o'clock, the temperature had gone down 30 degrees. What was the temperature at 10 o'clock? 10°F

Fill in the change diagram by writing:

1. 40 in the Start box.

2. −30 in the Change box.

3. ? in the End box.

Remind children that the minus sign in −30 indicates a change to less: the temperature goes down, and it gets colder. Once children conclude that the final temperature is 10 degrees, write 10 in the End box.

Expand the range of temperatures to include two 2-digit numbers whose difference is a multiple of 10. *For example:*

- If the temperature is 72°F, and it goes down 20 degrees, what is the new temperature? 52°F

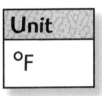

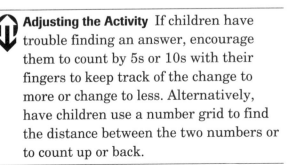

Adjusting the Activity If children have trouble finding an answer, encourage them to count by 5s or 10s with their fingers to keep track of the change to more or change to less. Alternatively, have children use a number grid to find the distance between the two numbers or to count up or back.

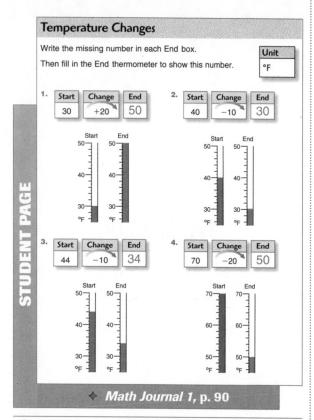

Temperature Changes

Write the missing number in each End box.
Then fill in the End thermometer to show this number.

Unit: °F

1. Start **30** | Change **+20** | End **50**
2. Start **40** | Change **−10** | End **30**
3. Start **44** | Change **−10** | End **34**
4. Start **70** | Change **−20** | End **50**

✦ *Math Journal 1, p. 90*

 Adjusting the Activity On journal pages 90 and 91, children can place the top of a card or ruler horizontally at the top of the "mercury" in one thermometer. They then slide the card up or down, counting by 2s until the card reaches the top of the other "mercury."

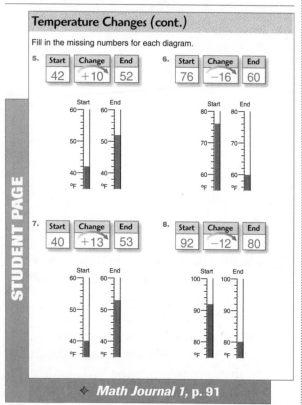

Temperature Changes (cont.)

Fill in the missing numbers for each diagram.

5. Start **42** | Change **+10** | End **52**
6. Start **76** | Change **−16** | End **60**
7. Start **40** | Change **+13** | End **53**
8. Start **92** | Change **−12** | End **80**

✦ *Math Journal 1, p. 91*

✦ Reading and Showing Temperatures and Solving Temperature-Change Problems
(*Math Journal 1*, pp. 90 and 91)

PARTNER ACTIVITY

Partners work through the journal pages and check each other's work. Problems include practice in reading temperatures, marking a thermometer to show a temperature, and using change diagrams. Circulate to evaluate and help as needed.

2 Ongoing Learning & Practice

✦ Solving Parts-and-Total Number Stories
(*Math Journal 1*, p. 92)

INDEPENDENT ACTIVITY

Children solve parts-and-total number stories. They complete parts-and-total diagrams and write number models for these stories.

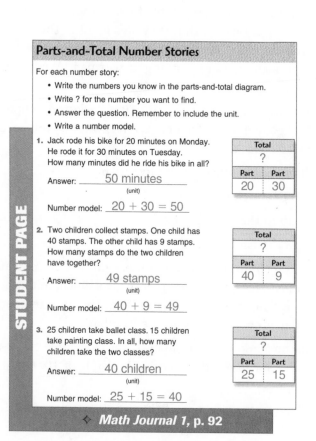

Parts-and-Total Number Stories

For each number story:
- Write the numbers you know in the parts-and-total diagram.
- Write ? for the number you want to find.
- Answer the question. Remember to include the unit.
- Write a number model.

1. Jack rode his bike for 20 minutes on Monday. He rode it for 30 minutes on Tuesday. How many minutes did he ride his bike in all?

Answer: **50 minutes** (unit)

Number model: **20 + 30 = 50**

Total
?

Part	Part
20	30

2. Two children collect stamps. One child has 40 stamps. The other child has 9 stamps. How many stamps do the two children have together?

Answer: **49 stamps** (unit)

Number model: **40 + 9 = 49**

Total
?

Part	Part
40	9

3. 25 children take ballet class. 15 children take painting class. In all, how many children take the two classes?

Answer: **40 children** (unit)

Number model: **25 + 15 = 40**

Total
?

Part	Part
25	15

✦ *Math Journal 1, p. 92*

◆ Math Boxes 4.4 (*Math Journal 1*, p. 93)

Mixed Review This journal page provides opportunities for cumulative review or assessment of concepts and skills.

◆ Home Link 4.4 (*Math Masters*, pp. 284 and 285)

Home Connection The Home Link provides children practice with two skills: reading the temperature shown on a thermometer and marking a thermometer to show a given temperature.

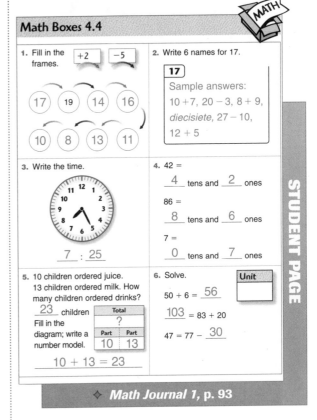

Math Boxes 4.4

1. Fill in the frames. $+2$ -5

   17 19 14 16

   10 8 13 11

2. Write 6 names for 17.

   17
   Sample answers:
   $10 + 7$, $20 - 3$, $8 + 9$,
   diecisiete, $27 - 10$,
   $12 + 5$

3. Write the time.

   7 : 25

4. 42 =
   __4__ tens and __2__ ones

   86 =
   __8__ tens and __6__ ones

   7 =
   __0__ tens and __7__ ones

5. 10 children ordered juice. 13 children ordered milk. How many children ordered drinks?

   __23__ children
   Fill in the diagram; write a number model.

Total
?

Part	Part
10	13

   $10 + 13 = 23$

6. Solve. **Unit**

   $50 + 6 = $ __56__

   __103__ $= 83 + 20$

   $47 = 77 - $ __30__

◆ *Math Journal 1*, p. 93

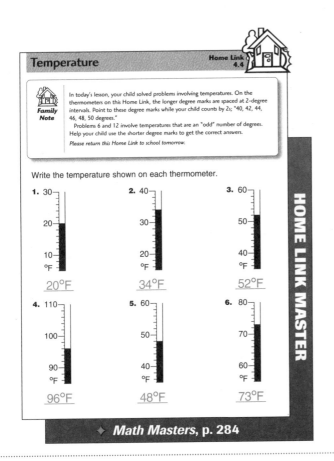

Temperature Home Link 4.4

Family Note In today's lesson, your child solved problems involving temperatures. On the thermometers on this Home Link, the longer degree marks are spaced at 2-degree intervals. Point to these degree marks while your child counts by 2s: "40, 42, 44, 46, 48, 50 degrees."
Problems 6 and 12 involve temperatures that are an "odd" number of degrees. Help your child use the shorter degree marks to get the correct answers.
Please return this Home Link to school tomorrow.

Write the temperature shown on each thermometer.

1. 30 / 20 / 10 / °F __20°F__

2. 40 / 30 / 20 / 10 / °F __34°F__

3. 60 / 50 / 40 / °F __52°F__

4. 110 / 100 / 90 / °F __96°F__

5. 60 / 50 / 40 / °F __48°F__

6. 80 / 70 / 60 / °F __73°F__

◆ *Math Masters*, p. 284

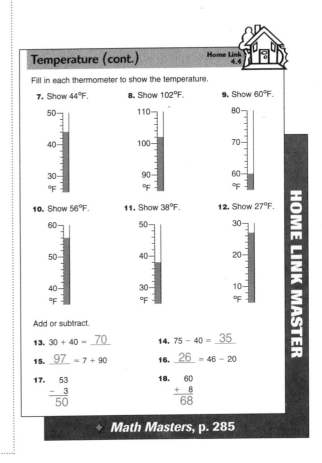

Temperature (cont.) Home Link 4.4

Fill in each thermometer to show the temperature.

7. Show 44°F.
   50 / 40 / 30 / °F

8. Show 102°F.
   110 / 100 / 90 / °F

9. Show 60°F.
   80 / 70 / 60 / °F

10. Show 56°F.
    60 / 50 / 40 / °F

11. Show 38°F.
    50 / 40 / 30 / °F

12. Show 27°F.
    30 / 20 / 10 / °F

Add or subtract.

13. $30 + 40 = $ __70__

14. $75 - 40 = $ __35__

15. __97__ $= 7 + 90$

16. __26__ $= 46 - 20$

17. $\begin{array}{r} 53 \\ -\ 3 \\ \hline 50 \end{array}$

18. $\begin{array}{r} 60 \\ +\ 8 \\ \hline 68 \end{array}$

◆ *Math Masters*, p. 285

♦ ENRICHMENT Identifying Situations as Change to More or Change to Less
(*Math Masters*, p. 66)

INDEPENDENT ACTIVITY   5–15 min

Children are asked to identify various situations as change to more or change to less. Children make up their own situations and identify them as change to more or change to less.

♦ EXTRA PRACTICE Minute Math

SMALL-GROUP ACTIVITY   5–15 min

To offer children more experience with solving problems about temperature, see the following page in *Minute Math*:

Number Stories: p. 97

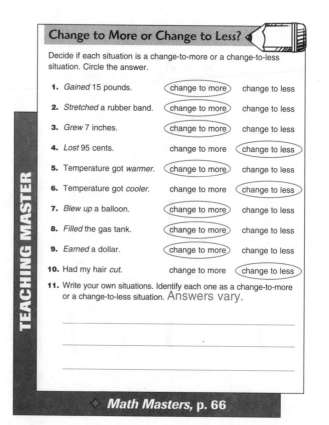

Change to More or Change to Less?

Decide if each situation is a change-to-more or a change-to-less situation. Circle the answer.

1. *Gained* 15 pounds. — (change to more) — change to less
2. *Stretched* a rubber band. — (change to more) — change to less
3. *Grew* 7 inches. — (change to more) — change to less
4. *Lost* 95 cents. — change to more — (change to less)
5. Temperature got *warmer*. — (change to more) — change to less
6. Temperature got *cooler*. — change to more — (change to less)
7. *Blew up* a balloon. — (change to more) — change to less
8. *Filled* the gas tank. — (change to more) — change to less
9. *Earned* a dollar. — (change to more) — change to less
10. Had my hair *cut*. — change to more — (change to less)
11. Write your own situations. Identify each one as a change-to-more or a change-to-less situation. Answers vary.

TEACHING MASTER

♦ *Math Masters*, p. 66

4.5

Estimating Costs

OBJECTIVE To use estimation to solve problems for which an exact answer is not necessary.

summaries	materials

1 Teaching the Lesson

Children are introduced to estimation. They use estimation to solve problems and share their solutions. [Numeration; Operations and Computation]

- ☐ *Math Journal 1*, p. 94
- ☐ Home Link 4.4
- ☐ Home Link transparency (*Math Masters*, pp. 284 and 285; optional)

***See* Advance Preparation**

2 Ongoing Learning & Practice

Children use the symbols <, >, and = to compare numbers and money amounts. [Numeration]

Children practice and maintain skills through Math Boxes and Home Link activities.

- ☐ *Math Journal 1*, pp. 95 and 96
- ☐ Home Link Master (*Math Masters*, p. 286)

3 Options for Individualizing

Enrichment Children use estimation to compare sums of weights. [Numeration; Operations and Computation]

Reteaching Children review mnemonic devices for remembering the meanings of < and >. [Numeration]

- ☐ *Math Journal 1*, p. 80

Additional Information

Advance Preparation For the Home Link 4.4 Follow-Up, you may want to create overhead transparencies of *Math Masters*, pages 284 and 285.

Vocabulary • **estimate** • <, >, =

Getting Started

Mental Math and Reflexes

The class counts orally in unison:

- by 10s from 0 to 100.
- by 10s from 100 back to 0.
- by 2s from 0 to 20.
- by 2s from 20 back to 10.
- by 2s from 50 to 60
- by 2s from 70 to 80.
- by 2s from 90 back to 80.

Math Message

Eraser: 28¢

Notebook: 69¢

You have $1.00. Do you have enough money to pay for both items? yes

Home Link 4.4 Follow-Up

You may want to use an overhead transparency of Home Link 4.4 as you review the answers. Pay special attention to Problems 6 and 12, in which the temperature is an odd number of degrees; children must read between the 2-degree intervals to get the correct answer.

◆ Math Message Follow-Up

WHOLE-CLASS DISCUSSION

Ask children to share their solution strategies. Some children may have tried to find the exact cost of the two items ($28¢ + 69¢ = 97¢$). Others may have found that they had enough money without actually finding the exact cost. *For example:*

▷ Some children might have reasoned that $69¢ + 20¢$ is $89¢$, and adding another $8¢$ would not bring the cost to more than $1.00.

▷ Other children might have thought that $69¢$ is just a little less than $70¢$. Since $70¢ + 28¢$ is $98¢$, the actual cost must be slightly less than $1.00.

◆ Discussing Estimation

WHOLE-CLASS DISCUSSION

There are many problems for which an exact answer is not required. The Math Message problem, for example, asks only whether the total cost is $1.00 or less; the exact total is not needed.

Ask children to think of other questions for which a "close" answer is good enough. *For example:*

▷ How old am I?

▷ What is the temperature today?

▷ What is the distance from my home to school?

Careful counting or measuring can furnish precise answers, but close answers are usually good enough for these situations. A close answer is called an **estimate.**

◆ Solving Problems by Estimation
(*Math Journal 1*, p. 94)

WHOLE-CLASS DISCUSSION

Use the information at the top of journal page 94 to make up estimation problems for children to solve. Tell them that it is not necessary to calculate exact answers. Close answers, or estimates, will be good enough to answer the questions.

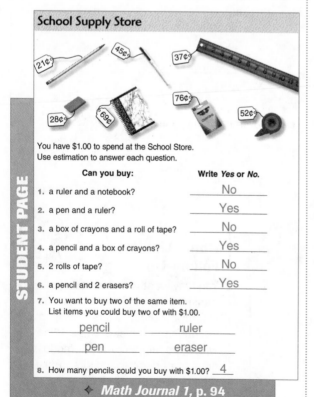

School Supply Store

21¢ *45¢* *37¢* *76¢* *28¢* *69¢* *52¢*

You have $1.00 to spend at the School Store.
Use estimation to answer each question.

Can you buy: Write *Yes* or *No.*

1. a ruler and a notebook? — No
2. a pen and a ruler? — Yes
3. a box of crayons and a roll of tape? — No
4. a pencil and a box of crayons? — Yes
5. 2 rolls of tape? — No
6. a pencil and 2 erasers? — Yes
7. You want to buy two of the same item.
   List items you could buy two of with $1.00.

   pencil   ruler

   pen   eraser

8. How many pencils could you buy with $1.00? __4__

✦ *Math Journal 1*, p. 94

To get an estimate, children should use numbers that are close to the numbers in the problems but easier to work with.

Examples

1. Is $1.00 enough to pay for a notebook and tape? No; each item costs more than 50¢, so the total must be more than $1.00.

2. You have 80¢ to spend. You buy a pen. Do you have enough money left to buy a ruler? No; the pen costs 45¢ and the ruler costs 37¢. 40¢ + 30¢ = 70¢. Since 5¢ + 7¢ is greater than 10¢, the total is greater than 80¢.

3. You buy an eraser and a ruler. The clerk says, "That will be 80 cents." Should you pay that amount? No; 28¢ + 37¢ is less than 30¢ + 40¢, which is 70¢. The clerk is wrong.

At this time, it is best not to teach any formal estimation techniques, such as rounding, since children may then rotely use such techniques for all problems.

Have children share estimation strategies. Encourage them to devise a variety of strategies of their own, and then have them choose the strategy that best fits a particular situation.

 Adjusting the Activity Challenge children with estimation problems about more than two items. For example, is $2.00 enough to buy a ruler, a box of crayons, and a notebook? Yes, 37¢ + 76¢ + 69¢ is less than 40¢ + 80¢ + 70¢, which is $1.90. $1.90 is less than $2.00.

◆ Solving Problems by Estimation
(*Math Journal 1*, p. 94)

PARTNER ACTIVITY

Once children feel comfortable dealing with estimation situations, have them complete journal page 94 with a partner. Do not permit the use of calculators. Circulate and help as needed.

 Adjusting the Activity Some children may find it helpful to write the cost of each item directly above its name in the problem.

NOTE: Many children think there is little reason to estimate when they know how to calculate an exact answer to a problem. As a result, many children do not consider estimation to be as important as exact computation.

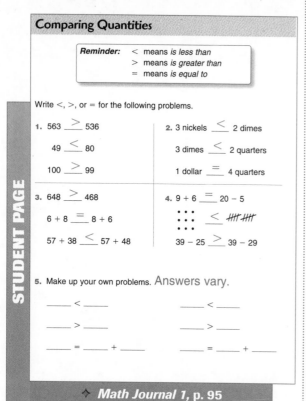

Comparing Quantities

Reminder: < means *is less than*
> means *is greater than*
= means *is equal to*

Write <, >, or = for the following problems.

1. 563 $>$ 536

   49 $<$ 80

   100 $>$ 99

2. 3 nickels $<$ 2 dimes

   3 dimes $<$ 2 quarters

   1 dollar $=$ 4 quarters

3. 648 $>$ 468

   6 + 8 $=$ 8 + 6

   57 + 38 $<$ 57 + 48

4. 9 + 6 $=$ 20 − 5

    $<$ ⫽⫽⫽ ⫽⫽⫽

   39 − 25 $>$ 39 − 29

5. Make up your own problems. Answers vary.

   ____ < ____   ____ < ____

   ____ > ____   ____ > ____

   ____ = ____ + ____   ____ = ____ + ____

STUDENT PAGE

✦ *Math Journal 1, p. 95*

Ongoing Learning & Practice

✦ Comparing Quantities Using <, >, or =
(*Math Journal 1*, p. 95)

INDEPENDENT ACTIVITY 👤

Children complete the page on their own. If necessary, review with children the meanings of the <, >, and = symbols at the top of the page.

✦ Math Boxes 4.5 (*Math Journal 1*, p. 96)

INDEPENDENT ACTIVITY 👤

Mixed Review This journal page provides opportunities for cumulative review or assessment of concepts and skills.

✦ Home Link 4.5 (*Math Masters*, p. 286)

Home Connection Children use estimation to solve problems about buying items at the grocery store. They also determine whether they can buy two items with $1.00.

Math Boxes 4.5

1. What temperature is it?

   Unit
   °F

   50°F

   (thermometer showing 40–60 °F, reading at 50)

2. I bought a sandwich and ice cream. Each cost 35¢. How much did I spend?

   70 ¢

   Fill in the diagram and write a number model.

Total
?

Part	Part
35	35

   35 + 35 = 70

3. Solve.

   57
   − 7
   50

   Unit

   43 = 40 + 3

   79 − 9 = 70

   80 = 85 − 5

4. Fill in the frames.

   Rule
   −2

   94 → 92 → 90 → 88

   86

5. I had $0.35. I spent $0.15. How much change do I have?

   $ 0.20

6. Fill in the missing numbers.

	102	103
	112	113
121	122	123

STUDENT PAGE

✦ *Math Journal 1, p. 96*

Shopping at the Grocery Store
Home Link 4.5

🏠 Family Note

Many problems in and out of the classroom require estimates rather than exact answers. In Problems 1–5 below, you need to know only whether the total cost is greater than $1.00 or less than $1.00; you do not need to know the exact total cost. In Problem 1, for example, help your child notice that the price of the can of frozen orange juice (98¢) is almost $1.00. Since a lemon is 10¢, your child could not buy both items.

Please return this Home Link to school tomorrow.

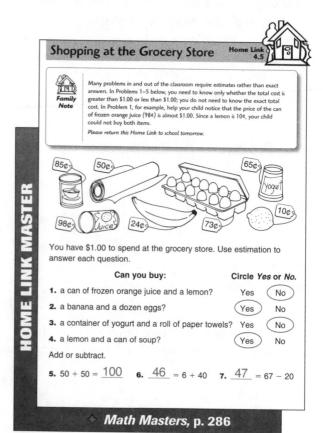

You have $1.00 to spend at the grocery store. Use estimation to answer each question.

Can you buy:	Circle *Yes* or *No*.
1. a can of frozen orange juice and a lemon?	Yes **(No)**
2. a banana and a dozen eggs?	**(Yes)** No
3. a container of yogurt and a roll of paper towels?	Yes **(No)**
4. a lemon and a can of soup?	**(Yes)** No

Add or subtract.

5. 50 + 50 = 100   6. 46 = 6 + 40   7. 47 = 67 − 20

HOME LINK MASTER

✦ *Math Masters, p. 286*

Options for Individualizing

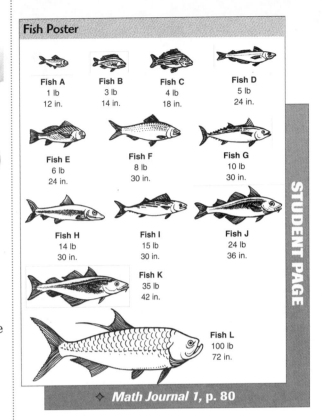

Fish Poster

Fish A
1 lb
12 in.

Fish B
3 lb
14 in.

Fish C
4 lb
18 in.

Fish D
5 lb
24 in.

Fish E
6 lb
24 in.

Fish F
8 lb
30 in.

Fish G
10 lb
30 in.

Fish H
14 lb
30 in.

Fish I
15 lb
30 in.

Fish J
24 lb
36 in.

Fish K
35 lb
42 in.

Fish L
100 lb
72 in.

◆ *Math Journal 1*, p. 80

STUDENT PAGE

◆ ENRICHMENT Using Estimation to Compare Sums of Weights (*Math Journal 1*, p. 80)

INDEPENDENT ACTIVITY   15–30 min

Give children problems about the Fish Poster on journal page 80 to practice using estimation skills. *For example:*

▷ Choose a fish and ask children to name pairs of fish whose combined weights are less than, greater than, or equal to the weight of the chosen fish. For example, Fish A and Fish D together weigh less than Fish G. Children should explain why they think the weight of the pair is less than, greater than, or equal to that of the chosen fish.

▷ Name two pairs of fish. For example, Fish E and Fish C are one pair, and Fish H and Fish J are the other pair. Ask, *Which pair weighs more?* or *Which pair weighs less?* Ask children to explain their answers.

◆ RETEACHING Mnemonic Devices for < and >

SMALL-GROUP ACTIVITY   15–30 min

Review the mnemonic devices that were mentioned in Unit 1 for remembering the meanings of < and >:

▷ Use animal analogies, such as "the duck's mouth must be bigger to swallow the bigger number."

▷ The symbol for "less than" (<) looks like the left-hand finger and thumb. Also, *less* and *left* start with the same letter.

▷ The meeting point of the two lines is next to the smaller number.

▷ Draw dots on each of the open ends of the symbol and one on the vertex or point. The number that is larger is on the side with two dots. The number that is smaller is on the side with one dot.

▷ Draw two dots next to the larger number and one dot next to the smaller number. Connect each of the two dots to the single dot and the symbol will be correct.

PLANNING AHEAD

For the Language Diversity activity in Lesson 4.7, you may want to prepare a poster like the one shown on page 262.

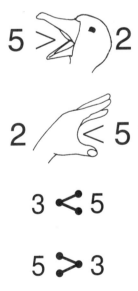

Mnemonic devices for *less than* and *greater than*

4.6

A Shopping Activity

OBJECTIVES To develop strategies for adding 2-digit numbers mentally; to calculate the total cost of two items; and to make change for whole-dollar amounts up to $100.

summaries	materials
1 Teaching the Lesson	
Children discuss strategies for adding 2-digit numbers. Then they add 2-digit numbers to solve problems about buying items. [Operations and Computation] Children calculate the total cost for a pair of items and use play money to pay and make change by playing *Shopping*. [Operations and Computation; Measurement and Reference Frames]	☐ *Math Journal 1*, pp. 97 and 98 ☐ Home Link 4.5 Per partnership: ☐ Teaching Master (*Math Masters*, p. 61) ☐ *Shopping* cards cut from *Math Masters*, p. 67 ☐ calculator; nine $1 bills, and eight $10 bills ☐ one $100 bill (optional) **See Advance Preparation**
2 Ongoing Learning & Practice	
Children practice adding 2-digit numbers by playing *Addition Spin*. [Operations and Computation] Children practice and maintain skills through Math Boxes and Home Link activities.	☐ *Math Journal 1*, pp. 86 and 99 ☐ Home Link Master (*Math Masters*, p. 287) Per partnership: ☐ Teaching Master (*Math Masters*, p. 62) ☐ paper clip; calculator
3 Options for Individualizing	
Reteaching Children add multiples of 10. [Numeration; Operations and Computation]	☐ Teaching Master (*Math Masters*, p. 61; optional) ☐ base-10 blocks: 18 longs

---

Additional Information

Advance Preparation If you need more bills before playing *Shopping* in Part 1, make copies of *Math Masters,* pages 5–8.

Getting Started

Mental Math and Reflexes

Solve each problem.

$36 + 40 = ?$ 76 $87 + 30 = ?$ 117 $50 + 24 = ?$ 74

$? = 60 + 69$ 129 $? = 58 + 20$ 78 $? = 70 + 33$ 103

Pose other addition problems with addends that are a multiple of 10 and any 2-digit number.

Math Message

You buy a clock that costs $78. You pay with a $100 bill. How much is your change?

Home Link 4.5 Follow-Up

Ask volunteers to explain their answers.

Teaching the Lesson

◆ Math Message Follow-Up

WHOLE-CLASS DISCUSSION

Ask children to share their solution strategies. In Unit 3, children practiced making change by counting up with coins. Invite a volunteer to make change for the clock purchase by counting up with play money. *For example:*

▷ Start with $78—the cost of the clock. Count up to $100—the money used to pay. Say *79, 80, 90, 100* while putting down two $1 bills and then two $10 bills. The change is $22.

Making change by counting up can be practiced as a variation of the *Shopping* activity.

◆ Strategies for Adding 2-Digit Numbers
(*Math Journal 1*, p. 98)

WHOLE-CLASS DISCUSSION

Select a pair of items from journal page 98, such as the telephone ($46) and the toaster ($29). Ask children how they might find the total cost of these two items.

You or the children might suggest the following strategies:

Strategy 1
Start with the larger addend, 46. To add 29, note that there are 2 tens in 29. Count up by 10s. 56, 66 Then add 9. $66 + 9 = 75$ The total cost is $75.

Strategy 2
Think of $10 bills and $1 bills. Add the $10 bills. 4 tens + 2 tens = 6 tens, or $60 Add the $1 bills. 6 ones + 9 ones = 15 ones, or $15 Add the tens and the ones. $60 + $15 = $75

Strategy 3
29 is 1 less than 30. Add 30 to 46. $30 + 46 = 76$ Then subtract 1 to make up for the extra 1. $76 - 1 = 75$

Strategy 4
29 is 1 less than 30, and 46 is 4 less than 50. Add 30 and 50. $30 + 50 = 80$ Then subtract the extra 1 and the extra 4. $1 + 4 = 5; 80 - 5 = 75$ or $80 - 1 = 79; 79 - 4 = 75$

◆ *Math Masters,* p. 67

NOTE: The items and prices shown on *Math Masters,* page 67 are the same as those shown on journal page 98.

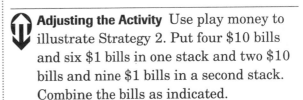

Adjusting the Activity Use play money to illustrate Strategy 2. Put four $10 bills and six $1 bills in one stack and two $10 bills and nine $1 bills in a second stack. Combine the bills as indicated.

Shopping

Play *Shopping* with a partner.

Materials
- ☐ *Shopping* cards (*Math Masters*, p. 67)
- ☐ *Math Masters*, p. 61
- ☐ calculator
- ☐ play money for each partner: at least nine $1 bills and eight $10 bills; one $100 bill (optional)

Directions

1. Partners take turns being the "Customer" and the "Clerk."

2. The Customer draws two cards and turns them over. These are the items the Customer is buying.

3. The Customer places the two cards on the parts-and-total diagram—one card in each Part box.

4. The Customer figures out the total cost of the two items without using a calculator.

5. The Customer counts out bills equal to the total cost. The Customer places the bills in the Total box on the parts-and-total diagram.

6. The Clerk uses a calculator to check that the Customer has figured the correct total cost.

7. Partners switch roles.

8. Play continues until all eight cards have been used.

Another Way to Play

Instead of counting out bills, the Customer says or writes the total. The Customer gives the Clerk a $100 bill to pay for the items. The Clerk must return the correct change.

✦ *Math Journal 1, p. 97*

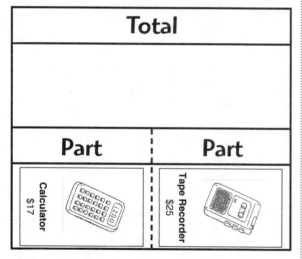

Children play *Shopping* with the *Shopping* cards from *Math Masters*, page 67 and the parts-and-total diagram from *Math Masters*, page 61.

NOTE: The main objective of this lesson is to develop and practice strategies for mental addition of 2-digit numbers. Making change by counting up is also practiced. *Shopping* is played using *Math Masters*, page 61 to keep the parts-and-total diagram in children's minds.

Discuss solution strategies for a few more problems.

NOTE: At this point, do not take the time to teach children a traditional paper-and-pencil algorithm for addition. The purpose of this lesson is to allow children to experiment with their own mental addition methods. Formal addition methods are addressed in Lessons 4.8 and 4.9.

ONGOING ASSESSMENT

Watch for children who still have difficulty adding multiples of 10. They need to practice this skill in anticipation of the partial-sums addition algorithm in Lesson 4.9. See the Reteaching activity in this lesson for a suggestion.

✦ Playing *Shopping*

(*Math Journal 1*, p. 97; *Math Masters*, p. 61 and *Shopping* Cards Cut from *Math Masters*, p. 67)

PARTNER ACTIVITY 👥

Divide the class into partnerships. Partners place the *Shopping* cards facedown on the playing surface. There should be 8 cards per partnership. Partners take turns being Customer and Clerk. Partners follow the steps given on journal page 97.

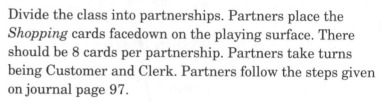 **Adjusting the Activity** If some children are having difficulty finding the total cost, they can count out the bills for each item separately. (If this is done, a player would need seventeen $1 bills.) For example, if the selected items are a camera ($43) and an iron ($32), the player can count out $43 and place these bills in one Part box, and then count out $32 and place these bills in the second Part box. The player then combines the bills, slides them to the Total box, and counts the bills to determine the total cost.

For a more challenging way to play, the Customer does not count out bills. Instead, the Customer says or writes the total cost of the selected items. The Customer pays with a $100 bill. The Clerk must return the correct change.

✦ Solve Shopping Problems
(*Math Journal 1*, p. 98)

PARTNER ACTIVITY

Children solve the problems with their partners. Partners check each other's work. There is more than one possible correct answer for Problems 3–5. For Problems 1 and 2, children should indicate the known and missing information in the parts-and-total diagram.

Adjusting the Activity Some children find that it is helpful to write words or short phrases in the parts-and-total diagram to remind them what the numbers mean. See examples below.

Total	
?	
Part	**Part**
43	32

Only essential information is recorded.

Total	
? cost of both	
Part	**Part**
$43 camera	*$32 iron*

Information with added descriptions

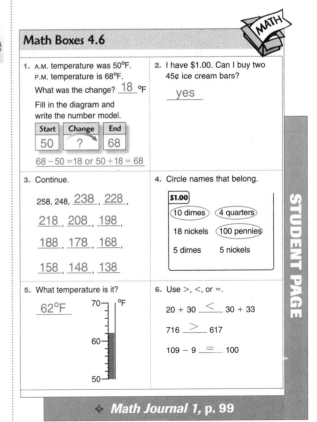

Shopping Problems

Telephone $46 · Camera $43 · Tape Recorder $25 · Calculator $17 · Toaster $29 · Iron $32 · Compact Disc $14 · Radio $38

1. You buy a telephone and an iron.
   What is the total cost? $ _78_
   Number model: _46 + 32 = 78_

Total	
?	
Part	Part
46	32

2. You buy a radio and a calculator.
   What is the total cost? $ _55_
   Number model: _38 + 17 = 55_

Total	
?	
Part	Part
38	17

Solve each problem.

3. You bought two items. The total cost is exactly $60. What did you buy?
   The telephone and compact disc or the camera and calculator

4. You bought two items. Together they cost the same as a telephone. What did you buy?
   The calculator and toaster or the iron and compact disc

5. You bought three items. The total cost is exactly $60. What did you buy?
   The calculator, compact disc, and toaster or iron and 2 compact discs

✦ *Math Journal 1*, p. 98

STUDENT PAGE

---

2 Ongoing Learning & Practice

✦ Playing *Addition Spin*
(*Math Journal 1*, p. 86; *Math Masters*, p. 62)

PARTNER ACTIVITY

Children use a spinner from *Math Masters*, page 62 to construct 2-digit addition problems.

The rules for *Addition Spin* are on journal page 86. The master includes two spin mats. Children should now use the mat at the bottom of the page.

✦ Math Boxes 4.6 (*Math Journal 1*, p. 99)

INDEPENDENT ACTIVITY

 Mixed Review This journal page provides opportunities for cumulative review or assessment of concepts and skills.

Math Boxes 4.6

1. A.M. temperature was 50°F. P.M. temperature is 68°F.
   What was the change? _18_ °F
   Fill in the diagram and write the number model.

Start	Change	End
50	?	68

   68 − 50 = 18 or 50 + 18 = 68

2. I have $1.00. Can I buy two 45¢ ice cream bars?
   yes

3. Continue.
   258, 248, _238_, _228_,
   _218_, _208_, _198_,
   _188_, _178_, _168_,
   _158_, _148_, _138_

4. Circle names that belong.

   $1.00
   (10 dimes)   (4 quarters)
   18 nickels   (100 pennies)
   5 dimes   5 nickels

5. What temperature is it?
   _62°F_

6. Use >, <, or =.
   20 + 30 _<_ 30 + 33
   716 _>_ 617
   109 − 9 _=_ 100

✦ *Math Journal 1*, p. 99

STUDENT PAGE

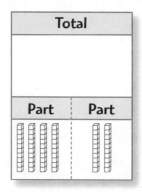

Total

Part	Part

$40 + 20 = ?$

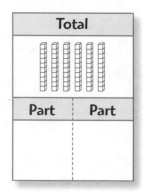

Total

Part	Part

Slide all longs to the Total box and count. $40 + 20 = 60$

Addition Number Stories

Home Link 4.6

Family Note

In today's lesson, your child solved problems by adding 2-digit numbers mentally. For example, to find 34 + 23, you might first add the tens: 30 + 20 = 50. Then add the ones: 4 + 3 = 7. Finally, combine the tens and ones: 50 + 7 = 57.

Please return this Home Link to school tomorrow.

Try to solve Problems 1 and 2 mentally. Fill in the diagrams. Then write the answers and number models.

1. Ruth had 20 marbles in her collection. Her brother gave her 10 more. How many marbles does Ruth have now?

Start	Change	End
20	+10	30

Answer: __30 marbles__
(unit)

Number model:

__20 + 10 = 30__

2. Tim baked 30 ginger snaps and 24 sugar cookies. How many cookies did he bake?

Total	
?	
Part	Part
30	24

Answer: __54 cookies__
(unit)

Number model:

__30 + 24 = 54__

Try to do each problem mentally. Then write the answer.

Unit
raisins

3. __100__ = 40 + 60

4. 90 + 50 = __140__

5. __79__ = 70 + 9

6. 80 + 3 = __83__

7. 30 + 64 = __94__

8. __77__ = 27 + 50

Math Masters, p. 287

◆ Home Link 4.6 (*Math Masters*, p. 287)

Home Connection Children use change diagrams to solve problems mentally. They also solve computation problems involving multiples of 10.

3 Options for Individualizing

◆ RETEACHING Adding Multiples of 10

INDEPENDENT ACTIVITY **15–30 min**

Pose sets of problems like the following:

4 + 2 = __ 6	9 + 3 = __ 12	__ = 7 + 9 16
40 + 20 = __ 60	90 + 30 = __ 120	__ = 70 + 90 160

Remind children that another way to think of 40 is as 4 tens or 4 [10s]. Another way to think of 20 is as 2 tens or 2 [10s]. So 40 + 20 = 4 [10s] + 2 [10s] = 6 [10s] or 60.

The sets of problems can then be rewritten as follows:

4 [1s] + 2 [1s] = __ [1s] 6
4 [10s] + 2 [10s] = __ [10s] 6

9 [1s] + 3 [1s] = __ [1s] 12
9 [10s] + 3 [10s] = __ [10s] 12

__ [1s] = 7 [1s] + 9 [1s] 16
__ [10s] = 7 [10s] + 9 [10s] 16

You may wish to use base-10 blocks on a parts-and-total diagram (*Math Masters*, page 61) to demonstrate further. An example is given in the margin.

PLANNING AHEAD

In Lesson 4.7, children will need tape measures for their tool kits. Be sure to add the tool-kit numbers to the tape measures.

4.7 EXPLORATIONS

Exploring Length, Area, and Attributes

OBJECTIVES To measure lengths and distances to the nearest inch and centimeter; to explore area by tiling surfaces; and to sort attribute blocks according to rules.

summaries / materials

1 Teaching the Lesson

Children examine and discuss inch and centimeter scales. [Measurement and Reference Frames]	☐ Home Link 4.6
	☐ tape measure and yardstick
Exploration D: Children use a tape measure to measure lengths and distances in the classroom. [Measurement and Reference Frames]	**Exploration D:** Per small group:
	☐ *Math Journal 1*, pp. 100 and 101
	☐ tape measure
Exploration E: Children use pattern blocks, playing cards, and quarter-sheets of paper to tile surfaces. [Measurement and Reference Frames]	**Exploration E:** Per partnership:
	☐ *Math Journal 1*, pp. 102 and 103
	☐ pattern blocks; Pattern-Block Template
	☐ playing cards or Everything Math Deck cards, if available
	☐ slate; sheets of paper; scissors
	☐ *A Cloak for the Dreamer* (optional)
Exploration F: Children sort a set of attribute blocks by determining which blocks fit a given set of rules and which blocks do not. [Geometry]	**Exploration F:** Per group:
	☐ *Math Journal 1*, p. 104
	☐ Teaching Masters (*Math Masters*, pp. 68–70)
	☐ 1 set of attribute blocks; scissors; envelope
	***See* Advance Preparation**

2 Ongoing Learning & Practice

Children practice adding 2-digit numbers by playing *Shopping*. [Operations and Computation; Measurement and Reference Frames]	☐ *Math Journal 1*, pp. 97 and 105
	☐ Home Link Master (*Math Masters*, p. 288)
Children practice and maintain skills through Math Boxes and Home Link activities.	☐ Teaching Master (*Math Masters*, p. 61); per partnership
	☐ per partnership: calculator; *Shopping* cards; nine $1 bills; eight $10 bills; and one $100 bill (optional)

3 Options for Individualizing

Language Diversity Children model and review the meanings of *inch* and *centimeter*. [Measurement and Reference Frames]	☐ ruler marked in cm and in., objects with lengths of 1 cm
	☐ poster showing inch and centimeter (optional)

Additional Information

Advance Preparation Spend the most time on Explorations D and E. Before using them, children should write tool-kit numbers on their tape measures. If possible, have children use heavier stock paper for Exploration E. For Exploration E, you may want to obtain the book *A Cloak for the Dreamer* by Aileen Friedman (A Marilyn Burns Brainy Day Book. Scholastic, 1994). *Math Masters*, pages 68 and 69 give directions for Exploration F. You may want to place copies of them at workstations.

Vocabulary • **inch (in.)** • **centimeter (cm)** • **tiling** • **attribute blocks**

Math Message

Name two things you would measure with a ruler.

Name two things you would measure with a tape measure.

Home Link 4.6 Follow-Up

Ask volunteers to explain how they solved each problem. Assess whether most children were able to find the answers to the problems mentally.

Date   Time

Measuring Lengths with a Tape Measure (cont.)

4. Open your journal so that it looks like the drawing below.

a. Measure the long side and the short side to the nearest inch.

The long side is about __17__ inches.

The short side is about __11__ inches.

b. Now measure your journal to the nearest centimeter.

The long side is about __44__ centimeters.

The short side is about __28__ centimeters.

Math Journal 1, page 101

Measuring Lengths with a Tape Measure

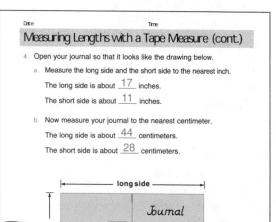

1. Measure the height from the top of your desk or table to the floor. Measure to the nearest inch.

The height from my desk or table to the

floor is about _____ inches.

Answers vary.

2. Measure the height from the top of your chair to the floor. Measure to the nearest inch.

The height from the top of my chair to the

floor is about _____ inches.

Answers vary.

3. Measure the width of your classroom door.

The classroom door is about

_____ inches wide.

Answers vary.

Math Journal 1, p. 100

STUDENT PAGE

---

1 Teaching the Lesson

◆ Math Message Follow-Up

WHOLE-CLASS DISCUSSION

Discuss children's answers. Sample answers: Ruler—the width of a hand, the length of a crayon; Tape measure— the width of a desk, the distance around a person's waist It is important to select the correct measuring tool for the task at hand. Children's tool-kit rulers are best suited for measuring lengths and distances that are shorter than the ruler. Tape measures and yardsticks are longer, and are useful for measuring lengths and distances that are greater than the ruler. Tape measures are useful for measuring things that are not flat, and for measuring around things.

Pull out a tool-kit tape measure to its full length (5 feet) and hold this alongside a yardstick. Ask why the tape measure would be a more convenient tool than the yardstick for measuring the heights of children in the class. Sample answer: All of the children are probably taller than a yardstick but shorter than the 5-foot tape.

◆ Examining Inch and Centimeter Scales

WHOLE-CLASS DISCUSSION

Discuss the **inch (in.)** and **centimeter (cm)** scales on rulers and tape measures. Ask children to examine their rulers and tape measures, and ensure that they can correctly identify the two scales on each. Say that the inch scale is more commonly used in the United States. In science, lengths are reported in centimeters or other metric units. Write the units and their abbreviations on the board.

Ask children which unit is longer—the inch or the centimeter. The inch Have children carefully pull their tape measures out to their full lengths. *How long is your tape measure?* 60 inches on the inch side; 150 cm on the centimeter side

Ask children to compare lengths on the two sides of their tape measures at different points along the tape. *For example:*

• It's 20 on the inch side and about 51 on the centimeter side.

• It's 30 on the inch side and about 76 on the centimeter side.

• It's 100 on the centimeter side and about 39 on the inch side.

Help children to summarize the comparison. If you measure a length in centimeters, you will get a larger number than if you measure the same length in inches.

◆ Exploration D: Measuring Lengths with a Tape Measure (*Math Journal 1,* pp. 100 and 101)

SMALL-GROUP ACTIVITY 👥👥

Children who used *Everyday Mathematics* in first grade have had considerable practice using rulers and tape measures to measure lengths to the nearest inch but limited practice in measuring to the nearest centimeter. As you circulate, make sure that children are lining up one end of the object or distance to be measured with the end (zero mark) of the tape measure. If a measured length falls between the inch (or centimeter) marks on their tapes, some children may need help in deciding which is the nearest inch (or centimeter).

 Adjusting the Activity Ask, *Can you find an object in our classroom that is about 50 inches long?*

Ask, *Can you find an object in our classroom that is about 50 centimeters long?*

◆ Exploration E: Tiling Surfaces with Different Shapes (*Math Journal 1,* pp. 102 and 103)

PARTNER ACTIVITY 👥

Children use multiples of the same pattern-block shape to cover as completely as possible a card from the Everything Math Deck, if available. There should be no spaces between the blocks, nor should the blocks overlap or extend beyond the card. This activity is called **tiling.**

Tiling Surfaces with Shapes

Materials ☐ pattern blocks
☐ slates
☐ sheets of paper
☐ Pattern-Block Template
☐ scissors
☐ Everything Math Deck cards, if available

1. Pick one pattern-block shape. **Tile** a card by covering it with blocks of this shape.

• Lay the blocks flat on the card.

• Don't leave any spaces between blocks.

• Keep the blocks inside the edges of the card. There may be open spaces along the edges.

Count the blocks on the card. If a space could be covered by more than half of a block, count the space as one block. Do not count spaces that could be covered by less than half of a block.

Which pattern-block shape did you use?
  Answers vary.

Number of blocks needed to tile the card:
  Answers vary.

Trace the card. Use your Pattern-Block Template to draw the blocks you used to tile the card.

◆ *Math Journal 1,* p. 102

NOTE: If children are using retractable tape measures, teach and enforce the "2-inch, no zap" rule: Do not "zap" the tape measure until no more than 2 inches are showing. Following this rule will extend the life of the tape measures.

Tiling Surfaces with Shapes (cont.)

2. Use Everything Math Deck cards to tile both a slate and a Pattern-Block Template. How many cards were needed to tile them?

Slate: _____ cards Answers vary.

Pattern-Block Template: _____ cards Answers vary.

3. Fold a sheet of paper into fourths. Cut the fourths apart. Use them to tile larger surfaces, such as a desktop.

Surface	Number of Fourths
Answers vary.	

Follow-Up

With a partner, find things in the classroom that are tiled or covered with patterns. Make a list. Be ready to share your findings.

◆ *Math Journal 1,* p. 103

An Attribute Rule

Choose an Attribute Rule Card. Copy the rule below.

Rule: _Rules, drawings, and descriptions vary._

Draw or describe all of the attribute blocks that fit the rule.

Draw or describe all of the attribute blocks that *do not* fit the rule.

These blocks fit the rule:

_____

_____

_____

These blocks *do not* fit the rule:

_____

_____

_____

_____

✦ *Math Journal 1*, p. 104

"What's My Attribute?"

Work with a small group.

Materials
- ❏ *Math Journal 1*, p. 104
- ❏ Attribute Rule Cards (*Math Masters*, p. 70)
- ❏ scissors
- ❏ 2 sheets of paper
- ❏ 1 set of attribute blocks: triangles, circles, squares (large and small; red, yellow, and blue)
- ❏ red, yellow, and blue crayons

Directions
1. Cut apart the Attribute Rule Cards on *Math Masters,* page 70.
2. Mix the cards. Stack them facedown.
3. Label one sheet of paper "These fit the rule."
4. Label another sheet "These do not fit the rule."
5. Take turns being the "Rule Maker."
6. The Rule Maker takes the top card from the stack.
7. The Rule Maker puts the card faceup for everyone to see.
8. Group members take turns choosing a block.

✦ *Math Masters*, p. 68

Children record the number of block shapes needed to tile the card. Any space around the edges of the card that cannot be covered by a whole block, but that can be covered by more than half a block, can be counted as 1 block. Any uncovered spaces less than half of a block should not be counted.

Next, children tile their slates and templates with playing cards or Everything Math Deck cards, and record the result. Then they fold a sheet of $8\frac{1}{2}$" by 11" paper into fourths, cut out the fourths, and use them to tile larger items, such as their desktops or a tabletop. Again, they record what they did.

Adjusting the Activity To extend the activity, ask children to find things in the room that are tiled or covered with a pattern.

Literature Link *A Cloak for the Dreamer* by Aileen Friedman (A Marilyn Burns Brainy Day Book. Scholastic, 1994) is a story about tailors designing patchwork cloaks. One cloak is made of rectangles, another of triangles, and a third of squares. The fourth is unacceptable because it is made of circles and full of open spaces.

✦ Exploration F: Sorting Attribute Blocks
(*Math Journal 1*, p. 104; *Math Masters,* pp. 68–70)

SMALL-GROUP ACTIVITY 👥👥

Children do the following to sort **attribute blocks:**

1. Cut apart the cards on *Math Masters,* page 70.

2. Shuffle the cards and put them in a pile facedown.

3. Label one sheet of paper "These fit the rule." Label a second sheet "These do not fit the rule."

4. Group members take turns being the Rule Maker. The Rule Maker draws a card from the shuffled pile and puts it out for all to see.

5. The rest of the group members take turns putting blocks on the appropriate sheets labeled "These fit the rule" and "These do not fit the rule."

Adjusting the Activity Allow children to work in partnerships when taking turns putting blocks on the appropriate sheet. In this way, children are able to discuss their choices. Alternately, the whole group can work together as a team to decide which blocks fit the rule and which do not.

Challenge children to make up their own rules and write them on the two blank cards on *Math Masters,* page 70.

Children record one of their rules on journal page 104 and describe those attribute blocks that fit the rule and those that don't.

NOTE: The Attribute Rule Cards from *Math Masters,* page 70 will be needed again in Lesson 5.1. Collect the cards and store them in envelopes.

 "What's My Attribute?" (cont.)

9. If the block fits the rule on the card, place it on the paper that says "These fit the rule."

10. If the block does not fit the rule, place it on the paper that says "These do not fit the rule."

11. Repeat Steps 6–10 until everyone has been the Rule Maker.

Follow-Up

• Write one of the rules on journal page 104.

• Draw or describe all of the blocks that fit the rule.

• Draw or describe all of the blocks that do not fit the rule.

Challenge

Make up two rules of your own. Write them on the two blank cards given on *Math Masters,* page 70.

TEACHING MASTER

◆ *Math Masters,* p. 69

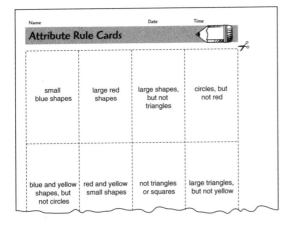

Name		Date	Time
Attribute Rule Cards			
small blue shapes	large red shapes	large shapes, but not triangles	circles, but not red
blue and yellow shapes, but not circles	red and yellow small shapes	not triangles or squares	large triangles, but not yellow

❷ Ongoing Learning & Practice

◆ Playing *Shopping*
(*Math Journal 1,* p. 97; *Math Masters,* p. 61, and *Shopping* Cards Cut from *Math Masters,* p. 67)

PARTNER ACTIVITY

This activity was introduced in Lesson 4.6. If children have not previously done this activity using the variation described at the bottom of the journal page, you may wish to have children do so now.

Shopping

Play *Shopping* with a partner.

Materials ☐ *Shopping* cards (*Math Masters,* p. 67)
☐ *Math Masters,* p. 61
☐ calculator
☐ play money for each partner: at least nine $1 bills and eight $10 bills; one $100 bill (optional)

Directions

1. Partners take turns being the "Customer" and the "Clerk."

2. The Customer draws two cards and turns them over. These are the items the Customer is buying.

3. The Customer places the two cards on the parts-and-total diagram—one card in each Part box.

4. The Customer figures out the total cost of the two items without using a calculator.

5. The Customer counts out bills equal to the total cost. The Customer places the bills in the Total box on the parts-and-total diagram.

6. The Clerk uses a calculator to check that the Customer has figured the correct total cost.

7. Partners switch roles.

8. Play continues until all eight cards have been used.

Another Way to Play

Instead of counting out bills, the Customer says or writes the total. The Customer gives the Clerk a $100 bill to pay for the items. The Clerk must return the correct change.

STUDENT PAGE

◆ *Math Journal 1,* p. 97

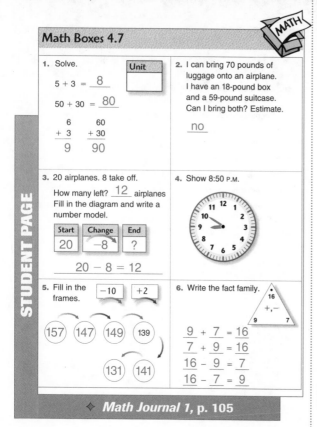

Math Boxes 4.7

1. Solve.

$5 + 3 = \underline{8}$

$50 + 30 = \underline{80}$

6	60
+ 3	+ 30
9	90

Unit

2. I can bring 70 pounds of luggage onto an airplane. I have an 18-pound box and a 59-pound suitcase. Can I bring both? Estimate.

_no_

3. 20 airplanes. 8 take off.

How many left? <u>12</u> airplanes
Fill in the diagram and write a number model.

Start	Change	End
20	−8	?

$20 - 8 = 12$

4. Show 8:50 P.M.

5. Fill in the frames.

−10   +2

(157) (147) (149) (139)

(131) (141)

6. Write the fact family.

16
+,−
9   7

$9 + 7 = 16$
$7 + 9 = 16$
$16 - 9 = 7$
$16 - 7 = 9$

♦ *Math Journal 1, p. 105*

STUDENT PAGE

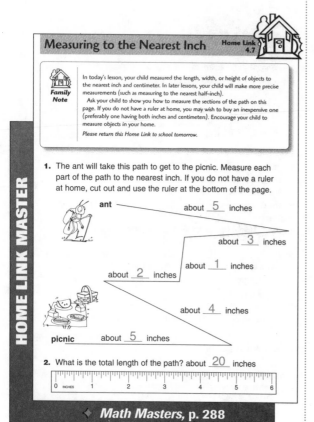

Measuring to the Nearest Inch

Home Link 4.7

Family Note

In today's lesson, your child measured the length, width, or height of objects to the nearest inch and centimeter. In later lessons, your child will make more precise measurements (such as measuring to the nearest half-inch).

Ask your child to show you how to measure the sections of the path on this page. If you do not have a ruler at home, you may wish to buy an inexpensive one (preferably one having both inches and centimeters). Encourage your child to measure objects in your home.

Please return this Home Link to school tomorrow.

1. The ant will take this path to get to the picnic. Measure each part of the path to the nearest inch. If you do not have a ruler at home, cut out and use the ruler at the bottom of the page.

ant

about <u>5</u> inches

about <u>3</u> inches

about <u>1</u> inches

about <u>2</u> inches

about <u>4</u> inches

picnic   about <u>5</u> inches

2. What is the total length of the path? about <u>20</u> inches

Math Masters, p. 288

HOME LINK MASTER

♦ **Math Boxes 4.7** (*Math Journal 1*, p. 105)

INDEPENDENT ACTIVITY

Mixed Review This journal page provides opportunities for cumulative review or assessment of concepts and skills.

♦ **Home Link 4.7** (*Math Masters,* p. 288)

Home Connection Children measure sections of a path to the nearest inch. Then they combine their measurements to find the total length of the path.

3 Options for Individualizing

♦ **LANGUAGE DIVERSITY** **Demonstrating Inch and Centimeter Scales**

PARTNER ACTIVITY 👥   **15–30 min**

You may want children familiar with the metric system to show examples of classroom objects whose measures are one, two, or three centimeters.

For children unfamiliar with U.S. customary measures of length, you may need to go over the meaning of *inch*. You may want to show children a ruler with the inch mark and measure 1-inch objects, such as a piece of chalk. You may also want to display a poster on the board showing the word *inch* spelled out, the abbreviation for inch (in.), the length of an inch, and perhaps a translation in children's languages.

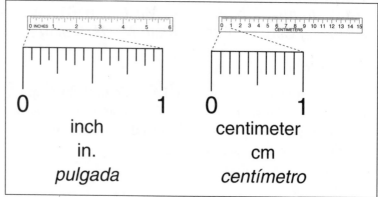

A teacher-created poster that uses *Math Masters*, pages 146 and 147 to display Spanish and English measurement names

4.8 Paper-and-Pencil Addition Strategies

OBJECTIVES To develop paper-and-pencil strategies for adding 2-digit and 3-digit numbers; and to use estimation to check if answers are reasonable.

summaries

materials

1 Teaching the Lesson

Children solve 2-digit addition problems, record their work with paper and pencil, share solution strategies, and use ballpark estimates to check if their answers are reasonable. Children practice adding 2-, 3-, and 4-digit numbers.
[Operations and Computation; Numeration]

- ☐ *Math Journal 1*, p. 106
- ☐ Home Link 4.7
- ☐ base-10 blocks (optional): 18 cubes, 18 longs, and 6 flats

2 Ongoing Learning & Practice

Children solve "What's My Rule?" and Frames-and-Arrows problems. [Patterns, Functions, and Algebra; Operations and Computation]

Children practice and maintain skills through Math Boxes and Home Link activities.

- ☐ *Math Journal 1*, pp. 107 and 108
- ☐ Home Link Masters (*Math Masters*, pp. 289 and 290)

3 Options for Individualizing

Reteaching Children use base-10 blocks to review place-value concepts. [Numeration]

Extra Practice Children add and subtract multiples of 10.
[Operations and Computation; Patterns, Functions, and Algebra]

- ☐ Teaching Masters (*Math Masters*, pp. 35 and 71)
- ☐ number cards (from the Everything Math Deck, if available)
- ☐ base-10 blocks: 9 cubes, 9 longs, and 9 flats
- ☐ *Minute Math®*, p. 42

Additional Information

Advance Preparation Plan to spend three days on this lesson and on Lesson 4.9.

Vocabulary • **ballpark estimate**

Vocabulary (teacher) • **algorithm**

Getting Started

Mental Math and Reflexes

Pose pairs of problems similar to the following:

- 30 + 40 = ? 70   30 + 46 = ? 76
- ? = 50 + 20 70   ? = 58 + 20 78
- ? = 60 + 30 90   ? = 60 + 37 97

Math Message

Add. Be ready to tell how you found each answer.

43 + 4 = ___ 47

___ = 75 + 8 83

57 + 22 = ___ 79

Unit
pennies

Home Link 4.7 Follow-Up

Review answers as necessary. Ask children to explain how they determined the nearest inch and their strategies for finding the total length of the path.

---

1 Teaching the Lesson

◆ Math Message Follow-Up

WHOLE-CLASS ACTIVITY

Have children share their solution strategies. For each problem, record on the board any strategies that result in the correct answer. Emphasize that there are many good ways to get correct answers to problems.

◆ Discussing the Use of Ballpark Estimates to Check Answers

WHOLE-CLASS DISCUSSION

Remind the class that one way to decide whether an answer is reasonable is to make a **ballpark estimate**—an answer that may not be exact but that is "close enough." One way to estimate a sum is to change the addends to "close-but-easier" numbers and then to add those numbers.

$$
\begin{array}{rcr}
57 & \rightarrow & 60 \\
22 & \rightarrow & +20 \\
\hline
 & & 80
\end{array}
$$

For the Math Message problem 57 + 22, suggest changing the first addend to 60 and the second addend to 20. Since 60 + 20 = 80, any answer not close to 80 is likely to be incorrect.

✦ Solving Addition Problems; Keeping a Paper-and-Pencil Record

SMALL-GROUP ACTIVITY 👥👥👥👥

In Lesson 4.6, children discussed mental arithmetic strategies for adding 2-digit numbers. In this lesson, children continue to develop and share their own solution strategies for solving addition problems and keep a paper-and-pencil record of their solutions. (The paper record will make it easier for children to recall and describe their methods.)

The goal is to develop, over time, a number of systematic paper-and-pencil procedures—**algorithms**—that can be applied to any addition problem, including those with 3- and 4-digit addends.

Write problems like the following on the board, some in a horizontal format and some in a vertical format. Ask someone to suggest a unit and record it in a unit box.

▷ 47 + 33 80

▷ 29 + 37 66

▷ 52 + 29 81

▷ 26 + 74 100

▷ 55 + 83 138

▷ 76 + 28 104

▷ 163 + 56 219

▷ 219 + 352 571

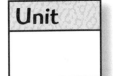

Unit

> NOTE: Although problems written in a horizontal format probably encourage more varied responses than problems written in a vertical format, the vertical format is often more efficient when children need to perform more complex computations.

Divide the class into small groups and have children work on the problems together. Tell them to record their work with paper and pencil, and to check whether each answer is reasonable by making a ballpark estimate.

After groups have done two or three problems, bring the class together to share solution strategies. Record successful strategies on the board or on the Class Data Pad if you want to start a class collection. Once most children seem to be catching on, let groups complete the rest of the problems. Then bring the class together for discussion.

Adjusting the Activity Have children act out the problems with base-10 blocks, using longs and cubes to represent each addend separately. Then have children combine the longs and cubes into a single pile. If 10 or more cubes are in the pile, children replace 10 cubes with one long (regrouping). Then they simply count the number of longs (10s) and the number of cubes (1s) to find the sum.

Some children may be curious about problems with 3-digit addends. Show them how to reduce such problems to 2-digit addition. For example, with $219 + 352$, add the hundreds first: $200 + 300 = 500$ Record or remember this. That leaves $19 + 52$. Find this sum. 71 Add 500 to get the final answer. 571

Children usually use three major types of strategies:

Counting On

$47 + 33 = ?$	← "My problem"
$47 \quad 57 \quad 67 \quad 77$	← "Start at 47. Count up 30 more."
$\underline{+3}$	← "Add on 3 more."
80	← "The answer is 80."

Combining Groups (1s, 10s, ...) Separately

$29 + 37 = ?$	← "My problem"
$20 + 30 = 50$	← "Add the tens."
$9 + 7 = \underline{16}$	← "Add the ones."
66	← "Put these together. The answer is 66."

Adjusting and Compensating

$52 + 29 = ?$	← "My problem"
30	← "30 is close to 29, just 1 more."
$52 + 30 = 82$	← "52 plus 30 is 82."
$\underline{-1}$	← "Take away 1, because I added 30 instead of 29."
81	← "The answer is 81."

◆ Finding the Sum of Two Multidigit Numbers
(Math Journal 1, p. 106)

PARTNER ACTIVITY

Partners work together to solve addition problems. Tell children to show their computations in the workspaces on the journal page.

STUDENT PAGE

Addition Practice

Add. Show your work in the workspaces. Check your work. Write a number model to show the ballpark estimate. Sample estimates:

1. $\begin{array}{r} 39 \\ +26 \end{array}$	**Answer** 65	2. $18 + 45$	**Answer** 63	3. $52 + 28$	**Answer** 80

Ballpark estimate: $40 + 30 = 70$ Ballpark estimate: $20 + 50 = 70$ Ballpark estimate: $50 + 30 = 80$

4. $54 + 79$	**Answer** 133	5. $115 + 32$	**Answer** 147	6. $\begin{array}{r} 327 \\ +146 \end{array}$	**Answer** 473

Ballpark estimate: $50 + 80 = 130$ $120 + 30 = 150$ $300 + 150 = 450$

Add. In each problem, use the first sum to help you find the other two sums.

7. $17 + 8 = \underline{25}$
$17 + 8 + 25 = \underline{50}$
$17 + 8 + 25 + 12 = \underline{62}$

8. $\begin{array}{r} 15 \\ +9 \\ \hline 24 \end{array}$ $\begin{array}{r} 15 \\ 9 \\ +6 \\ \hline 30 \end{array}$ $\begin{array}{r} 15 \\ 9 \\ 6 \\ +22 \\ \hline 52 \end{array}$

9. $19 + 6 = \underline{25}$
$19 + 6 + 5 = \underline{30}$
$19 + 6 + 5 + 70 = \underline{100}$

10. $\begin{array}{r} 24 \\ +4 \\ \hline 28 \end{array}$ $\begin{array}{r} 24 \\ 4 \\ +7 \\ \hline 35 \end{array}$ $\begin{array}{r} 24 \\ 4 \\ 7 \\ +35 \\ \hline 70 \end{array}$

◆ *Math Journal 1*, p. 106

Children should record their answers and write a number model for their ballpark estimate to check their work. Remember that ballpark estimates can vary depending on which close, but easier to add, numbers are used. Problems 7–10 extend addition to problems with more than two addends. Children can use the first sum to find the second sum, the second sum to find the third sum, and the third sum to find the fourth sum.

ONGOING ASSESSMENT

Circulate and listen to the interactions as children work on the problems, but let them figure out the answers with as little help from you as possible. If children are having difficulty, suggest that they try one of the procedures that you recorded on the board earlier.

2 Ongoing Learning & Practice

✦ Solving "What's My Rule?" and Frames-and-Arrows Problems (*Math Journal 1,* p. 107)

INDEPENDENT ACTIVITY

In Problems 1 and 2, remind children to look at the completed rows in the tables to help them determine the rule.

✦ Math Boxes 4.8 (*Math Journal 1,* p. 108)

INDEPENDENT ACTIVITY

Mixed Review This journal page provides opportunities for cumulative review or assessment of concepts and skills.

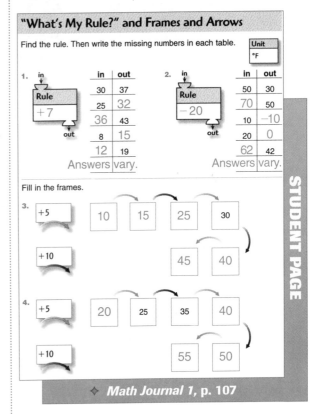

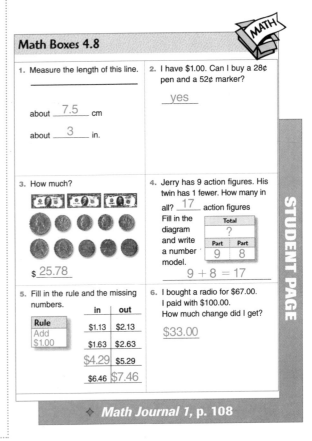

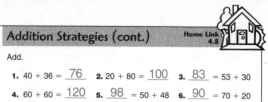

Addition Strategies (cont.)

Add.

1. $40 + 36 =$ __76__   2. $20 + 80 =$ __100__   3. __83__ $= 53 + 30$

4. $60 + 60 =$ __120__   5. __98__ $= 50 + 48$ 6. __90__ $= 70 + 20$

Add. Show your work in the workspaces.

Check your work. Write a number model to show your ballpark estimate. Answers vary.

| 7. 34 $+ 59$ | **Answer** 93 | 8. $17 + 68$ | **Answer** 85 |

Ballpark estimate: $30 + 60 = 90$ Ballpark estimate: $20 + 70 = 90$

| 9. $46 + 25$ | **Answer** 71 | 10. $56 + 27$ | **Answer** 83 |

Ballpark estimate: $50 + 30 = 80$ Ballpark estimate: $60 + 30 = 90$

| 11. $123 + 46$ | **Answer** 169 | 12. 318 $+ 226$ | **Answer** 544 |

Ballpark estimate: $120 + 50 = 170$ Ballpark estimate: $300 + 200 = 500$

◆ *Math Masters, p. 290*

Base-10 Blocks

For each problem, draw a new set of base-10 blocks that uses the fewest possible number of flats, longs, and cubes.

1.
2.
3.
4.
5.
6.

◆ *Math Masters, p. 71*

◆ Home Link 4.8 (*Math Masters*, pp. 289 and 290)

Home Connection Children add two multidigit numbers and record their strategies.

The Family Note on the Home Link explains paper-and-pencil strategies other than the traditional right-to-left method.

3 Options for Individualizing

◆ RETEACHING Reviewing Place-Value Concepts (*Math Masters*, pp. 35 and 71)

PARTNER ACTIVITY   5–15 min

If children are having trouble discovering a strategy for adding 2- and 3-digit numbers, it may be beneficial for them to do one or both of the following place-value activities.

Use base-10 blocks: Partners shuffle number cards, place the deck facedown between them, and draw two cards. They place the first card in the ones column on the Place-Value Mat (*Math Masters,* page 35) and the second card in the tens column. They use the *fewest* base-10 blocks possible to build the number. On a sheet of paper, they record the number shown, as well as the number of tens (longs) and the number of ones (cubes).

Then partners switch the two cards on the mat and repeat the procedure. Vary the activity by having children draw three cards to make 3-digit numbers.

Use Math Masters, *page 71:* This page shows collections of longs (10s) and cubes (1s). For each group of base-10 blocks, children represent the same number using the fewest longs and cubes possible. The last two problems show flats (100s), longs, and cubes.

◆ EXTRA PRACTICE Minute Math

SMALL-GROUP ACTIVITY   5–15 min

To offer children more experience with adding multiples of 10, see the following page in *Minute Math:*

Operations: p. 42

4.9 The Partial-Sums Addition Algorithm

OBJECTIVE To introduce and practice the partial-sums addition algorithm.

summaries / materials

1 Teaching the Lesson

Children are introduced to the partial-sums algorithm using both base-10 blocks and paper and pencil. Children practice adding 2- and 3-digit numbers using the partial-sums algorithm and make ballpark estimates to check their answers. [Numeration; Operations and Computation]

- ☐ *Math Journal 1*, p. 109
- ☐ Home Link 4.8
- ☐ base-10 blocks (optional): 2 flats, 18 longs, and 18 cubes
- ☐ overhead base-10 blocks (optional): 8 longs and 13 cubes

***See* Advance Preparation**

2 Ongoing Learning & Practice

Children answer questions about the times before or after the given time of an event. [Measurement and Reference Frames]

Children practice and maintain skills through Math Boxes and Home Link activities.

- ☐ *Math Journal 1*, pp. 110 and 111
- ☐ Home Link Master (*Math Masters*, p. 291)

3 Options for Individualizing

Enrichment Children explore pattern-block designs to reinforce the idea that there are usually many ways to solve a problem. [Geometry]

Per child or partnership:
- ☐ Teaching Masters (*Math Masters*, pp. 72 and 73)
- ☐ pattern blocks
- ☐ Pattern-Block Template

Additional Information

Background Information The problems in Mental Math and Reflexes give children practice doing mental addition quickly. This skill is needed for making ballpark estimates and carrying out the partial-sums algorithm.

Advance Preparation Plan to spend three days on this lesson. Before starting this lesson, decide how you will demonstrate the partial-sums algorithm using base-10 blocks—on a flat surface with children gathered around or with blocks on the overhead projector.

Vocabulary • **algorithm**

Getting Started

Mental Math and Reflexes

Pose pairs of problems, such as the following:

- 30 + 40 = ? 70
  300 + 400 = ? 700
- ? = 20 + 50 70
  ? = 200 + 500 700
- 90 + 30 = ? 120
  900 + 300 = ? 1,200

Math Message

Make a ballpark estimate for each answer.

Write a number model for each estimate.

37 + 58 = ?

473 + 234 = ?

Unit
people

Home Link 4.8 Follow-Up

Review answers and ask volunteers to explain the strategies they used to add and to make ballpark estimates. Problems 11 and 12 involve adding 3-digit numbers.

---

1 Teaching the Lesson

✦ Math Message Follow-Up

WHOLE-CLASS ACTIVITY

Remind children that one way to make a ballpark estimate is to change the numbers in the problem to "close-but-easier" numbers that can be added mentally. *For example:*

- 37 + 58 is close to 40 + 60, or 100. The exact answer to 37 + 58 should be close to 100.

- 473 + 234 is close to 500 + 200, or 700. The exact answer should be near 700. Or notice that 400 + 200 is 600. That leaves 73 + 34, which is close to 70 + 30, or 100. Thus, 473 + 234 is close to 600 + 100, or 700.

✦ Introducing the Partial-Sums Addition Algorithm Using Base-10 Blocks

WHOLE-CLASS DISCUSSION

Explain to the class that they will be able to calculate the answers to addition problems with larger numbers much more easily if they can use the same strategy for all problems. Today children will learn and practice a single strategy for addition that they will be expected to know. (You should, of course, encourage children to continue using other favorite strategies they may have for adding numbers.)

Write these two problems on the board, in vertical form:

$$45 \\ +\ 22$$ $$26 \\ +\ 57$$

Ask children to gather around as you demonstrate how to use base-10 blocks. You may wish to use base-10 blocks on an overhead. Refer to the longs as "tens" and the cubes as "ones." For each problem, model addition as a three-part operation: adding the 10s, adding the 1s, and then adding the partial sums.

Example: Model 45 + 22 with base-10 blocks.

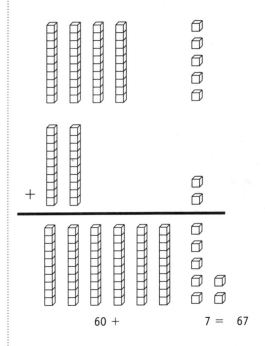

1. Count out 4 tens and 5 ones to represent 45. Count out 2 tens and 2 ones to represent 22.

2. Arrange the blocks so that they resemble the vertical addition problem. (See the first model in the margin.)

3. Collect the tens into one pile. Collect the ones into a second pile.

4. Count the tens. 6 tens, or 60

5. Count the ones. 7 ones, or 7

6. Add the counts of tens and ones. 60 + 7 = 67

Example: Model 26 + 57 with base-10 blocks.

1. Count out 2 tens and 6 ones to represent 26. Count out 5 tens and 7 ones to represent 57.

2. Arrange the blocks so that they resemble the vertical addition problem. (See the second model in the margin.)

3. Collect the tens into one pile. Collect the ones into a second pile.

4. Count the tens. 7 tens, or 70

5. Count the ones. 13 ones, or 13

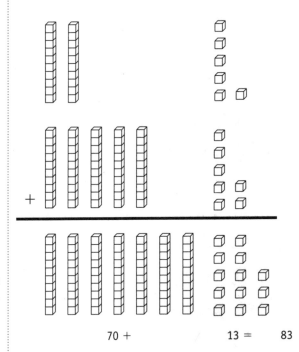

Some children may notice that the 13 cubes in the ones pile can be replaced by fewer blocks: 1 ten and 3 ones. This is fine, and you can make this substitution. There are still two piles of blocks: the tens pile (with 7 tens), and the revised ones pile (with 1 ten and 3 ones).

6. Add the counts of tens and ones. 70 + 13 = 83

Summary

These examples using base-10 blocks illustrate the steps of the partial-sums method for addition:

1. Add the tens.

2. Add the ones.

3. Add the partial sums of tens and ones to obtain the final answer.

WHOLE-CLASS DISCUSSION 👥👥👥

On the board or overhead, demonstrate the paper-and-pencil method using the same two problems (45 + 22 and 26 + 57). Remind children that in the vertical format, numbers are written one below the other and lined up in columns according to place value. As a reminder of place value, write "10s" and "1s" above the columns. (See the margin.)

Work each problem in the same order as before, and use the same language to describe 10s and 1s.

Example: 45 + 22

1. Add the tens. 4 tens + 2 tens = 6 tens, or 60. Write 60 below the line.

2. Add the ones. 5 ones + 2 ones = 7 ones, or 7. Write 7 below 60.

3. Add the partial sums. Draw a second line beneath 60 and 7. Write 67 beneath this line.

Example: 26 + 57

1. Add the tens. 2 tens + 5 tens = 7 tens, or 70. Write 70 below the line.

2. Add the ones. 6 ones + 7 ones = 13 ones, or 13. Write 13 below the 70.

3. Add the partial sums. Draw a second line beneath 70 and 13. Write 83 beneath this line.

In these examples, the tens were added first. However, the partial sums may be calculated in either order—it does not matter whether the tens or the ones are added first.

Tell children that the method illustrated by these examples is called an **algorithm.** An algorithm is a step-by-step set of instructions for doing something—in this case, for calculating a sum.

◆ **Practicing the Partial-Sums Algorithm**
(*Math Journal 1,* p. 109)

WHOLE-CLASS DISCUSSION 👥👥👥

Write several multidigit addition problems on the board. Most problems should have 2-digit addends, but include at least one problem with 3-digit addends.

10s	1s
4	5
+ 2	2
6	0
+	7
6	7

10s	1s
2	6
+ 5	7
7	0
+ 1	3
8	3

Addition Practice

Add. Show your work. Check your work. Write a number model to show your ballpark estimate.

1. 59 + 8   Answer: 67

Ballpark estimate:
60 + 10 = 70

2. 67 + 7   Answer: 74

Ballpark estimate:
70 + 10 = 80

3. 47 + 32   Answer: 79

Ballpark estimate:
50 + 30 = 80

4. 43 + 37   Answer: 80

Ballpark estimate:
40 + 40 = 80

5. 28 + 57   Answer: 85

Ballpark estimate:
30 + 60 = 90

6. 49 + 29   Answer: 78

Ballpark estimate:
50 + 30 = 80

7. 58 + 26   Answer: 84

Ballpark estimate:
60 + 30 = 90

8. 122 + 53   Answer: 175

Ballpark estimate:
120 + 50 = 170

9. 136 + 157   Answer: 293

Ballpark estimate:
140 + 160 = 300

STUDENT PAGE

◆ *Math Journal 1,* p. 109

Ask children to work these problems at the board. Have them describe exactly what they are doing at each step. Correct errors in calculation and in method. Make sure that the numbers that children write are properly aligned in columns.

When you discuss the problem with 3-digit addends, write "100s," "10s," and "1s" above the columns as a reminder of place value. Most children will quickly realize that the partial-sums method works the same way, and nearly as easily, for 3-digit problems as for 2-digit problems. The additional step is adding the hundreds and then including this partial sum in the final step when the partial sums are added.

Assign journal page 109. Children should show their work in the spaces provided on the page. Remind children to make ballpark estimates to check their answers, writing a number model for each estimate. They should look for mistakes if an answer is way off. After they have finished all of the problems on the page, bring the class together to check answers.

100s	10s	1s
4	7	3
+ 2	3	4
6	0	0
1	0	0
+		7
7	0	7

ONGOING ASSESSMENT

This is the first time that children have been exposed to a formal paper-and-pencil addition algorithm. Children will have plenty of opportunities to practice the partial-sums algorithm throughout the year. Please do not expect all children to be able to perform the algorithm at the conclusion of this lesson.

 Adjusting the Activity For children who are ready for a challenge, pose several 4-digit addition problems.

 Ongoing Learning & Practice

◆ Review Telling Time (*Math Journal 1*, p. 110)

INDEPENDENT ACTIVITY

Children answer questions in which they determine the times before or after the given time of an event.

This activity is related to the partial-sums algorithm. In adding an initial time and an elapsed time, a common strategy is to add the hours and minutes separately and then trade 60 minutes for an hour if the total number of minutes is 60 or greater.

The Time of Day

For Problems 1–4, draw the hour hand and the minute hand to show the time.

1. Dina got up at 7:00.
   She had breakfast an hour later.
   Show the time when she had breakfast.

2. Mel left home at 8:15.
   It took him half an hour to get to school. Show the time when he arrived at school.

3. Mia finished reading a story at 10:30.
   It took her 15 minutes. Show the time when she started reading.

4. The second graders went on a field trip.
   They left school at 12:30.
   They got back 2 hours later.
   Show the time when they got back.

5. The clock shows when Bob went to bed.
   He went to sleep 15 minutes later.
   At what time did he go to sleep?
   __9__ : __30__

◆ *Math Journal 1*, p. 110

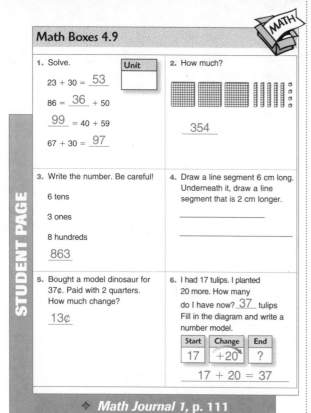

Math Boxes 4.9

1. Solve.

Unit

$23 + 30 = \underline{53}$

$86 = \underline{36} + 50$

$\underline{99} = 40 + 59$

$67 + 30 = \underline{97}$

2. How much?

354

3. Write the number. Be careful!

6 tens

3 ones

8 hundreds

863

4. Draw a line segment 6 cm long. Underneath it, draw a line segment that is 2 cm longer.

5. Bought a model dinosaur for 37¢. Paid with 2 quarters. How much change?

13¢

6. I had 17 tulips. I planted 20 more. How many do I have now? _37_ tulips Fill in the diagram and write a number model.

Start	Change	End
17	+20	?

$17 + 20 = 37$

◆ *Math Journal 1,* p. 111

◆ Math Boxes 4.9 (*Math Journal 1,* p. 111)

INDEPENDENT ACTIVITY

Mixed Review This journal page provides opportunities for cumulative review or assessment of concepts and skills.

◆ Home Link 4.9 (*Math Masters,* p. 291)

Home Connection Children use the partial-sums algorithm to solve multidigit addition problems.

---

3 Options for Individualizing

◆ ENRICHMENT Exploring Pattern-Block Designs (*Math Masters,* pp. 72 and 73)

INDEPENDENT ACTIVITY   15–30 min

Everyday Mathematics stresses the idea that there are many ways to name numbers and many ways to solve problems. While the partial-sums algorithm is stressed in this lesson as a method to solve multidigit addition problems, it is not the only method that a child may use. This activity reinforces the idea that there are usually many ways to solve a problem.

Children use various pattern blocks to cover each of the 5 hexagons on *Math Masters,* page 73 in a different way. They record their work by drawing in their block-shapes using the Pattern-Block Template and by making colored Xs to match the colors of the actual pattern blocks they used. Children compare results to find out how many different ways they found to cover the small and large hexagons.

Portfolio Ideas

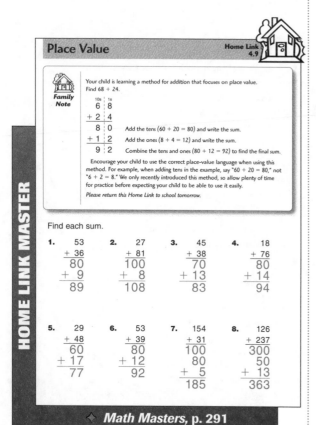

Place Value

Home Link 4.9

Family Note Your child is learning a method for addition that focuses on place value. Find 68 + 24.

```
     10s  1s
      6   8
  +   2   4
      8   0    Add the tens (60 + 20 = 80) and write the sum.
  +   1   2    Add the ones (8 + 4 = 12) and write the sum.
      9   2    Combine the tens and ones (80 + 12 = 92) to find the final sum.
```

Encourage your child to use the correct place-value language when using this method. For example, when adding tens in the example, say "60 + 20 = 80," not "6 + 2 = 8." We only recently introduced this method, so allow plenty of time for practice before expecting your child to be able to use it easily.

Please return this Home Link to school tomorrow.

Find each sum.

1.
```
   53
 + 36
   80
 +  9
   89
```

2.
```
   27
 + 81
  100
 +  8
  108
```

3.
```
   45
 + 38
   70
 + 13
   83
```

4.
```
   18
 + 76
   80
 + 14
   94
```

5.
```
   29
 + 48
   60
 + 17
   77
```

6.
```
   53
 + 39
   80
 + 12
   92
```

7.
```
  154
 + 31
  100
   80
 +  5
  185
```

8.
```
  126
 + 237
  300
   50
 + 13
  363
```

◆ *Math Masters,* p. 291

4.10

Unit 4 Review and Assessment

OBJECTIVE To review and assess children's progress on the material covered in Unit 4.

1 Assess Progress

learning goals

4a **Developing Goal** Devise and use strategies for finding sums of 2-digit numbers. **(Lessons 4.1 and 4.6–4.9)**

4b **Developing Goal** Devise and use strategies for finding differences of 2-digit numbers. **(Lesson 4.4)**

4c **Developing Goal** Estimate approximate costs and sums. **(Lessons 4.5 and 4.8)**

4d **Developing Goal** Read °F on a thermometer. **(Lessons 4.3 and 4.4)**

4e **Secure Goal** Add and subtract multiples of 10. **(Lessons 4.1–4.3 and 4.6–4.9)**

activities

❑ Slate Assessment, Problem 1
❑ Written Assessment, Problems 1, 2, and 9–12

❑ Slate Assessment, Problem 2
❑ Written Assessment, Problems 3 and 4

❑ Slate Assessment, Problems 3 and 4

❑ Written Assessment, Problems 5–8

❑ Slate Assessment, Problems 1 and 2

materials

❑ *Math Journal 1,* pp. 86, 88, and 97
❑ Home Link 4.9
❑ Assessment Masters (*Math Masters,* pp. 424 and 425)
❑ Teaching Masters (*Math Masters,* pp. 62 or 63)
❑ *Shopping* cards (cut from *Math Masters,* p. 67)

❑ play money for each player: at least nine $1 bills and at least eight $10 bills; one $100 bill (optional)
❑ calculator
❑ paper clip
❑ slate

2 Build Background for Unit 5

summaries

Children practice and maintain skills through Math Boxes and Home Link activities.

materials

❑ *Math Journal 1,* p. 112
❑ Home Link Masters (*Math Masters,* pp. 292–295)

Each **learning goal** listed above indicates a level of performance that might be expected at this point in the *Everyday Mathematics* K–6 curriculum. For a variety of reasons, the levels indicated may not accurately portray your class's performance.

Additional Information

Advance Information For additional information on assessment for Unit 4, see the *Assessment Handbook,* pages 50–52. For assessment checklists, see *Math Masters,* pages 454–455 and 485–488.

Getting Started

Math Message
Time to Reflect *Open your journal to page 88.
Is the temperature in your home more likely to be
30°F or 70°F?*

Home Link 4.9 Follow-Up
Review answers. Ask volunteers to demonstrate
on the board or an overhead how they used the
partial-sums algorithm to find the answers.

Fahrenheit Thermometer / Celsius Thermometer

Fahrenheit Thermometer °F	Celsius Thermometer °C

Water boils. 212°F, 100°C

Normal body temperature 98.6°F, 37°C

Room temperature 70°F, 21°C

Water freezes. 32°F, 0°C

Thermometers from journal page 88

1 Assess Progress

◆ Math Message Follow-Up

WHOLE-CLASS DISCUSSION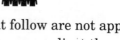

Ask children how they know that 70°F is the more
sensible measure. Sample response: Water freezes at
32°F. My house must be warmer than that!

It is important for children to be able to read a
thermometer. It is also important that they have a sense
of how hot or cold the temperature is. Pose additional
temperature situations, and ask children to identify the
more sensible measure.

- A good day for swimming outside: 28°C or 60°C? 28°C

- A good day for ice fishing: 50°F or 20°F? 20°F

- A good day to watch a baseball game outside: 20°C or
  40°F? 20°C

◆ Slate Assessment

SMALL-GROUP ACTIVITY

If the suggested problems that follow are not appropriate
for your class's level of performance, adjust the numbers
in the problems—or adjust the problems themselves—to
better assess your children's abilities.

Slate Assessment Suggestions

1. Write the sums.

   - 40 + 50 90, 30 + 20 50, 60 + 10 70, 70 + 50 120
     Goal 4e

   - 20 + 9 29, 30 + 8 38, 50 + 6 56, 70 + 3 73 **Goal 4a**

   - 12 + 30 42, 40 + 16 56, 50 + 27 77, 60 + 15 75
     Goal 4a

2. Write the differences.

- 90 − 20 70, 80 − 40 40, 100 − 60 40, 140 − 80 60
  Goal 4e

- 37 − 7 30, 62 − 2 60, 49 − 9 40, 56 − 6 50 **Goal 4b**

- 45 − 30 15, 62 − 20 42, 59 − 40 19, 87 − 50 37
  Goal 4b

3. Pose the following estimation number stories. Children write yes or no on their slates and then explain their answers.

- A hamburger costs 65 cents. An apple costs 15 cents. You have 1 dollar. Do you have enough to pay for both items? yes **Goal 4c**

- A slice of cherry pie costs 40 cents. You have 1 dollar. Do you have enough to buy 3 slices? no **Goal 4c**

- You buy a ruler for 37 cents and a pencil for 21 cents. The clerk says, "That will be 70 cents." Should you pay that amount? no **Goal 4c**

- You have 90 cents. You buy a box of crayons for 76 cents. Do you have enough money left to buy an eraser for 28 cents? no **Goal 4c**

4. Ask children to make ballpark estimates for sums, aloud or on their slates, and to explain the strategies that they used. For example, "48 is close to 50, and 53 is close to 50. 50 + 50 = 100. 100 is a ballpark estimate for 48 + 53." *Suggested problems:*

- 48 + 53 50 + 50 = 100 **Goal 4c**

- 17 + 42 20 + 40 = 60 **Goal 4c**

- 38 + 47 40 + 50 = 90 **Goal 4c**

- 309 + 482 300 + 500 = 800 or 700 + 10 + 80 = 790 **Goal 4c**

Telling time is a goal of the preceding unit. It is worthwhile to check how well children are doing on this skill. Set the demonstration clock to the following times and have children record the times shown on their slates. *Suggested times:*

- 4:05, 3:45, 1:55, 6:15, 2:10, 12:35

NOTE: Many of these assessment suggestions relate to learning goals that have been addressed in previous units. Now is a good time to evaluate children's progress toward those goals.

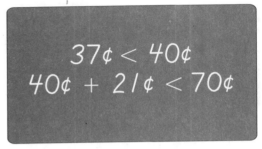

The clerk must be wrong.

Unit 4 Checking Progress

In the diagram for each number story:

- Write the numbers you know.
- Write ? for the number you want to find.
- Write the answer. Don't forget to include the unit.
- Write a number model.

1. Arlene has 20 dolls. Katie has 7 dolls. How many dolls do Arlene and Katie have in all?

Total	
?	
Part	**Part**
20	7

Answer: __27 dolls__
(unit)

Number model: __20 + 7 = 27__

2. On Monday, Jen painted 30 beads for her necklace. On Tuesday, she painted 12 beads. How many beads did Jen paint in all?

Total	
?	
Part	**Part**
30	12

Answer: __42 beads__
(unit)

Number model: __30 + 12 = 42__

3. At 2:30 in the afternoon, the temperature was 68°F. During the night, it went down 20 degrees. What was the new temperature?

Start	Change	End
68	−20	?

Answer: __48°F__
(unit)

Number model: __68 − 20 = 48 or 20 + 48 = 68__

◆ *Math Masters, p. 424*

Unit 4 Checking Progress (cont.)

4. Kevin brought 36 cupcakes to school for his birthday. He gave 10 away during lunch. How many cupcakes did he have then?

Start	Change	End
36	−10	?

Answer: __26 cupcakes__
(unit)

Number model: __36 − 10 = 26 or 10 + 26 = 36__

Write the temperature shown on each thermometer.

5. °F — __62__ °F

6. °F — __21__ °F

Mark each thermometer to show the temperature.

7. 30°F

8. 49°F

Solve the addition problems.

9.	**10.**	**11.**	**12.**
53	27	34	95
+ 66	+ 48	+ 37	+ 63
119	75	71	158

◆ *Math Masters, p. 425*

◆ Written Assessment
(Math Masters, pp. 424 and 425)

WHOLE-CLASS ACTIVITY

Read through the problems with the class. You may want to do examples with the class for some of the problems.

If appropriate, work through the problems together. Wait for children to complete a problem before reading the next one.

If your class can work independently, have children work alone or with a partner on this review page. Circulate and assist.

- In the diagram for each number story: Write the numbers you know. Write ? for the number you want to find. Write the answer. Don't forget to include the unit. Write a number model. (Problems 1–4) **Goals 4a and 4b**

- Write the temperature shown on each thermometer. Mark each thermometer to show the temperature. (Problems 5–8) **Goal 4d**

- Solve the addition problems. (Problems 9–12) **Goal 4a**

◆ ALTERNATIVE ASSESSMENT OPTION
Play *Shopping*
(Math Journal 1, p. 97; Math Masters, p. 67)

PARTNER ACTIVITY

Observe children as they play *Shopping* to assess children's ability to add 2-digit numbers. On a sheet of paper, children record a number model for the total cost of the items purchased. For example, if a child purchased a camera for $43 and an iron for $32, she or he would write 43 + 32 = 75. Collect the sheets and assess.

See Lesson 4.6 for directions.

◆ ALTERNATIVE ASSESSMENT OPTION
Play *Addition Spin*
(Math Journal 1, p. 86; Math Masters, pp. 62 or 63)

PARTNER ACTIVITY

This game was introduced in Lesson 4.2. Observe children as they play *Addition Spin* to assess their ability to add 2-digit numbers. Choose a spin mat appropriate to the skill level that you would like to assess. The top mat on *Math Masters*, page 62 provides an opportunity to assess

ASSESSMENT MASTER

addition of 2-digit multiples of 5. The bottom mat on *Math Masters*, page 62 provides an opportunity to assess addition of 2-digit numbers requiring no regrouping. *Math Masters*, page 63 is a blank *Addition Spin* mat. You can customize this mat to assess more difficult 2-digit or 3-digit addition.

For each round, ask children to record a number model on a sheet of paper. Collect the sheets and assess.

Build Background for Unit 5

 Math Boxes 4.10 (*Math Journal 1*, p. 112)

INDEPENDENT ACTIVITY

Mixed Review This journal page provides opportunities for cumulative review or assessment of concepts and skills.

 Home Link 4.10 (*Math Masters*, pp. 292–295)

Home Connection This Home Link is a four-page newsletter that introduces parents and guardians to Unit 5's topics and terms. The letter also offers ideas for home-based mathematics activities that are supportive of classroom work.

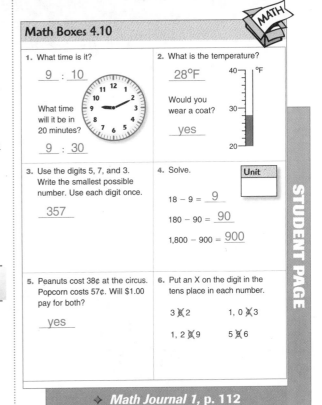

Math Boxes 4.10

1. What time is it?

9 : 10

What time will it be in 20 minutes?

9 : 30

2. What is the temperature?

28°F

Would you wear a coat?

yes

3. Use the digits 5, 7, and 3. Write the smallest possible number. Use each digit once.

357

4. Solve.

Unit

$18 - 9 = 9$

$180 - 90 = 90$

$1,800 - 900 = 900$

5. Peanuts cost 38¢ at the circus. Popcorn costs 57¢. Will $1.00 pay for both?

yes

6. Put an X on the digit in the tens place in each number.

3 X 2   1, 0 X 3

1, 2 X 9   5 X 6

Math Journal 1, p. 112

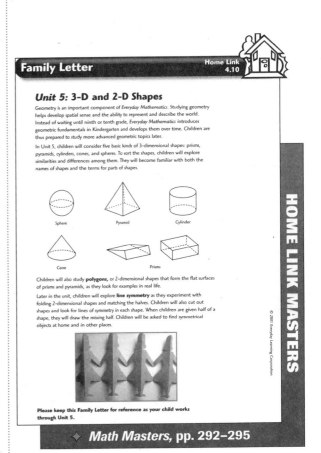

Family Letter

Home Link 4.10

Unit 5: 3-D and 2-D Shapes

Geometry is an important component of *Everyday Mathematics*. Studying geometry helps develop spatial sense and the ability to represent and describe the world. Instead of waiting until ninth or tenth grade, *Everyday Mathematics* introduces geometric fundamentals in Kindergarten and develops them over time. Children are thus prepared to study more advanced geometric topics later.

In Unit 5, children will consider five basic kinds of 3-dimensional shapes: prisms, pyramids, cylinders, cones, and spheres. To sort the shapes, children will explore similarities and differences among them. They will become familiar with both the names of shapes and the terms for parts of shapes.

Sphere   Pyramid   Cylinder

Cone   Prism

Children will also study **polygons**, or 2-dimensional shapes that form the flat surfaces of prisms and pyramids, as they look for examples in real life.

Later in the unit, children will explore **line symmetry** as they experiment with folding 2-dimensional shapes and matching the halves. Children will also cut out shapes and look for lines of symmetry in each shape. When children are given half of a shape, they will draw the missing half. Children will be asked to find symmetrical objects at home and in other places.

Please keep this Family Letter for reference as your child works through Unit 5.

Math Masters, pp. 292–295

Unit 5
3-D and
2-D Shapes

overview

This unit contains mathematical terms that may be new to your students. The primary purpose of this unit, however, is to develop classification skills, not to teach vocabulary. This objective is accomplished through hands-on activities, in which children observe similarities and differences among various shapes and explore spatial relationships. These activities, as well as geometry Explorations, should be viewed as preliminary exposures to ideas that will appear in later lessons.

contents

UNIT

5

learning goals	links to the past	links to the future
5a **Developing Goal** Identify 3-dimensional shapes, such as rectangular prisms, cylinders, pyramids, cones, and spheres. **(Lessons 5.7 and 5.8)**	Children have been working with 3-dimensional shapes since Kindergarten, when they began to create a Shapes Museum. First graders explored the cube as a special rectangular prism, and constructed paper tetrahedrons. *(Related Grade 2 lessons: 1.2, 2.10, 3.4, 4.3)*	Beyond third grade, lessons will highlight clear notation, definitions, comparisons, and statements of properties and relationships. *(Related Grade 2 lesson: 9.7)*
5b **Developing Goal** Identify symmetrical figures. **(Lesson 5.9)**	In Kindergarten, children began exploring symmetry through art activities. In first grade, children used pattern blocks and did a symmetry project with leaves. *(Related Grade 2 lesson: 3.4)*	In third grade, students will explore the properties of symmetrical shapes. *(Related Grade 2 lessons: 6.7, 9.7)*
5c **Developing Goal** Find common attributes of shapes. **(Lessons 5.1 and 5.2)**	Children in Kindergarten and first grade sorted attribute blocks and played games such as the Attribute Train Game. *(Related Grade 2 lessons: 3.4, 4.3, 4.7)*	Attribute game puzzles, which involve the identification of common attributes in a set of figures, will be introduced in third grade. *(Related Grade 2 lesson: 7.6)*
5d **Developing Goal** Identify parallel and nonparallel line segments. **(Lesson 5.5)**	In first grade, children explored parallel line segments through experiences with polygons.	In third grade, children will construct 2- and 3-dimensional figures to model and explore the relationship among parallel and intersecting line segments, lines, and rays. *(Related Grade 2 lesson: 9.7)*
5e **Developing/Secure Goal** Draw line segments. **(Lessons 5.4 and 5.5)**	In earlier grades, children were introduced to rulers and straightedges. They also measured and drew line segments to the nearest centimeter. *(Related Grade 2 lesson: 1.2)*	In third grade, children will identify, draw, and name line segments, lines, and rays. *(Related Grade 2 lesson: 7.7)*
5f **Secure Goal** Identify 2-dimensional shapes. **(Lessons 5.2, 5.3, and 5.6)**	Children began to examine the properties of 2-dimensional shapes in Kindergarten. They created models of polygons in first grade. *(Related Grade 2 lessons: 3.4, 4.3, 4.7)*	Exploration and construction of 2-dimensional shapes will continue in third grade. Using their knowledge of shapes, children will be able to classify 3-dimensional shapes. *(Related Grade 2 lessons: 6.7, 10.7)*

assessment
ongoing • product • periodic

✓ Informal Assessment

Math Boxes These *Math Journal* pages provide opportunities for cumulative review or assessment of concepts and skills.

Ongoing Assessment: Kid Watching Use the Ongoing Assessment suggestions in the following lessons to make quick, on-the-spot observations about children's understanding of:
• Measurement and Reference Frames **(Lesson 5.1)**
• Geometry **(Lesson 5.3)**

Portfolio Ideas Samples of children's work may be obtained from the following assignments:
• Exploring Equal Sharing **(Lesson 5.2)**
• Making Centimeter-Cube Arrays **(Lesson 5.3)**
• Making a Dollar **(Lesson 5.3)**
• Creating a Booklet or Bulletin-Board Display of Parallel Line Segments **(Lesson 5.5)**
• Making Shapes Out of Triangles and Rectangles **(Lesson 5.6)**
• Making a Symmetry Booklet **(Lesson 5.9)**
• Making Symmetrical Shapes **(Lesson 5.10)**

✓ Unit 5 Review and Assessment

Math Message Use the question in Lesson 5.10 to assess children's progress toward the following learning goal: Goal 5c

Slate Assessments Use slate assessments during Lesson 5.10 to assess children's progress toward the following learning goals: Goal From Previous Unit: 4a

Written Assessment Use a written review during Lesson 5.10 to assess children's progress toward the following learning goals: Goals 5a, 5b, 5c, 5d, 5e, and 5f

assessment handbook

For more information on how to use different types of assessment in Unit 5, see the Assessment Overview on pages 53–55 in the *Assessment Handbook*. The following Assessment Masters can be found in the *Math Masters* book:

• Unit 5 Checking Progress, pp. 426 and 427
• Unit 5 Class Checklist, p. 456
• Unit 5 Individual Profile of Progress, p. 457
• Class Progress Indicator, p. 488
• Math Logs, pp. 493–495
• Self-Assessment Forms, pp. 496 and 497
• Interest Inventory, pp. 491 and 492

problem**solving**

A process of modeling everyday situations using tools from mathematics

Encourage children to use a variety of strategies when attacking a given problem—and to explain those strategies. *Strategies children might use in this unit:*

- Identifying a pattern
- Identifying important information
- Making an organized list
- Using logical reasoning
- Acting out the problem

Four Problem-Solving REPRESENTATIONS

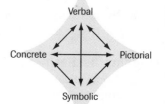

Lessons that teach *through* problem solving, not just *about* problem solving

Lesson	Activity	Lesson	Activity
5.1	Figuring out attribute rules	5.2	Solving equal sharing problems
5.1	Giving and following directions to make figures on a geoboard	5.3	Finding coin combinations to make one dollar
5.2	Finding attribute blocks that differ by one or more attributes	5.6, 5.7	Finding similarities and differences among shapes
5.2	Splitting a triangle into 2, 3, and 4 triangles		

For more information about problem solving in *Everyday Mathematics,* see the *Teacher's Reference Manual,* pp. 197–208.

cross-curricularlinks

literature and art

- Read *The Art of Shapes for Children and Adults,* which focuses on the polygons found in famous works of art. **(Lessons 5.3 and 5.7)**
- Read *Lao Lao of Dragon Mountain* and learn about the Chinese art of cutting shapes from paper. **(Lesson 5.9)**
- Find and identify polygons and other shapes in *Shapes, Shapes, Shapes.* **(Lessons 5.3 and 5.7)**

literature

- Read *The Greedy Triangle,* a book that explores the characteristics of different polygons. **(Lesson 5.3)**
- Read about a shape-changing competition in *Grandfather Tang's Story.* **(Lesson 5.6)**

language arts

- Show children that polygons are named according to number of sides and angles. **(Lesson 5.3)**
- Help children explore definitions of the word *point.* **(Lesson 5.4)**

social studies

- Look at the step-by-step process of building an ancient Egyptian pyramid and compare the characteristics of the Egyptian pyramid with the pyramids made in class. **(Lesson 5.8)**

meeting INDIVIDUAL needs

UNIVERSAL ACCESS

✦ RETEACHING

The following features provide additional instructional support:

Adjusting the Activity
- **Lesson 5.1, Part 1**
- **Lesson 5.2, Part 1**
- **Lesson 5.5, Part 1**
- **Lesson 5.7, Part 1**
- **Lesson 5.8, Part 1**

Options for Individualizing
- **Lesson 5.4** Drawing Line Segments
- **Lesson 5.5** Modeling Parallel Line Segments on a Geoboard
- **Lesson 5.6** Playing *Touch-and-Match Quadrangles*
- **Lesson 5.9** Exploring Line Symmetry with Geoboards

✦ ENRICHMENT

The following features suggest enrichment and extension activities:

Adjusting the Activity
- **Lesson 5.1, Part 1**
- **Lesson 5.3, Part 1**
- **Lesson 5.5, Part 1**
- **Lesson 5.6, Part 1**
- **Lesson 5.8, Part 1**

Options for Individualizing
- **Lesson 5.5** Creating a Booklet or Bulletin-Board Display of Parallel Line Segments
- **Lesson 5.6** Exploring Tangrams
- **Lesson 5.8** Constructing a Decagon Out of Triangles
- **Lesson 5.8** Making a Connection between Pyramids in Math and Social Studies
- **Lesson 5.9** Exploring Line Symmetry in Literature

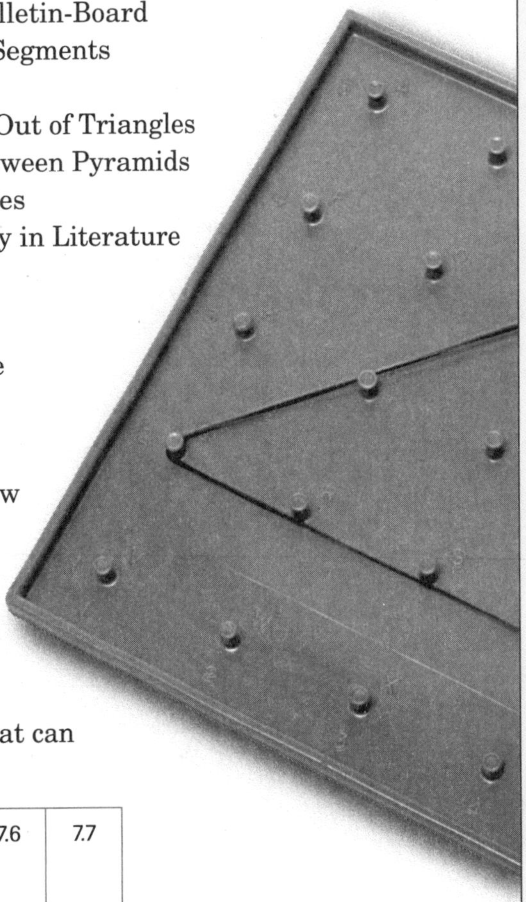

✦ LANGUAGE DIVERSITY

The following features suggest ways to support children who are acquiring proficiency in English:

Adjusting the Activity
- **Lesson 5.4, Part 1**
- **Lesson 5.5, Part 1**
- **Lesson 5.7, Part 1**
- **Lesson 5.9, Part 1**

Options for Individualizing
- **Lesson 5.4** Making Up Codes to Draw Capital Letters with Line Segments

✦ MULTIAGE CLASSROOM

The following chart lists related lessons from Grades 1 and 3 that can help you meet your instructional needs:

Grade 1	4.7 6.10 7.1	4.7 7.1 7.2	7.1– 7.4 8.2	1.3 2.7 4.5	2.7 4.5 7.4	7.3 7.4	7.5 7.6 10.5	7.6	7.7
Grade 2	5.1	5.2	5.3	5.4	5.5	5.6	5.7	5.8	5.9
Grade 3	1.4	4.3 6.4 9.7	1.9 4.8 6.6	6.1	6.2	3.5 6.5 9.3	6.11 6.12	6.11	6.9

materials

lesson	📖 math masters pages	🧊 manipulative kit items	✂ other items
5.1	Home Link Master, p. 296 Teaching Masters, pp. 62, 63, 70, and 74–79 **See Advance Preparation, p. 290**	attribute blocks 1 six-sided die geoboard; rubber bands clock-face stamp stamp pad	Attribute Rule Cards index cards paper clip; envelope calculator **See Advance Preparation, p. 290**
5.2	Home Link Master, p. 297 Teaching Masters, pp. 80–83	attribute blocks geoboard; rubber bands 1 regular die or number cube	bills counters calculator *Shopping* cards **See Advance Preparation, p. 295**
5.3	Home Link Master, p. 298 Teaching Masters, pp. 84–87	Pattern-Block Template geoboard; rubber bands base-10 blocks 2 six-sided dice	straightedge coins (optional) *Dollar Rummy* cards literature selections **See Advance Preparation, p. 300**
5.4	Home Link Master, p. 299 Teaching Masters, pp. 77–79, 88, and 89		straightedge *Clock Concentration* cards
5.5	Home Link Master, p. 300	geoboard; rubber bands	straightedge magazines and newspapers different colors of yarn or different markers
5.6	Home Link Master, p. 301 Teaching Masters, pp. 90–93	Pattern-Block Template	index cards (optional) paper clips box or bag *Grandfather Tang's Story* by Ann Tompert **See Advance Preparation, p. 314**
5.7	Home Link Master, p. 302	slate	3-D Shapes Poster (optional) 3-dimensional models items from home for the Shapes Museum labeled index cards literature selections (optional) **See Advance Preparation, p. 319**
5.8	Home Link Master, p. 303 Teaching Masters, pp. 94–97	slate straws	*Pyramid* by David Macauley models of a cone and a pyramid twist-ties **See Advance Preparation, p. 325**
5.9	Home Link Master, p. 304 Teaching Masters, pp. 98–99	slate geoboard; rubber bands Pattern-Block Template	*Lao Lao of Dragon Mountain* by Margaret Bateson-Hill magazines backing paper
5.10	Home Link Masters, pp. 305–308 Teaching Master, p. 100 Assessment Masters, pp. 426 and 427	slate Pattern-Block Template	

planning tips

Pacing

Pacing depends on a number of factors, such as children's individual needs and how long your school has been using *Everyday Mathematics*. At the beginning of Unit 5, review your Contents by Strand Poster to help you set a monthly pace.

← MOST CLASSROOMS →		
D E C E M B E R	J A N U A R Y	F E B R U A R Y

Home Communication

Share Home Links 5.1–5.9 with families to help them understand the content and procedures in this unit. At the end of the unit, use Home Link 5.10 to introduce Unit 6. Supplemental information can be found in the *Home Connection Handbook*.

NCTM Standards

Standard	1	2	3	4	5	6	7	8	9	10
Unit 5 Lessons	2, 3, 8	1–4, 6, 8	1–9	1, 3	1	1–9	1–9	1–9	1–9	1–9

Content Standards
1 Number and Operation
2 Patterns, Functions, and Algebra
3 Geometry and Spatial Sense
4 Measurement
5 Data Analysis, Statistics, and Probability

Process Standards
6 Problem Solving
7 Reasoning and Proof
8 Communication
9 Connections
10 Representations

PRACTICE *through* Games

Everyday Mathematics uses games to help children develop good fact power and other math skills.

- Practice adding 2- or 3-digit numbers with *Addition Spin* **(Lesson 5.1)**
- Practice exchanging coins for dollars in *Dollar Rummy* **(Lesson 5.3)**
- Match digital notation with clocks in *Clock Concentration* **(Lessons 5.1 and 5.4)**
- Practice identifying quadrangles by playing *Touch-and-Match Quadrangles* **(Lesson 5.6)**

unit 5 content highlights

The notes below highlight the major content ideas presented in Unit 5. These notes may help you establish instructional priorities.

Explorations (Lessons 5.1, 5.2, and 5.3)

Unit 5 begins with nine Explorations. Four of the Explorations develop children's abilities to classify shapes, identify similarities and differences among shapes, and represent shapes on paper. The remaining five Explorations cover giving and following directions, time, readiness for multiplication and division, and coin values.

Polygons (Lessons 5.3, 5.6, and following)

Polygons are 2-dimensional closed figures whose sides are all line segments. Children identify shapes that are polygons and nonpolygons. They note that it is possible to trace the sides of a polygon and come back to the starting point without retracing or crossing any part. They classify and name polygons according to the numbers of sides and angles. Children focus in greater detail on one kind of polygon by finding similarities and differences among various quadrilaterals (in Lesson 5.6). Later, they observe that the bases of pyramids are in the shapes of various polygons.

These lessons include many hands-on activities. Children draw polygons by tracing pattern blocks; they make polygons out of triangular and rectangular pieces; they draw polygons with a straightedge; and they form them on a geoboard.

Points and Line Segments (Lessons 5.4 and 5.5)

Everyday Mathematics develops the fundamental concepts of *point* and *line segment*. Parallel line segments—segments that are the same distance apart and that will not meet no matter how far they are extended—are considered. Children learn how to name line segments, draw line segments that are parallel, and draw line segments that are not parallel.

3-D Shapes (Lessons 5.7 and 5.8)

Before you begin Lesson 5.7, you and the children should bring enough 3-dimensional objects to school to create an extensive Shapes Museum. These objects are sorted into basic categories: prisms, pyramids, cylinders, cones, spheres, cubes, and others. Referring to these objects

> NOTE: Many vocabulary words are used in this unit. Children are not expected to memorize them, but they should be encouraged to use them. It may be helpful to write the words on a "Word Wall" so that children can refer to them as often as needed. Next to each word, include a picture as well as a written description.
>
> Numerous suggestions for the "Word Wall" are given throughout this unit.

and to a 3-D Shapes Poster (*Math Journal 1,* page 126), children observe the similarities and differences among shapes, such as flat and curved surfaces. Children also identify the parts of shapes, such as faces, bases, edges, and vertices. In Lesson 5.8, they use straws and twist-ties to construct pyramids whose bases are squares, triangles, rectangles, pentagons, and hexagons.

As you use the names of the shapes and their parts, children will be exposed to many words that are probably unfamiliar to them. Don't let this deter you from using the words, but do keep in mind that you should not expect children to memorize them at this time. With repeated exposure, these words will gradually become part of the children's vocabularies. Most children will be able to identify these shapes by the end of second grade. Children will have a good understanding of shapes and their characteristics by the end of third grade.

Line Symmetry (Lesson 5.9)

Children explore symmetry through folding and drawing activities. As with other topics, they look to the real world for examples of symmetry.

Review and Assessment (Lesson 5.10)

Unit goals for geometry are assessed on the review pages. Questions suggested for the slate assessment address the following skills: addition, estimation, telling time, and reading a thermometer.

For **additional information** on the following topics, see the *Teacher's Reference Manual:*

- lines, segments, and rays
- parallel and perpendicular
- Pattern-Block Template
- pattern blocks and geometric solids
- polygons
- solid figures
- straws and twist-ties
- symmetry
- teaching geometry

5.1 EXPLORATIONS

Exploring Rules, Directions, and Time

OBJECTIVES To identify rules used to classify shapes; to give and follow directions; and to tell time using digital and analog notation.

summaries | materials

1 Teaching the Lesson

Exploration A: Children play "What's My Attribute Rule" to determine the rule (involving color, shape, and size) used to sort a set of attribute blocks. [Geometry; Patterns, Functions, and Algebra]

Exploration B: Children give and follow directions for making shapes on a geoboard. [Geometry]

Exploration C: Children make game cards and play *Clock Concentration,* in which they match clock faces with digital times. [Measurement and Reference Frames]

Exploration A: Per group:
- ☐ Teaching Masters (*Math Masters,* pp. 74 and 75)
- ☐ Attribute Rule Cards (cut from *Math Masters,* p. 70)
- ☐ 2 sheets of paper and a marking pen
- ☐ set of attribute blocks; 1 six-sided die

Exploration B: Per partnership:
- ☐ Teaching Master (*Math Masters,* p. 76)
- ☐ rubber bands; 2 geoboards

Exploration C: Per group:
- ☐ Teaching Masters (*Math Masters,* pp. 77 and 78)
- ☐ 10 index cards or 2 copies of *Math Masters,* p. 79
- ☐ clock-face stamp and stamp pad (or *Math Masters,* p. 79)
- ☐ scissors; envelope

See **Advance Preparation**

2 Ongoing Learning & Practice

Children practice adding 2-digit numbers by playing *Addition Spin.* [Operations and Computation]

Children practice and maintain skills through Math Boxes and Home Link activities.

- ☐ *Math Journal 1,* pp. 86 and 113
- ☐ Teaching Masters (*Math Masters,* pp. 62 or 63; per group)
- ☐ per group: paper clip; calculator
- ☐ Home Link Master (*Math Masters,* p. 296)

3 Options for Individualizing

Extra Practice Children tell time to the nearest hour, half-hour, and 5-minute interval. [Measurement and Reference Frames]

- ☐ *Minute Math®,* p. 71

Additional Information

Advance Preparation Before assigning the Math Message, draw three large circles—one yellow, one blue, and one red—on a piece of paper. Color the interiors of the circles. Label the sheet: **These fit the rule.** On another piece of paper, draw a small yellow triangle, a small blue square, and a small red circle. Color the interiors of these shapes. Label this sheet: **These do NOT fit the rule.** (Alternatively, you could tape actual attribute blocks to the labeled pieces of paper.) Post both sheets near the Math Message. (See the illustration on the next page.)

Math Masters, pages 74–78 give directions for the Explorations. Plan to spend most of your time working with children on Exploration A. You may want to place copies of these masters at workstations. Aides or volunteers can then use the masters as they work with small groups or partnerships.

Getting Started

Mental Math and Reflexes

Problems like the following give children practice in the quick mental-addition skills that are needed for making ballpark estimates and for carrying out the partial-sums algorithm:

50 + 30 = ? 80	500 + 300 = ? 800
? = 40 + 60 100	? = 400 + 600 1,000
70 + 40 = ? 110	700 + 400 = ? 1,100

Math Message

(See Advance Preparation.)
I am the Rule Maker. Look at the pictures of the attribute blocks labeled "These fit the rule." Look at the pictures labeled "These do NOT fit the rule." What is my rule?

1 Teaching the Lesson

◆ Math Message Follow-Up

WHOLE-CLASS DISCUSSION

The rule is "only large shapes." Instead of explaining the rule, ask a child to bring you an attribute block that fits the rule. Say "yes" if the block fits the rule, and place it on the paper labeled "These fit the rule." If the block does not fit the rule, say "no," and place the block on the paper labeled "These do NOT fit the rule."

Continue until the majority of the class has figured out the rule.

NOTE: At the beginning of this activity, children may logically think that the rule is "only circles." Point out to children, however, that a small red circle does not fit the rule.

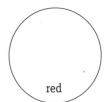 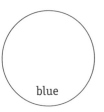

These fit the rule.

These do NOT fit the rule.

TEACHING MASTER

Materials	☐ set of attribute blocks
	☐ Attribute Rule Cards (*Math Masters*, p. 70)
	☐ 1 six-sided die
Players	3 or more

Directions

1. Label one sheet of paper: **These fit the rule.**

2. Label another sheet of paper: **These do NOT fit the rule.**

3. Take turns. Roll the die once. The player with the lowest number is the first "Rule Maker."

4. The Rule Maker mixes the Attribute Rule Cards and then stacks them facedown.

5. The Rule Maker turns over the top Attribute Rule Card but does not show it to the other players or tell them what the rule is.

> large shapes,
> but not
> triangles

Sample Attribute Rule Card

Math Masters, p. 74

Adjusting the Activity If children are having difficulty giving or following directions, you may wish to revisit the activity found in Exploration C of Lesson 3.4—Making Shapes on a Geoboard.

"What's My Attribute Rule?" (cont.)

TEACHING MASTER

6. The Rule Maker chooses 3 or 4 attribute blocks that fit the rule on the card. The Rule Maker puts them on the sheet labeled "These fit the rule."

7. The Rule Maker chooses 3 or 4 blocks that do NOT fit the rule. The Rule Maker puts them on the sheet labeled "These do NOT fit the rule."

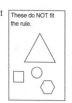

8. The other players are the "Guessers." The Guessers take turns. Each one chooses a block that he or she thinks might fit the rule.

9. The Rule Maker tells each Guesser "yes" or "no." The Guesser puts the block on the correct sheet. The Guesser suggests what the rule might be. The Rule Maker tells the Guesser if his or her rule is correct.

10. The Guessers continue until someone figures out the rule. Then that player becomes the Rule Maker for the next round.

Math Masters, p. 75

◆ Exploration A: Figuring Out Attribute Rules
(*Math Masters,* pp. 70, 74, and 75)

SMALL-GROUP ACTIVITY 👥👥

Children play the game "What's My Attribute Rule?," which is similar to the Math Message activity. See *Math Masters,* pages 74 and 75 for game instructions. In Lesson 4.7, children cut out the necessary Attribute Rule Cards from *Math Masters,* page 70.

Adjusting the Activity If needed, select two children to be Rule Makers. Together, they can choose the initial blocks that do and do not fit the rule and determine if the blocks chosen by the Guessers fit the rule.

To make the activity more challenging, ask the Rule Maker to make up his or her own rule rather than using an Attribute Rule Card. The Rule Maker can record the rule on a separate sheet of paper before laying out blocks that do and do not fit the rule.

◆ Exploration B: Giving and Following Directions to Make Figures on a Geoboard
(*Math Masters,* p. 76)

PARTNER ACTIVITY 👥

One partner makes a simple shape or design on a geoboard—without the other partner watching. The goal of this activity is for the partner who made the shape or design to give the best directions possible to help the other partner duplicate the shape or design.

◆ Exploration C: Making and Playing *Clock Concentration*
(*Math Masters,* pp. 77–79)

SMALL-GROUP ACTIVITY 👥👥

Each group makes a set of *Clock Concentration* cards using a clock-face stamp and index cards. Once the cards are made, children match times given on a clock face and in digital notation to sharpen time-telling skills. Game directions are on *Math Masters,* pages 77 and 78.

NOTE: If clock stamps are not available, make copies of *Math Masters,* page 79, preferably on tagboard. If you use ordinary paper, tell children to write the times and draw the hands of the clocks lightly in pencil. By doing this, the times and clocks will not show through the paper when the cards are turned facedown. Have children cut the clock cards apart.

 Adjusting the Activity Challenge children to write the time in words rather than digital notation. Children should use expressions like *quarter-past 6, ten till 7, half-past 9,* and *noon.*

If children are having difficulty playing *Clock Concentration,* limit the number of pairs in the array. For example, instead of 10 **C**s and 10 **T**s, use only 5 **C**s and 5 **T**s. Then, after each game, change the set of cards to provide practice using all 20 cards. Alternatively, play with all of the cards faceup. For some children, matching the **C** and **T** cards is enough of a challenge, without having to cope with the memory aspect of the game.

✓ ONGOING ASSESSMENT

Children should have no difficulty creating cards that show times on the hour and the half-hour. Expect that the majority of children can show times to 5-minute intervals. Some children may be able to show times to the minute.

Clock Concentration

Materials	☐ 10 index cards
	☐ clock-face stamp
	☐ stamp pad
	☐ envelope
	☐ scissors
Players	4 to 6

Directions

Make a set of *Clock Concentration* cards.

1. Fold each index card in half. Then unfold it.

2. Stamp a clock face on one half of the card. Then draw an hour hand and a minute hand on the face to show a time.

3. Write the matching digital time on the other half. Check one another's work.

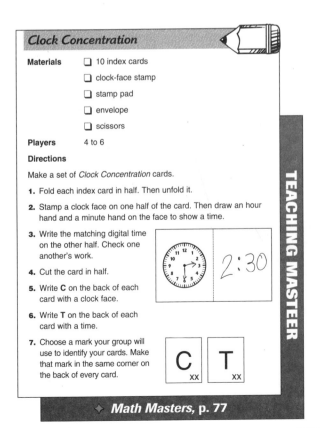

4. Cut the card in half.

5. Write **C** on the back of each card with a clock face.

6. Write **T** on the back of each card with a time.

7. Choose a mark your group will use to identify your cards. Make that mark in the same corner on the back of every card.

◆ *Math Masters,* p. 77

Secret Shapes ✏

Work with a partner.

Materials ☐ 2 geoboards
☐ rubber bands

Directions

1. One partner makes an easy shape, design, or picture on his or her geoboard. The other partner does not watch.

2. The first partner gives directions to the other partner for making the picture on the geoboard. The directions should be very clear so that the pictures will look alike.

Example

Make a flag on a flagpole.
The flagpole is 4 units long.
The flag is a rectangle.
It is 2 units long and 1 unit high.
The flag is at the top of the flagpole.

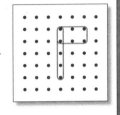

3. Partners compare pictures. How are they alike? How are they different?

4. Partners change roles and do Steps 1–3 again.

◆ *Math Masters,* p. 76

Math Masters, page 79 includes
5 sets of *Clock Concentration* cards.

Clock Concentration (cont.) ✏

Play *Clock Concentration.*

1. One player shuffles the cards and places them facedown in an array.

2. Take turns. For each turn, a player turns a **C** card and a **T** card faceup. If the cards match, that player takes both cards and takes another turn.

3. If the cards do not match, put them back in the array facedown. Then the next player takes a turn.

4. Play until the time is up or until all the cards have been taken. The player with the most cards wins.

5. Store your group's cards in an envelope until you play again.

◆ *Math Masters,* p. 78

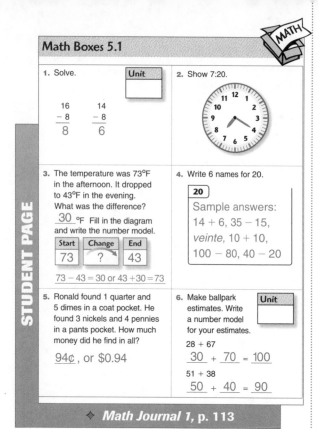

Math Boxes 5.1

1. Solve.

Unit ____

$$\begin{array}{r} 16 \\ -\ 8 \\ \hline 8 \end{array} \qquad \begin{array}{r} 14 \\ -\ 8 \\ \hline 6 \end{array}$$

2. Show 7:20.

3. The temperature was 73°F in the afternoon. It dropped to 43°F in the evening. What was the difference?

__30__ °F Fill in the diagram and write the number model.

Start	Change	End
73	?	43

$73 - 43 = 30$ or $43 + 30 = 73$

4. Write 6 names for 20.

20

Sample answers:
$14 + 6$, $35 - 15$,
veinte, $10 + 10$,
$100 - 80$, $40 - 20$

5. Ronald found 1 quarter and 5 dimes in a coat pocket. He found 3 nickels and 4 pennies in a pants pocket. How much money did he find in all?

__94¢__ , or $0.94

6. Make ballpark estimates. Write a number model for your estimates.

Unit ____

$28 + 67$
__30__ + __70__ = __100__

$51 + 38$
__50__ + __40__ = __90__

✦ *Math Journal 1, p. 113*

HOME LINK MASTER

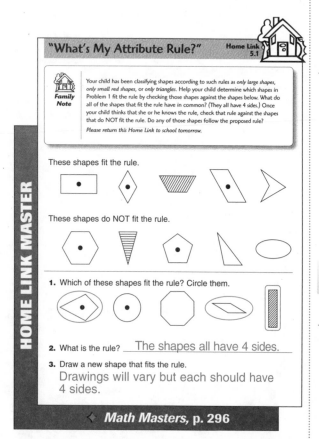

"What's My Attribute Rule?"   Home Link 5.1

Family Note Your child has been classifying shapes according to such rules as *only large shapes, only small red shapes,* or *only triangles.* Help your child determine which shapes in Problem 1 fit the rule by checking those shapes against the shapes below. What do all of the shapes that fit the rule have in common? (They all have 4 sides.) Once your child thinks that she or he knows the rule, check that rule against the shapes that do NOT fit the rule. Do any of those shapes follow the proposed rule?

Please return this Home Link to school tomorrow.

These shapes fit the rule.

These shapes do NOT fit the rule.

1. Which of these shapes fit the rule? Circle them.

2. What is the rule? The shapes all have 4 sides.

3. Draw a new shape that fits the rule.
   Drawings will vary but each should have 4 sides.

✦ *Math Masters, p. 296*

Ongoing Learning & Practice

✦ Playing *Addition Spin*
(*Math Journal 1*, p. 86; *Math Masters*, pp. 62 or 63)

PARTNER ACTIVITY

This game was introduced in Lesson 4.2. (The instructions are on journal page 86.) You can customize the game for your class in different ways. If children use the top mat on *Math Masters*, page 62, they will practice adding 2-digit numbers that are multiples of 5. If they use the bottom mat on *Math Masters*, page 62, they will practice adding 2-digit numbers with no regrouping. *Math Masters*, page 63 is a blank *Addition Spin* mat. You can write numbers on this mat so that your children can practice adding 2-digit numbers with regrouping or practice adding 3-digit numbers.

✦ Math Boxes 5.1 (*Math Journal 1*, p. 113)

INDEPENDENT ACTIVITY

Mixed Review This journal page provides opportunities for cumulative review or assessment of concepts and skills.

✦ Home Link 5.1 (*Math Masters*, p. 296)

Home Connection Children determine an unknown rule by looking at shapes that fit the rule and shapes that do not fit the rule. Children then write the rule and choose and draw shapes that fit it.

Options for Individualizing

✦ EXTRA PRACTICE Minute Math

SMALL-GROUP ACTIVITY   5–15 min

To offer children more experience in telling time, see the following page in *Minute Math*:

Measurement: p. 71

5.2 EXPLORATIONS

Exploring Attributes, Triangles, and Sharing

OBJECTIVES To explore similarities and differences among attribute blocks and among triangles; and to develop readiness for division.

summaries	materials

1 Teaching the Lesson

Exploration D: Children find sets of attribute blocks that differ by at least one attribute: size, shape, or color. [Geometry]

Exploration E: Children form triangles on a geoboard, copy those triangles on dot paper, and list similarities and differences among the triangles. [Geometry]

Exploration F: Children act out an equal-sharing situation. [Operations and Computation]

☐ Home Link 5.1

Exploration D: Per partnership or group:
☐ *Math Journal 1,* p. 114
☐ attribute blocks; 1 sheet of paper
☐ red, yellow, and blue crayons or pencils

Exploration E: Per partnership:
☐ Teaching Masters (*Math Masters,* p. 80, and p. 82 or 83)
☐ geoboard; rubber bands

Exploration F: Per partnership:
☐ Teaching Master (*Math Masters,* p. 81)
☐ quarter-sheets of paper
☐ about 35 centimeter cubes, pennies, dried beans, or other small counters
☐ 1 regular die or number cube; paper for recording

***See* Advance Preparation**

2 Ongoing Learning & Practice

Children practice adding 2-digit numbers, making change, and counting up to 100 by playing *Shopping.* [Operations and Computation; Measurement and Reference Frames]

Children practice and maintain skills through Math Boxes and Home Link activities.

☐ *Math Journal 1*, pp. 97 and 115

Per partnership:
☐ Teaching Master (*Math Masters,* p. 61)
☐ *Shopping* cards cut from *Math Masters,* p. 67
☐ nine $1 bills, eight $10 bills
☐ one $100 bill (optional)
☐ calculator
☐ Home Link Master (*Math Masters,* p. 297)

3 Options for Individualizing

Extra Practice Children identify shapes in their classroom and other locations. [Geometry]

☐ *Minute Math*®, p. 17

Additional Information

Advance Preparation Prepare a set of attribute blocks for the Math Message.

Math Masters, pages 80 and 81 give directions for Explorations E and F. You may want to place copies of these masters at workstations. Aides or volunteers can then use the masters as they work with small groups or partnerships.

Getting Started

Mental Math and Reflexes

Pose problems like the following:

60 + 20 = ? 80

600 + 200 = ? 800

? = 40 + 80 120

? = 400 + 800 1,200

90 + 50 = ? 140

900 + 500 = ? 1,400

Math Message

Take one attribute block. What shape is it? What color is it?

Home Link 5.1 Follow-Up

Review the rule. Ask volunteers to draw shapes that fit the rule on the board.

Attributes

Materials
- ☐ attribute blocks
- ☐ sheet of paper
- ☐ red, yellow, and blue crayons or pencils

Solve each problem. On a separate sheet of paper, trace and color the blocks to show your answers.

1. Find 2 blocks that are NOT the same size, NOT the same shape, and NOT the same color.

Drawings of a small yellow triangle and a large red rectangle

2. Find 2 blocks that have the same shape, but are NOT the same size and NOT the same color.

Drawings of a small yellow triangle and a large blue triangle

3. Find 3 blocks that are the same size and the same color, but are NOT the same shape.

Drawings of a large red triangle, a large red circle, and a large red square

4. Find 4 small blocks that are the same color, but are NOT the same shape.

Drawings of a small red triangle, a small red rectangle, a small red circle, and a small red square

Sample answers are given.

✦ *Math Journal 1, p. 114*

---

1 Teaching the Lesson

✦ Math Message Follow-Up

WHOLE-CLASS DISCUSSION

Call on two children to show their attribute blocks. Then ask:

- Are the blocks the same color?
- Are they the same shape?
- Are they the same size?
- How many attributes do the blocks have in common?

Repeat this routine several more times with other pairs of children.

✦ Exploration D: Finding Attribute Blocks That Differ by One Attribute or More
(*Math Journal 1*, p. 114)

SMALL-GROUP ACTIVITY

Children follow the directions on the journal page to find sets of attribute blocks that differ by at least one of the three attributes—size, shape, or color.

Encourage children to find sets of blocks that are not the same as those of other children.

Adjusting the Activity Some children may find it helpful if you give them the first block and then guide them through a process of elimination to find the second block. For example, you might guide them through Problem 1 as follows:

- Start with a small red triangle.

- The second block may not be small. Make a pile with only large blocks.

- The second block may not be a triangle. Remove all triangles from the pile of large yellow and blue blocks.

- The second block may not be red. Remove all red blocks from the pile of large blocks.

All of the shapes that remain in the pile are not the same size, shape, or color as the original block, the small red triangle.

✦ Exploration E: Investigating Shapes of Triangles
(*Math Masters,* pp. 80, 82, and 83)

PARTNER ACTIVITY

Partners form various triangles on a geoboard. They copy their triangles onto geoboard dot paper (*Math Masters,* page 82 or 83).

Partners also make a large triangle on their geoboard. With additional rubber bands, they try to split the triangle into 2, 3, and 4 or more triangles. They copy their results onto geoboard dot paper.

The Follow-Up section on *Math Masters,* page 80 asks the partnership or whole group to discuss and list how all the triangles are alike and how they differ. The triangles are alike because each triangle is a polygon with 3 sides and 3 corners, or vertices. The triangles are different in length of sides, in how much the sides slant, and in the amount of surface they cover.

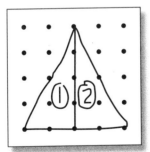 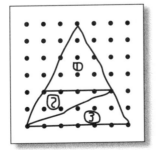

Children record their triangles on *Math Masters,* pages 82 or 83.

Geoboard Triangles

Work with a partner or a small group.

Materials
- ❑ geoboard
- ❑ rubber bands
- ❑ geoboard dot paper
- ❑ paper

Directions

1. How many different-looking triangles can you make on your geoboard? Each partner or person in your group should try to find out.

2. Draw your triangles on geoboard dot paper.

3. Make the largest triangle you can on your geoboard. Use more rubber bands to split the triangle into 2 triangles. Then split it into 3 triangles. Now split it into 4 triangles. Can you make more than 4 triangles? Try.

4. Draw your triangles on geoboard dot paper.

Follow-Up

Look at the triangles that your partnership or group drew.

- How are all the triangles alike? Make a list of the ways.

- How are some of the triangles different? Talk about the ways. Then make a list of the ways you found.

✦ *Math Masters,* p. 80

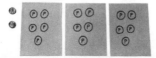

Sharing Equally

Work with a partner.

Materials
- ☐ quarter-sheets of paper
- ☐ plain paper
- ☐ 1 regular die or number cube
- ☐ centimeter cubes, pennies, or dried beans

Directions

1. Think of the quarter-sheets of paper as nests.
   Think of the cubes, pennies, or beans as eggs.

2. Choose a number between 8 and 32.
   Then count out that many "eggs."

3. Roll the die once. The number that lands faceup
   tells how many "nests" (quarter-sheets) to lay out.

4. Work together to share the eggs equally among all the
   nests. When you finish, count the eggs in each nest.
   Make sure each nest has the same number of eggs.

5. Make a record of your work on the sheet of plain paper.
   - Show the number of eggs you started with.
   - Show the nests and the eggs in each nest.
   - Show any eggs that were left over.

6. Choose a different number of eggs. Then follow Steps 1–5 again.

Math Masters, p. 81

TEACHING MASTER

◆ Exploration F: Exploring Equal Sharing
(*Math Masters*, p. 81)

PARTNER ACTIVITY 👥

Children choose numbers between 8 and 32 and take as many counters ("eggs") as the number they choose. Then they roll the die to determine how many quarter-sheets ("nests") to take. They share (divide) the eggs among the nests. Children keep a record of what they did by showing the number of eggs with which they started, the number of nests among which they shared the eggs, and the number of eggs in each nest. They also record how many, if any, eggs were left over (the remainder).

Portfolio Ideas

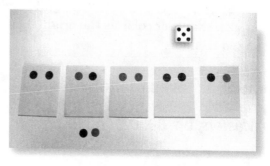

12 eggs are divided equally among 5 nests with 2 eggs left over.

Shopping

Play *Shopping* with a partner.

Materials
- ☐ *Shopping* cards (*Math Masters*, p. 67)
- ☐ *Math Masters*, p. 61
- ☐ calculator
- ☐ play money for each partner: at least nine $1 bills and eight $10 bills; one $100 bill (optional)

Directions

1. Partners take turns being the "Customer" and the "Clerk."

2. The Customer draws two cards and turns them over.
   These are the items the Customer is buying.

3. The Customer places the two cards on the parts-and-total
   diagram—one card in each Part box.

4. The Customer figures out the total cost of the two items without
   using a calculator.

5. The Customer counts out bills equal to the total cost. The Customer
   places the bills in the Total box on the parts-and-total diagram.

6. The Clerk uses a calculator to check that the Customer has
   figured the correct total cost.

7. Partners switch roles.

8. Play continues until all eight cards have been used.

Another Way to Play

Instead of counting out bills, the Customer says or writes the total.
The Customer gives the Clerk a $100 bill to pay for the items.
The Clerk must return the correct change.

Math Journal 1, p. 97

STUDENT PAGE

---

② Ongoing Learning & Practice

◆ Playing *Shopping*
(*Math Journal 1*, p. 97;
Math Masters, p. 61;
and *Shopping* Cards from *Math Masters*, p. 67)

PARTNER ACTIVITY 👥

This activity, which was introduced in Lesson 4.6, helps children practice strategies for the mental addition of 2-digit numbers. The variation described at the bottom of the journal page provides practice in making change and counting up to 100.

◆ Math Boxes 5.2 (*Math Journal 1,* p. 115)

INDEPENDENT ACTIVITY

Mixed Review This journal page provides opportunities for cumulative review or assessment of concepts and skills.

◆ Home Link 5.2 (*Math Masters,* p. 297)

Home Connection In each problem, three of the shapes have something in common that is not a feature of the fourth shape. The attributes considered are size (small or large), shape (square, circle, or triangle), and face (smile or frown). Children decide which shape is different.

3 Options for Individualizing

◆ EXTRA PRACTICE Minute Math

SMALL-GROUP ACTIVITY   5–15 min

To offer children more experience with identifying shapes, see the following page in *Minute Math:*

Basic Routines: p. 17

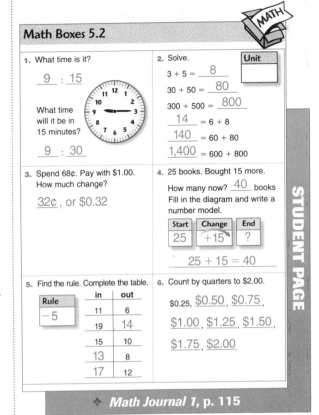

◆ *Math Journal 1,* p. 115

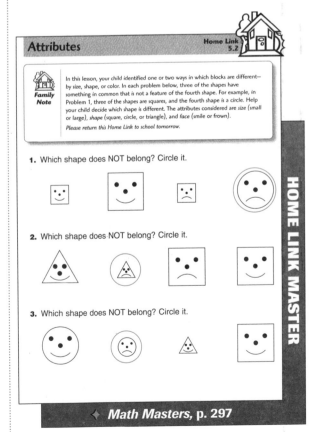

◆ *Math Masters,* p. 297

5.3 EXPLORATIONS

Exploring Polygons, Arrays, and Coins

OBJECTIVES To name and classify polygons; to develop readiness for multiplication; and to find coin combinations equivalent to $1.00.

summaries

materials

1 Teaching the Lesson

Children review the shapes on the Pattern-Block Template and the characteristics and names of polygons. [Geometry]

□ *Math Journal 1*, p. 116
□ Home Link 5.2
□ Pattern-Block Template
□ *The Greedy Triangle* (optional)

Exploration G: Children construct polygons on their geoboards following specifications, copy those polygons onto dot paper, and compare their polygons to those of other children. [Geometry]

Exploration G: Per group:
□ Teaching Master (*Math Masters*, p. 84)
□ geoboard; rubber bands; straightedge
□ *Shapes, Shapes, Shapes* (optional)
□ *The Art of Shapes for Children and Adults* (optional)

Exploration H: Children explore multiplication concepts by making rectangular arrays with centimeter cubes and recording them on grid paper. [Numeration; Operations and Computation]

Exploration H: Per partnership or group:
□ Teaching Masters (*Math Masters*, pp. 85 and 86)
□ about 40 centimeter cubes; 2 six-sided dice

Exploration I: Children make and record different combinations of nickels, dimes, and quarters that are equivalent to $1.00. [Measurement and Reference Frames; Operations and Computation]

Exploration I: Per group:
□ Teaching Master (*Math Masters*, p. 87)
□ 20 nickels, 10 dimes, 4 quarters; 2 half-dollars (optional)

***See* Advance Preparation**

2 Ongoing Learning & Practice

Children practice identifying complements of 100 by playing *Dollar Rummy*. [Numeration; Operations and Computation]

Children practice and maintain skills through Math Boxes and Home Link activities.

□ *Math Journal 1*, pp. 63 and 117
□ Home Link Master (*Math Masters*, p. 298)
□ *Dollar Rummy* cards (cut from *Math Masters*, pp. 48 and 49)

3 Options for Individualizing

Extra Practice Children identify an unknown 2-dimensional shape by asking *yes* and *no* questions. [Geometry]

□ *Minute Math*®, p. 18

Additional Information

Advance Preparation You may wish to obtain *The Greedy Triangle* by Marilyn Burns (Scholastic, 1994) to use with this lesson. You may want to write the vocabulary words below on the "Word Wall," as suggested on page 288.

For Exploration G, you may want to obtain the books *Shapes, Shapes, Shapes* by Tana Hoban (Greenwillow Books, 1986) and *The Art of Shapes for Children and Adults* by Margaret Steele and Cindy Estes (FotoFolio, 1997).

Vocabulary • **trapezoid** • **rhombus** • **polygon** • **side** • **vertex (*plural:* vertices)** • **angle** • **triangle** • **quadrangle** • **pentagon** • **hexagon** • **heptagon** • **octagon**

Getting Started

Mental Math and Reflexes

Say a number and ask children to record the 100-complement of that number on their slates. For example, you say 90 and the class writes 10. Write the number model on the board: $90 + 10 = 100$.

Suggestions:

- Multiples of 10: 90, 40, 70
- Multiples of 25: 50, 25, 75
- Multiples of 5: 95, 45, 65

Math Message

Name the Pattern-Block Template shapes.

Hexagon, circle, triangle, trapezoid, rhombus, square

Home Link 5.2 Follow-Up

For each problem, children name the shape that doesn't belong. Ask them to explain how they chose that shape.

1 Teaching the Lesson

◆ Math Message Follow-Up

WHOLE-CLASS DISCUSSION

As children identify shapes on their Pattern-Block Templates, draw the shapes and write their names on the board. Remind children that the square, **trapezoid,** larger triangle, hexagon, and two **rhombuses** are the same size and shape as the pattern blocks. To distinguish between the two rhombuses, you might refer to them as the "narrow" rhombus and the "wide" rhombus.

◆ Reviewing Characteristics of Polygons
(*Math Journal 1,* p. 116)

WHOLE-CLASS DISCUSSION

Remind the class that the pattern-block shapes are examples of **polygons.** Draw a polygon on the board. Identify and discuss its parts.

▷ Polygons are made up of straight **sides** (line segments).

▷ Sides meet at their endpoints. A point at which two sides meet is called a **vertex** of the polygon. The plural of *vertex* is **vertices.**

▷ Any two sides that meet form an **angle.**

With children, examine the shapes on the journal page. Mention that polygons are "closed" figures—you can trace their sides and come back to where you started without retracing or crossing any part. Ask children to trace a couple of the polygons with their fingers.

NOTE: Although the word *diamond* is often used to describe a rhombus, and even though *rhombus* is defined in this way by some dictionaries, use the word *rhombus* since it is the formal term used in geometry.

Polygons

Triangles	Quadrangles or Quadrilaterals

Pentagons	Hexagons

Heptagons	Octagons

These are NOT polygons.

◆ *Math Journal 1,* p. 116

STUDENT PAGE

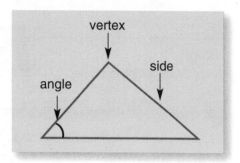

vertex

angle   side

Literature Link

The book *The Greedy Triangle* by Marilyn Burns (Scholastic, 1994) focuses on the characteristics of different polygons. A triangle, dissatisfied with its life, goes to the "Shapeshifter" and asks for one more angle and one more side. Then the shape explores life as a square. The story goes on with the shape continually asking the Shapeshifter for one more angle and one more side.

ONGOING ASSESSMENT

Do not require children to memorize the shape names at this time. Most children will be able to do so by the end of second grade.

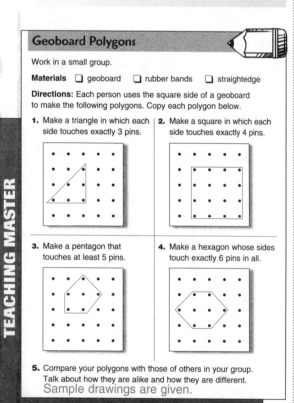

Geoboard Polygons

Work in a small group.

Materials ☐ geoboard   ☐ rubber bands   ☐ straightedge

Directions: Each person uses the square side of a geoboard to make the following polygons. Copy each polygon below.

1. Make a triangle in which each side touches exactly 3 pins.

2. Make a square in which each side touches exactly 4 pins.

3. Make a pentagon that touches at least 5 pins.

4. Make a hexagon whose sides touch exactly 6 pins in all.

5. Compare your polygons with those of others in your group. Talk about how they are alike and how they are different.
Sample drawings are given.

◆ *Math Masters*, p. 84

Call children's attention to the last two rows of the journal page and discuss why these shapes are not polygons. Children should have no trouble with most of the shapes. Ask them to trace each of the three shapes located on the right of the final row. First, draw a dot anywhere on the shape to identify a starting point. Can they return to the starting point without retracing or crossing any part of the shape? no

◆ Naming Polygons by the Number of Their Sides or Angles (*Math Journal 1*, p. 116)

WHOLE-CLASS DISCUSSION

Language Arts Link Explain that the word *polygon* comes from the Greek language: *poly-* means many, and *-gon* means angle. Point out that polygons are named according to the number of sides or angles they have.

3 Sides or Angles

Ask: *How many angles does a* **triangle** *have?* 3 *How many sides?* 3 Point out that *tri-* means *three*. Ask children to name other words that start with *tri-*. Sample answers: tricycle, triple, triceratops (a dinosaur with three horns)

4 Sides or Angles

Ask: *How many angles does a* **quadrangle** *have?* 4 *How many sides?* 4 Point out that *quad-* means *four*. Other words that start with *quad-* include *quadruped* (a four-legged animal), *quadruple* (to multiply by four), and *quadrille* (a square dance for four couples; also a card game played by four people).

Quadrangles are often called *quadrilaterals*. The root *-later* means *side*.

5 and More Sides or Angles

Discuss the other polygons on the page in a similar manner: **pentagon**—5 angles and 5 sides; **hexagon**—6 angles and 6 sides; **heptagon**—7 angles and 7 sides; and **octagon**—8 angles and 8 sides.

◆ Exploration G: Constructing Polygons on a Geoboard (*Math Masters*, p. 84)

SMALL-GROUP ACTIVITY

Children make a triangle, a square, a pentagon, and a hexagon on a square geoboard. Children use their straightedges to copy each polygon onto dot paper. Note the restrictions: The rubber band may touch only a given number of pins. This is done in order to limit the size of the constructions.

When everyone in a group has copied all four shapes, ask group members to compare their shapes. Children should notice that polygons come in many sizes and shapes.

✦ Exploration H: Making Centimeter-Cube Arrays (*Math Masters*, pp. 85 and 86)

PARTNER ACTIVITY

Partners or group members complete the steps to make arrays with centimeter cubes. Together, group members record at least 5 rectangular arrays by filling in the correct number and arrangement of centimeter-grid squares. For each array, group members write how many rows, how many in each row, and how many in all.

Portfolio Ideas

NOTE: You might want to provide children with additional copies of the centimeter grid paper on *Math Masters*, page 86.

✦ Exploration I: Making a Dollar (*Math Masters*, p. 87)

SMALL-GROUP ACTIVITY

Before children begin, ask them to think about an organized way to determine the different groups of coins equivalent to $1.00. Children are given a hint: Find ways of using 3 quarters and other coins.

Portfolio Ideas

Children plan how to, and then record, the groups of coins using Ⓝ, Ⓓ, and Ⓠ.

Coin combinations

Adjusting the Activity To extend the activity, add 2 half-dollars to the set of coins.

TEACHING MASTER

Cube Arrays

Work with a partner or a small group.

Materials
- ☐ centimeter grid paper from *Math Masters*, p. 86
- ☐ 2 six-sided dice
- ☐ about 40 centimeter cubes

Directions

Follow these steps to build arrays with centimeter cubes:

1. Pick one member of your group to roll the dice.

2. Use the number that is faceup on one die for the number of rows in the array. Use the number that is faceup on the other die for the number of cubes in each row.

Example: If you roll this: You can make either array:

3. Work together. Use centimeter cubes to build the array.

4. On grid paper, fill in squares to show your array. Underneath the array, write
   - how many rows are in the array
   - how many cubes are in each row
   - how many cubes there are in all

   5 rows
   3 cubes in each row
   15 cubes in all

5. Take turns rolling the dice. Together, make at least five different arrays. Record each array on grid paper.

✦ *Math Masters*, p. 85

◯ Literature and Art Link

- *Shapes, Shapes, Shapes* by Tana Hoban (Greenwillow Books, 1986)

- *The Art of Shapes for Children and Adults* by Margaret Steele and Cindy Estes (FotoFolio, 1997)

Make a Dollar

Work together in a small group.

Materials
- ☐ 20 nickels
- ☐ 10 dimes
- ☐ 4 quarters
- ☐ paper and pencil

Directions

1. Use the coins to find as many different ways as you can to make $1.00.

2. Before you begin, THINK about how to do this. *Hint:* First, make a dollar using 3 quarters and some other coins.

3. Plan how you will record the different ways to make $1.00.

4. On a sheet of paper, record the different ways you find to make $1.00. Use Ⓝ, Ⓓ, and Ⓠ to show the coins.

Follow-Up

- How many ways did you find to make $1.00? Check with other groups to see if they thought of any ways that your group didn't find.

- Did you have a plan to find all the combinations? Compare your plan with the plan used by another group.

TEACHING MASTER

✦ *Math Masters*, p. 87

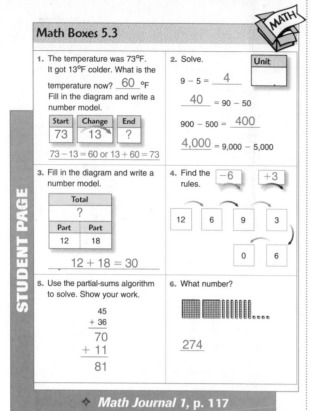

Math Boxes 5.3

1. The temperature was 73°F. It got 13°F colder. What is the temperature now? __60__ °F
Fill in the diagram and write a number model.

Start	Change	End
73	13	?

73 − 13 = 60 or 13 + 60 = 73

2. Solve.

Unit

9 − 5 = __4__

__40__ = 90 − 50

900 − 500 = __400__

__4,000__ = 9,000 − 5,000

3. Fill in the diagram and write a number model.

Total
?

Part	Part
12	18

12 + 18 = 30

4. Find the rules.

5. Use the partial-sums algorithm to solve. Show your work.

```
   45
 + 36
 ----
   70
 + 11
 ----
   81
```

6. What number?

274

◆ Math Journal 1, p. 117

Polygons

Home Link 5.3

Family Note

In this lesson, your child has been learning the names of different polygons. A polygon is a closed figure made up of straight sides, and you can trace and come back to where you started without retracing or crossing any part. Different types of polygons are shown below. Examples of polygons can be found in real-life objects. For example, a stop sign is an octagon and this page is a rectangle. As your child cuts out pictures of polygons, discuss each shape. Count the sides and angles and try to name the polygons. Talk about how the polygons are alike and different.

Please return this Home Link to school tomorrow or as requested by the teacher.

1. Cut out pictures from newspapers and magazines that show triangles, quadrangles, and other polygons. Ask an adult for permission first.

2. Paste each picture on a sheet of paper.

3. Write the names of some of the polygons under the pictures.

4. Bring your pictures to school.

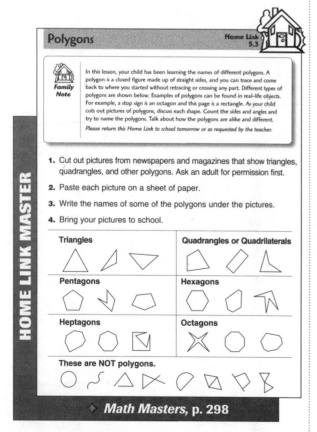

Triangles	Quadrangles or Quadrilaterals
Pentagons	Hexagons
Heptagons	Octagons

These are NOT polygons.

◆ Math Masters, p. 298

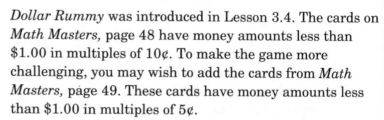

Ongoing Learning & Practice

◆ Playing *Dollar Rummy*
(*Math Journal 1*, p. 63;
Math Masters, pp. 48 and 49)

PARTNER ACTIVITY

Dollar Rummy was introduced in Lesson 3.4. The cards on *Math Masters*, page 48 have money amounts less than $1.00 in multiples of 10¢. To make the game more challenging, you may wish to add the cards from *Math Masters*, page 49. These cards have money amounts less than $1.00 in multiples of 5¢.

◆ Math Boxes 5.3 (*Math Journal 1*, p. 117)

INDEPENDENT ACTIVITY

Mixed Review This journal page provides opportunities for cumulative review or assessment of concepts and skills.

◆ Home Link 5.3 (*Math Masters*, p. 298)

Home Connection Children cut out pictures of polygons from newspapers and magazines. They bring the pictures to school to use in a bulletin-board display or class polygon book. You may wish to allow children to have more than one day to complete this assignment. If so, be sure to tell the children.

Options for Individualizing

◆ EXTRA PRACTICE Minute Math

SMALL-GROUP ACTIVITY **5–15 min**

To offer children more experience with identifying shapes, see the following page in *Minute Math:*

Basic Routines: p. 18

5.4 Points and Line Segments

OBJECTIVE To define, name, and draw line segments.

summaries	**materials**
1 **Teaching the Lesson**	
Children define and name points and line segments with letter labels. They also practice drawing line segments with a straightedge according to a code. [Geometry]	☐ *Math Journal 1,* p. 118 ☐ Home Link 5.3 ☐ straightedge
2 **Ongoing Learning & Practice**	
Children match clock faces with digital times by playing *Clock Concentration.* [Measurement and Reference Frames] Children practice and maintain skills through Math Boxes and Home Link activities.	☐ *Math Journal 1,* p. 119 ☐ Teaching Masters (*Math Masters,* pp. 77 and 78) ☐ *Clock Concentration* cards (made from index cards or from *Math Masters,* p. 79; per small group) ☐ Home Link Master (*Math Masters,* p. 299)
3 **Options for Individualizing**	
Language Diversity Children create codes for drawing capital letters composed of line segments. [Geometry] **Reteaching** Children practice drawing line segments using a straightedge. [Geometry]	☐ Teaching Masters (*Math Masters,* pp. 88 and 89) ☐ straightedge

Additional Information

Vocabulary • **point** • **straightedge** • **line segment** • **endpoint**

Getting Started

Mental Math and Reflexes

Pose number stories with "harder" addition and subtraction facts:

- Alexi has 8 toy cars. Theo has 7 toy cars. How many do they have in all?
- Jillian had 9 crayons. She found 6 more. How many crayons in all?
- Lara brought 14 lollipops to school. She gave away 8 during lunch. How many does she have now?
- Bobby went down the slide 17 times during recess. Jason went down 9 times. Bobby went down the slide how many more times than Jason?

Math Message

Write a sentence that has the word point *or* points *in it.*

Home Link 5.3 Follow-Up

Ask children how they identified shapes in pictures they brought to school.

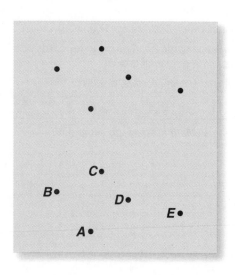

1 Teaching the Lesson

◆ Math Message Follow-Up

WHOLE-CLASS DISCUSSION

Write a few of the children's sentences on the board. If interest in this activity is high, add a few sentences of your own. *For example:*

▷ My pencil has a sharp *point.*

▷ The football team scored 21 *points.*

▷ This number has a decimal *point* in it.

▷ Can you *point* out the picture you like the best?

Discuss the meaning of the word ***point*** in geometry—a location in space, the tiniest part of a figure, an object without length, something represented by a dot, and so on.

The idea of a geometric point is so basic that the term *point* is usually regarded as undefined. Similarly, *line* is usually considered undefined.

◆ Discussing How Points Are Named

WHOLE-CLASS DISCUSSION

Draw five dots on the board. Ask someone to choose one of the dots and to tell you which one it is without pointing to it. He or she will probably have a hard time doing this.

Explain that an easy way to talk about points is to give them labels. Points are usually labeled with capital letters, such as *A, B,* and *C.* Label each of the dots on the board, calling them by name as you do so: "Point *A,*" "Point *B,*" and so on.

◆ Defining and Naming Line Segments

WHOLE-CLASS ACTIVITY

Ask children what they think *straight* means. "Not curved" or "goes in one direction" are good responses. Point out that a **straightedge** is a tool used for drawing straight lines.

On blank sheets of paper, have children draw two dots as you do the same on the board. Label the dots *A* and *B*. Then demonstrate how to draw a "straight line" connecting them: Place the straightedge just under the dots and draw from point to point, not from letter to letter, and not past the points. Tell children that they just drew a **line segment** whose **endpoints** are points *A* and *B*. The segment can be called "line segment *AB*" or "line segment *BA*"—the names of the endpoints can be in either order. Write $\overline{AB}$ and $\overline{BA}$ on the board and say that sometimes the symbols are used for "line segment *AB*" or "line segment *BA*."

Ask children to draw three points (that are not in a straight line) on their papers and to label each point with a *different* letter. Explain that in any problem or example, all of the points must have different names; two points may not have the same letter label. Have children use a straightedge to connect each of the three points to each of the other points. Ask children to name the shape they have formed. A triangle

✦ Drawing Line Segments with a Straightedge
(*Math Journal 1*, p. 118)

PARTNER ACTIVITY 👥

The first part of the journal page shows points connected by line segments, along with a code that specifies the sequence in which the points have been connected. For example, the code $A{\rightarrow}B{\rightarrow}C{\rightarrow}A$ means: "First draw a line segment from *A* to *B*, then a line segment from *B* to *C*, and finally one from *C* to *A*." Give partners 2 or 3 minutes to figure out the codes. Then go over the three codes with the class.

In the second part of the activity, children draw line segments according to given codes. Partners can work on these problems independently while you circulate and assist children who need help.

Drawing a line segment labeled *AB*

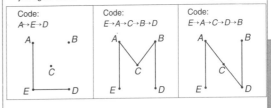

Adjusting the Activity Consider posting *point, straightedge, line segment,* and *endpoint* on the "Word Wall" so that children can refer to them as necessary. Include a picture, as well as a written description, next to each word.

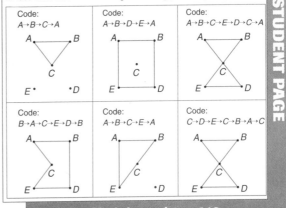

✦ *Math Journal 1*, p. 118

STUDENT PAGE

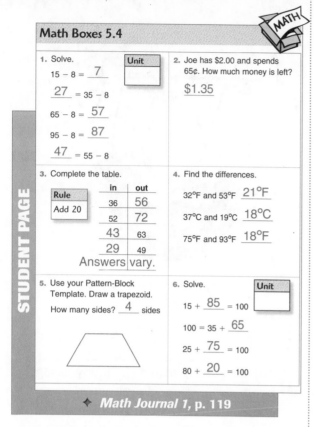

Math Boxes 5.4

1. Solve.

$15 - 8 = \underline{7}$ Unit

$\underline{27} = 35 - 8$

$65 - 8 = \underline{57}$

$95 - 8 = \underline{87}$

$\underline{47} = 55 - 8$

2. Joe has $2.00 and spends 65¢. How much money is left?

$1.35

3. Complete the table.

Rule	in	out
Add 20	36	56
	52	72
	43	63
	29	49

Answers vary.

4. Find the differences.

32°F and 53°F $\underline{21°F}$

37°C and 19°C $\underline{18°C}$

75°F and 93°F $\underline{18°F}$

5. Use your Pattern-Block Template. Draw a trapezoid.

How many sides? $\underline{4}$ sides

6. Solve. Unit

$15 + \underline{85} = 100$

$100 = 35 + \underline{65}$

$25 + \underline{75} = 100$

$80 + \underline{20} = 100$

Math Journal 1, p. 119

STUDENT PAGE

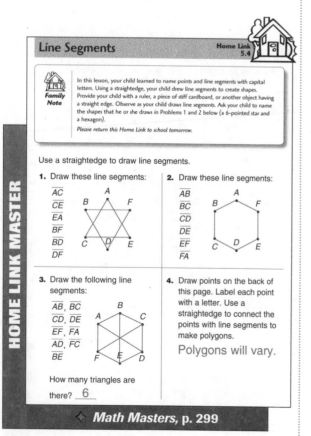

Line Segments Home Link 5.4

Family Note

In this lesson, your child learned to name points and line segments with capital letters. Using a straightedge, your child drew line segments to create shapes. Provide your child with a ruler, a piece of stiff cardboard, or another object having a straight edge. Observe as your child draws line segments. Ask your child to name the shapes that he or she draws in Problems 1 and 2 below (a 6-pointed star and a hexagon).

Please return this Home Link to school tomorrow.

Use a straightedge to draw line segments.

1. Draw these line segments:

$\overline{AC}$
$\overline{CE}$
$\overline{EA}$
$\overline{BF}$
$\overline{BD}$
$\overline{DF}$

2. Draw these line segments:

$\overline{AB}$
$\overline{BC}$
$\overline{CD}$
$\overline{DE}$
$\overline{EF}$
$\overline{FA}$

3. Draw the following line segments:

$\overline{AB}, \overline{BC}$
$\overline{CD}, \overline{DE}$
$\overline{EF}, \overline{FA}$
$\overline{AD}, \overline{FC}$
$\overline{BE}$

How many triangles are there? $\underline{6}$

4. Draw points on the back of this page. Label each point with a letter. Use a straightedge to connect the points with line segments to make polygons.

Polygons will vary.

Math Masters, p. 299

HOME LINK MASTER

Ongoing Learning & Practice

◆ **Playing *Clock Concentration***
(*Math Masters*, pp. 77–79)

SMALL-GROUP ACTIVITY

Clock Concentration was introduced in Lesson 5.1. If children have not played this game, they will need to follow the directions to make a set of *Clock Concentration* cards. The game can be modified to meet the needs of children having difficulty by using fewer pairs of cards or by playing the game with the cards showing faceup.

◆ **Math Boxes 5.4** (*Math Journal 1*, p. 119)

INDEPENDENT ACTIVITY

Mixed Review This journal page provides opportunities for cumulative review or assessment of concepts and skills.

◆ **Home Link 5.4** (*Math Masters*, p. 299)

Home Connection Children connect 6 points with line segments in two different ways to form a 6-pointed star and a hexagon. Children also connect other line segments and answer a question about the triangles that are formed.

3 Options for Individualizing

◆ **LANGUAGE DIVERSITY** **Making Up Codes to Draw Capital Letters with Line Segments**
(*Math Masters*, p. 88)

INDEPENDENT ACTIVITY   **15–30 min**

Children make up codes that specify capital letters. For the Challenge letter *Z*, they also name line segments.

◆ **RETEACHING** **Drawing Line Segments**
(*Math Masters*, p. 89)

INDEPENDENT ACTIVITY   **15–30 min**

This master provides additional practice for any children who are having difficulty drawing line segments or using a straightedge. Ask children to describe the picture after they have drawn all of the line segments. A house

---

PLANNING AHEAD

In preparation for the Shapes Museum that will be introduced in Lesson 5.7, collect a few objects or pictures of objects having the following shapes:

Cylinders: coffee cans, rolls of paper towels, rolls of toilet paper, drinking straws, mugs, fluorescent lightbulbs

Spheres: tennis balls, oranges, globes

Rectangular prisms: books, cereal boxes, cartons, chalkboard erasers, pictures of a file cabinet, pictures of a bookcase

Cones: ice cream cones, party hats, conical paper cups, pictures of traffic cones

Pyramids: pictures of pyramids or pyramid-shaped roofs

Cubes: notepaper cubes, regular dice, centimeter cubes, a liter (cubic decimeter) box

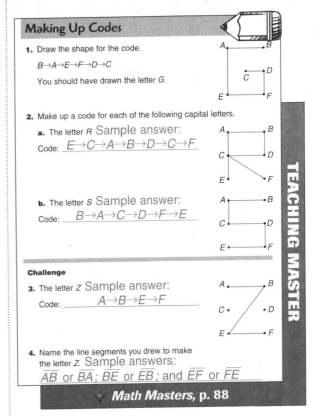

Making Up Codes

1. Draw the shape for the code.

$B \rightarrow A \rightarrow E \rightarrow F \rightarrow D \rightarrow C$

You should have drawn the letter *G*.

2. Make up a code for each of the following capital letters.
   a. The letter *R* Sample answer:
   Code: $E \rightarrow C \rightarrow A \rightarrow B \rightarrow D \rightarrow C \rightarrow F$

   b. The letter *S* Sample answer:
   Code: $B \rightarrow A \rightarrow C \rightarrow D \rightarrow F \rightarrow E$

Challenge

3. The letter *Z* Sample answer:
   Code: $A \rightarrow B \rightarrow E \rightarrow F$

4. Name the line segments you drew to make the letter *Z*. Sample answers:
   $\overline{AB}$ or $\overline{BA}$; $\overline{BE}$ or $\overline{EB}$; and $\overline{EF}$ or $\overline{FE}$

◇ *Math Masters*, p. 88

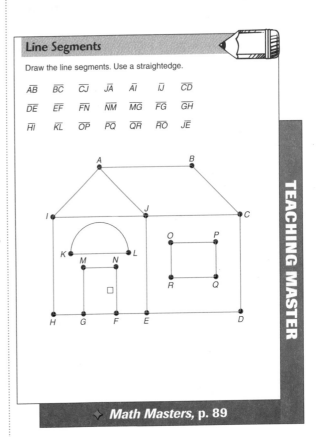

Line Segments

Draw the line segments. Use a straightedge.

$\overline{AB}$ $\overline{BC}$ $\overline{CJ}$ $\overline{JA}$ $\overline{AI}$ $\overline{IJ}$ $\overline{CD}$

$\overline{DE}$ $\overline{EF}$ $\overline{FN}$ $\overline{NM}$ $\overline{MG}$ $\overline{FG}$ $\overline{GH}$

$\overline{HI}$ $\overline{KL}$ $\overline{OP}$ $\overline{PQ}$ $\overline{QR}$ $\overline{RO}$ $\overline{JE}$

◇ *Math Masters*, p. 89

5.5 Parallel Line Segments

OBJECTIVE To introduce the concept of *parallel;* and to apply this concept to parallel line segments.

summaries	materials

1 Teaching the Lesson

Children are introduced to the meaning of the word *parallel*, and they identify examples of parallel line segments in the real world. They also examine diagrams of parallel and nonparallel line segments, draw parallel and nonparallel line segments, and identify parallel and nonparallel sides of quadrangles. [Geometry]

- ☐ *Math Journal 1*, pp. 120, 122, and 123
- ☐ Home Link 5.4
- ☐ straightedge

2 Ongoing Learning & Practice

Children practice and maintain skills through Math Boxes and Home Link activities.

- ☐ *Math Journal 1*, p. 121
- ☐ Home Link Master (*Math Masters,* p. 300)

3 Options for Individualizing

Enrichment Children collect examples of parallel line segments from magazines or newspapers. [Geometry]

Reteaching Children form parallel line segments on a geoboard. [Geometry]

- ☐ magazines and newspapers
- ☐ different-color markers, or glue and different colors of yarn
- ☐ straightedge (optional)
- ☐ geoboard; rubber bands

Additional Information
Vocabulary • parallel

Getting Started

Mental Math and Reflexes

Pose problems about making change. *Suggestions:*

- You buy a candy bar for 55 cents. You pay with a $1 bill. How much change should you receive? 45 cents
- You buy a notebook for 68 cents. You pay with a $1 bill. How much change should you receive? 32 cents
- You buy a pen for 37 cents. You pay with 2 quarters. How much change should you receive? 13 cents
- You buy a can of soup for 66 cents. You pay with 3 quarters. How much change should you receive? 9 cents

Math Message

Think of the lines printed on a sheet of notebook paper. Imagine that the lines could go on forever. Do you think that the lines would ever meet?

Home Link 5.4 Follow-Up

Quickly check children's drawings to see if they drew the correct line segments. Ask volunteers to identify the shapes that were drawn in Problems 1 and 2. A 6-pointed star and a hexagon Ask several children to show the line segments and polygons they drew for Problem 4. If possible, have children name the specific polygons.

1 Teaching the Lesson

◆ Math Message Follow-Up

WHOLE-CLASS DISCUSSION

Although we cannot see a line that goes on "forever" in the real world, it is possible to imagine it. Ask children to give reasons they think the lines printed on the notebook paper would or would not meet if extended forever in both directions. Some children may understand intuitively that the lines on notebook paper will always be the same distance apart.

◆ Discussing the Meaning of Parallel Line Segments (*Math Journal 1,* p. 120)

WHOLE-CLASS DISCUSSION

Mention that the "lines" on notebook paper are really line segments. Discuss the idea of **parallel** in the real world; for example, parallel railroad tracks, lane markers on roads, shelves on bookcases, and so on. The lines on notebook paper are parallel line segments.

Ask children to suggest other examples of parallel line segments in the classroom or hallway. Sample answers: parallel edges of doors and windows, radiator sections, opposite edges of books and journals, opposite edges of chalkboards

With the children, examine the parallel line segments at the top of the journal page. Mention that parallel line segments do not need to be the same length. Discuss why the line segments in the second row are not parallel. Sample answers: Some of the line segments meet; other line segments would meet if they were extended.

NOTE: Theoretically, the lines on notebook paper would never meet, if extended infinitely. But in practice, no lines drawn on paper are perfectly parallel, and so they would meet at some point.

Adjusting the Activity Display a sheet of notebook paper rather than asking children to visualize the lines on the sheet. Tape the sheet to the board and use a ruler and chalk to extend the lines in either or both directions.

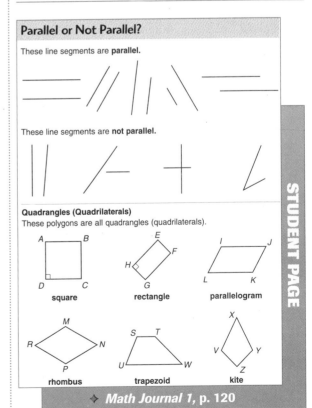

Math Journal 1, p. 120

Parallel Line Segments

Use a straightedge.

1. Draw line segments *AB* and *CD*.

   Are line segments *AB* and *CD* parallel?

   <u>yes</u>

2. Draw line segment *EF*.

   Are line segments *AB* and *EF* parallel?

   <u>yes</u>

3. Draw line segment *LM*.

4. Draw a line segment that is parallel to line segment *LM*. Label its endpoints *R* and *S*.

5. Draw a line segment that is NOT parallel to line segment *LM*. Label its endpoints *T* and *U*. Line segments drawn may vary. Sample line segments *RS* and *TU* are shown.

6. Draw a quadrangle that has NO parallel sides.

   Quadrangles drawn may vary. Sample drawing is shown.

✦ *Math Journal 1, p. 122*

NOTE: Some children may ask about the symbol in the corner of the square and the rectangle. It is used to indicate a right angle. Tell children it simply means *square corner*. Square corners will be covered in the next lesson.

Parallel Line Segments (cont.)

7. Draw a quadrangle in which opposite sides are parallel.

   Quadrangles drawn may vary. Sample drawing is shown. Possible drawings are a square, rectangle, rhombus, or parallelogram.

8. Draw a quadrangle in which all four sides are the same length.

   What is another name for this shape?

   <u>square or rhombus</u>

   Quadrangles drawn may vary. Sample drawing is shown. Possible drawings are a square or a rhombus.

9. Draw a quadrangle in which 2 opposite sides are parallel and the other 2 opposite sides are NOT parallel.

   Trapezoids drawn may vary. Sample drawing is shown.

✦ *Math Journal 1, p. 123*

Next, examine the quadrangles at the bottom of the page. Have children point to opposite sides that are parallel and to opposite sides that are not parallel.

 Adjusting the Activity Add the word *parallel* to the "Word Wall," along with a picture and a written description. Include a mnemonic device to help children remember the meaning: "The three *l*s in *para**ll**el* are parallel!"

✦ Drawing Line Segments That Are or Are Not Parallel (*Math Journal 1*, pp. 122 and 123)

INDEPENDENT ACTIVITY

In Problems 1–5, children draw line segments that are parallel, as well as those that are not parallel. In Problems 6–9, children apply their knowledge of parallel line segments to drawing quadrangles. These problems prepare children for further work with quadrangles in Lesson 5.6, so they should complete the problems before going on to the next lesson.

 Adjusting the Activity Some children may be interested in the mathematical symbol that is used to indicate parallel line segments. For example, "Line segment *AB* is parallel to line segment *CD*" can be written symbolically as "$\overline{AB} \parallel \overline{CD}$."

Ongoing Learning & Practice

✦ Math Boxes 5.5 (*Math Journal 1*, p. 121)

INDEPENDENT ACTIVITY

Mixed Review This journal page provides opportunities for cumulative review or assessment of concepts and skills.

◆ Home Link 5.5 (*Math Masters*, p. 300)

Home Connection Children draw line segments and identify parallel line segments. They also begin collecting 3-dimensional objects for the Shapes Museum that will be introduced in Lesson 5.7.

3 Options for Individualizing

◆ ENRICHMENT Creating a Booklet or Bulletin-Board Display of Parallel Line Segments

INDEPENDENT ACTIVITY   30+ min

Encourage children to look through newspapers and magazines to find examples of parallel line segments. Have them highlight the parallel line segments by using colored markers and a straightedge. If more than one pair of line segments is highlighted within a picture, different colors can be used.

Portfolio Ideas

Children can also highlight parallel line segments by gluing pieces of brightly colored yarn on top of the chosen segments. Display children's collections on a bulletin board or in a class book.

◆ RETEACHING Modeling Parallel Line Segments on a Geoboard

SMALL-GROUP ACTIVITY   5–15 min

It may be helpful to use geoboards with children who are still struggling with the concept of parallel line segments. You might make a line segment on your geoboard and ask children to copy it on their geoboards. Then ask children to make a line segment parallel to the one they just created.

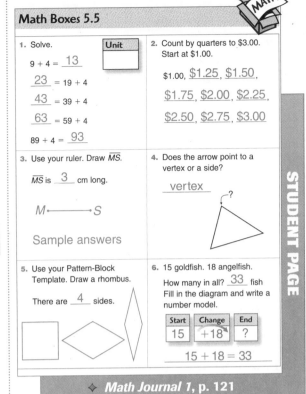

Math Boxes 5.5

1. Solve.   Unit

   $9 + 4 =$ __13__

   __23__ $= 19 + 4$

   __43__ $= 39 + 4$

   __63__ $= 59 + 4$

   $89 + 4 =$ __93__

2. Count by quarters to $3.00. Start at $1.00.

   $1.00, __$1.25__, __$1.50__,

   __$1.75__, __$2.00__, __$2.25__,

   __$2.50__, __$2.75__, __$3.00__

3. Use your ruler. Draw $\overline{MS}$.

   $\overline{MS}$ is __3__ cm long.

   M •———→• S

   Sample answers

4. Does the arrow point to a vertex or a side?

   vertex

5. Use your Pattern-Block Template. Draw a rhombus.

   There are __4__ sides.

6. 15 goldfish. 18 angelfish.

   How many in all? __33__ fish Fill in the diagram and write a number model.

Start	Change	End
15	+18	?

   $15 + 18 = 33$

◆ *Math Journal 1*, p. 121

Parallel Line Segments   Home Link 5.5

Family Note Parallel line segments are always the same distance apart. They would never meet, even if they were extended forever in either or both directions. In Problem 1, line segment DC is parallel to line segment AB, and line segment AD is parallel to line segment BC. There are no parallel line segments in Problem 2.

*Please return the **top part** of this Home Link to school tomorrow.*

1. Draw line segments *AB*, *BC*, *CD*, and *DA*.

   Put a red **X** on the line segment that is parallel to line segment *AB*.

   Put a blue **X** on the line segment that is parallel to line segment *BC*.

2. Draw line segments *AB*, *BC*, and *CA*.

   Is any line segment in your drawing parallel to line segment *AB*? __no__

Special Family Note In Lesson 5.7, your child will be studying 3-dimensional shapes. Help your child gather 3-dimensional objects for a class collection that we call the "Shapes Museum." You and your child might want to separate the objects you collect according to shape.

Shapes Museum

For the next few days, your class will collect things to put into a Shapes Museum. Starting tomorrow, bring items like boxes, soup cans, party hats, pyramids, and balls to school. Ask an adult for permission before bringing in these items. Make sure that the things you bring are clean.

◆ *Math Masters*, p. 300

5.6

Quadrangles

OBJECTIVES To identify the names and the characteristics of various quadrangles; and to explore similarities and differences among quadrangles.

summaries	materials

1 Teaching the Lesson

Children discuss features and names of various quadrangles and identify the types of quadrangles they drew in Lesson 5.5. They also cut out triangles and rectangles, put them together to make other shapes, and write the names of the shapes. [Geometry]

- ☐ *Math Journal 1*, pp. 120 and 123
- ☐ Home Link 5.5
- ☐ Teaching Masters (*Math Masters*, pp. 90 and 91)
- ☐ Pattern-Block Template
- ☐ index card (optional)
- ☐ scissors; glue or tape; paper clip

***See* Advance Preparation**

2 Ongoing Learning & Practice

Children practice and maintain skills through Math Boxes and Home Link activities.

- ☐ *Math Journal 1*, p. 124
- ☐ Home Link Master (*Math Masters*, p. 301)

3 Options for Individualizing

Enrichment Children explore tangrams (geometry puzzles in which the challenge is to form a square from 7 polygons). [Geometry]

Reteaching Children identify an unknown, hidden shape by touching and matching it to a shape they can see. [Geometry]

- ☐ tangram shapes and square (cut from *Math Masters*, p. 92)
- ☐ two sets of quadrangles (cut from *Math Masters*, p. 93)
- ☐ box or bag
- ☐ *Grandfather Tang's Story* (optional)

***See* Advance Preparation**

Additional Information

Advance Preparation The *Making Shapes Out of Triangles and Rectangles* activity in Part 1 may take more than one day. On the first day, children can cut out the shapes and begin to form other shapes. On the second day, children can finish forming new shapes. This activity works best if the triangles and rectangles have been carefully cut out. Therefore, before beginning the activity, you may wish to ask a more skilled child or a classroom volunteer to prepare a set of triangles and rectangles for any child who is not skillful with scissors.

Before beginning the optional Enrichment activity in Part 3, copy *Math Masters*, page 92 (tangram shapes) onto cardstock paper. Then cut it in half along the dotted line and cut apart the 7 tangram shapes (on the top half) and put them in an envelope. The bottom half of this master is used as a template. You may also wish to obtain the book *Grandfather Tang's Story* by Ann Tompert (Crown, 1990). Before beginning the optional Reteaching activity, make two copies of *Math Masters*, page 93 on cardstock paper, cut out all of the quadrangles, and keep the the quadrangles from each copy separate.

Vocabulary • **square corner** • **square** • **rhombus** • **rectangle** • **trapezoid** • **parallelogram** • **kite**

Getting Started

Mental Math and Reflexes

Children make ballpark estimates for sums. Ask them to record the number models on their slates. Pose problems like the following:

29 + 46 30 + 50 = 80

17 + 84 20 + 80 = 100; or 15 + 85 = 100

67 + 98 70 + 100 = 170

153 + 239 150 + 240 = 390

198 + 256 200 + 250 = 450; or 200 + 256 = 456

Math Message

Trace each quadrangle that you find on your Pattern-Block Template.

Home Link 5.5 Follow-Up

Review answers. Discuss why there are no parallel line segments in Problem 2. Sample answer: Each line segment meets the other two line segments.

1 Teaching the Lesson

◆ Math Message Follow-Up

WHOLE-CLASS DISCUSSION

Briefly check children's drawings. Ask which shapes have **square corners.** The square

If children are unable to determine which corners are square corners, they can check the shapes by using the corner of an index card.

You may wish to tell children that square corners are also called *right angles.*

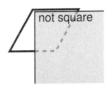

◆ Exploring Similarities and Differences among Quadrilaterals (*Math Journal 1,* pp. 120 and 123)

WHOLE-CLASS DISCUSSION

Ask children to examine the quadrangles on journal page 120. Call attention to the symbol ⌐ in the square and rectangle, indicating square corners. Discuss the features and names of the quadrangles. Ask questions like the following:

- How are the **square** and the **rhombus** alike? All four sides are the same length. How are they different? A square has square corners; a rhombus may or may not have square corners.

- How are the **square** and the **rectangle** alike? Both have four square corners. How are they different? All four sides of a square are the same length; the adjacent sides of a rectangle do not need to be the same length.

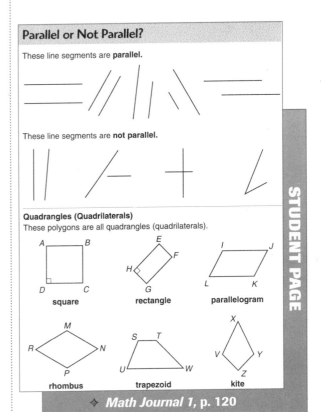

◆ *Math Journal 1,* p. 120

STUDENT PAGE

Parallel Line Segments (cont.)

7. Draw a quadrangle in which opposite sides are parallel.

Quadrangles drawn may vary. Sample drawing is shown. Possible drawings are a square, rectangle, rhombus, or parallelogram.

8. Draw a quadrangle in which all four sides are the same length.

What is another name for this shape?

 square or rhombus

Quadrangles drawn may vary. Sample drawing is shown. Possible drawings are a square or a rhombus.

9. Draw a quadrangle in which 2 opposite sides are parallel and the other 2 opposite sides are NOT parallel.

Trapezoids drawn may vary. Sample drawing is shown.

✦ *Math Journal 1, p. 123*

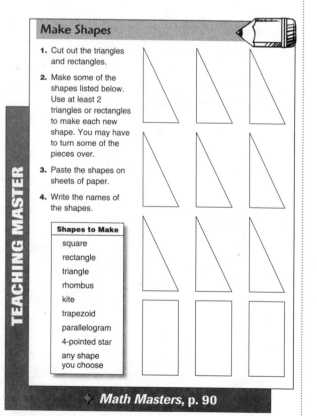

Make Shapes

1. Cut out the triangles and rectangles.

2. Make some of the shapes listed below. Use at least 2 triangles or rectangles to make each new shape. You may have to turn some of the pieces over.

3. Paste the shapes on sheets of paper.

4. Write the names of the shapes.

Shapes to Make

square
rectangle
triangle
rhombus
kite
trapezoid
parallelogram
4-pointed star
any shape you choose

✦ *Math Masters, p. 90*

- How are the **trapezoid** and **parallelogram** different? A parallelogram has two pairs of parallel sides. A trapezoid has only one pair of parallel sides.

- How are the **parallelogram** and the **kite** alike? Both have two pairs of sides that are the same length. **How are they different?** The opposite sides of a parallelogram are parallel; the opposite sides of a kite are not parallel. The sides of a kite that are the same length meet at a vertex; the sides of a parallelogram that are the same length may or may not meet at a vertex.

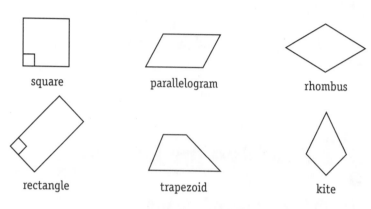

square   parallelogram   rhombus

rectangle   trapezoid   kite

NOTE: A square is a special kind of rhombus, one with all square corners. Similarly, a square is a special kind of rectangle, one with all sides the same length. Squares, rectangles, and rhombuses are all special kinds of parallelograms, shapes with two pairs of parallel sides. This kind of classification of quadrangles will be discussed in *Third Grade Everyday Mathematics*.

Adjusting the Activity If children are familiar with Venn diagrams, use them as a tool to organize the information about similarities and differences between the shapes. *For example:*

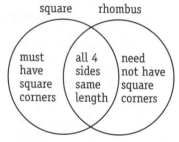

square   rhombus

must have square corners | all 4 sides same length | need not have square corners

Ask the class to turn to journal page 123. Volunteers show and name the shapes they drew in Problems 7, 8, and 9. If the class did not come up with all possible shapes for Problem 7 or 8, ask, *What other shape could you have drawn?*

Making Shapes Out of Triangles and Rectangles

(*Math Masters,* pp. 90 and 91)

INDEPENDENT ACTIVITY

Children cut out the triangles and rectangles on *Math Masters,* page 90. They put them together to form various shapes, which they paste or tape onto sheets of paper.

If children need more triangles and rectangles, they can cut out additional shapes from *Math Masters,* page 91.

Below are some possible constructions. Encourage children who enjoy this activity to attempt more complex constructions.

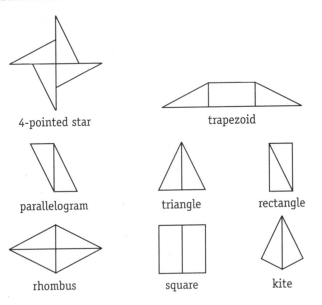

4-pointed star   trapezoid

parallelogram   triangle   rectangle

rhombus   square   kite

2 Ongoing Learning & Practice

◆ Math Boxes 5.6 (*Math Journal 1,* p. 124)

INDEPENDENT ACTIVITY

 Mixed Review This journal page provides oportunities for cumulative review or assessment of concepts and skills.

◆ Home Link 5.6 (*Math Masters,* p. 301)

 Home Connection In each set of four quadrangles, three quadrangles have something in common that is not a feature of the fourth. Children decide which quadrangle is different.

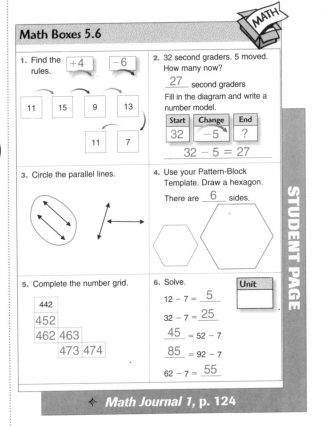

STUDENT PAGE

1. Find the rules. $+4$ -6

| 11 | 15 | 9 | 13 |

| 11 | 7 |

2. 32 second graders. 5 moved. How many now?

   __27__ second graders

   Fill in the diagram and write a number model.

Start	Change	End
32	-5	?

   $32 - 5 = 27$

3. Circle the parallel lines.

4. Use your Pattern-Block Template. Draw a hexagon.

   There are __6__ sides.

5. Complete the number grid.

442	
452	
462	463
	473	474

6. Solve.

   Unit

   $12 - 7 = \underline{5}$

   $32 - 7 = \underline{25}$

   $\underline{45} = 52 - 7$

   $\underline{85} = 92 - 7$

   $62 - 7 = \underline{55}$

◆ *Math Journal 1,* p. 124

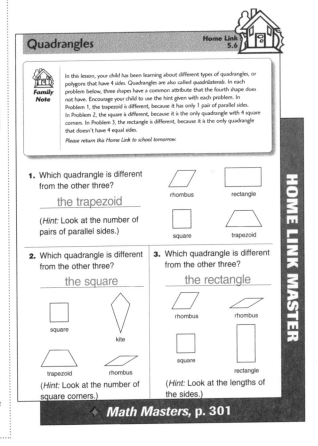

HOME LINK MASTER

Quadrangles
Home Link 5.6

Family Note In this lesson, your child has been learning about different types of quadrangles, or polygons that have 4 sides. Quadrangles are also called *quadrilaterals.* In each problem below, three shapes have a common attribute that the fourth shape does not have. Encourage your child to use the hint given with each problem. In Problem 1, the trapezoid is different, because it has only 1 pair of parallel sides. In Problem 2, the square is different, because it is the only quadrangle with 4 square corners. In Problem 3, the rectangle is different, because it is the only quadrangle that doesn't have 4 equal sides.

Please return this Home Link to school tomorrow.

1. Which quadrangle is different from the other three?

   __the trapezoid__

   (*Hint:* Look at the number of pairs of parallel sides.)

   rhombus   rectangle

   square   trapezoid

2. Which quadrangle is different from the other three?

   __the square__

   square   kite

   trapezoid   rhombus

   (*Hint:* Look at the number of square corners.)

3. Which quadrangle is different from the other three?

   __the rectangle__

   rhombus   rhombus

   square   rectangle

   (*Hint:* Look at the lengths of the sides.)

◆ *Math Masters,* p. 301

Lesson 5.6   **317**

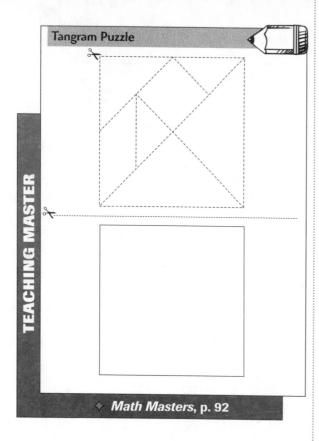

Tangram Puzzle

Math Masters, p. 92

TEACHING MASTER

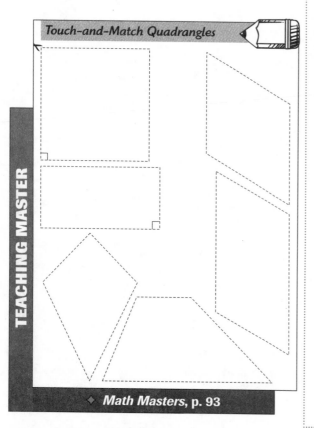

Touch-and-Match Quadrangles

Math Masters, p. 93

TEACHING MASTER

3 Options for Individualizing

✦ ENRICHMENT Exploring Tangrams
(*Math Masters*, p. 92)

PARTNER ACTIVITY   5–15 min

Some children may have enjoyed the challenge of making shapes out of triangles and rectangles. These children may also enjoy working with tangrams—a popular kind of geometric puzzle.

Copy *Math Masters*, page 92 onto cardstock paper. Then cut it in half along the dashed line, and cut apart the 7 tangram shapes on the top half of the page. (Children can store the pieces in an envelope.) Provide the bottom half of the master as a template. Challenge children to put the 7 pieces together to form the square.

If interest in this activity is high, additional tangram puzzles can be found in many commercially available books.

Literature Link *Grandfather Tang's Story* by Ann Tompert (Crown, 1990) is about two foxes, Chou and Wu Ling, and their quest to outdo each other by changing themselves into different animals. Both foxes are represented by the 7 tangram pieces. Each time one of the foxes changes into a new animal, the tangram pieces are rearranged to represent that animal.

✦ RETEACHING Playing *Touch-and-Match Quadrangles* (*Math Masters*, p. 93)

SMALL-GROUP ACTIVITY   5–15 min

For children who need additional practice identifying similarities and differences among quadrangles, make two copies of *Math Masters*, page 93 onto cardstock paper. Cut out all of the quadrilaterals, and place one set in full view on a table.

Without the child seeing, place one of the quadrilaterals from the other set in a bag or box. The child reaches inside, feels the shape without looking, and tries to find the matching shape among those on the table.

Ask the child to explain how he or she made the match. Expect responses like the following: "The shape I was holding had 4 square corners, but I knew it was the square and not the rectangle, because all of the sides were the same length."

5.7 3-Dimensional Shapes

OBJECTIVE To compare and contrast the characteristics of 3-dimensional shapes.

1 Teaching the Lesson

Children review the names and parts of 3-dimensional objects by using the 3-D Shapes Poster and models. They also compare and contrast 3-dimensional shapes, collect objects for a Shapes Museum, and classify real objects by the names of their 3-dimensional shapes. [Geometry]

- ☐ *Math Journal 1,* pp. 126 and 127
- ☐ Home Link 5.6
- ☐ 3-D Shapes Poster (optional)
- ☐ 3-dimensional models: rectangular prism, cube, cylinder, cone, sphere, and pyramid
- ☐ slate
- ☐ items from home for the Shapes Museum
- ☐ labeled index cards for the Shapes Museum
- ☐ *Shapes, Shapes, Shapes* (optional)
- ☐ *The Art of Shapes for Children and Adults* (optional)

***See* Advance Preparation**

2 Ongoing Learning & Practice

Children draw and count line segments and triangles. [Geometry]

Children practice and maintain skills through Math Boxes and Home Link activities.

- ☐ *Math Journal 1,* pp. 125 and 128
- ☐ Home Link Master (*Math Masters,* p. 302)

3 Options for Individualizing

Extra Practice Children identify an unknown 3-dimensional shape by asking *yes* and *no* questions. [Geometry]

- ☐ *Minute Math®,* p. 18

Additional Information

Advance Preparation For Part 1, you might make a large poster with a labeled picture of each shape to help children learn the names of the various 3-dimensional shapes. Keep the poster on display for the rest of the school year. For the Shapes Museum, write the words *rectangular prism, cube, cylinder, cone, sphere, pyramid,* and *other* on index cards. Also, gather models of 3-D shapes and items for the museum. See the Planning Ahead section on page 309 for suggestions.

For examples of 3-dimensional shapes to use for the *Starting a Shapes Museum* activity in Part 1, you may wish to obtain the books *Shapes, Shapes, Shapes* by Tana Hoban (Greenwillow Books, 1986) and *The Art of Shapes for Children and Adults* by Margaret Steele and Cindy Estes (FotoFolio, 1997).

Vocabulary • **cylinder** • **cone** • **sphere** • **curved surface** • **rectangular prism** • **cube** • **pyramid** • **flat surface** • **face** • **edge** • **vertex (*plural:* vertices)**

Getting Started

Mental Math and Reflexes

Make a ballpark estimate for each sum. Record a number model on your slate.

48 + 46 *50 + 50 = 100; or 50 + 45 = 95*

13 + 59 *10 + 60 = 70*

76 + 88 *80 + 90 = 170*

183 + 211 *180 + 210 = 390; or 200 + 200 = 400*

296 + 173 *300 + 173 = 473*

Math Message

Find two things in the room that have only flat sides. Find two things that have round sides. Sample answers: A book and a desk have flat sides. A roll of paper towels and a piece of chalk have round sides.

Home Link 5.6 Follow-Up

For each problem, have children name the quadrangle that doesn't belong and explain how they chose that quadrangle.

---

1 Teaching the Lesson

◆ Math Message Follow-Up

WHOLE-CLASS DISCUSSION

Children name the objects they found in the room. If children are having difficulty finding items, pose the question in the following way: *Find two things in the room that will not roll. Find two things that will roll.*

◆ Reviewing the Names of the Basic 3-Dimensional Shapes *(Math Journal 1, p. 126)*

WHOLE-CLASS DISCUSSION

Ask children to examine the shapes on your class's 3-D Shapes Poster (see Advance Preparation) or on the journal page and to say their names. Then use your models of 3-D shapes to name the parts of each shape. Introduce the following terms:

▷ **Cylinders, cones,** and **spheres** have **curved surfaces.**

▷ **Rectangular prisms, cubes, pyramids, cylinders,** and **cones** have **flat surfaces,** called **faces.**

▷ An **edge** of a prism or pyramid is a line segment where two faces meet.

▷ A **vertex** (plural: **vertices**) of a prism or pyramid is a point at which two edges meet.

 Adjusting the Activity Add the shape words in the text column below to the "Word Wall" so that children can refer to them as often as necessary. Include a picture, as well as a written description, for each word.

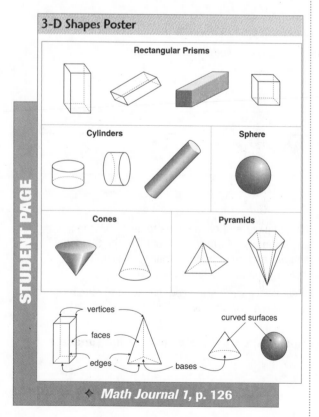

3-D Shapes Poster

Rectangular Prisms

Cylinders

Sphere

Cones

Pyramids

vertices

faces

edges

bases

curved surfaces

STUDENT PAGE

✦ *Math Journal 1,* p. 126

◆ Discussing Similarities and Differences among Shapes

WHOLE-CLASS DISCUSSION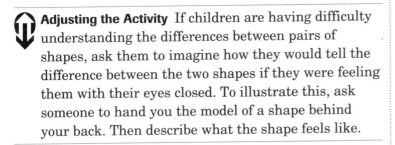

Compare and contrast shapes, two at a time.

Cylinder and Cone

Hold up the models of the cylinder and the cone. How are they alike? How are they different? Ask children to describe the shapes; expect and accept unclear and informal descriptions. *Some possible responses:*

▷ Both the cylinder and the cone have a round side, but they don't look the same. The round side of the cylinder goes straight up and down. The round side of the cone comes to a point.

▷ Both the cylinder and the cone can roll.

▷ The cylinder has two (flat) faces; the cone has only one (flat) face.

▷ The (flat) faces in both shapes are circles.

Models of a cone and cylinder

Adjusting the Activity If children are having difficulty understanding the differences between pairs of shapes, ask them to imagine how they would tell the difference between the two shapes if they were feeling them with their eyes closed. To illustrate this, ask someone to hand you the model of a shape behind your back. Then describe what the shape feels like.

Continue the discussion with other pairs of shapes. *For example:*

Pyramid and Cone

▷ The pyramid has no curved surfaces and can't be rolled.

▷ Both shapes come to a point.

▷ The faces of the pyramid that come to a point at the top are all triangles.

▷ The cone has a curved edge. The pyramid has only straight edges.

Models of a pyramid and cone

Models of a pyramid and rectangular prism

Models of a cylinder and rectangular prism

Models of a rectangular prism and cube

Pyramid and Rectangular Prism

▷ Both have vertices.

▷ Both have faces.

▷ Both have edges.

▷ Neither has a curved surface.

▷ The faces (except for the bottom face) of the pyramid come to a point. The faces of the rectangular prism come to a point in groups of three.

▷ At least two of the faces of the rectangular prism are rectangles. At least three of the faces of the pyramid are triangles.

▷ If you turn the prism upside down, it sits flat. If you turn the pyramid upside down, it tips over.

Cylinder and Rectangular Prism

▷ The cylinder has a curved surface; the prism does not.

▷ The cylinder has no vertices; the rectangular prism has eight vertices.

▷ The cylinder has two curved edges but no straight edges; the prism has 12 straight edges but no curved edges.

▷ If you closed your eyes and your partner turned a cylinder or prism upside down, you wouldn't be able to tell that the shape had been turned upside down by touching it.

Cube and Rectangular Prism

▷ They have the same number of faces and vertices.

▷ All of the faces of a cube are squares.

▷ The faces of a rectangular prism can be squares or rectangles. Those that have all square faces are cubes. A cube is a special kind of rectangular prism.

Continue to compare and contrast pairs of shapes only as long as children remain interested. You can revisit other pairs of shapes in future lessons.

Adjusting the Activity In Lesson 5.6, Venn diagrams were suggested as a way to help children compare the traits of shapes in an organized manner. If the diagrams proved to be a useful tool, consider using them for this activity.

Starting a Shapes Museum with a Display of 3-Dimensional Objects

WHOLE-CLASS ACTIVITY

Tell children that they are going to make a Shapes Museum. Help them set up the museum by placing the items they brought from home near the correct name cards. Shapes that do not fit in any of the six categories are placed near the "other" card. Add some of your own items to the museum.

 Literature and Art Link As you assemble your Shapes Museum, you may wish to use the following books suggested in Lesson 5.3: *Shapes, Shapes, Shapes* by Tana Hoban (Greenwillow Books, 1986) and *The Art of Shapes for Children and Adults* by Margaret Steele and Cindy Estes (FotoFolio, 1997). Children can look through the books to find examples of 3-dimensional shapes.

Identifying the Shapes of Real Objects
(*Math Journal 1*, p. 127)

INDEPENDENT ACTIVITY

Children complete the page on their own. Point out to children that real-life objects can resemble 3-dimensional shapes, but they often have other parts as well. For example, the wrapped package in Problem 3 is a rectangular prism, but it also has a bow attached to it.

2 Ongoing Learning & Practice

Drawing and Counting Line Segments
(*Math Journal 1*, p. 128)

INDEPENDENT ACTIVITY

For Problems 1 and 2, children draw line segments between pairs of points and count the total number of line segments they drew. In Problem 3, children draw line segments and then identify triangles and a 4-sided figure.

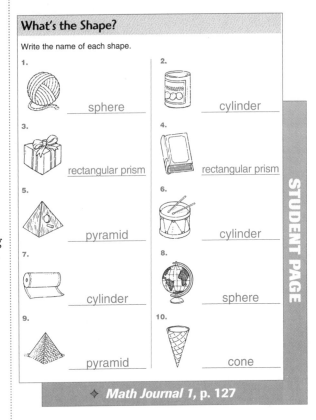

✦ *Math Journal 1*, p. 127

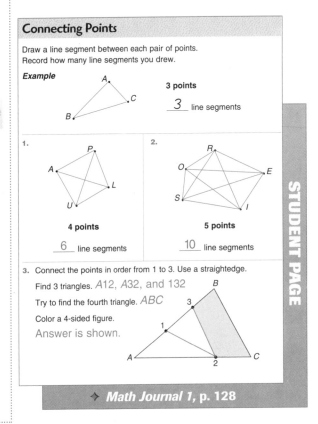

✦ *Math Journal 1*, p. 128

Math Boxes 5.7

1. Make ballpark estimates. Write a number model for each estimate.

	Unit

$32 + 59$

$\underline{30} + \underline{60} = \underline{90}$

$51 + 27$

$\underline{50} + \underline{30} = \underline{80}$

2. Write 6 names in the 32-box.

32

Sample answers:
$30 + 2$, $67 - 35$,
treinta y dos, $16 + 16$,
$8 + 8 + 8 + 8$, $34 - 2$

3. Each cookie costs 30¢. I have $1.00. Can I buy 3 cookies?

yes

4. Use the partial-sums algorithm to solve. Show your work.

$$\begin{array}{r} 39 \\ + 46 \\ \hline 70 \\ + 15 \\ \hline 85 \end{array}$$

5. This is a trapezoid. Put an **X** on the line segments that are parallel.

6. Use 5, 7, and 12. Write 2 addition and 2 subtraction facts.

$5 + 7 = 12$

$7 + 5 = 12$

$12 - 7 = 5$

$12 - 5 = 7$

Math Journal 1, p. 125

STUDENT PAGE

◆ **Math Boxes 5.7** (*Math Journal 1*, p. 125)

INDEPENDENT ACTIVITY

Mixed Review This journal page provides opportunities for cumulative review or assessment of concepts and skills.

◆ **Home Link 5.7** (*Math Masters*, p. 302)

Home Connection Children make a list of things they see on their way home and classify those things according to shape.

3 Options for Individualizing

◆ **EXTRA PRACTICE** **Minute Math**

SMALL-GROUP ACTIVITY **5–15 min**

To offer children more experience with identifying shapes, see the following page in *Minute Math:*

Basic Routines: p. 18

PLANNING AHEAD

Before beginning Lesson 5.8, you may wish to familiarize yourself with straw constructions by building your own square pyramid out of straws and twist-ties. Follow the five steps shown on page 327.

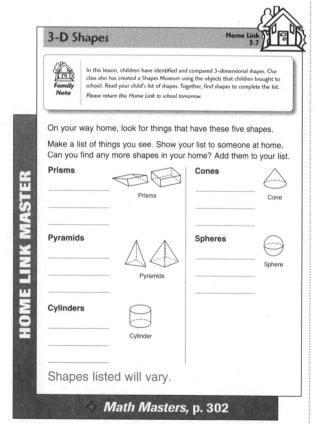

3-D Shapes

Home Link 5.7

Family Note In this lesson, children have identified and compared 3-dimensional shapes. Our class also has created a Shapes Museum using the objects that children brought to school. Read your child's list of shapes. Together, find shapes to complete the list. *Please return this Home Link to school tomorrow.*

On your way home, look for things that have these five shapes.

Make a list of things you see. Show your list to someone at home. Can you find any more shapes in your home? Add them to your list.

Prisms
_____
_____ Prisms

Cones
_____
_____ Cone

Pyramids
_____
_____ Pyramids

Spheres
_____
_____ Sphere

Cylinders
_____
_____ Cylinder

Shapes listed will vary.

Math Masters, p. 302

HOME LINK MASTER

5.8 Pyramids

OBJECTIVES To construct pyramids; and to explore the relationship among the number of faces, edges, and vertices in pyramids.

summaries	materials

1 Teaching the Lesson

Children construct pyramids whose bases are squares, triangles, rectangles, pentagons, and hexagons. [Geometry]

Children count the numbers of edges, faces, and vertices in different kinds of pyramids. [Geometry; Numeration]

- ☐ Teaching Masters (*Math Masters,* p. 94; optional)
- ☐ Home Link 5.7
- ☐ models of a cone and a pyramid
- ☐ slate
- ☐ 8 straws; 12 twist-ties
- ☐ per partnership: 15 four-inch straws, 15 six-inch straws, and 20 twist-ties

***See* Advance Preparation**

2 Ongoing Learning & Practice

Children practice and maintain skills through Math Boxes and Home Link activities.

- ☐ *Math Journal 1,* p. 129
- ☐ Home Link Master (*Math Masters,* p. 303)
- ☐ Teaching Master (*Math Masters,* p. 97; optional)

3 Options for Individualizing

Enrichment Children construct a decagon out of triangles and determine the numbers of faces, edges, and vertices in a decagonal pyramid. [Geometry; Patterns, Functions, and Algebra]

Enrichment Children connect pyramids in math and social studies by investigating the building of ancient Egyptian pyramids. [Geometry]

- ☐ Teaching Masters (*Math Masters,* pp. 95 and 96)
- ☐ scissors
- ☐ glue or tape
- ☐ *Pyramid*

***See* Advance Preparation**

Additional Information

Advance Preparation Plan to spend two days on this lesson. You may want to construct the pyramids on the first day and discuss the constructions on the second day.

Before children begin the Math Message, place 8 straws of equal length and 12 twist-ties per child (and a few extras) in separate boxes near the Message.

For the pyramid constructions in Part 1, you might want to place the straws and twist-ties listed above in three separate boxes or containers before beginning the lesson.

For the second optional Enrichment activity in Part 3, you will need to obtain the book *Pyramid* by David Macaulay (Houghton Mifflin, 1982).

Vocabulary • **base (of cones and pyramids)** • **apex (of cones and pyramids)** • **square pyramid** • **triangular pyramid** • **rectangular pyramid** • **pentagonal pyramid** • **hexagonal pyramid**

Getting Started

Mental Math and Reflexes

Have children record addition problems and their sums on slates. *For example:*

37 + 41 = ? 78   ? = 257 + 136 393

66 + 79 = ? 145   ? = 152 + 146 298

36 + 48 = ? 84

Math Message

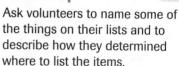

Take 8 straws and 12 twist-ties. How are pyramids and cones alike and different?

Home Link 5.7 Follow-Up

Ask volunteers to name some of the things on their lists and to describe how they determined where to list the items.

---

1 Teaching the Lesson

DAY 1

✦ Math Message Follow-Up

WHOLE-CLASS DISCUSSION

Briefly discuss similarities and differences between cones and pyramids. List children's responses on the board. *Possible responses:*

▷ Both shapes come to a point.

▷ The cone has one (flat) face; the pyramid has more than one (flat) face.

▷ The cone can be rolled; the pyramid cannot.

▷ The cone has a curved edge; the pyramid has only straight edges.

Place a model of a cone on its flat face. Say that this face is called the **base** of the cone. The "tip" of the cone—the vertex opposite the base—is called the **apex.**

Next, place a model of a pyramid in the same position as the cone. The face on which the pyramid "sits" is also called the **base,** and the tip of the pyramid is also called the **apex.** All of the faces of the pyramid, except the base, meet at the apex of the pyramid.

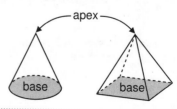

◆ Constructing a Pyramid Out of Straws

 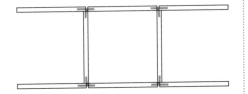

Demonstrate how to build a pyramid, one step at a time, as children follow your directions. As indicated in the Math Message, each child should have 8 straws of equal length and 12 twist-ties.

Step 1   **Step 2**

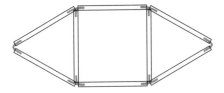

Step 3

Step 4   **Step 5**

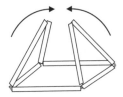   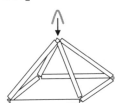

When children have finished their constructions, ask them to name the shape of the base of their pyramids. A square Tell them that a pyramid is named after the shape of its base—a pyramid whose base is a square is called a **square pyramid.**

Ask: *Do you think you can build a cone out of straws? Why or why not?* Sample response: No. The base of a cone is a circle. You can't make a circle out of straight straws.

NOTE: Since a square is a special kind of rectangle, a square pyramid is a special kind of rectangular pyramid.

Pyramid Base Cards

Use straws and twist-ties to build a **triangular pyramid**.	Use straws and twist-ties to build a **rectangular pyramid**.
Use short straws for the base. Use long straws for the other edges.	Use 2 short straws and 2 long straws for the base. Use long straws for the other edges.
The base of a triangular pyramid is a triangle:	The base of a rectangular pyramid is a rectangle:
Use straws and twist-ties to build a **pentagonal pyramid**.	Use straws and twist-ties to build a **hexagonal pyramid**.
Use short straws for the base. Use long straws for the other edges.	Use short straws for the base. Use long straws for the other edges.
The base of a pentagonal pyramid is a pentagon:	The base of a hexagonal pyramid is a hexagon:

◇ *Math Masters,* p. 94

✦ Constructing Four Kinds of Pyramids Out of Straws (*Math Masters,* p. 94)

PARTNER ACTIVITY

Children are to work in partnerships. Each partnership will make one pyramid.

Each partnership should have 15 four-inch straws, 15 six-inch straws, and about 20 twist-ties. Assign each of the following pyramids, one to each partnership: **triangular pyramid, rectangular pyramid, pentagonal pyramid,** or **hexagonal pyramid.** Children should use the shorter straws for the base. If they are building the rectangular pyramid, they will need to use 2 shorter straws and 2 longer straws. Children should use longer straws for the other edges.

If you wish, provide each partnership with the appropriate "Pyramid Base Card" from *Math Masters,* page 94 to help them with their constructions.

Circulate and assist. Store children's constructions for use during the next math class.

Adjusting the Activity The triangular pyramid base is the easiest to build because it involves the fewest number of straws. For this reason, you may wish to assign it to children who had difficulty constructing the square pyramid earlier in the lesson.

Challenge children by asking them to use a mixture of short and long straws for the bases and edges of the pyramids. Be aware that these constructions are more difficult to make.

Encourage children to pay close attention to the resulting faces of the pyramids. The triangular faces will no longer be identical. Ask children to notice the position of the apex. Using both short and long straws will result in an apex not directly above the center of the base.

In some cases, the apex may not be above the base at all, but rather skewed to one side.

Assure children that these are all examples of pyramids.

DAY 2

◆ Discussing Pyramid Constructions

WHOLE-CLASS DISCUSSION

The purpose of this discussion is to observe patterns and relationships among various parts of pyramids.

A pyramid whose base is a triangle is called a **triangular pyramid.** Ask children who have constructed triangular pyramids to display them. Then ask:

- How many faces does your pyramid have? 4 Do these pyramids all have the same number of faces? yes

- How many edges does your pyramid have? 6 Do these pyramids all have the same number of edges? yes

- How many vertices does your pyramid have? 4 Do these pyramids all have the same number of vertices? yes

- Are all of the faces the same kind of polygon? Yes, triangles

NOTE: Any face of a triangular pyramid can be chosen to be its base. Once a face is chosen as a base, the other three faces are not bases. You need not discuss this with children unless the question comes up.

Record the information in a table on the board. Repeat the procedure for the other three kinds of pyramids. The completed table should look like this:

Pyramid	Shape of Base	Number of Sides in Base	Number of Edges	Number of Faces	Number of Vertices
triangular	triangle	3	6	4	4
rectangular	rectangle	4	8	5	5
pentagonal	pentagon	5	10	6	6
hexagonal	hexagon	6	12	7	7

Ask: *What is the shape of the faces that meet at the apex of any pyramid?* triangle

NOTE: It is not important that children master this new vocabulary at this time. They should understand that pyramids are named after the shape of the base and that all pyramids with the same-shape base have the same number of faces, edges, and vertices.

Adjusting the Activity To extend the activity, ask children to imagine a pyramid whose base has 10 sides. *How many edges would such a pyramid have?* 20: 10 edges around the base and 10 edges that meet at the apex of the pyramid *How many faces?* 11: 1 base and 10 triangles *How many vertices?* 11: 10 vertices at the base and 1 vertex at the apex

A 10-sided polygon is a decagon, so a pyramid whose base is a decagon is called a *decagonal pyramid.*

Another way to extend the activity is to ask children to use the table to describe the relationship among the numbers of edges, faces, and vertices in a pyramid. The relationship is:

$$\textbf{number of edges} + \textbf{2} = \textbf{number of faces} + \textbf{number of vertices}$$

This relationship is true for these four kinds of pyramids and for other 3-dimensional shapes (polyhedra) as well.

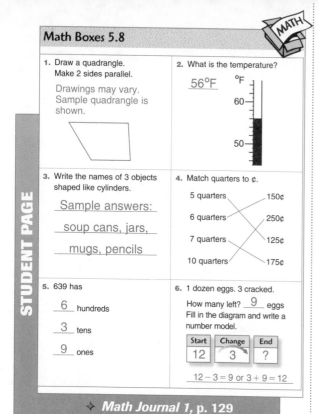

1. Draw a quadrangle. Make 2 sides parallel.

Drawings may vary. Sample quadrangle is shown.

2. What is the temperature?

56°F

3. Write the names of 3 objects shaped like cylinders.

Sample answers: soup cans, jars, mugs, pencils

4. Match quarters to ¢.

5 quarters — 150¢
6 quarters — 250¢
7 quarters — 125¢
10 quarters — 175¢

5. 639 has

6 hundreds
3 tens
9 ones

6. 1 dozen eggs. 3 cracked.

How many left? 9 eggs
Fill in the diagram and write a number model.

Start	Change	End
12	3	?

12 − 3 = 9 or 3 + 9 = 12

Math Journal 1, p. 129

STUDENT PAGE

Ongoing Learning & Practice

◆ **Math Boxes 5.8** (*Math Journal 1,* p. 129)

INDEPENDENT ACTIVITY

Mixed Review This journal page provides opportunities for cumulative review or assessment of concepts and skills.

◆ **Home Link 5.8** (*Math Masters,* p. 303)

Home Connection Children construct a triangular pyramid out of a paper pattern. If you wish to have children construct a square pyramid as well, send home *Math Masters,* page 97.

HOME LINK MASTER

Make a Triangular Pyramid   Home Link 5.8

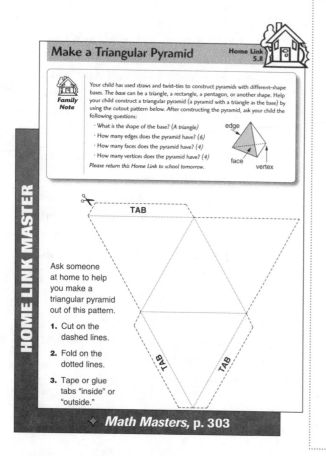

Family Note

Your child has used straws and twist-ties to construct pyramids with different-shape bases. The *base* can be a triangle, a rectangle, a pentagon, or another shape. Help your child construct a triangular pyramid (a pyramid with a triangle as the base) by using the cutout pattern below. After constructing the pyramid, ask your child the following questions:

· What is the shape of the base? (*A triangle*)
· How many edges does the pyramid have? (*6*)
· How many faces does the pyramid have? (*4*)
· How many vertices does the pyramid have? (*4*)

Please return this Home Link to school tomorrow.

TAB

Ask someone at home to help you make a triangular pyramid out of this pattern.

1. Cut on the dashed lines.

2. Fold on the dotted lines.

3. Tape or glue tabs "inside" or "outside."

Math Masters, p. 303

TEACHING MASTER

Make a Square Pyramid

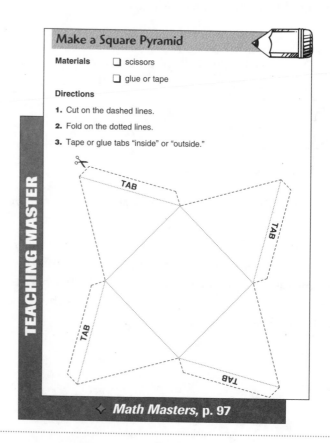

Materials   ☐ scissors
              ☐ glue or tape

Directions

1. Cut on the dashed lines.

2. Fold on the dotted lines.

3. Tape or glue tabs "inside" or "outside."

TAB

Math Masters, p. 97

---

3 Options for Individualizing

♦ **ENRICHMENT Constructing a Decagon Out of Triangles** (*Math Masters,* pp. 95 and 96)

INDEPENDENT ACTIVITY **15–30 min**

Children construct a decagon out of the 10 identical triangles found on *Math Masters,* page 96.

♦ **ENRICHMENT Making a Connection between Pyramids in Math and Social Studies**

SMALL-GROUP DISCUSSION **5–15 min**

Social Studies Link The book *Pyramid* by David Macaulay (Houghton Mifflin, 1982) contains pen-and-ink illustrations for the step-by-step process of building an ancient Egyptian pyramid. The text may be too difficult for many children to read on their own, but the illustrations will capture the interest of most. Point out to children the traits that the ancient Egyptian pyramids have in common with the pyramids children have constructed.

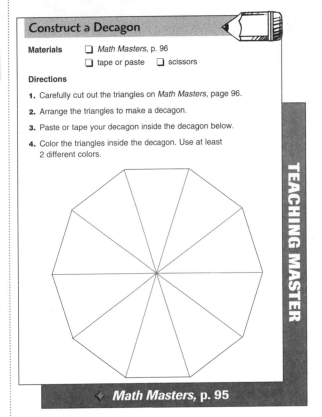

Construct a Decagon

Materials ☐ *Math Masters,* p. 96
☐ tape or paste ☐ scissors

Directions

1. Carefully cut out the triangles on *Math Masters,* page 96.
2. Arrange the triangles to make a decagon.
3. Paste or tape your decagon inside the decagon below.
4. Color the triangles inside the decagon. Use at least 2 different colors.

✧ Math Masters, p. 95

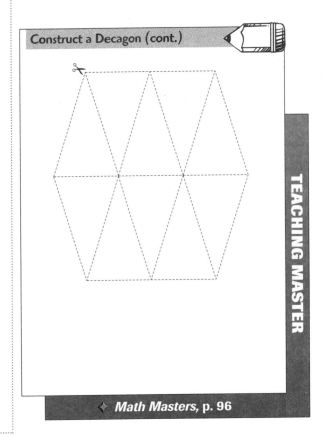

Construct a Decagon (cont.)

✧ Math Masters, p. 96

5.9

Line Symmetry

OBJECTIVES To find lines of symmetry in objects; and to complete drawings to create symmetrical shapes.

summaries	materials
1 Teaching the Lesson	
Children name examples of symmetrical objects, fold pictures to find lines of symmetry and identify lines of symmetry in objects, and complete half-pictures to draw symmetrical template shapes. [Geometry]	□ *Math Journal 1*, p. 130 □ Home Link 5.8 □ Teaching Masters (*Math Masters*, p. 98; per partnership: *Math Masters*, p. 99) □ slate; scissors; Pattern-Block Template ***See* Advance Preparation**
2 Ongoing Learning & Practice	
Children practice and maintain skills through Math Boxes and Home Link activities.	□ *Math Journal 1*, p. 131 □ Home Link Master (*Math Masters*, p. 304)
3 Options for Individualizing	
Enrichment Children read *Lao Lao of Dragon Mountain* to further explore line symmetry. [Geometry] **Reteaching** Children create symmetrical shapes on a geoboard. [Geometry] **Extra Practice** Children cut symmetrical pictures from magazines and create a booklet. [Geometry]	□ *Lao Lao of Dragon Mountain* □ geoboard; rubber bands □ magazines; backing paper ***See* Advance Preparation**

Additional Information

Advance Preparation Before doing the Home Link 5.8 Follow-Up, use Home Link 5.8 to make a triangular pyramid.

For the optional Enrichment activity in Part 3, obtain the book *Lao Lao of Dragon Mountain* by Margaret Bateson-Hill (De Agostini Children's Books, 1996).

Vocabulary • line symmetry • line of symmetry • symmetrical

Getting Started

Mental Math and Reflexes

Children record addition problems and their sums on slates. *Suggestions:*

? = 236 + 148 384   58 + 87 = ? 145
? = 124 + 133 257   27 + 46 = ? 73

Math Message

Take a copy of Math Masters, page 98. It shows half of a picture. Guess what the whole picture looks like.

Home Link 5.8 Follow-Up

Display a triangular pyramid made from the pattern. Review names of the parts of a pyramid. Ask children to explain their answers.

Teaching the Lesson

Math Masters, p. 98

◆ Math Message Follow-Up
(*Math Masters,* p. 98)

WHOLE-CLASS ACTIVITY

Briefly go over the answer. A star *How many points does the star have?* 5

Ask children to do the following:

1. Fold the paper along the dotted fold line.

2. Carefully cut along the solid lines.

3. Unfold the cutout picture.

Point out that when the picture is folded, the two halves match. Such shapes are said to have **line symmetry.** The fold line is called the **line of symmetry.**

> **Adjusting the Activity** Add the terms *line symmetry* and *line of symmetry* to the "Word Wall" so that children may refer to them as often as necessary. Include a picture, as well as a written description, next to each term.

Ask the class to give other examples of things that look **symmetrical.** If children have trouble getting started, suggest categories. *For example:*

▷ Things in nature: pumpkins, leaves, butterflies

▷ Things in school: tables, open books

▷ Things at home: spoons, chairs

▷ Tools: scissors, screwdrivers

▷ Things outside: buildings, fences

◆ Finding Lines of Symmetry
(*Math Masters,* p. 99)

PARTNER ACTIVITY

Pass out a copy of *Math Masters,* page 99 to each partnership. Partners cut out each shape.

Cut out each shape. Find all the lines of symmetry for each shape by folding it in half.

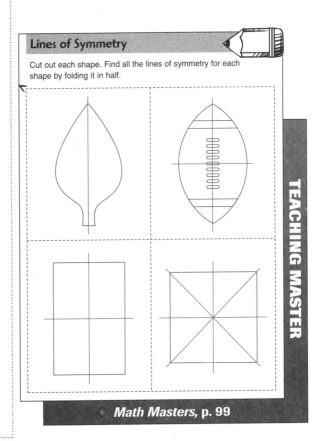

Math Masters, p. 99

Start with the leaf. Ask children to fold it so that the two halves match. Can they fold it another way so that the two halves match? no The leaf has just one line of symmetry.

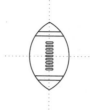

Repeat the process with the football. Can they fold it in more than one way? Yes, in 2 ways The football has two lines of symmetry.

Partners look for all lines of symmetry in the rectangle and the square. Ask for volunteers to demonstrate how they got their answers. Rectangle: 2 lines of symmetry; square: 4 lines of symmetry

✦ Completing Half-Pictures of Template Shapes
(*Math Journal 1,* p. 130)

INDEPENDENT ACTIVITY

Go over the example. Make sure children understand that the dotted line is a line of symmetry for the whole shape. Children use their templates to complete each shape. Circulate and assist as needed.

After children have completed the page, discuss how many lines of symmetry the circle has. An unlimited or infinite number

Ask volunteers to draw any additional lines of symmetry for some of the other shapes. *How many lines of symmetry does the rhombus have?* 2 *The trapezoid?* 1 *The square?* 4 *The hexagon?* 6 *The triangle?* 3

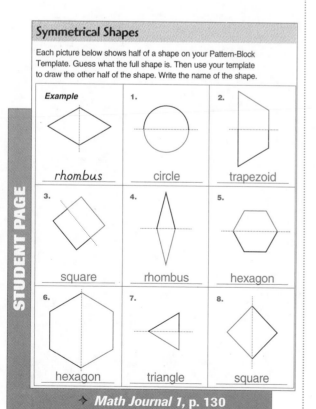

Symmetrical Shapes

Each picture below shows half of a shape on your Pattern-Block Template. Guess what the full shape is. Then use your template to draw the other half of the shape. Write the name of the shape.

Example	1.	2.
rhombus	circle	trapezoid
3.	4.	5.
square	rhombus	hexagon
6.	7.	8.
hexagon	triangle	square

✦ *Math Journal 1,* p. 130

2. Ongoing Learning & Practice

◆ Math Boxes 5.9 (*Math Journal 1,* p. 131)

INDEPENDENT ACTIVITY

 Mixed Review This journal page provides opportunities for cumulative review or assessment of concepts and skills.

◆ Home Link 5.9 (*Math Masters,* p. 304)

 Home Connection Children make a list of symmetrical objects found in their homes and draw a picture of one of those objects.

Math Boxes 5.9

1. What time is it?

_1_ : _00_

In ½ hour, it will be

_1_ : _30_ .

2. Make ballpark estimates. Write a number model for each estimate.

Unit

73 − 49

_70_ − _50_ = _20_

87 − 21

_90_ − _20_ = _70_

3. Match dimes to ¢.

5 dimes — 100¢
10 dimes — 150¢
15 dimes — 50¢
18 dimes — 180¢

4. Use the partial-sums algorithm to solve. Show your work.

```
   46
 + 35
 ____
   70
 + 11
 ____
   81
```

5. Solve.

Unit

_11_ = 6 + 5

16 + 5 = _21_

46 + 5 = _51_

_81_ = 76 + 5

86 + 5 = _91_

6. Write the names of 3 objects shaped like rectangular prisms.

Sample answers: boxes, books, CD cases, dresser

◆ Math Journal 1, p. 131

---

3. Options for Individualizing

◆ ENRICHMENT Exploring Line Symmetry in Literature

SMALL-GROUP DISCUSSION **15–30 min**

 Literature/Art Link The book *Lao Lao of Dragon Mountain* by Margaret Bateson-Hill (De Agostini Children's Books, 1996) tells the story of a woman who makes beautiful paper cutouts for children in her village. A greedy emperor imprisons her and demands that she make a chestful of jewels for him. The book includes patterns for some of the symmetrical shapes. Children can use them to explore the Chinese art of paper cutting.

Symmetry Hunt

Home Link 5.9

Family Note

In this lesson, your child has been determining if shapes are symmetrical. A shape has *symmetry* if it has two halves that look alike but face in opposite directions. A *line of symmetry* divides the shape into two matching parts. Lines of symmetry are shown in the objects below. Help your child find other objects that are symmetrical. Remember that some shapes, such as the mirror below, may be symmetrical in more than one way.

Please return this Home Link to school tomorrow.

1. Ask someone to help you make a list of things at home that have symmetry. For example, you might list a window, a sofa, or a mirror.

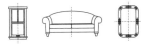

My List: _____

_____

2. Draw a picture of one thing on your list. Draw as many lines of symmetry as you can.

3. If you find pictures in books or magazines that show symmetry, bring them to school.

◆ Math Masters, p. 304

✦ RETEACHING Exploring Line Symmetry with Geoboards

INDEPENDENT ACTIVITY   **5–15 min**

If children are still struggling with the concept of symmetry, consider the following activity:

Directions _____

1. Use a rubber band to divide the geoboard in half.

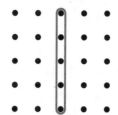

2. Use a rubber band to create a simple shape on the right-hand side.

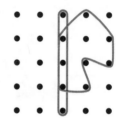

3. Ask a child to create the other half of the shape.

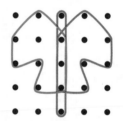

✦ EXTRA PRACTICE Making a Symmetry Booklet

INDEPENDENT ACTIVITY   **15–30 min**

Provide a variety of magazines for children to look through and from which they can cut out pictures of things that look symmetrical. The pictures can be displayed in "symmetrical" booklets.

5.10

Unit 5 Review and Assessment

OBJECTIVE To review and assess children's progress on the material covered in Unit 5.

1   Assess Progress

learning goals

5a **Developing Goal** Identify 3-dimensional shapes, such as rectangular prisms, cylinders, pyramids, cones, and spheres. **(Lessons 5.7 and 5.8)**

5b **Developing Goal** Identify symmetrical figures. **(Lesson 5.9)**

5c **Developing Goal** Find common attributes of shapes. **(Lessons 5.1 and 5.2)**

5d **Developing Goal** Identify parallel and nonparallel line segments. **(Lesson 5.5)**

5e **Developing/Secure Goal** Draw line segments. **(Lessons 5.4 and 5.5)**

5f **Secure Goal** Identify 2-dimensional shapes. **(Lessons 5.2, 5.3, and 5.6)**

activities

❑ Written Assessment, Problems 6–8

❑ Written Assessment, Problem 9

❑ Written Assessment, Problem 10

❑ Written Assessment, Problems 2 and 3

❑ Written Assessment, Problems 1–3

❑ Written Assessment, Problems 4 and 5

materials

☐ Home Link 5.9
☐ Assessment Masters (*Math Masters,* pp. 426 and 427)

☐ Teaching Master (*Math Masters,* p. 100)
☐ scissors; Pattern-Block Template; slate

2   Build Background for Unit 6

summaries

Children practice and maintain skills through Math Boxes and Home Link activities.

materials

☐ *Math Journal 1,* p. 132
☐ Home Link Masters (*Math Masters,* pp. 305–308)

Each **learning goal** listed above indicates a level of performance that might be expected at this point in the *Everyday Mathematics* K–6 curriculum. For a variety of reasons, the levels indicated may not accurately portray your class's performance.

Additional Information

Advance Preparation For additional information on assessment for Unit 5, see the *Assessment Handbook,* pages 53–55. For assessment checklists, see *Math Masters,* pages 456–457 and 485–488.

Getting Started

Math Message

Pick 2 different objects from the Shapes Museum. Write down the names of the objects. How are the 2 objects different? How are they similar?

Home Link 5.9 Follow-Up

Volunteers name some of the things on their lists. Consider making a class symmetry book or bulletin board out of children's drawings.

1 Assess Progress

◆ Math Message Follow-Up

WHOLE-CLASS ACTIVITY

Have several children share the similarities and differences of the 2 objects that they chose. Encourage children to use such terms as *face*, *vertex*, *flat surface*, *curved surface*, *base*, and *parallel*.

◆ Slate Assessments

SMALL-GROUP ACTIVITY

If the suggested problems below are not appropriate for your class's level of performance, adjust the numbers in the problems or adjust the problems themselves to better assess your children's abilities.

Suggestions

1. Say a number and have children record the 100-complement of that number on their slates; for example, 80. Answer: 20 Begin with multiples of 10, then multiples of 25, and finally, multiples of 5.

2. Pose extended addition facts while children record the sums.

   • 30 + 40 = 70
   • 300 + 400 = 700
   • 120 = 50 + 70
   • 1,200 = 500 + 700
   • 20 + 90 = 110
   • 200 + 900 = 1,100
   • 120 = 60 + 60
   • 1,200 = 600 + 600

NOTE: Many of these assessment suggestions relate to learning goals that have been addressed in previous units. Now is a good time to evaluate children's progress toward those goals.

3. Have children make a ballpark estimate, with a number model, for each sum.

- $37 + 48 = ?$ $40 + 50 = 90$
- $12 + 77 = ?$ $10 + 80 = 90$
- $59 + 43 = ?$ $60 + 40 = 100$
- $172 + 47 = ?$ $170 + 50 = 220$

4. Have children record addition problems and their sums.

- $53 + 26 = 79$
- $38 + 56 = 94$
- $67 + 54 = 121$
- $134 + 123 = 257$
- $167 + 154 = 321$

5. Show times on a demonstration clock. Children record the times on their slates; for example, 4:05, 3:45, 1:55, 6:15, 2:10, 12:35.

6. Show temperatures on the classroom thermometer. Children record the temperatures on their slates; for example, 80°F, 56°F, 45°F, 20°C, 24°C, and 11°C.

✦ Written Assessment
(*Math Masters,* pp. 426 and 427)

INDEPENDENT ACTIVITY

Read through the problems with the class. You may want to work through examples for some of the problems.

If appropriate, work through the problems together. Wait for children to complete a problem before reading the next one.

Circulate and assist as children work.

- Draw line segment *AB*. (Problem 1) **Goal 5e**

- Draw a line segment that is parallel to line segment *AB*. Label its endpoints *C* and *D*. (Problem 2) **Goals 5d and 5e**

- Draw a line segment that is not parallel to line segment *AB*. Label its endpoints *E* and *F*. (Problem 3) **Goals 5d and 5e**

- Fill in the oval next to the correct answer. [Identify the pictured shape.] (Problems 4–8) **Goals 5a and 5f**

- Which things have a line of symmetry? (Problem 9) **Goal 5b**

- Which shape doesn't belong? Circle it. (Problem 10) **Goal 5c**

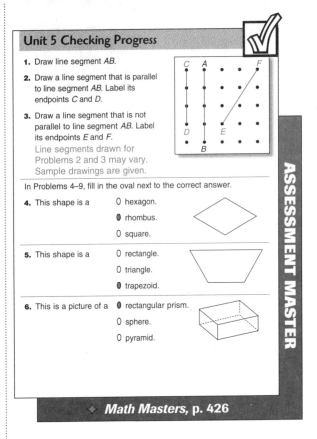

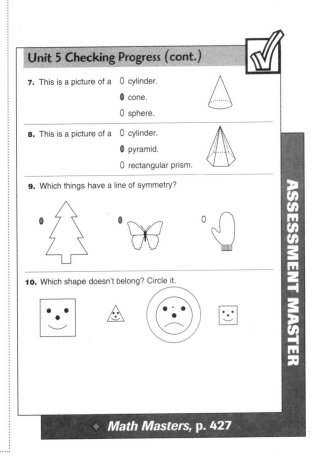

"My design is symmetrical because the two sides match."

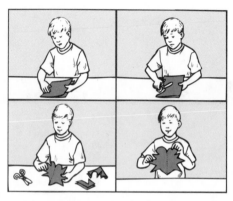

"My design is symmetrical because the two sides look exactly alike, even though they face in opposite directions."

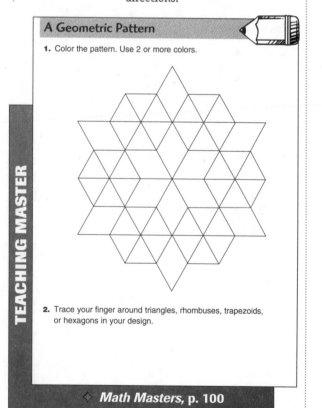

A Geometric Pattern

1. Color the pattern. Use 2 or more colors.

2. Trace your finger around triangles, rhombuses, trapezoids, or hexagons in your design.

✦ *Math Masters*, p. 100

Make Symmetrical Shapes

INDEPENDENT ACTIVITY

Activity 1

1. Fold a sheet of paper and unfold it.

2. Use a pencil or crayon to draw a design on one side of the fold.

3. Color the inside of the shape up to the fold.

4. Close the paper and rub over the design with a hard object, such as the blunt end of a pair of scissors.

5. Unfold the paper.

6. Explain why the design is symmetrical.

Activity 2

1. Fold a sheet of paper.

2. Cut out a shape that contains part of the fold.

3. Unfold the cutout piece.

4. Explain why the design is symmetrical.

Use a Template to Draw a 6-Pointed Star

INDEPENDENT ACTIVITY

Ask for volunteers to share their methods for drawing a 6-pointed star using their templates. Some children may have traced a hexagon and then traced a triangle onto each side of the hexagon.

If none have done so, show children how to make a 6-pointed star by drawing two triangles pointing in opposite directions.

Ask children why the 6-pointed star is not a polygon. Refer children to journal page 116 if they need help. Sample answer: You cannot trace the sides of the star without retracing or crossing any path.

ALTERNATIVE ASSESSMENT OPTION
Color a Geometric Pattern
(*Math Masters*, p. 100)

INDEPENDENT ACTIVITY

Children use at least 2 colors to color the pattern. When children have completed their coloring, ask them to identify visible polygons, such as rhombuses, triangles, trapezoids, or hexagons.

2 Build Background for Unit 6

◆ Math Boxes 5.10 (*Math Journal 1*, p. 132)

INDEPENDENT ACTIVITY

 Mixed Review This journal page provides opportunities for cumulative review or assessment of concepts and skills. The skill in Problem 6 is prerequisite for Unit 6.

◆ Home Link 5.10: *Unit 6 Family Letter*
(*Math Masters*, pp. 305–308)

Home Connection This Home Link is a four-page newsletter that introduces parents and guardians to Unit 6's topics and terms. This letter also offers ideas for home-based mathematics activities that are supportive of classroom work.

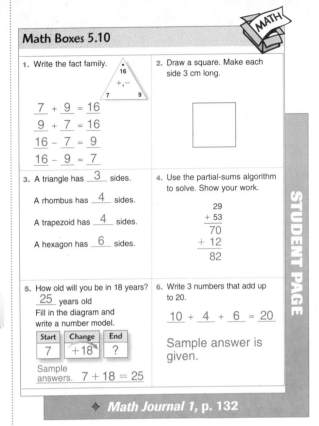

Math Boxes 5.10

1. Write the fact family.

   $7 + 9 = 16$
   $9 + 7 = 16$
   $16 - 7 = 9$
   $16 - 9 = 7$

2. Draw a square. Make each side 3 cm long.

3. A triangle has __3__ sides.

   A rhombus has __4__ sides.

   A trapezoid has __4__ sides.

   A hexagon has __6__ sides.

4. Use the partial-sums algorithm to solve. Show your work.

   $$\begin{array}{r} 29 \\ + 53 \\ \hline 70 \\ + 12 \\ \hline 82 \end{array}$$

5. How old will you be in 18 years?
   __25__ years old
   Fill in the diagram and write a number model.

Start	Change	End
7	+18	?

   Sample answers. $7 + 18 = 25$

6. Write 3 numbers that add up to 20.

   $10 + 4 + 6 = 20$

   Sample answer is given.

◆ *Math Journal 1*, p. 132

STUDENT PAGE

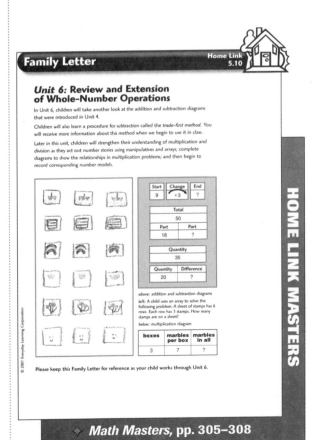

Family Letter

Home Link 5.10

Unit 6: Review and Extension of Whole-Number Operations

In Unit 6, children will take another look at the addition and subtraction diagrams that were introduced in Unit 4.

Children will also learn a procedure for subtraction called the *trade-first method*. You will receive more information about this method when we begin to use it in class.

Later in this unit, children will strengthen their understanding of multiplication and division as they act out number stories using manipulatives and arrays; complete diagrams to show the relationships in multiplication problems; and then begin to record corresponding number models.

Start	Change	End
9	+3	?

Total	
50	
Part	Part
18	?

Quantity	
35	
Quantity	Difference
20	?

above: addition and subtraction diagrams

left: A child uses an array to solve the following problem: A sheet of stamps has 6 rows. Each row has 3 stamps. How many stamps are on a sheet?

below: multiplication diagram

boxes	marbles per box	marbles in all
3	7	?

Please keep this Family Letter for reference as your child works through Unit 6.

© 2001 Everyday Learning Corporation

◆ *Math Masters*, pp. 305–308

HOME LINK MASTERS

Unit **6**
Whole-Number Operations and Number Stories

overview

In the context of number stories, children review earlier work with addition and subtraction and begin formal work with multiplication and division.

Comparison number stories are used to begin development of a subtraction algorithm. Stories about multiples of equal groups are used to introduce a multiplication diagram and multiplication number models. Equal-sharing and equal-grouping stories provide some initial work with division.

contents

UNIT
6

learning goals in perspective

learning goals	links to the past	links to the future
6a **Beginning/Developing Goal** Solve stories about multiples of equal groups. **(Lessons 6.8, 6.9, and 6.11)**	Children have previously explored multiples of equal groups informally and by skip counting. *(Related Grade 2 lessons: 2.7, 5.3)*	*Third Grade Everyday Mathematics* focuses extensively on multiplication. *(Related Grade 2 lessons: 7.6, 8.3, 11.3)*
6b **Beginning/Developing Goal** Solve equal-grouping and equal-sharing division problems. **(Lessons 6.11 and 6.12)**	Children have had many informal experiences with equal grouping and equal sharing in Kindergarten and first grade. *(Related Grade 2 lessons: 2.7, 5.2)*	Equal sharing is closely related to fractions, which will be a focus of Unit 8. Division number models will be introduced in Unit 11. *(Related Grade 2 lessons: 7.6, 8.3, 11.3, 11.4)*
6c **Developing Goal** Use the trade-first method to solve 2-digit subtraction problems. **(Lessons 6.6, 6.10, and 6.12)**	In Kindergarten and first grade, children found ways to subtract smaller numbers. In second grade children worked with subtraction strategies in Unit 2. *(Related Grade 2 lessons: 2.6, 2.8, 2.10–2.13)*	In third grade, children will extend the use of this algorithm to include larger numbers. *(Related Grade 2 lesson: 7.3)*
6d **Developing Goal** Make ballpark estimates of exact answers. **(Lessons 6.1, 6.4, 6.6, 6.7, 6.10, and 6.11)**	In Kindergarten, children were introduced to the idea of estimation. In first grade, estimation was extended to include money, measurement, and time. *(Related Grade 2 lessons: 4.5, 4.6, 4.9)*	Estimation and mental arithmetic are found throughout *Everyday Mathematics*. In Unit 10, children will do some further work with estimating costs. *(Related Grade 2 lesson: 10.5)*
6e **Developing Goal** Model multiplication problems with arrays. **(Lessons 6.9 and 6.10)**	Children have had informal experiences with arrays in Kindergarten and first grade. *(Related Grade 2 lessons: 2.7, 5.3)*	Work with arrays will continue in *Third Grade Everyday Mathematics*. *(Related Grade 2 lesson: 11.3)*
6f **Developing Goal** Add three 2-digit numbers mentally. **(Lessons 6.1, 6.6, and 6.11)**	In Kindergarten and first grade, children found ways to add smaller numbers. In second grade children worked with 2-digit addition in Unit 4. *(Related Grade 2 lessons: 1.4, 1.13, 2.1–2.5, 2.10, 4.6, 4.8, 4.9)*	In third grade, children will add larger numbers and will use three addends in problem situations. *(Related Grade 2 lessons: 7.4, 11.1)*
6g **Developing/Secure Goal** Add and subtract with multiples of 10. **(Lessons 6.1, 6.5, and 6.10)**	Children began counting by 10s in Kindergarten. Previous experiences with number grids will also contribute to success with this goal. *(Related Grade 2 lessons: 1.4, 1.6, 1.8, 1.9, 1.11, 1.13, 2.1–2.6, 2.12, 2.13, 3.1, 3.2, 3.4, 4.6, 4.8, 4.9)*	In Unit 7, children will use counting patterns to help with mental arithmetic. *(Related Grade 2 lessons: 7.1–7.4, 10.5, 11.1, 11.2)*
6h **Developing/Secure Goal** Solve addition and subtraction number stories. **(Lessons 6.2–6.4 and 6.7)**	Children began telling and solving number stories in Kindergarten, and continued throughout first grade. *(Related Grade 2 lessons: 2.1, 4.1, 4.2, 4.6)*	Throughout the grades, children will continue to create and solve number stories. *(Related Grade 2 lessons: 8.7, 11.1, 11.2)*
6i **Secure Goal** Add three 1-digit numbers mentally. **(Lessons 6.1, 6.4, and 6.7)**	Mental math is emphasized throughout *Everyday Mathematics*. *(Related Grade 2 lessons: 2.2–2.6, 2.11, 3.7, 4.5, 4.6)*	In Unit 7, children will use counting patterns to help with mental arithmetic. *(Related Grade 2 lessons: 7.1–7.4, 10.5, 11.1, 11.2)*

assessment
ongoing • product • periodic

✔ Informal Assessment

Math Boxes These *Math Journal* pages provide opportunities for cumulative review or assessment of concepts and skills.

Ongoing Assessment: Kid Watching Use the Ongoing Assessment suggestions in the following lessons to make quick, on-the-spot observations about children's understanding of:
• Operations and Computation **(Lessons 6.1, 6.2, and 6.4–6.8)**

Portfolio Ideas Samples of children's work may be obtained from the following assignments:
• Favorite-Food Data **(Lesson 6.3)**
• Number Stories **(Lesson 6.4)**
• Creating Pattern-Block Symmetry **(Lesson 6.7)**
• Drawing and describing arrays **(Lesson 6.9)**
• Describe a method used to solve a subtraction problem **(Lesson 6.12)**
• Make up and solve number stories **(Lesson 6.12)**

✔ Unit 6 Review and Assessment

Math Message Use the question in Lesson 6.12 to assess children's progress toward the following learning goal: Goal 6b

Oral and Slate Assessments Use oral or slate assessments during Lesson 6.12 to assess children's progress toward the following learning goals: Goals 6a, 6b, 6c, 6d, 6e, 6g, 6h, and 6i

Written Assessment Use a written review during Lesson 6.12 to assess children's progress toward the following learning goals: Goals 6c, 6e, 6f, 6h, and 6i

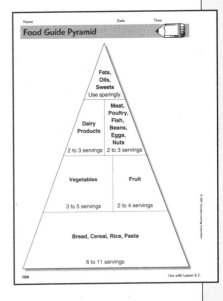

assessment handbook

For more information on how to use different types of assessment in Unit 6, see the Assessment Overview on pages 56–58 in the *Assessment Handbook*. The following Assessment Masters can be found in the *Math Masters* book:

• Unit 6 Checking Progress, p. 428
• Unit 6 Class Checklist, p. 458
• Unit 6 Individual Profile of Progress, p. 459
• Class Progress Indicator, p. 488
• Math Logs, pp. 493 and 495
• Self-Assessment Forms, pp. 496 and 497
• Interest Inventory, pp. 491 and 492
• Class Checklist: 2nd Quarter, pp. 475 and 476
• Individual Profile of Progress: 2nd Quarter, p. 477
• Midyear Assessment, pp. 438–440

problem→solving

A process of modeling everyday situations using tools from mathematics

Encourage children to use a variety of strategies when attacking a given problem—and to explain those strategies. *Strategies children might use in this unit:*

- Using a situation diagram
- Writing a number model
- Using and making a graph
- Using information in a picture
- Trying and checking
- Modeling with manipulatives
- Drawing a picture

Four Problem-Solving REPRESENTATIONS

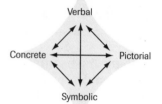

Lessons that teach *through* problem solving, not just *about* problem solving

Lesson	Activity	Lesson	Activity
6.2	Solving comparison number stories	6.3	Comparing lengths of fish
6.3	Finding the most popular food among the class	6.4	Solving addition and subtraction diagram problems
6.4	Solving a mixed set (addition and subtraction) of number stories	6.11	Solving number stories about equal groups of things, about equal sharing, and about equal grouping

For more information about problem solving in *Everyday Mathematics,* see the *Teacher's Reference Manual,* pp. 197–208.

cross-curricularlinks

literature

- Read *Each Orange Had Eight Slices: A Counting Book* and *Sea Squares* to explore multiplication. **(Lesson 6.8)**

- Read *One Hundred Hungry Ants*, in which a group of ants uses arrays to find the most efficient way to get to a picnic. **(Lesson 6.9)**

- Read *A Remainder of One*, a book about an ant who is always left out of arrays. **(Lesson 6.11)**

language arts

- Children write and illustrate addition and subtraction number stories. **(Lessons 6.4 and 6.6)**

art

- Children make symmetrical designs with paper and pattern blocks. **(Lesson 6.7)**

science

- Children cut out grocery store sale ads and use them to make food-group collages. **(Lesson 6.3)**

meeting INDIVIDUAL needs

✦ RETEACHING

The following features provide additional instructional support:

Adjusting the Activity
- **Lesson 6.2, Part 1**
- **Lesson 6.3, Part 1**
- **Lesson 6.4, Part 1**
- **Lesson 6.6, Part 1**
- **Lesson 6.9, Part 1**

Options for Individualizing
- **Lesson 6.1** Adding Using Base-10 Blocks
- **Lesson 6.2** Playing *Penny Grab*
- **Lesson 6.5** Building and Renaming Numbers
- **Lesson 6.5** Subtracting with Coins
- **Lesson 6.10** Building Arrays to Model Multiplication
- **Lesson 6.11** Using a Number Line to Model Equal Sharing and Equal Grouping

✦ ENRICHMENT

The following features suggest enrichment and extension activities:

Adjusting the Activity
- **Lesson 6.1, Part 1**
- **Lesson 6.3, Part 3**
- **Lesson 6.4, Part 3**
- **Lesson 6.7, Part 1**
- **Lesson 6.8, Part 1**
- **Lesson 6.9, Parts 1, 3**
- **Lesson 6.10, Part 1**

Options for Individualizing
- **Lesson 6.1** *Three Addends*–Multiples of 10
- **Lesson 6.3** Categorizing Foods
- **Lesson 6.3** Favorite-Food Data
- **Lesson 6.4** Number Stories
- **Lesson 6.6** Making Up and Solving Subtraction Number Stories
- **Lesson 6.8** Equal Groups in Literature
- **Lesson 6.9** Describing Arrays Found in Literature
- **Lesson 6.10** Extending *Array Bingo*
- **Lesson 6.11** Describing Division Situations Found in Literature

✦ LANGUAGE DIVERSITY

The following features suggest ways to support children who are acquiring proficiency in English:

Adjusting the Activity
- **Lesson 6.9, Part 3**

Options for Individualizing
- **Lesson 6.9** Array Display or Booklet

✦ MULTIAGE CLASSROOM

The following chart lists related lessons from Grades 1 and 3 that can help you meet your instructional needs:

Grade 1	5.9 6.7 6.8	1.13 2.13 5.7	3.13 6.12 10.1	3.6 5.6–5.8	9.2–9.4	8.5 9.2–9.4	7.7 8.6 9.5				8.6
Grade 2	6.1	6.2	6.3	6.4	6.5	6.6	6.7	6.8	6.9	6.10	6.11
Grade 3	2.9	2.6	1.5 11.2–11.9	1.10 2.4–2.6	1.7 2.2 2.8	1.7 2.8	4.2–4.4 6.9	4.2–4.4 4.8	4.2–4.4 4.7	4.2–4.4 4.8	4.4 7.6 9.1

materials

lesson	📖 *math masters* pages	📦 manipulative kit items	✂️ other items
6.1	Home Link Masters, pp. 309 and 310 Teaching Masters, pp. 101 and 102	number cards 0–20 base-10 blocks	
6.2	Home Link Masters, pp. 311 and 312 Teaching Master, p. 103 *See* **Advance Preparation, p. 360**	number cards 0–20	30 pennies or other small counters
6.3	Home Link Masterd, p. 313 Teaching Masters, pp. 104 and 107 transparency of Teaching Masters, pp. 104–106 *See* **Advance Preparation, p. 366**		magazines, newspapers, and grocery-store fliers *See* **Advance Preparation, p. 366**
6.4	Home Link Masters, pp. 314 and 315 Teaching Masters, pp. 108 and 109	slate	
6.5	Home Link Masters, pp. 316 and 317 Teaching Masters, pp. 35, 41, and 42	base-10 blocks overhead base-10 blocks (optional) number cards 0–9	coins
6.6	Home Link Masters, pp. 318 and 319 Teaching Master, p. 109	base-10 blocks (optional)	Fact Triangles in an envelope
6.7	Home Link Master, p. 320 Teaching Masters, pp. 101 and 110–114 *See* **Advance Preparation, p. 390**	geoboard; rubber bands slate Pattern-Block Template pattern blocks 1 regular die per group number cards 0–20 per partnership	overhead geoboard (optional) straightedge pennies or other counters
6.8	Home Link Master, p. 321		40 pennies or other counters per group 6 boxes or bags Fact Triangles in an envelope literature selections *See* **Advance Preparation, p. 395**
6.9	Home Link Master, p. 322 Teaching Masters, pp. 115 and 116 transparency of Teaching Master, p. 115 *See* **Advance Preparation, p. 400**		50 pennies or other counters per partnership newspapers and magazines *One Hundred Hungry Ants* by Elinor Pinczes *See* **Advance Preparation, p. 400**
6.10	Home Link Masters, pp. 323 and 324 Teaching Masters, pp. 117–121 *See* **Advance Preparation, p. 405**	dice or number cards per group Pattern-Block Template pattern blocks dice or egg carton per group	40 counters per partnership 40 overhead counters paper clips; envelope 16 index cards
6.11	Home Link Master, p. 325	slate	30 counters per group *A Remainder of One* by Elinor Pinczes *See* **Advance Preparation, p. 410**
6.12	Home Link Masters, pp. 326–329 Assessment Masters, pp. 428 and 438–440 Teaching Masters, pp. 22, 101, and 108	slate number cards 0–20 per partnership	100 counters

planningtips

Pacing

Pacing depends on a number of factors, such as children's individual needs and how long your school has been using *Everyday Mathematics*. At the beginning of Unit 6, review your Content by Strand Poster to help you set a monthly pace.

← MOST CLASSROOMS →		
JANUARY	FEBRUARY	MARCH

Using the Projects

Use Project 5 during Unit 4, Unit 6, or Unit 8 to experiment with paper folding, creating snowflakes that represent real 6-sided water crystals. The Projects can be found at the back of this book.

Home Communication

Share Home Links 6.1–6.11 with families to help them understand the content and procedures in this unit. At the end of the unit, use Home Link 6.12 to introduce Unit 7. Supplemental information can be found in the *Home Connection Handbook*.

NCTM Standards

Standard	1	2	3	4	5	6	7	8	9	10
Unit 6 Lessons	1–11	1, 2, 4, 5, 7–9	7, 9, 10	6, 10	3	1–11	1–11	1–11	1–11	1–11

Content Standards
1 Number and Operation
2 Patterns, Functions, and Algebra
3 Geometry and Spatial Sense
4 Measurement
5 Data Analysis, Statistics, and Probability

Process Standards
6 Problem Solving
7 Reasoning and Proof
8 Communication
9 Connections
10 Representations

PRACTICE *through* Games

Everyday Mathematics uses games to help children develop good fact power and other math skills.

- Practice addition skills with three addends in *Three Addends* **(Lessons 6.1 and 6.7)**
- Practice addition with four addends and comparing sums in *Addition Top-It* **(Lesson 6.2)**
- Compare handfuls of pennies by finding the difference in *Penny Grab* **(Lesson 6.2)**
- Match numbers with the total number of dots in arrays with *Array Bingo* **(Lesson 6.10)**

The notes below highlight the major content ideas presented in Unit 6. These notes may help you establish instructional priorities.

Addition and Subtraction (Lesson 6.1 and following)

In *Everyday Mathematics,* the operations are developed gradually, in three stages:

1. Children explore an operation by using concrete objects (such as counters, pictures, doodles, or tallies) to solve real-life problems.

2. Children are exposed to more formal representations through diagrams and number models, but they are not yet expected to produce these representations by themselves.

3. Children choose and fill in appropriate diagrams; they also represent their solutions by writing number models.

Start	Change	End
40	+20	?

A change diagram

Quantity
25

Quantity	Difference
17	?

A comparison diagram

Total
?

Part	Part
12	23

A parts-and-total diagram

Up to this point, the first two stages of the process have been used in developing addition and subtraction. Children solved simple problems with concrete objects in Kindergarten and first grade. Then, in the first five units of second grade, they were exposed to addition and subtraction diagrams and number models. This was done informally: The teacher drew diagrams as part of the discussion, but children were not expected to do so themselves. In Unit 6, the development of addition and subtraction is extended to the third stage. The following procedure for solving addition and subtraction problems is formally established:

1. Choose an appropriate addition/subtraction diagram: change, comparison, or parts-and-total.

2. Enter the known quantities, and identify which quantity is unknown.

3. Choose the operation needed to find the missing information.

4. Solve the problem and write a number model.

NOTE: Children are accustomed to seeing horizontal addition and subtraction problems with the answer (or answer spaces) written to the right of the equal sign. In *Everyday Mathematics,* children will also see problems with the answer (or answer spaces) written to the left of the equal sign. It is important that children regularly see both of these horizontal forms of addition and subtraction.

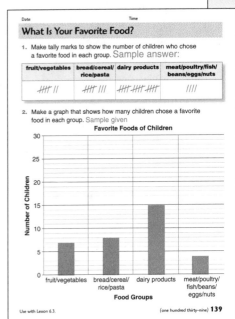

Data Day (Lesson 6.3)

The important topic of nutrition provides a context for the collection, analysis, and representation of data. The teacher discusses the basic food groups, referring to the Food Guide Pyramid. Food preferences of children are surveyed, tallied, and graphed.

Multiplication and Division (Lesson 6.7 and following)

Children have been exposed to the underlying concepts of multiplication and division in a variety of contexts: addition involving equal groups of objects; oral counts by 1-digit numbers; counting by using a calculator; arrays; equal sharing; and finding fractional quantities (for example, give your friend half of your counters).

Explorations A and C in Lesson 6.7 continue this exposure: Children make arrays on geoboards, record these arrays, and sort different arrays for the same number. Then they determine how many groups of n objects can be made from a specified number of objects.

Extending these activities in Lessons 6.8–6.11, children act out problems with counters. They solve problems about equal groups, some of which involve objects that form arrays in real life. They make arrays consisting of a certain number of rows with the same number of objects in each row,

Children use arrays to explore the meaning of multiplication.

and they write number models to represent those arrays. Arrays will become increasingly important in building an understanding of the link between multiplication and division and in learning multiplication and division facts.

The diagram introduced for multiplication serves two purposes: It specifies the unit associated with each quantity, and it identifies the known and unknown quantities in the problem. While it is recommended that you ask children to help you complete such diagrams when discussing a problem, do not expect them to come up with such diagrams on their own. Repeated exposure to such diagrams will help children understand the meanings of multiplication and division.

rows	eggs per row	eggs in all
2	6	?

Since few children have difficulty with equal-sharing problems that involve "leftovers," you need not avoid problems with remainders, even at this early stage in the development of division. But because number models for division with remainders are somewhat more complex than those for other operations, the introduction of division number models will be postponed until a later unit.

Review and Assessment (Lesson 6.1 and following)

This is a good time to pause and assess children's progress on the topics covered in the first five units. Rather than waiting until the end of this unit, try to schedule frequent small-group assessment sessions throughout the unit. By now, children should have become proficient in reading, writing, and comparing 3-digit numbers; finding equivalent names for numbers; telling time; counting money and making change; and finding the sums and differences of 2-digit numbers by using mental arithmetic. Also, children should know most of the addition and subtraction facts.

Addition and subtraction skills are assessed in Lesson 6.12, as are skills for modeling multiplication with arrays and solving simple equal-sharing and equal-grouping problems.

If you are planning a quarterly assessment for Units 4–6, you may want to refer to the *Assessment Handbook*. The quarterly learning goals listed on the Class Checklist and Individual Profile of Progress checklist (*Math Masters,* pages 275–277) are useful tools for keeping track of children's progress.

For **additional information** on the following topics, see the *Teacher's Reference Manual:*

- algorithms and procedures
- data collection, organization, and analysis
- number models and number sentences
- operations and use classes
- problem solving
- standard and alternative algorithms

6.1 Addition with Several Addends

OBJECTIVE To review strategies for solving addition problems, with emphasis on problems having three addends.

summaries	materials
1 Teaching the Lesson	
Children review strategies for solving addition problems, such as counting on, making diagrams, adding mentally, and using the partial-sums algorithm. They identify the easiest order in which to add three numbers, write number models, and practice adding three or more 1-digit and 2-digit numbers. [Operations and Computation]	☐ *Math Journal 1*, p. 133 ☐ Teaching Master (*Math Masters*, p. 101; optional) ☐ number cards 0–20 per partnership (from the Everything Math Deck, if available)
2 Ongoing Learning & Practice	
Children estimate sums and use the partial-sums algorithm. [Operations and Computation] Children practice and maintain skills through Math Boxes and Home Link activities.	☐ *Math Journal 1*, pp. 134 and 135 ☐ Home Link Masters (*Math Masters*, pp. 309 and 310)
3 Options for Individualizing	
Enrichment Children practice adding multiples of 10 by playing *Three Addends*. [Operations and Computation] **Reteaching** Children use base-10 blocks to practice addition. [Operations and Computation]	☐ Teaching Masters (*Math Masters*, pp. 101 and 102) ☐ base-10 blocks: 27 cubes and 9 longs

Getting Started

Mental Math and Reflexes
Pose addition and subtraction problems that feature multiples of 10.
Suggestions:

$70 + 20 = 90$	$20 + 8 = 28$
$83 = 70 + 13$	$50 = 70 - 20$
$65 - 5 = 60$	$89 - 49 = 40$

Math Message
(Use names of children in your class.)

Lia has 13 pencils. Thomas has 6 pencils. Nate has 7. How many pencils do they have in all?
26 pencils

✦ Math Message Follow-Up

WHOLE-CLASS DISCUSSION

Review strategies for solving addition problems.

Draw a unit box on the board. Ask: *What is the Math Message story about?* Sample answer: Finding the total number of pencils 3 children have *What label should go in the unit box?* pencils

Invite children to share strategies for solving the Math Message problem. Encourage them to doodle or calculate with pencil and paper if they need to. *Suggestions:*

▷ Use counters or fingers as an aid for counting on.

▷ Draw pictures or tally marks. (See below.)

▷ Use a parts-and-total diagram. (See below.)

▷ Solve by mental arithmetic.

▷ Use the partial-sums method. (See below.)

Unit
pencils

✦ Adding Three Numbers in Any Order

WHOLE-CLASS DISCUSSION

Write number models for the Math Message problem in horizontal format. Then ask:

• Does the order in which the numbers are written make a difference as far as the sum? no

• Which order makes it easiest to find the sum?

Option 1

Add 13 and 6 first to make 19; then add 7.

$13 + 6 + 7 =$
$\vee$
$19 + 7 = 26$

Option 2

Add 13 and 7 first to make 20; then add 6.

$13 + 7 + 6 =$
$\vee$
$20 + 6 = 26$

Option 3

Add 6 and 7 first to make 13; then double 13.

$6 + 7 + 13 =$
$\vee$
$13 + 13 = 26$

Write other number triplets on the board, and ask children to decide which order makes it easiest for them to find the sum. *See the following suggestions.*

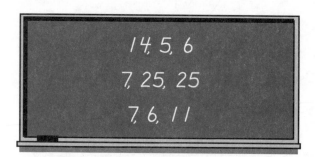

Encourage children to make up similar problems for the class to solve. Some number triplets—for example, 7, 9, and 17—do not have an "easiest" order for addition.

Summary: Three or more numbers can be added in any order. Also, they can be ordered in a way that makes it easiest to find the sum.

Adjusting the Activity Challenge children by including triplets with 3-digit numbers. For example,
$140 + 150 + 60$ 350

◆ Playing *Three Addends*
(*Math Journal 1*, p. 133; *Math Masters*, p. 101)

PARTNER ACTIVITY

Three Addends gives partners the opportunity to add three numbers in different orders. Instructions are found on journal page 133.

NOTE: *Math Masters*, page 101 is available if children need more space to record numbers and number models.

ONGOING ASSESSMENT
Use children's records of *Three Addends* to assess whether they are looking for easy-to-add combinations.

Ongoing Learning & Practice

◆ Practicing Estimation and the Partial-Sums Algorithm (*Math Journal 1*, p. 134)

INDEPENDENT ACTIVITY

Review the instructions for the journal page with children. Have them begin by making a ballpark estimate for each sum.

▷ If the estimated sum is less than 50, they should not add the numbers.

▷ If the estimated sum is 50 or greater, they should add the numbers.

NOTE: Many children don't recognize the value of making a ballpark estimate. However, most children should see the value of making an estimate if it will allow them to do less work! In Lesson 6.4, children return to this journal page and solve each problem for which the estimated sum is less than 50.

ONGOING ASSESSMENT
The partial-sums algorithm was introduced in Unit 4. Use journal page 134 to assess children's progress with addition of 2-digit numbers.

Three Addends

Materials ☐ number cards 0–20

Players 2

Directions

• Shuffle the cards. Place the deck number-side down.

• Turn over the top 3 cards. Each partner writes the 3 numbers.

• Add the numbers. Write a number model to show the order in which you added.

• Compare your answers with your partner's.

Example Numbers and number models vary in Problems 1–6.

The cards 6, 5, and 14 are turned over. Gillian records the numbers. She adds 14 and 6 first and then adds 5. She records her number model and compares her answer with her partner's.

Numbers: _6_, _5_, _14_ Number model: _14_ + _6_ + _5_ = _25_

1. Numbers: ____, ____, ____	2. Numbers: ____, ____, ____
Number model:	Number model:
____ + ____ + ____ = ____	____ + ____ + ____ = ____
3. Numbers: ____, ____, ____	4. Numbers: ____, ____, ____
Number model:	Number model:
____ = ____ + ____ + ____	____ = ____ + ____ + ____
5. Numbers: ____, ____, ____	6. Numbers: ____, ____, ____
Number model:	Number model:
____ + ____ + ____ = ____	____ + ____ + ____ = ____

◆ *Math Journal 1*, p. 133

Adjusting the Activity For a more challenging version of *Three Addends*, children draw 4 cards at each turn and solve problems with 4 addends.

Addition Practice

Fill in the unit box. Then, for each problem:

• Make a ballpark estimate before you add.

• Write a number model for your estimate.

• If your estimate is less than 50, you do not have to add the numbers. Leave the answer box empty.

• If your estimate is 50 or more, add the numbers. Write your answer in the answer box.

Unit ☐

1. $29 + 7$ Answer	2. $87 + 9$ Answer 96	3. $37 + 42$ Answer 79
Ballpark estimate: $30 + 10 = 40$	Ballpark estimate: $90 + 10 = 100$	Ballpark estimate: $40 + 40 = 80$
4. $27 + 13$ Answer	5. $38 + 46$ Answer 84	6. $42 + 28$ Answer 70
Ballpark estimate: $30 + 10 = 40$	Ballpark estimate: $40 + 50 = 90$	Ballpark estimate: $40 + 30 = 70$

◆ *Math Journal 1*, p. 134

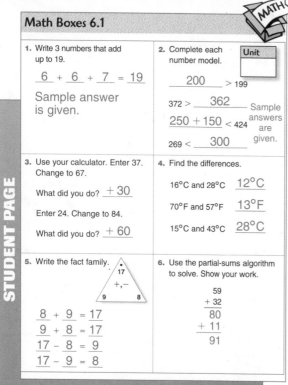

Math Boxes 6.1

1. Write 3 numbers that add up to 19.

$\underline{6} + \underline{6} + \underline{7} = 19$

Sample answer is given.

2. Complete each number model.

Unit

$\underline{200} > 199$

$372 > \underline{362}$

$\underline{250 + 150} < 424$

$269 < \underline{300}$

Sample answers are given.

3. Use your calculator. Enter 37. Change to 67.

What did you do? $\underline{+\,30}$

Enter 24. Change to 84.

What did you do? $\underline{+\,60}$

4. Find the differences.

16°C and 28°C $\quad \underline{12°C}$

70°F and 57°F $\quad \underline{13°F}$

15°C and 43°C $\quad \underline{28°C}$

5. Write the fact family.

$\underline{8} + \underline{9} = \underline{17}$
$\underline{9} + \underline{8} = \underline{17}$
$\underline{17} - \underline{8} = \underline{9}$
$\underline{17} - \underline{9} = \underline{8}$

6. Use the partial-sums algorithm to solve. Show your work.

$$
\begin{array}{r}
59 \\
+\ 32 \\
\hline
80 \\
+\ 11 \\
\hline
91
\end{array}
$$

Math Journal 1, p. 135

◆ **Math Boxes 6.1** (*Math Journal 1*, p. 135)

INDEPENDENT ACTIVITY

Mixed Review This journal page provides opportunities for cumulative review or assessment of concepts and skills.

◆ **Home Link 6.1** (*Math Masters*, pp. 309 and 310)

Home Connection Children practice adding three numbers in the easiest order. Children also practice using the partial-sums method for adding three numbers.

3 Options for Individualizing

◆ **ENRICHMENT** *Three Addends*—Multiples of 10 (*Math Masters*, p. 101)

PARTNER ACTIVITY

Modify the rules for *Three Addends* by challenging children to think of each card as a multiple of 10. For

---

Adding Three Numbers

Home Link 6.1

Family Note

Sometimes the order in which you add numbers can make it easier to find the sum. For example, when adding 17, 19, and 23, some people may first calculate 17 + 23 *(which equals 40)* and then add 19 *(40 + 19 = 59)*. For Problems 1–4, help your child look for easy combinations. Before working on Problems 5–10, you might go over the example with your child.

Please return this Home Link to school tomorrow.

For each problem: Sample number models shown

- Think about an easy way to add the numbers.
- Write a number model to show the order in which you are adding the numbers.
- Find each sum. Tell someone at home why you added the numbers in that order.

1. (13 6 7)

Number model:

$\underline{13} + \underline{7} + \underline{6} = \underline{26}$

2. (22 8 5)

Number model:

$\underline{8} + \underline{22} + \underline{5} = \underline{35}$

3. (15 9 25)

Number model:

$\underline{15} + \underline{25} + \underline{9} = \underline{49}$

4. (29 11 6)

Number model:

$\underline{29} + \underline{11} + \underline{6} = \underline{46}$

Math Masters, p. 309

Adding Three Numbers (cont.)

Home Link 6.1

Add. Use the partial-sums method.

Example

$$
\begin{array}{r}
33 \\
42 \\
+\ 11 \\
\end{array}
$$

Add the tens. $\rightarrow (30 + 40 + 10) \rightarrow 80$

Add the ones. $\rightarrow (3 + 2 + 1) \rightarrow 6$

Add the partial sums. $\rightarrow (80 + 6) \rightarrow 86$

5.
$$
\begin{array}{r}
23 \\
32 \\
+\ 14 \\
\hline
60 \\
9 \\
\hline
69
\end{array}
$$

6.
$$
\begin{array}{r}
14 \\
29 \\
+\ 27 \\
\hline
50 \\
20 \\
\hline
70
\end{array}
$$

7.
$$
\begin{array}{r}
8 \\
19 \\
+\ 35 \\
\hline
40 \\
22 \\
\hline
62
\end{array}
$$

8.
$$
\begin{array}{r}
46 \\
25 \\
+\ 12 \\
\hline
70 \\
13 \\
\hline
83
\end{array}
$$

9.
$$
\begin{array}{r}
40 \\
45 \\
+\ 63 \\
\hline
140 \\
8 \\
\hline
148
\end{array}
$$

10.
$$
\begin{array}{r}
9 \\
85 \\
+\ 96 \\
\hline
170 \\
20 \\
\hline
190
\end{array}
$$

Math Masters, p. 310

example, suppose the cards drawn are 4, 7, and 6. Think of these cards as 40, 70, and 60. Children might find 40 + 60 first 100 and then find 100 + 70 170. Children would then write the following number model:
40 + 60 + 70 = 170.

◆ RETEACHING Adding Using Base-10 Blocks
(*Math Masters,* p. 102)

INDEPENDENT ACTIVITY

Children can represent each addend by placing base-10 blocks—longs and cubes—on *Math Masters,* page 102. The problem 14 + 5 + 6 = ? might be represented as follows:

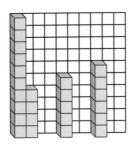

14 + 5 + 6 = ?

Encourage children to look for a combination that will result in trading ones for tens. *For example:*

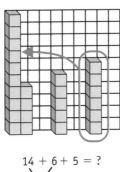

14 + 6 + 5 = ?
20 + 5 = 25

PLANNING AHEAD
For an optional Enrichment activity in Lesson 6.3, begin collecting magazines, newspapers, and, especially, grocery-store sale flyers for children to cut apart.

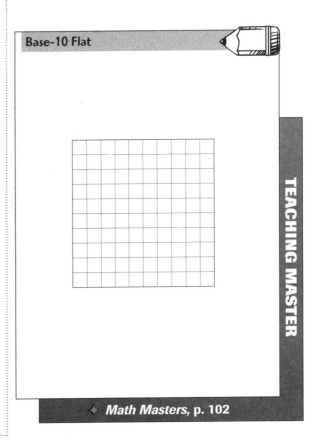

Three Addends Record Sheet

For each turn:
• Write the 3 numbers.
• Add the numbers.
Numbers and number models vary.
• Write a number model to show the order in which you added.

1. Numbers: ____, ____, ____
   Number model:
   ____ + ____ + ____ = ____

2. Numbers: ____, ____, ____
   Number model:
   ____ + ____ + ____ = ____

3. Numbers: ____, ____, ____
   Number model:
   ____ = ____ + ____ + ____

4. Numbers: ____, ____, ____
   Number model:
   ____ = ____ + ____ + ____

5. Numbers: ____, ____, ____
   Number model:
   ____ + ____ + ____ = ____

6. Numbers: ____, ____, ____
   Number model:
   ____ + ____ + ____ = ____

7. Numbers: ____, ____, ____
   Number model:
   ____ + ____ + ____ = ____

8. Numbers: ____, ____, ____
   Number model:
   ____ + ____ + ____ = ____

9. Numbers: ____, ____, ____
   Number model:
   ____ = ____ + ____ + ____

10. Numbers: ____, ____, ____
   Number model:
   ____ = ____ + ____ + ____

◆ *Math Masters,* p. 101

Base-10 Flat

◇ *Math Masters,* p. 102

TEACHING MASTER

TEACHING MASTER

6.2 Comparison Number Stories

OBJECTIVE To solve comparison number stories by using comparison diagrams.

summaries	materials
1 Teaching the Lesson	
Children are introduced to the comparison diagram as a tool for recording known and missing information in a comparison number story. Children then solve comparison number stories by using comparison diagrams and writing number models. [Operations and Computation; Patterns, Functions, and Algebra]	☐ *Math Journal 1*, pp. 136 and 137 ☐ Home Link 6.1 ☐ Teaching Master transparency (*Math Masters*, p. 103; optional) ***See* Advance Preparation**
2 Ongoing Learning & Practice	
Children practice adding three or four numbers by playing a more advanced version of *Addition Top-It*. [Numeration; Operations and Computation] Children practice and maintain skills through Math Boxes and Home Link activities.	☐ *Math Journal 1*, p. 138 ☐ Teaching Master (*Math Masters*, p. 101; optional) ☐ Home Link Masters (*Math Masters*, pp. 311 and 312) ☐ number cards 0–20 (from the Everything Math Deck, if available)
3 Options for Individualizing	
Reteaching Children compare numbers by playing *Penny Grab*. [Numeration; Operations and Computation]	☐ 30 pennies or other small counters

Additional Information

Advance Preparation For the *Solving Comparison Number Stories* activity in Part 1, decide how you will display a comparison diagram. Some possibilities:

▷ Make an overhead transparency of *Math Masters*, page 103.

▷ Draw a comparison diagram on the board with semipermanent chalk. (Read about semipermanent chalk in the *Teacher's Reference Manual*.)

▷ Draw and erase comparison diagrams on the board as needed.

Vocabulary • comparison number story • difference • comparison diagram

Getting Started

Mental Math and Reflexes

Write multiple-addend problems like the following on the board. Encourage children to look for combinations that will make the addition easier.

$3 + 9 + 7 = ?$ 19 $14 + 8 + 6 = ?$ 28 $? = 21 + 5 + 9$ 35 $? = 8 + 5 + 12 + 5$ 30

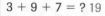

Home Link 6.1 Follow-Up

Ask volunteers to share how they found the answer to each problem and why they chose the order in which they added the three numbers.

1 Teaching the Lesson

◆ Math Message Follow-Up

WHOLE-CLASS DISCUSSION

Use the Math Message problem to start a discussion of **comparison number stories.** Comparison stories involve the **difference** between two quantities.

You can compare things that are counted. *For example:*

▷ Beth scored 14 points. Ivy scored 8 points. So Beth scored 6 more points than Ivy. (Alternatively, Ivy scored 6 fewer points than Beth.) The difference in points scored is 6 points.

You can also compare things that are measured. *For example:*

▷ The big fish is 14 inches long. The small fish is 8 inches long. So the small fish is 6 inches shorter. (Alternatively, the big fish is 6 inches longer.) The difference in length is 6 inches.

Draw a picture on the board (see the margin) and show how children can solve the Math Message problem by matching the two quantities one to one. The quantity that is left unmatched is the difference. In the Math Message problem, the difference tells how many more CDs Silva has than Mark.

Display a **comparison diagram.** In it, write the numbers 17, 8, and 9, as shown in the margin. Say that the diagram is a convenient way to represent the CD comparison story. The longer Quantity cell shows the larger number of CDs that Silva has. The shorter Quantity cell shows the smaller number of CDs that Mark has. The Difference cell shows how many more CDs Silva has.

17

○○○○○○○ ○○○○○○○○○
| | | | | | | |
○○○○○○○○

8 matched   9 more unmatched

Quantity
Silva 17 CDs

Quantity	Difference
Mark 8 CDs	9

Whenever a comparison diagram is provided, children should always write the known and missing information on the diagram. Some children may also find it helpful to write words or short phrases on the diagram, as a reminder of what the numbers mean. For the Math Message problem, the names of the children might be written as reminders.

If children have difficulty writing a number model, have them think of 17, 8, and 9 as the numbers on a Fact Triangle. Ask them what addition and subtraction statements they can make using the three numbers.

Quantity
30 Joey

Quantity	Difference
10 Max	?

Quantity
47 radio

Quantity	Difference
20 watch	?

Ask children to write a number model for this problem. Any one of the number models $8 + 9 = 17$, $9 + 8 = 17$, $17 - 8 = 9$, or $17 - 9 = 8$ summarizes the problem. The choice of a number model depends on how a child thinks about the problem.

Beneath the filled-in comparison diagram, list the four number models named above. Add a title: "Four possible number models."

◆ Solving Comparison Number Stories

WHOLE-CLASS DISCUSSION

Display a comparison diagram. Work with the children to solve several comparison stories.

Example 1

Joey scored 30 points. Max scored 10 points. How many more points did Joey score than Max? 20 points

Fill in the comparison diagram as shown in the margin. Write ? for the difference, which is the number to be found.

Invite children to share mental-arithmetic strategies for finding the difference between 30 and 10. *For example:*

▷ Count on from 10 to 30.

▷ Think, "What must I add to 10 to get 30?"

▷ Think of the comparison diagram as a Fact Triangle. Think, "30 − 10 is the difference I want."

Write the difference in the Difference cell. 20 Ask volunteers to come to the board and write a number model that summarizes the problem.

▷ A child who counted on from 10 to 30 might write $10 + 20 = 30$.

▷ A child who found the difference by subtracting would likely write $30 - 10 = 20$, or perhaps $30 - 20 = 10$.

Example 2

A radio costs $47. A watch costs $20. How much more does the radio cost? $27

This problem is similar to the previous example. Fill in the comparison diagram as shown in the margin. Once children find the difference 27, write 27 in the Difference space. Then have children write a number model for the story. Sample answers: $27 + 20 = 47$, $20 + 27 = 47$, $47 - 20 = 27$, or $47 - 27 = 20$

Example 3

A radio costs $47. A calculator costs $12 less than the radio. How much does the calculator cost? $35

Fill in the diagram as shown in the margin. This example differs from the previous ones—this time, the smaller quantity is not known, but the difference is known. Make sure that children understand this. The strategies for solving this problem are the same as before, except that counting up is replaced by counting back *(start at 47, count back 12)*. Once children find the calculator cost 35, write 35 in the short Quantity cell. Then have children write a number model for the story. Sample answers: $47 - 12 = 35$, $12 + 35 = 47$, or $47 - 35 = 12$, $35 + 12 = 47$

Quantity
47 radio

Quantity	Difference
? calculator	12

✦ Solving Comparison Number Stories
(*Math Journal 1*, pp. 136 and 137)

PARTNER ACTIVITY 👥

Partners complete the problems on the journal pages. Check that children are recording the known information in the comparison diagram and that they're writing ? to represent the unknown number. For most problems, the difference will be the unknown number. For some problems, however, the difference will be known and one of the two quantities will be unknown.

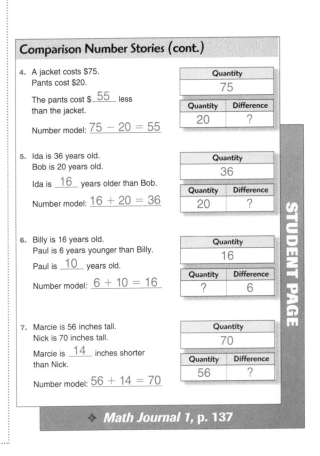

Comparison Number Stories

For each number story:
- Write the numbers you know in the comparison diagram.
- Write ? for the number you want to find.
- Solve the problem.
- Write a number model. Number models vary.

1. Barb scored 27 points.
   Cindy scored 10 points.

   Barb scored __17__ more points than Cindy.

   Number model: $27 - 10 = 17$

Quantity
27

Quantity	Difference
10	?

2. Jack scored 13 points.
   Jack scored 6 more points than Eli.

   Eli scored __7__ points.

   Number model: $7 + 6 = 13$

Quantity
13

Quantity	Difference
?	6

3. Frisky lives on the 16th floor.
   Fido lives on the 7th floor.

   Frisky lives __9__ floors higher than Fido.

   Number model: $16 - 9 = 7$

Quantity
16

Quantity	Difference
7	?

✦ *Math Journal 1*, p. 136

Comparison Number Stories (cont.)

4. A jacket costs $75.
   Pants cost $20.

   The pants cost $__55__ less than the jacket.

   Number model: $75 - 20 = 55$

Quantity
75

Quantity	Difference
20	?

5. Ida is 36 years old.
   Bob is 20 years old.

   Ida is __16__ years older than Bob.

   Number model: $16 + 20 = 36$

Quantity
36

Quantity	Difference
20	?

6. Billy is 16 years old.
   Paul is 6 years younger than Billy.

   Paul is __10__ years old.

   Number model: $6 + 10 = 16$

Quantity
16

Quantity	Difference
?	6

7. Marcie is 56 inches tall.
   Nick is 70 inches tall.

   Marcie is __14__ inches shorter than Nick.

   Number model: $56 + 14 = 70$

Quantity
70

Quantity	Difference
56	?

✦ *Math Journal 1*, p. 137

STUDENT PAGE

Children may use number lines, number grids, or any other learning tool except calculators. It is fine for children to draw pictures and doodles.

2 Ongoing Learning & Practice

◆ Playing *Addition Top-It*

PARTNER ACTIVITY

Addition Top-It was introduced in Lesson 1.4 to practice facts and compare sums. A domino version was played in Lesson 2.5.

Children now play a more advanced version with the numbers 0 through 20 by using all of the cards in the Everything Math Deck and by drawing 3 or 4 cards at each turn to practice addition with 3 or 4 addends.

> NOTE: Some children may prefer to play *Three Addends* from Lesson 6.1 again. *Math Masters*, page 101 is available for children to record their numbers and number models.

ONGOING ASSESSMENT
On a sheet of paper, ask children to record a number model showing the order in which they added the cards. Ask children to also write the sum of their partner's cards and to write $<$, $>$, or $=$ to compare the sums.

Collect papers and assess children's progress on:

· adding 1- and 2-digit numbers

· comparing numbers.

◆ Math Boxes 6.2 (*Math Journal 1*, p. 138)

INDEPENDENT ACTIVITY

Mixed Review This journal page provides opportunities for cumulative review or assessment of concepts and skills.

Math Boxes 6.2

1. Use $<$, $>$, or $=$.

   Unit

   $7 + 5 + 30 \;\underline{>}\; 40$

   $11 + 6 + 4 \;\underline{<}\; 26$

   $32 \;\underline{>}\; 18 + 7 + 2$

   $19 \;\underline{<}\; 13 + 9 + 1$

2. Write three names for 15.

   $\underline{12} + \underline{1} + \underline{2} = 15$

   $15 = \underline{8} + \underline{4} + \underline{3}$

   $\underline{5} + 9 + \underline{1} = 15$

   Sample answers are given.

3. Make a ballpark estimate. Write a number model for your estimate.

   $49 + 51$

   $\underline{50} + \underline{50} = \underline{100}$

4. Use your calculator. Enter 49. Change to 99.

   What did you do? $\underline{+50}$

   Enter 15. Change to 85.

   What did you do? $\underline{+70}$

5. Tim harvested 12 bushels of corn and 19 bushels of tomatoes. How many bushels in all? $\underline{31}$ bushels

   Fill in the diagram and write a number model.

Total	
?	
Part	**Part**
12	19

   $12 + 19 = 31$

6. Draw a line segment 8 cm long.

   _____

   Draw a line segment 3 cm shorter than the one you just drew.

   _____

◆ *Math Journal 1*, p. 138

Home Connection Children solve comparison number stories. They fill in a comparison diagram and write a number model for each problem. The explanation in the Family Note will help parents and guardians feel comfortable when participating in these activities with their children.

Children also practice addition by using the partial-sums method.

3 Options for Individualizing

◆ RETEACHING Playing *Penny Grab*

PARTNER ACTIVITY   5–15 min

Some children may benefit from comparing small numbers of counters before they solve comparison number stories. *Penny Grab* is played as follows:

1. Place a pile of pennies or other counters on a table between two children.

2. Each child grabs a handful of pennies, counts them, and records the amount.

3. Partners compare their amounts by lining up the pennies side by side and finding the difference.

4. Partners work together to record number models that describe the lined-up pennies. For example, 9 − 6 = 3.

Encourage such remarks as, "I have 3 more than you. You have 3 less than I do."

The difference between 9 and 6 is 3.

Comparison Number Stories

Home Link 6.2

Family Note Today your child learned about a device that is useful when solving number stories. We call it a "comparison diagram." Diagrams like these can help your child organize the information in a problem. When the information is organized, it is easier to decide which operation (+, −, ×, or ÷) to use to solve the problem. Comparison diagrams are used to represent problems in which two quantities are given, and the question is how much more or less one quantity is than the other (the difference).

Example 1: There are 49 fourth graders and 38 third graders. How many more fourth graders are there than third graders?

Note that the number of fourth graders is being compared with the number of third graders.

· *Answer:* There are 11 more fourth graders than third graders.

· *Possible number models:* Children who think of the problem in terms of subtraction will write 49 − 38 = 11. Other children may think of the problem in terms of addition: "Which number added to 38 will give me 49?" They will write the number model as 38 + 11 = 49.

Quantity
49 fourth graders

Quantity	Difference
38 third graders	?

Your child may write words in the diagram as a reminder of what the numbers mean.

Example 2: There are 53 second graders. There are 10 more second graders than first graders. How many first graders are there?

Note that sometimes the difference is known, and one of the two quantities is to be found.

· *Answer:* There are 43 first graders.

· *Possible number models:* 53 − 10 = 43 or 10 + 43 = 53

Quantity
53

Quantity	Difference
?	10

For Problems 1 and 2, ask your child to explain the number model that he or she wrote. Also ask your child to explain the steps needed to solve Problems 4–6.

Please return the **second page** of this Home Link to school tomorrow.

◆ Math Masters, p. 311

HOME LINK MASTER

Comparison Stories (cont.)

Home Link 6.2

In each number story:

- Write the numbers you know in the comparison diagram.
- Write ? for the number you want to find.
- Solve the problem. Then write a number model.

Sample number models are given.

1. Ross has $29 in his bank account. Omeida has $10.

Ross has $ _19_ more than Omeida.

Number model: 29 − 10 = 19

Quantity
29

Quantity	Difference
10	?

2. Omar swam 35 laps in the pool. Anthony swam 20 laps.

Anthony swam _15_ fewer laps than Omar.

Number model: 20 + 15 = 35

Quantity
35

Quantity	Difference
20	?

3. Claudia's birthday is June 10. Tisha's birthday is 12 days later.

Tisha's birthday is June _22_.

Number model: 10 + 12 = 22

Quantity
?

Quantity	Difference
10	12

Add. Use the partial-sums method.

4. 39   90
   + 62   + 11
   ─────   ─────
    101   101

5. 48   40
   + 7   + 15
   ─────   ─────
    55   55

6. 33   80
   + 54   + 7
   ─────   ─────
    87   87

◆ Math Masters, p. 312

HOME LINK MASTER

6.3 Data Day: The Four Food Groups

OBJECTIVE To collect, sort, tally, and graph data.

summaries	materials

1 Teaching the Lesson

Children are introduced to the basic food groups and the Food Guide Pyramid. Then they make a data-table tally of favorite class foods, analyze the data table, and make a bar graph of the favorite-food data. [Data and Chance]

- ☐ *Math Journal 1*, p. 139
- ☐ Home Link 6.2
- ☐ Teaching Master (*Math Masters*, p. 104)
- ☐ Teaching Master transparencies (*Math Masters*, pp. 104, 105, and 106; optional)

See Advance Preparation

2 Ongoing Learning & Practice

Children solve comparison number stories about lengths of fish on the Fish Poster. [Operations and Computation]

Children practice and maintain skills through Math Boxes and Home Link activities.

- ☐ *Math Journal 1*, p. 80, optional; and pp. 140–142
- ☐ Home Link Master (*Math Masters*, p. 313)

3 Options for Individualizing

Enrichment Children classify pictures of food by making a food-groups collage. [Data and Chance]

Enrichment Children survey adults about favorite foods, make a bar graph of the results, and compare data collected from children to data collected from adults. [Data and Chance]

- ☐ Teaching Master (*Math Masters*, p. 107)
- ☐ magazines, newspapers, and grocery-store sale flyers

See Advance Preparation

Additional Information

Advance Preparation For the teaching activities in Part 1, you may want to make overhead transparencies for *Math Masters*, pages 104–106.

For the first optional Enrichment activity in Part 3, collect magazines, newspapers, and, especially, grocery-store sale flyers for children to cut apart.

Vocabulary • **basic food groups** • **Food Guide Pyramid** • **data table** • **bar graph**

Getting Started

Mental Math and Reflexes

Pose comparison number stories like the following:

- It takes Maurice about 15 minutes to get to school in the morning. It takes Eva about 8 minutes. About how much longer does it take Maurice to get to school? About 7 minutes longer
- Josh read 25 pages. Steven read 15 pages. How many fewer pages did Steven read than Josh? 10 fewer pages
- Joe collected 54 cans. Rosi collected 30. How many more cans did Joe collect than Rosi? 24 cans

Math Message
What is your favorite food?
(Candy and soda don't count!)

Home Link 6.2 Follow-Up
Review answers as necessary. As time permits, have children share the strategies they used to do the computation.

1 Teaching the Lesson

◆ Math Message Follow-Up
(Math Masters, p. 104)

WHOLE-CLASS DISCUSSION

Before talking about favorite foods, talk with children about good nutrition.

People need to eat balanced diets in order to stay healthy. There are 4 **basic food groups:**

1. bread, cereal, rice, and pasta—the Grain Group

2. fruit and vegetables—the Fruit/Vegetables Group

3. dairy products (milk, yogurt, and cheese)—the Milk Group

4. meat, poultry, fish, beans, eggs, and nuts—the Meat Group

The **Food Guide Pyramid** (*Math Masters*, page 104) shows the recommended number of servings per day from each of the 4 basic food groups. Explain to children that the Food Guide Pyramid shows *six* food groups because the U.S. Department of Agriculture put fruit and vegetables into separate groups and added another group for fats, oils, and sweets.

On the Food Guide Pyramid, the foods that a person should eat the most of—bread, cereal, rice, pasta, fruit, and vegetables—are near the bottom. Foods that a person should eat less of—dairy products, meat, poultry, fish, beans, eggs, and nuts—are near the top. Things to be eaten sparingly—fats, oils, and sweets—are at the top.

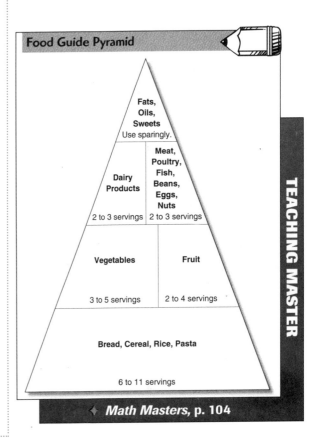

TEACHING MASTER

Math Masters, p. 104

NOTE: Some teachers have reported that assigning a favorite food to a single group can be confusing and time-consuming. For example, are pepperoni pizzas and beef enchiladas in the bread, dairy, or meat groups? Other teachers have said that this activity has not been problematic and that children have come to a consensus about the primary ingredient in a food item and then assigned that favorite food to a food group based on that criterion.

If you foresee having problems in your classroom, consider the following option: Display an overhead transparency of *Math Masters,* page 105. This master lists foods that belong in each of the four food groups. (See the facing page.) Based on the examples of foods that belong in each of the groups, ask children to pick the "group" that they like best. The foods listed as belonging in that group may not be their favorite foods, but they do represent types of foods that children like.

There is room on *Math Masters,* page 105 to tailor the list to include special foods that may be popular in your region or with children in your school.

◆ Collecting Data on Favorite Foods
(*Math Journal 1,* p. 139; *Math Masters,* pp. 104 and 106)

WHOLE-CLASS ACTIVITY

On the board, draw a table like the one shown in Problem 1 on the journal page or use an overhead transparency of *Math Masters,* page 106. Ask each child to name his or her favorite food. As a class, assign each food named to the most appropriate food group. Make a tally mark in the table on the board as children do the same on the journal page.

Use the Food Guide Pyramid on *Math Masters,* page 104 as a reference. (You may choose to use an overhead transparency of this page during your discussion.) For the more problematic foods, you can make suggestions or act as the final authority. Continue until each child has named a favorite food and each food named has been assigned to one of the 4 food groups.

◆ Discussing the Favorite-Food Data Table
(*Math Journal 1,* p. 139)

WHOLE-CLASS DISCUSSION

Discuss the resulting **data table** with children. Ask:

* Which is the most popular food group among children in the class?

* Which is the least popular?

* Why do you think children prefer one food group to another?

* Do you think children in other parts of the world would have similar results on their data tables?

* Do you think adults prefer the same foods as children?

Adjusting the Activity If there are other second grade classrooms in your school, share data-table results and make comparisons between the classrooms. For example: *Which is the most popular food group in Mr. Mazzuca's classroom? Is it the same food group as in our classroom? Do you think all children have similar tastes in food?*

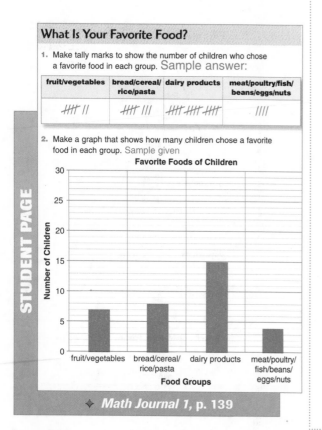

✦ Making a Bar Graph of the Favorite-Food Data

(*Math Journal 1*, p. 139; *Math Masters*, p. 106)

WHOLE-CLASS ACTIVITY

Display an overhead transparency of *Math Masters*, page 106 as children follow along in their journals. Remind children how a **bar graph** is drawn using vertical or horizontal bars to represent data. Ask questions such as the following about the bar graph in their journals:

- What do the labels at the bottom of the graph refer to? The 4 food groups What do the numbers on the left side of the graph refer to? The number of children

- Suppose 15 children had chosen a dairy product as their favorite food. How would you show this on the graph? Color the "dairy products" column up to the line for 15.

- How would you show on the graph that 7 children had chosen a fruit or vegetable as their favorite food? Color the "fruit/vegetables" column up to the line for 7.

Show children how to graph the data for the fruit/vegetables group on the overhead transparency of *Math Masters*, page 106. Children can use crayons or coloring pencils to color the bars of the graphs in their journals.

Adjusting the Activity Some children may find it helpful to lay a straightedge or piece of paper across the vertical axis to help them determine how far up they should color each bar. This will be especially helpful for the bars that are farthest from the numbers.

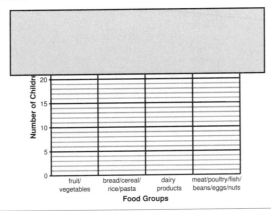

Partners should work together to complete the bar graph. Children who used *Everyday Mathematics* in first grade should be familiar with bar graphs. However, if children have difficulty, complete the graph as a whole-class activity.

fruit/ vegetables	bread/cereal/ rice/pasta	dairy products	meat/poultry/ fish/ beans/ eggs/nuts
watermelon	pancakes	ice cream	hamburgers
bananas	fried rice	Swiss cheese	omelets
grapes	French toast	yogurt	almonds
pears	cornflakes	chocolate milk	peanut butter
apples	muffins	cream cheese	chicken
broccoli	crackers	milk shakes	fish
corn	spaghetti	frozen yogurt	pork chops
potatoes	bagels		black beans
carrots	English muffins		refried beans
squash	waffles		scrambled eggs
raisins			turkey
strawberries			bacon

✦ *Math Masters*, p. 105

TEACHING MASTER

What Is Your Favorite Food?

1. Make tally marks to show the number of children who chose a favorite food in each group. Answers vary.

fruit/ vegetables	bread/cereal/ rice/pasta	dairy products	meat/poultry/ fish/beans/ eggs/nuts

2. Make a graph that shows how many children chose a favorite food in each group.

Favorite Foods of Children

✦ *Math Masters*, p. 106

TEACHING MASTER

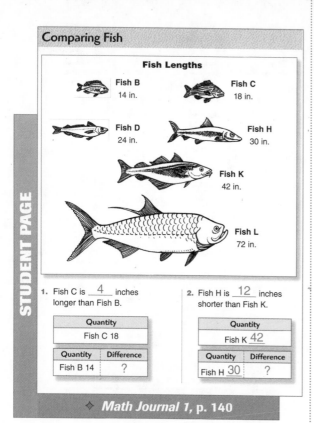

Comparing Fish

Fish Lengths

Fish B — 14 in.
Fish C — 18 in.
Fish D — 24 in.
Fish H — 30 in.
Fish K — 42 in.
Fish L — 72 in.

1. Fish C is __4__ inches longer than Fish B.

Quantity
Fish C 18

Quantity	Difference
Fish B 14	?

2. Fish H is __12__ inches shorter than Fish K.

Quantity
Fish K 42

Quantity	Difference
Fish H 30	?

Math Journal 1, p. 140

2 Ongoing Learning & Practice

◆ Comparing Lengths of Fish on the Fish Poster
(*Math Journal 1*, pp. 140 and 141)

INDEPENDENT ACTIVITY

If necessary, guide children through Problem 1.

Adjusting the Activity To extend the activity, refer children to the Fish Poster on journal page 80. Use the complete set of data to challenge children to make *difference comparisons* (Fish I is 6 inches shorter than Fish J.) or to make *ratio comparisons* (Fish D is twice as long as Fish A.)

◆ Math Boxes 6.3 (*Math Journal 1*, p. 142)

INDEPENDENT ACTIVITY

Mixed Review This journal page provides opportunities for cumulative review or assessment of concepts and skills.

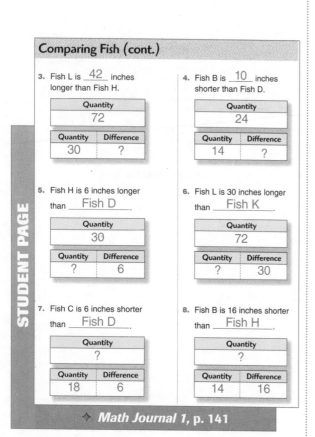

Comparing Fish (cont.)

3. Fish L is __42__ inches longer than Fish H.

Quantity
72

Quantity	Difference
30	?

4. Fish B is __10__ inches shorter than Fish D.

Quantity
24

Quantity	Difference
14	?

5. Fish H is 6 inches longer than __Fish D__.

Quantity
30

Quantity	Difference
?	6

6. Fish L is 30 inches longer than __Fish K__.

Quantity
72

Quantity	Difference
?	30

7. Fish C is 6 inches shorter than __Fish D__.

Quantity
?

Quantity	Difference
18	6

8. Fish B is 16 inches shorter than __Fish H__.

Quantity
?

Quantity	Difference
14	16

Math Journal 1, p. 141

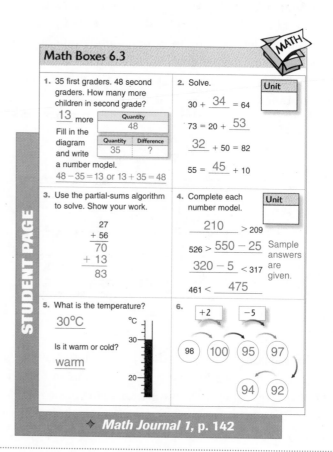

Math Boxes 6.3

1. 35 first graders. 48 second graders. How many more children in second grade?

__13__ more

Fill in the diagram and write a number model.

Quantity
48

Quantity	Difference
35	?

$48 - 35 = 13$ or $13 + 35 = 48$

2. Solve.   Unit

$30 + \underline{34} = 64$

$73 = 20 + \underline{53}$

$\underline{32} + 50 = 82$

$55 = \underline{45} + 10$

3. Use the partial-sums algorithm to solve. Show your work.

```
   27
 + 56
 ----
   70
 + 13
 ----
   83
```

4. Complete each number model.   Unit

$\underline{210} > 209$

$526 > \underline{550 - 25}$

$\underline{320 - 5} < 317$

$461 < \underline{475}$

Sample answers are given.

5. What is the temperature?

__30°C__

Is it warm or cold?

__warm__

°C
30
20

6.

$+2$ -5

98   100   95   97

94   92

Math Journal 1, p. 142

◆ **Home Link 6.3** (*Math Masters,* p. 313)

Home Connection Children use survey data about favorite fruit to make a bar graph. They then use the information to draw conclusions about fruit preferences.

3 Options for Individualizing

◆ **ENRICHMENT** Categorizing Foods

INDEPENDENT ACTIVITY   **30+ min**

Science Link Children look through magazines and newspapers (especially grocery-store sale flyers) to find pictures of food. They cut out the pictures and arrange these to form collages showing the basic food groups.

Label each collage, and display all collages in the classroom. You might wish to create a collage in the shape of the Food Guide Pyramid. If you decide to do this, children will need to find relatively more pictures to illustrate the bread, cereal, rice, and pasta group and relatively fewer pictures of fats, oils, and sweets.

◆ **ENRICHMENT** Favorite-Food Data
(*Math Masters,* p. 107)

INDEPENDENT ACTIVITY   **30+ min**

Children survey adults around school or at home, asking adults to name their favorite food.

Children tally their data as they collect it, using the table at the top of *Math Masters,* page 107. They use their tallied data to make a bar graph, make comparisons between the adult data and the class data collected in this lesson, and report their findings to the class.

Graphing Data
Home Link 6.3

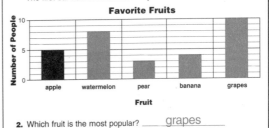

Family Note

The class has been collecting and graphing data about favorite foods. Ask your child about the graph he or she made in class. In the table below, help your child count the tally marks below the name of each fruit. To decide how high up to color each bar, your child could lay a straightedge across the columns.

Please return this Home Link to school tomorrow.

In a survey, people were asked to name their favorite fruit. The table below shows the results.

apple	watermelon	pear	banana	grapes
⅄⅄⅄	⅄⅄⅄ ///	///	////	⅄⅄⅄ ⅄⅄⅄

1. Make a bar graph that shows how many people chose each fruit. The first bar has been colored for you.

Favorite Fruits

2. Which fruit is the most popular? ___grapes___

   Which fruit is the least popular? ___pear___

   What is your favorite kind of fruit? ___Answers vary.___

◆ *Math Masters,* p. 313

Adults: What's Your Favorite Food?

1. Make tally marks to show the number of adults who chose a favorite food in each group. Answers vary.

fruit/ vegetables	bread/cereal/ rice/pasta	dairy products	meat/poultry/ fish/beans/ eggs/nuts

2. Make a graph that shows how many adults chose a favorite food in each group.

Favorite Foods of Adults

◆ *Math Masters,* p. 107

6.4 Mixed Addition and Subtraction Stories

OBJECTIVE To select and complete an appropriate diagram to help solve an addition or subtraction problem.

---

summaries | materials

1 Teaching the Lesson

Children categorize number stories as change, parts-and-total, or comparison problems; fill in an appropriate diagram to record known and missing information; and write number models to summarize their solutions. [Operations and Computation; Patterns, Functions, and Algebra]

- ☐ *Math Journal 1,* p. 143
- ☐ Home Link 6.3
- ☐ Teaching Master (*Math Masters,* p. 108): 2 copies per child
- ☐ Teaching Master transparency (*Math Masters,* p. 108; optional)
- ☐ slate

***See* Advance Preparation**

2 Ongoing Learning & Practice

Children practice estimation and the partial-sums algorithm. [Operations and Computation]

Children practice and maintain skills through Math Boxes and Home Link activities.

- ☐ *Math Journal 1,* pp. 134 and 144
- ☐ Home Link Masters (*Math Masters,* pp. 314 and 315)

3 Options for Individualizing

Enrichment Children make up, illustrate, and solve addition and subtraction number stories. [Operations and Computation]

Extra Practice Children make up addition number stories. [Operations and Computation]

- ☐ Teaching Master (*Math Masters,* p. 109)
- ☐ *Minute Math®,* p. 16

Additional Information

Advance Preparation For the second activity in Part 1, you may want to make an overhead transparency of *Math Masters,* page 108.

Getting Started

Mental Math and Reflexes

Write multiple-addend problems on the board. Encourage children to look for combinations that will make the addition easier.

? = 43 + 5 + 7 55

6 + 8 + 9 = ? 23; no particularly easy way to add these numbers

? = 1 + 15 + 29 + 5 50

Math Message

Make a list of some of the things you like to collect.

Home Link 6.3 Follow-Up

Ask comparison questions, such as the following, about the survey data:

- How many more people like watermelon than like grapes?

Ask parts-and-total questions, such as the following:

- What is the total number of people who like apples and pears?

1 Teaching the Lesson

◆ Math Message Follow-Up
(*Math Journal 1*, p. 143)

INDEPENDENT ACTIVITY

Ask children to describe some of the things they like to collect. Record their responses on the board. Sample answers: coins, shells, sports cards, dolls, stuffed animals

Have each child select 2 items to use as topics for number stories on the journal page. Different children may select different things.

Problems 3 and 4 on the journal page have answer blanks within their number stories. Ask children to select one item for each problem and to write that item in all of the empty boxes. *For example:*

Suppose "coins" is one of the selected items. Problem 3 would be completed as follows:

Colin has 20 <u>coins</u>. Fiona has 30 <u>coins</u>. How many <u>coins</u> do they have in all?

◆ Selecting Diagrams and Solving Number Stories
(*Math Journal 1*, p. 143; *Math Masters*, p. 108)

INDEPENDENT ACTIVITY

Until now, lessons have focused on one type of number story at a time. For example, the problems in Lesson 6.2 were all based on comparison stories, and the comparison diagram was the only diagram used. In this lesson, children are asked to categorize addition and subtraction stories: They must decide which type of story (change, parts-and-total, or comparison) best matches the problem at hand and then use the appropriate diagram to find a solution.

The journal page contains 4 number stories, and the master has 2 sets of diagrams. Each set includes a change diagram, a parts-and-total diagram, and a comparison diagram.

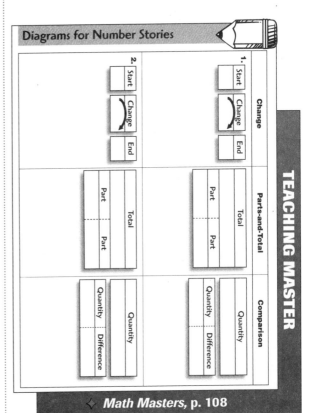

Adjusting the Activity If children are having difficulty choosing a diagram, ask them first to explain how they view the problem. Then direct them toward the diagram that best matches their way of thinking. Alternatively, pick a diagram and ask children if they are able to explain how to solve the problem at hand by using the parts of that diagram.

Start	Change	End
17	?	26

Change diagram

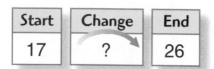

Quantity	
26	

Quantity	Difference
17	?

Comparison diagram

Total	
26	

Part	Part
17	?

Parts-and-total diagram

For each number story, children do the following:

1. Choose one diagram they think is appropriate.
2. Fill in the diagram by writing known numbers in the appropriate places and by writing ? to represent the unknown number.
3. Calculate the sum or difference and solve the problem.
4. Write a number model to summarize the problem.

Solve Problems 1 and 2 with the class. Display an overhead transparency of *Math Masters,* page 108, or draw the three kinds of diagrams on the board. Ask a volunteer to select one of the diagrams, explain his or her choice, and model the solution at the board. When the problem has been solved in one way, ask if anyone selected one of the other diagrams and solved it in a different way.

Do not force any number story into a particular mold or say that there is a "best" diagram for the problem. As the following examples show, there may be several ways to view a problem—and to select a diagram:

Example 1: Problem 1 viewed as a change problem

Think: Last year there were 17 slides (the Start number). New slides were added (the Change number). Now, this year, there are 26 slides (the End number). I want to find the Change number.

Example 2: Problem 1 viewed as a comparison problem

Think: I'm comparing the number of slides this year (the larger Quantity, 26) to the number of slides last year (the smaller Quantity, 17). I want to find how many more slides there are this year (the Difference).

Example 3: Problem 1 viewed as a parts-and-total problem

Think: I know there are 26 slides in all (the Total). 17 of them (the first Part) were there last year, and some new slides (the second Part) were added this year. I want to find the second Part.

 Adjusting the Activity If the numbers used on the journal page are too difficult or too easy for some children, change the numbers so that the problems are tailored to the ability levels of individual children.

Summary: The purpose of diagrams is to help children organize the information in a number story, identify the missing information, and determine whether to add or subtract to solve the problem. Children should be encouraged to select the diagram that best matches the way they "see" the problem. There is no right or wrong diagram for any given problem; what matters is that the chosen diagram matches the child's thinking and is used as a tool for finding the correct answer.

ONGOING ASSESSMENT
Circulate as children work and ask them to explain why they chose a particular diagram for each problem. When children have completed their work, collect *Math Masters,* page 108. The diagrams that children selected will give you insight into their thought processes.

2 Ongoing Learning & Practice

◆ Reviewing Estimation and the Partial-Sums Algorithm (*Math Journal 1,* p. 134)

INDEPENDENT ACTIVITY

Children complete this journal page by calculating the remaining sums—the sums less than 50 (Problems 1 and 4). If some children did not have time to work on this page during Lesson 6.1, they should do the whole page now.

◆ Math Boxes 6.4 (*Math Journal 1,* p. 144)

INDEPENDENT ACTIVITY

Mixed Review This journal page provides opportunities for cumulative review or assessment of concepts and skills.

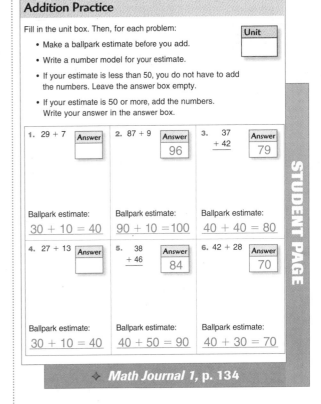

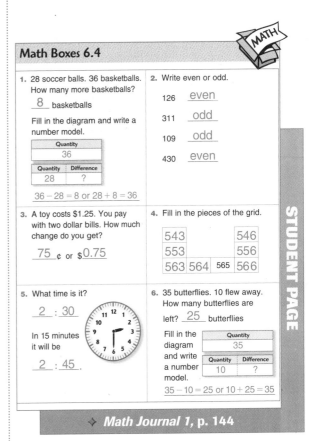

Family Note

In today's lesson, your child used diagrams to solve number stories. Listen to your child's stories. Ask your child to explain how each story relates to both the diagram and the number model. (See Home Link 5.10: Unit 6 Family Letter for information about number stories and diagrams.)

Please return this Home Link to school tomorrow.

Write number stories to match each diagram. Then finish the number model. Tell your stories to someone at home.

1.

Unit
building blocks

Start	Change	End
24	+6	?

Answers vary.

Finish the number model: 24 + 6 = __30__

2.

Unit
books

Total	
?	
Part	Part
15	13

Answers vary.

Finish the number model: 15 + 13 = __28__

HOME LINK MASTER

Home Connection Children make up number stories to match diagrams. Then they solve their number stories and complete a number model.

 Options for Individualizing

◆ **ENRICHMENT** Number Stories
(*Math Masters*, p. 109)

INDEPENDENT ACTIVITY   5–15 min

 Language Arts Link Children write addition and subtraction number stories, draw pictures to illustrate them, and find the solutions.

Portfolio Ideas

◆ **EXTRA PRACTICE** Minute Math

SMALL-GROUP ACTIVITY   5–15 min

To offer children more experience with making up number stories, see the following page in *Minute Math*:

Basic Routines: p. 16

3.

Unit
bananas

Quantity
28

Quantity	Difference
8	?

Answers vary.

Finish the number model: 28 − 8 = __20__

4.

Unit
baseball cards

Total	
50	
Part	Part
?	37

Answers vary.

Write a number model for your story.

Number model: __50 − 37 = 13 or 13 + 37 = 50__

HOME LINK MASTER

A Number Story

Answer to my number story: _____

Number model: _____

TEACHING MASTER

6.5 Modeling Subtraction with Base-10 Blocks

OBJECTIVE To use base-10 blocks to model subtraction of 2-digit numbers.

summaries	materials
1 Teaching the Lesson	
Children represent 1- and 2-digit numbers with base-10 blocks and use the blocks to model and solve subtraction problems that do and do not require trades. [Numeration; Operations and Computation]	☐ *Math Journal 1*, pp. 145 and 146 ☐ Home Link 6.4 ☐ base-10 blocks per partnership: 6 longs and 30 cubes ☐ overhead base-10 blocks (optional): 6 longs and 18 cubes
2 Ongoing Learning & Practice	
Children identify missing numbers in addition and subtraction diagrams. [Operations and Computation] Children practice and maintain skills through Math Boxes and Home Link activities.	☐ *Math Journal 1*, pp. 147 and 148 ☐ Home Link Masters (*Math Masters*, pp. 316 and 317)
3 Options for Individualizing	
Reteaching Children build and rename numbers with base-10 blocks. [Numeration] **Reteaching** Children model subtraction with dimes and pennies. [Operations and Computation]	☐ *Math Journal 1*, pp. 51 and 61 ☐ Teaching Masters (*Math Masters*, pp. 35, 41, and 42) ☐ base-10 blocks per partnership: 9 longs and 30 cubes ☐ number cards 0–9 (from the Everything Math Deck, if available) ☐ 6 dimes and 18 pennies ☐ 30 pennies per partnership

Additional Information
Advance Preparation Plan to spend two days on this lesson.

Vocabulary • **trade (a base-10 long for 10 cubes)** • **variable**

Vocabulary (teacher) • **minuend** • **subtrahend**

Getting Started

Mental Math and Reflexes
Pose subtraction problems that feature multiples of 10. *Suggestions:*

$48 - 10 = 38$	$28 = 48 - 20$	$48 - 30 = 18$	$63 - 20 = 43$	$33 = 73 - 40$
$72 - 10 = 62$	$52 = 72 - 20$	$72 - 50 = 22$	$95 - 60 = 35$	$15 = 95 - 80$

Math Message

Select a partner. Together, take 4 longs and 30 cubes. Show 25 two different ways using longs and cubes.

Home Link 6.4 Follow-Up

Invite several children to share their stories with the class. Collect children's stories to use when you need a quick "sponge" or filler activity or for use during future Mental Math and Reflexes sessions.

Teaching the Lesson

✦ Math Message Follow-Up

WHOLE-CLASS ACTIVITY

Ask children to represent 2-digit numbers with base-10 blocks. Vary the instructions for each number. *For example:*

- Show 25 using the smallest number of base-10 blocks. 2 longs and 5 cubes Now show 25 using only one long. 1 long and 15 cubes Now show 25 using all cubes. 25 cubes

Give similar instructions for 11, 23, and 30. Have children show additional numbers if they need more practice.

Ask children why it is easier to show numbers with both longs and cubes, instead of with only cubes. Sample answer: For larger numbers, there are too many ones to count out carefully. Each long shows 10 connected cubes, and it's easier to show and name a number using the greatest number of longs possible.

DAY 1

✦ Using Base-10 Blocks to Model Subtraction That Does Not Require Trades

WHOLE-CLASS ACTIVITY

Write the following problems on the board:

$$
\begin{array}{cccc}
18 & 45 & 36 & 57 \\
-\ 6 & -22 & -14 & -31 \\
\end{array}
$$

Ask partners to represent the top number (the **minuend**) with the fewest blocks possible. Then ask them to subtract the bottom number (the **subtrahend**) by removing the correct number of blocks.

Invite children to demonstrate and explain what they did. Have the class gather around a table as children demonstrate with actual blocks. You might want to use base-10 blocks for the overhead if you have them. Refer to the longs alternately as "longs" and as "10s"; refer to the cubes alternately as "cubes" and as "1s."

Example: Model 45 − 22 = ? as follows:

1. Count out four 10s and five 1s to represent 45. Lay these on the table, with longs to the left of the cubes.

2. Ask: *Are there enough longs and cubes on the table so that I can remove 22 (2 longs and 2 cubes)?* yes

3. Remove 22 (2 longs and 2 cubes) from the table.

4. Count the remaining blocks, and record the answer (the difference) on the board. 23

✦ Solving Subtraction Problems That Do Not Require Trades (*Math Journal 1*, p. 145)

PARTNER ACTIVITY

Partners work together to solve the subtraction problems. Each problem is written in vertical form, with the columns labeled as "longs/10s" and "cubes/1s."

Children are expected to continue using base-10 blocks to model these problems, when possible. With practice, however, many children should begin to visualize the operation of subtraction and to give the answer before actually removing any base-10 blocks.

NOTE: If children have a limited number of base-10 blocks, they may not be able to model problems that have large minuends. Solving these problems will force them to begin to visualize the operation of subtraction.

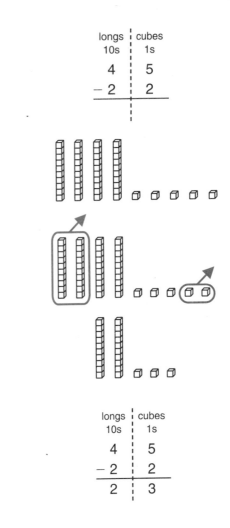

Subtraction with Base-10 Blocks

Use base-10 blocks to help you subtract.

	longs 10s	cubes 1s		longs 10s	cubes 1s		longs 10s	cubes 1s		longs 10s	cubes 1s
1.	1	9	2.	2	5	3.	4	4	4.	3	6
−		7	−	1	4	−	3	1	−	2	3
	1	2		1	1		1	3		1	3

	longs 10s	cubes 1s		longs 10s	cubes 1s		longs 10s	cubes 1s		longs 10s	cubes 1s
5.	2	9	6.	4	7	7.	3	8	8.	5	7
−	1	8	−	2	5	−	2	6	−	1	6
	1	1		2	2		1	2		4	1

	longs 10s	cubes 1s		longs 10s	cubes 1s		longs 10s	cubes 1s		longs 10s	cubes 1s
9.	6	8	10.	2	8	11.	2	8	12.	3	8
−	2	4	−	2	0	−		8	−	2	3
	4	4			8		2	0		1	5

Use mental math to solve these problems:

13. 76 − 46 = __30__   14. __27__ = 37 − 10

15. 20 + __34__ = 54   16. __67__ + 30 = 97

✦ *Math Journal 1*, p. 145

DAY 2

◆Using Base-10 Blocks to Model Subtraction That Requires Trades

PARTNER ACTIVITY

Write the problems shown below on the board, in vertical form:

$$
\begin{array}{r} 22 \\ -\ 7 \\ \hline \end{array}
\qquad
\begin{array}{r} 53 \\ -\ 35 \\ \hline \end{array}
\qquad
\begin{array}{r} 35 \\ -\ 9 \\ \hline \end{array}
\qquad
\begin{array}{r} 24 \\ -\ 16 \\ \hline \end{array}
$$

Ask partners to represent the top number (the minuend) with the fewest blocks possible. Then ask them to subtract the bottom number (the subtrahend) in any way they can.

Children cannot solve these problems by simply removing the appropriate number of blocks. Invite them to share their strategies. For example, to find 22 − 7, they might use one of the following strategies:

▷ Subtract 7 in two stages. First, remove 2 cubes, leaving 2 longs. Then cover up 5 cubes on one of the longs. That leaves one long (10 cubes), plus 5 cubes showing on the second long, for a total of 15.

▷ **Trade** one of the longs for 10 separate cubes so that 22 is represented by 1 long and 12 cubes. Then remove 7 cubes, leaving 1 long and 5 cubes, or 15.

Have the class gather around a table as children demonstrate with actual blocks. You might want to use base-10 blocks for the overhead if you have them. Refer to the longs alternately as "longs" and as "10s"; refer to the cubes alternately as "cubes" and as "1s."

Example: Model 53 − 35 = ? as follows:

1. Count out five 10s and three 1s to represent 53. Lay these on the table, with longs to the left of the cubes.

2. Ask: *Are there enough longs and cubes on the table so that I can remove exactly 35 (3 longs and 5 cubes)?* No. There are only 3 cubes on the table, so it's not possible to remove 5 cubes.

3. Trade a long for cubes: Remove one of the longs used to represent 53, and replace it with 10 cubes. 53 is now represented by 4 longs and 13 cubes.

4. Remove 35 (3 longs and 5 cubes) from the table.

5. Record the answer (the difference) on the board. 18

longs   cubes
10s   1s

$$
\begin{array}{c|c} 5 & 3 \\ -\ 3 & 5 \\ \hline \end{array}
$$

longs   cubes
10s   1s

$$
\begin{array}{c|c} 5 & 3 \\ -\ 3 & 5 \\ \hline 1 & 8 \end{array}
$$

✦ Solving Subtraction Problems That Require Trades (*Math Journal 1*, p. 146)

PARTNER ACTIVITY

Partners work together to solve the subtraction problems. Each problem is written in vertical form, with the columns labeled as "longs/10s" and "cubes/1s."

Children are expected to continue using base-10 blocks to model these problems, and many will actually trade 1 long for 10 cubes. Some children may trade by simply moving one of the longs next to the pile of cubes and will answer the problem without actually exchanging the long for cubes.

2 Ongoing Learning & Practice

✦ Solving Addition and Subtraction Diagram Problems (*Math Journal 1*, p. 147)

INDEPENDENT ACTIVITY

Each diagram on the journal page includes one missing number that is represented by a letter, or **variable.** Three possible values for the variable are given, and children are asked which value is correct for the diagram. Children can test these values by inserting them into the diagram until they find the one that works.

☑ ONGOING ASSESSMENT
Use the journal page to assess children's understanding of addition and subtraction diagrams.

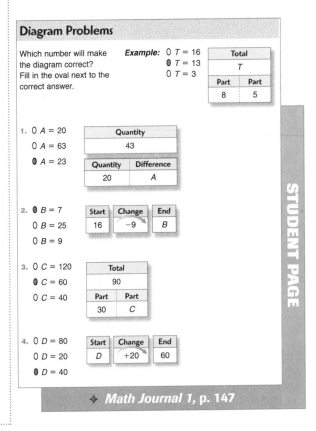

STUDENT PAGE

STUDENT PAGE

Math Boxes 6.5

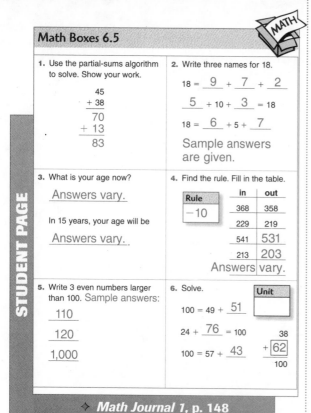

1. Use the partial-sums algorithm to solve. Show your work.

```
    45
  + 38
  ────
    70
  + 13
  ────
    83
```

2. Write three names for 18.

$18 = \underline{9} + \underline{7} + \underline{2}$

$\underline{5} + 10 + \underline{3} = 18$

$18 = \underline{6} + 5 + \underline{7}$

Sample answers are given.

3. What is your age now?

Answers vary.

In 15 years, your age will be

Answers vary.

4. Find the rule. Fill in the table.

Rule −10	in	out
	368	358
	229	219
	541	531
	213	203

Answers vary.

5. Write 3 even numbers larger than 100. Sample answers:

110

120

1,000

6. Solve.

Unit

$100 = 49 + \underline{51}$

$24 + \underline{76} = 100$

$100 = 57 + \underline{43}$

```
   38
 + 62
 ────
  100
```

Math Journal 1, p. 148

◆ Math Boxes 6.5 (*Math Journal 1*, p. 148)

INDEPENDENT ACTIVITY

Mixed Review This journal page provides opportunities for cumulative review or assessment of concepts and skills.

◆ Home Link 6.5 (*Math Masters,* pp. 316 and 317)

Home Connection Children subtract by "crossing out" cubes. Before sending this Home Link with the children, go over the example and make sure they understand that each long shows *10 connected cubes.*

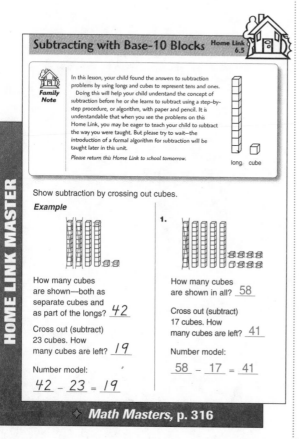

Subtracting with Base-10 Blocks — Home Link 6.5

Family Note

In this lesson, your child found the answers to subtraction problems by using longs and cubes to represent tens and ones.

Doing this will help your child understand the concept of subtraction before he or she learns to subtract using a step-by-step procedure, or algorithm, with paper and pencil. It is understandable that when you see the problems on this Home Link, you may be eager to teach your child to subtract the way you were taught. But please try to wait—the introduction of a formal algorithm for subtraction will be taught later in this unit.

Please return this Home Link to school tomorrow.

long   cube

Show subtraction by crossing out cubes.

Example

How many cubes are shown—both as separate cubes and as part of the longs? _42_

Cross out (subtract) 23 cubes. How many cubes are left? _19_

Number model:

_42_ – _23_ = _19_

1.

How many cubes are shown in all? _58_

Cross out (subtract) 17 cubes. How many cubes are left? _41_

Number model:

_58_ – _17_ = _41_

Math Masters, p. 316

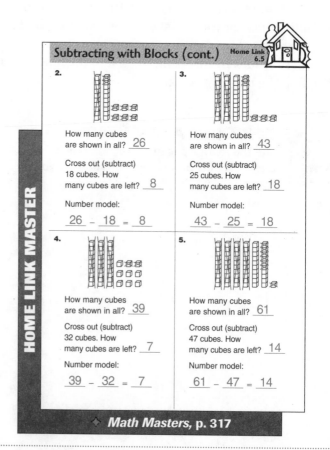

Subtracting with Blocks (cont.) — Home Link 6.5

2.

How many cubes are shown in all? _26_

Cross out (subtract) 18 cubes. How many cubes are left? _8_

Number model:

_26_ – _18_ = _8_

3.

How many cubes are shown in all? _43_

Cross out (subtract) 25 cubes. How many cubes are left? _18_

Number model:

_43_ – _25_ = _18_

4.

How many cubes are shown in all? _39_

Cross out (subtract) 32 cubes. How many cubes are left? _7_

Number model:

_39_ – _32_ = _7_

5.

How many cubes are shown in all? _61_

Cross out (subtract) 47 cubes. How many cubes are left? _14_

Number model:

_61_ – _47_ = _14_

Math Masters, p. 317

3 Options for Individualizing

◆ **RETEACHING** **Building and Renaming Numbers** (*Math Journal 1*, pp. 51 and 61; *Math Masters*, pp. 35, 41, and 42)

PARTNER ACTIVITY   **15–30 min**

Children who are having difficulty using base-10 blocks to model subtraction may benefit from reviewing Exploration A in Lesson 3.4.

◆ **RETEACHING** **Subtracting with Coins**

INDEPENDENT ACTIVITY

Choosing another manipulative may help children understand a concept. Some children may benefit from using coins rather than base-10 blocks to model subtraction.

Example: Model 53 − 35 as follows:

1. Count out 5 dimes and 3 pennies to represent 53. Ask: *Are there enough dimes and pennies to remove 35¢?* no

2. Trade 1 dime for 10 pennies. 53 is now represented by 4 dimes and 13 pennies.

3. Remove 3 dimes and 5 pennies. 1 dime and 8 pennies remain. That's 18¢.

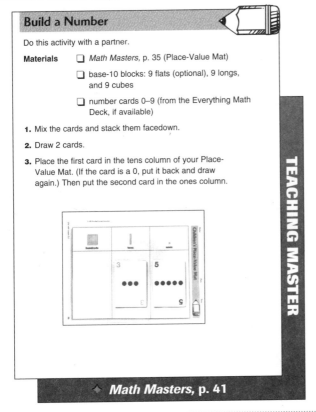

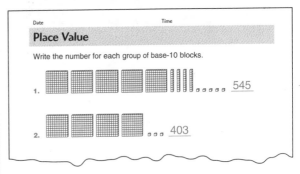

Place Value

Write the number for each group of base-10 blocks.

1. 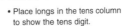 545

2. 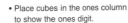 403

Math Journal 1, page 51

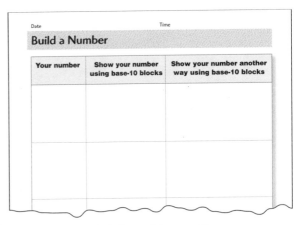

Build a Number

Your number	Show your number using base-10 blocks	Show your number another way using base-10 blocks

Math Journal 1, page 61

Build a Number (cont.)

4. Build the number.
   • Place longs in the tens column to show the tens digit.
   • Place cubes in the ones column to show the ones digit.

5. Record your work in the table on journal page 61. Draw pictures of the longs and cubes you used.

6. Use the Place-Value Mat and blocks to build the same number in a different way. Draw the longs and cubes you used.

7. Build 3 or 4 more numbers in the same way. Record your numbers and draw pictures to show the two ways you built each number.

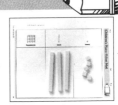

Challenge

Draw 3 cards instead of 2. Put 1 card in each column of the Place-Value Mat. Draw flats, longs, and cubes on journal page 61 to show your number.

Build the same number in a different way. Draw the blocks you used.

◆ *Math Masters, p. 42*

Build a Number

Do this activity with a partner.

Materials ❑ *Math Masters*, p. 35 (Place-Value Mat)

❑ base-10 blocks: 9 flats (optional), 9 longs, and 9 cubes

❑ number cards 0–9 (from the Everything Math Deck, if available)

1. Mix the cards and stack them facedown.

2. Draw 2 cards.

3. Place the first card in the tens column of your Place-Value Mat. (If the card is a 0, put it back and draw again.) Then put the second card in the ones column.

TEACHING MASTER

◆ *Math Masters, p. 41*

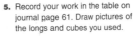

6.6

The Trade-First Subtraction Algorithm

OBJECTIVE To introduce and practice the trade-first subtraction algorithm.

summaries	materials
1 **Teaching the Lesson**	
Children learn the trade-first subtraction algorithm; use the algorithm to solve subtraction problems with and without trades; and make ballpark estimates to determine whether their answers to subtraction problems are reasonable. [Operations and Computation; Numeration]	☐ *Math Journal 1*, p. 149 ☐ Home Link 6.5 ☐ base-10 blocks (optional): 18 cubes and 7 longs
2 **Ongoing Learning & Practice**	
Children use Fact Triangles to practice addition and subtraction facts. [Operations and Computation] Children practice and maintain skills through Math Boxes and Home Link activities.	☐ *Math Journal 1*, p. 150 ☐ Home Link Masters (*Math Masters*, pp. 318 and 319) ☐ Fact Triangles in envelope
3 **Options for Individualizing**	
Enrichment Children make up, illustrate, and solve subtraction number stories. [Operations and Computation]	☐ Teaching Master (*Math Masters*, p. 109)

Additional Information

Vocabulary • **trade-first (subtraction)**

Vocabulary (teacher) • **algorithm**

Getting Started

Mental Math and Reflexes

Write problems like the following on the board. Mix horizontal and vertical formats. Ask children to subtract by counting up mentally.

50 − 43 = ? 7	50 − 35 = ? 15	30 − 7 = ? 23
70 − 39 = ? 31	60 − 14 = ? 46	80 − 56 = ? 24

Such practice reminds children that a good way to subtract is to ask, "How much do I add?" Subtracting this way gives children practice in using the efficient counting-up strategy, which is often used in situations involving making change.

1 Teaching the Lesson

◆ Math Message Follow-Up

WHOLE-CLASS DISCUSSION

Remind children that one way to make a ballpark estimate is to change the numbers in the problem to close but "easier" numbers that can be subtracted mentally. *For example:*

▷ 58 − 37 is close to 60 − 40, so the exact answer to 58 − 37 should be close to 20.

▷ 143 − 65 is close to either 140 − 60 or 140 − 70, so the exact answer should be near 80 or 70. The exact answer is 143 − 65 = 78. Point out that 65 is halfway between 60 and 70 on the number line and the same number of spaces away from 60 and 70 on the number grid. Therefore, either 60 or 70 may be used as an "easier" number substitute for 65.

◆ Demonstrating the Trade-First Algorithm without Trades

WHOLE-CLASS DISCUSSION

Explain to children that they will be able to calculate the answers to subtraction problems with larger numbers much more easily if they learn to use the same strategy for all problems.

Their task today will be to learn and practice a single paper-and-pencil strategy for subtraction that all children will be expected to know. You should, of course, encourage

```
longs ┊ cubes
10s   ┊  1s
 4    ┊  5
-2    ┊  2
─────────────
 2    ┊  3
```

children to continue using other favorite strategies, such as counting up, that they may have learned or devised for subtracting numbers.

Show the paper-and-pencil method for problems that do not require trading one 10 for ten 1s.

Example: 45 − 22

1. Write the problem on the board in vertical format. As a reminder, write "longs/10s" and "cubes/1s" above the columns. (See the margin.)

2. Draw 4 longs and 5 cubes on the board to represent the number 45.

3. Ask: *Are there enough longs and cubes so that I can remove 22 (2 longs and 2 cubes)?* Yes. There are 4 longs, so I can remove 2 longs. There are 5 cubes, so I can remove 2 cubes.

4. Subtract the tens. Erase 2 longs. Say, *4 longs minus 2 longs leaves 2 longs,* or *4 tens minus 2 tens leaves 2 tens.* Write 2 in the tens place of the answer space.

5. Subtract the ones. Erase 2 cubes. Say, *5 cubes minus 2 cubes leaves 3 cubes,* or *5 ones minus 2 ones leaves 3 ones.* Write 3 in the ones place of the answer space.

Repeat this demonstration with several other problems that do not require trades—for example, 79 − 34 and 87 − 15. Try to rely less and less on the longs-and-cubes pictures to illustrate the operation of subtraction.

◆ Demonstrating the Trade-First Algorithm with Trades

WHOLE-CLASS DISCUSSION

Example: 53 − 35

1. Write the problem on the board in vertical format. As a reminder, write "longs/10s" and "cubes/1s" above the columns. (See the margin.)

2. Draw 5 longs and 3 cubes on the board to represent the number 53.

3. Ask: *Are there enough longs and cubes so that I can remove 35 (3 longs and 5 cubes)?* No. There are only 3 cubes, so I can't remove 5 cubes.

```
longs ┊ cubes
10s   ┊  1s
 4    ┊  13
 5̸    ┊  3̸
-3    ┊  5
─────────────
 1    ┊  8
```

4. Trade a long for cubes. Erase 1 long and replace it by drawing 10 cubes. Ask: *How many longs and cubes make up 53 now?* 53 is now represented by 4 longs and 13 cubes. Mark the problem to reflect this action: Draw a slash mark through the 5 and write 4 above it; draw a slash mark through the 3 and write 13 above it.

5. Subtract the tens. Erase 3 longs from the picture. Say, *4 longs minus 3 longs leaves 1 long,* or *4 tens minus 3 tens leaves 1 ten.* Write 1 in the tens place of the answer space.

6. Subtract the ones. Erase 5 cubes from the picture. Say, *13 ones minus 5 ones leaves 8 ones.* Write 8 in the ones place of the answer space.

Repeat this demonstration with several other problems that require trades—for example, 72 − 38 and 80 − 17. Try to rely less and less on the tens-and-ones pictures to illustrate the operation of subtraction.

Summary: The method shown in these examples is called a subtraction **algorithm** because it gives a step-by-step set of instructions for solving a subtraction problem. It is called a **trade-first** algorithm because the first step is to identify whether any trade (such as one 10 for ten 1s) is required. If a trade is required, the trade is carried out first, followed by subtraction of the tens digits and the ones digits in either order. Use the term "trade-first" with children, but it is not necessary to use the term "algorithm."

✦ Practicing the Trade-First Algorithm
(*Math Journal 1,* p. 149)

INDEPENDENT ACTIVITY

On the board, write several 2-digit subtraction problems that require trading. Invite children to solve these problems at the board. Ask children to describe exactly what they did. Correct errors in calculation and in method. Make sure that the numbers children write are properly aligned in columns.

Many students will find it helpful if they are reminded about place value for the numbers they are subtracting. (See the margin.)

Assign journal page 149. Children may continue to use base-10 blocks to model the problems if they wish. Circulate and check to make sure that children are correctly marking the problems to show any trades.

Remind children to make ballpark estimates to check their answers and to look for mistakes if an answer is far away from an estimate. After they have finished all of the problems, they should check their answers with the answer key at the bottom of journal page 151.

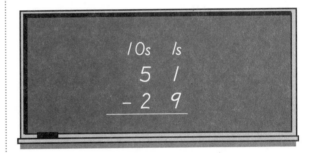

✦ *Math Journal 1, p. 149*

Encourage children to write "10s" and "1s" above the tens and ones columns of a problem.

ONGOING ASSESSMENT
As children work on the journal page, circulate and ask them to explain what they are doing. Watch for children who forget about place value. For example, in subtracting 78 − 35, children should say "7 tens minus 3 tens equals 4 tens" or "70 minus 30 equals 40," not "7 minus 3 equals 4."

STUDENT PAGE

Math Boxes 6.6

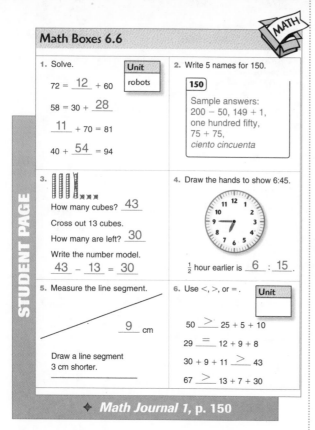

1. Solve.

Unit
robots

$72 = \underline{12} + 60$

$58 = 30 + \underline{28}$

$\underline{11} + 70 = 81$

$40 + \underline{54} = 94$

2. Write 5 names for 150.

150

Sample answers:
$200 - 50$, $149 + 1$,
one hundred fifty,
$75 + 75$,
ciento cincuenta

3. How many cubes? __43__

Cross out 13 cubes.

How many are left? __30__

Write the number model.

$\underline{43} - \underline{13} = \underline{30}$

4. Draw the hands to show 6:45.

$\frac{1}{2}$ hour earlier is __6__ : __15__ .

5. Measure the line segment.

__9__ cm

Draw a line segment
3 cm shorter.

6. Use <, >, or =.

Unit

$50 \underline{>} 25 + 5 + 10$

$29 \underline{=} 12 + 9 + 8$

$30 + 9 + 11 \underline{>} 43$

$67 \underline{>} 13 + 7 + 30$

◆ *Math Journal 1*, p. 150

HOME LINK MASTER

Trade-First Subtraction

Home Link
6.6

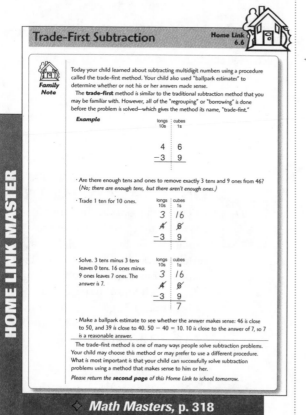

Family Note

Today your child learned about subtracting multidigit numbers using a procedure called the trade-first method. Your child also used "ballpark estimates" to determine whether or not his or her answers made sense.

The **trade-first** method is similar to the traditional subtraction method that you may be familiar with. However, all of the "regrouping" or "borrowing" is done before the problem is solved—which gives the method its name, "trade-first."

Example

	longs 10s	cubes 1s
	4	6
–	3	9

· Are there enough tens and ones to remove exactly 3 tens and 9 ones from 46? *(No; there are enough tens, but there aren't enough ones.)*

· Trade 1 ten for 10 ones.

	longs 10s	cubes 1s
	3	16
	4	6
–	3	9

· Solve. 3 tens minus 3 tens leaves 0 tens. 16 ones minus 9 ones leaves 7 ones. The answer is 7.

	longs 10s	cubes 1s
	3	16
	4	6
–	3	9
		7

· Make a ballpark estimate to see whether the answer makes sense: 46 is close to 50, and 39 is close to 40. $50 - 40 = 10$. 10 is close to the answer of 7, so 7 is a reasonable answer.

The trade-first method is one of many ways people solve subtraction problems. Your child may choose this method or may prefer to use a different procedure. What is most important is that your child can successfully solve subtraction problems using a method that makes sense to him or her.

*Please return the **second page** of this Home Link to school tomorrow.*

◆ *Math Masters*, p. 318

Adjusting the Activity You may want to pair children who are having difficulty with those who are having success. Another option is to work with a small group and use base-10 blocks to model the problems. More successful children will soon discover that they can begin to solve problems without the blocks.

2 Ongoing Learning & Practice

◆ Practicing with Addition/Subtraction Fact Triangles

PARTNER ACTIVITY

Have children work with a partner to use the Fact Triangles as flash cards.

◆ Math Boxes 6.6 (*Math Journal 1*, p. 150)

INDEPENDENT ACTIVITY

Mixed Review This journal page provides opportunities for cumulative review or assessment of concepts and skills.

◆ Home Link 6.6 (*Math Masters*, pp. 318 and 319)

Home Connection Children use the trade-first algorithm to solve subtraction problems.

The trade-first algorithm is similar to the subtraction method most parents learned, but the term may not be familiar to them. The explanation in the Family Note will help parents feel comfortable when participating in these activities with their children.

3 Options for Individualizing

◆ ENRICHMENT Subtraction Number Stories
(*Math Masters*, p. 109)

INDEPENDENT ACTIVITY   5–15 min

Language Arts Link Children write subtraction number stories, draw pictures to illustrate them, and find the solutions. You may wish to compile children's number stories into books. Children may look these over in their free time or check them out to take home.

Consider having children write subtraction stories again at the end of the year. Comparing the books made now and those made later offers a clear picture of the progress children have made. Children also enjoy and are motivated by comparing stories and judging their own progress.

 Portfolio Ideas

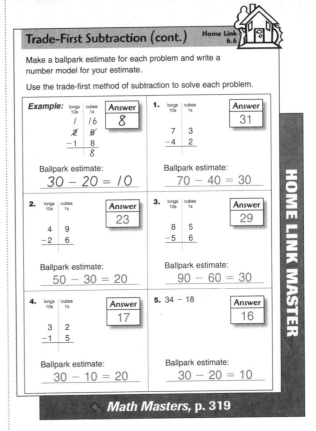

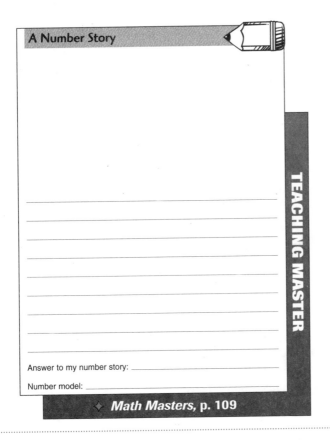

6.7
EXPLORATIONS

Exploring Arrays, Symmetry, and Division

OBJECTIVES To develop readiness for multiplication; to review symmetry; and to explore one meaning of division.

summaries	materials

1 Teaching the Lesson

Exploration A: Children make arrays on geoboards, record these arrays on dot paper, and sort arrays having the same number of dots into groups. [Operations and Computation]

Exploration B: Children use Pattern Block Templates to draw mirror images of pattern-block designs. [Geometry]

Exploration C: Children determine how many groups of *n* objects can be made from a specified number of objects and how many objects are left over. [Operations and Computation]

□ slate
□ Home Link 6.6
Exploration A: Per child (except per group where noted):
□ Teaching Masters (*Math Masters,* p. 110; and p. 111 or 112)
□ geoboard and rubber band
□ overhead geoboard (optional)
□ scissors per group
□ large sheet of paper and glue or paste per group (optional)
Exploration B: Per child:
□ Teaching Master (*Math Masters,* p. 113)
□ Pattern-Block Template; set of pattern blocks
□ 2 sheets of blank paper; straightedge
Exploration C: Per child (except per group where noted):
□ *Math Journal 1,* p. 151
□ Teaching Master (*Math Masters,* p. 114)
□ about 50 pennies or other counters per group
□ 1 regular die per group
***See* Advance Preparation**

2 Ongoing Learning & Practice

Children look for combinations of numbers that make those numbers easier to add by playing *Three Addends*. [Operations and Computation]

Children practice and maintain skills through Math Boxes and Home Link activities.

□ *Math Journal 1,* pp. 133 and 152
□ Teaching Master (*Math Masters,* p. 101)
□ Home Link Master (*Math Masters,* p. 320)
□ number cards 0–20 per partnership (from the Everything Math Deck, if available)

3 Options for Individualizing

Extra Practice Children identify an unknown 2-dimensional shape by asking *yes* and *no* questions. [Geometry]

□ *Minute Math*®, p. 18

Additional Information

Advance Preparation Plan to spend most of your time working on Exploration A with children. *Math Masters,* pages 110, 113, and 114 give directions for the Explorations. You may want to place copies of these masters at workstations. These masters can be especially useful if a teacher's aide or volunteer is helping children with the activities.

Vocabulary (teacher) • **equal-sharing division situations** • **equal-grouping division situations**

Getting Started

Mental Math and Reflexes

Write subtraction problems like the following on the board. Have children write ballpark estimates and the number models they used to make them on their slates.

98 − 42 100 − 40 = 60

45 − 22 45 − 20 = 25; or 40 − 20 = 20

173 − 39 170 − 40 = 130

Math Message
How many dots?

Home Link 6.6 Follow-Up

Review answers. Use base-10 blocks to model the problems as necessary. As children describe how they solved the subtraction problems, encourage them to pay careful attention to place value. For example, in subtracting 49 − 26, encourage children to say, "4 tens minus 2 tens equals 2 tens" or "40 minus 20 equals 20."

---

1 Teaching the Lesson

✦ Math Message Follow-Up

WHOLE-CLASS DISCUSSION

Ask:

- How many rows of dots are there? 2
- How many dots are in each row? 5
- How many dots are there in all? 10

Use an overhead geoboard to show children how to use a rubber band to enclose 10 pegs in a 2-by-5 rectangle, or demonstrate this on a regular geoboard and pass it around the classroom. Explain that in one of the Explorations in this lesson, children will use rubber bands to form rectangles and then count the number of pegs in the enclosed array.

✦ Exploration A: Making Geoboard Arrays
(*Math Masters*, p. 110; and p. 111 or 112)

INDEPENDENT ACTIVITY

Directions for making rectangles on a geoboard are found on *Math Masters*, page 110. Before proceeding, check the size of your class's geoboards. If the geoboards in your classroom are 5 × 5, use *Math Masters*, page 111. If the geoboards are 7 × 7, use *Math Masters*, page 112.

	How many rows?	How many dots in each row?	How many dots in all?
1.			
2.			
3.			
4.			

▼ Using *Math Masters,* page 110 and either page 111 or page 112, children record information about arrays.

Geoboard Arrays

Materials
- ☐ geoboard dot paper for each person
- ☐ geoboard for each person
- ☐ rubber band for each person
- ☐ scissors for the group
- ☐ glue or paste for the group (optional)
- ☐ large sheet of paper for the group (optional)

Work by yourself to complete Steps 1–5.

1. Use one rubber band to make a rectangle on your geoboard. The pegs inside the rubber band make an array.

2. Draw your array on the geoboard dot paper.

3. Write about your array at the bottom of the geoboard dot paper. Tell how many rows are in your rectangle, how many dots are in each row, and how many dots in all are in your rectangle.

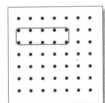

There are 2 rows of 5 pegs. 10 pegs are in the array.

4. Make 3 more arrays—all different. Draw each array on the geoboard dot paper. Write about each array at the bottom of the geoboard dot paper.

5. Cut apart the dot-paper records of your 4 arrays.

Work with your group to complete Step 6.

6. Sort your group's arrays into piles that have the same number of dots. You might want to use the arrays in each pile to make a display about that number.

✦ *Math Masters*, p. 110

TEACHING MASTER

◆ Exploration B: Creating Pattern-Block Symmetry (*Math Masters*, p. 113)

INDEPENDENT ACTIVITY

Portfolio Ideas

Art Link Using two sheets of paper, a straightedge, the Pattern-Block Template, pattern blocks, and crayons or coloring pencils, each child creates a symmetrical design.

Adjusting the Activity Challenge children to create a design on one side of the line for a friend to complete as a symmetrical design.

◆ Exploration C: Finding How Many Children Get *n* Things
(*Math Journal 1*, p. 151; *Math Masters*, p. 114)

SMALL-GROUP ACTIVITY

Using instructions from *Math Masters*, page 114, children make as many equal piles as possible. Then, on journal page 151, they record the total number of counters, how many counters are in each group, and how many groups there are. They also record how many counters are left over—how many are less than a full group.

NOTE: In Lesson 5.2, children had experience with **equal-sharing division situations.** In this activity, children work with **equal-grouping division situations.** It isn't important that children be able to distinguish between the two meanings of "division" at this point. However, it is important that they have had informal experience with both meanings. In Lesson 6.11, children will begin to formalize their equal-sharing and equal-grouping understandings.

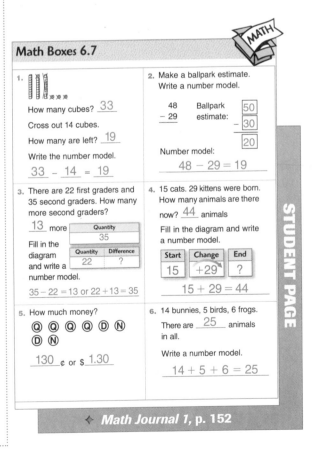

Three Addends Record Sheet

For each turn:
- Write the 3 numbers.
- Add the numbers.
- Write a number model to show the order in which you added.

Numbers and number models vary.

1. Numbers: ___, ___, ___
   Number model:
   ___ + ___ + ___ = ___

2. Numbers: ___, ___, ___
   Number model:
   ___ + ___ + ___ = ___

3. Numbers: ___, ___, ___
   Number model:
   ___ = ___ + ___ + ___

4. Numbers: ___, ___, ___
   Number model:
   ___ = ___ + ___ + ___

5. Numbers: ___, ___, ___
   Number model:
   ___ + ___ + ___ = ___

6. Numbers: ___, ___, ___
   Number model:
   ___ + ___ + ___ = ___

7. Numbers: ___, ___, ___
   Number model:
   ___ + ___ + ___ = ___

8. Numbers: ___, ___, ___
   Number model:
   ___ + ___ + ___ = ___

9. Numbers: ___, ___, ___
   Number model:
   ___ = ___ + ___ + ___

10. Numbers: ___, ___, ___
    Number model:
    ___ = ___ + ___ + ___

♦ *Math Masters*, p. 101

2 Ongoing Learning & Practice

♦ Playing *Three Addends*
(*Math Journal 1,* p. 133; *Math Masters,* p. 101)

PARTNER ACTIVITY

Children practice addition skills by playing *Three Addends.* For detailed instructions, see Lesson 6.1.

ONGOING ASSESSMENT
Children record a number model on *Math Masters,* page 101 to show the order in which they added three numbers. You can use this record to assess whether or not children understand the concept of looking for combinations of numbers that are easy to add.

♦ Math Boxes 6.7 (*Math Journal 1,* p. 152)

INDEPENDENT ACTIVITY

 Mixed Review This journal page provides opportunities for cumulative review or assessment of concepts and skills.

Math Boxes 6.7

1. How many cubes? __33__
   Cross out 14 cubes.
   How many are left? __19__
   Write the number model.
   __33__ − __14__ = __19__

2. Make a ballpark estimate.
   Write a number model.
   48 − 29   Ballpark estimate: 50 − 30 = 20
   Number model:
   48 − 29 = 19

3. There are 22 first graders and 35 second graders. How many more second graders?
   __13__ more
   Fill in the diagram and write a number model.

	Quantity
	35

Quantity	Difference
22	?

   35 − 22 = 13 or 22 + 13 = 35

4. 15 cats. 29 kittens were born. How many animals are there now? __44__ animals
   Fill in the diagram and write a number model.

Start	Change	End
15	+29	?

   15 + 29 = 44

5. How much money?
   Q Q Q Q D N
   D N
   __130__ ¢ or $ __1.30__

6. 14 bunnies, 5 birds, 6 frogs.
   There are __25__ animals in all.
   Write a number model.
   14 + 5 + 6 = 25

♦ *Math Journal 1,* p. 152

How Many?

Family Note

Your child has been working with arrays—rectangular arrangements of objects having the same number of objects in each row—to develop readiness for multiplication. Since this is a readiness activity, children have not yet written number models for multiplication, such as 4 × 5 = 20. Your child will do this in later lessons in this unit.

Please return this Home Link to school tomorrow.

---

1. Show someone at home this array.

```
X X X X X
X X X X X
X X X X X
X X X X X
```

How many rows? __4__

How many **X**s in each row? __5__

How many **X**s in all? __20__

2. Draw an array of 16 **X**s.

Sample answers:
```
X X X X X X X X
X X X X X X X X
```

How many rows? __2__

How many **X**s in each row? __8__

---

3. Draw an array of 24 **X**s.

Sample answers:
```
X X X X X X X X
X X X X X X X X
X X X X X X X X
```

How many rows? __3__

How many **X**s in each row? __8__

4. Draw a different array of 24 **X**s.

Sample answers:
```
X X X X X X
X X X X X X
X X X X X X
X X X X X X
```

How many rows? __4__

How many **X**s in each row? __6__

Math Masters, p. 320

HOME LINK MASTER

◆ **Home Link 6.7** (*Math Masters*, p. 320)

Home Connection Children draw arrays with specified numbers of Xs. For each array, children give the number of rows and the number of Xs in each row.

3 Options for Individualizing

◆ **EXTRA PRACTICE** Minute Math

SMALL-GROUP ACTIVITY   5–15 min

To offer children more experience with identifying shapes, see the following page in *Minute Math:*

Basic Routines: p. 18

6.8 Multiples of Equal Groups

OBJECTIVE To introduce multiplication as a way to find the total number of things in several equal groups.

summaries / materials

1 Teaching the Lesson

Children are introduced to diagrams to identify the known and unknown quantities in multiplication problems and to complete number models to summarize the solutions. Children also solve number stories about equal groups of things. [Operations and Computation; Patterns, Functions, and Algebra]

- ☐ *Math Journal 1*, p. 153
- ☐ Home Link 6.7
- ☐ 40 pennies or other counters per group of 4–5 students
- ☐ 6 boxes or bags to hold pennies or other counters

2 Ongoing Learning & Practice

Children use Fact Triangles to practice addition and subtraction facts. [Operations and Computation]

Children practice and maintain skills through Math Boxes and Home Link activities.

- ☐ *Math Journal 1*, p. 154
- ☐ Home Link Master (*Math Masters*, p. 321)
- ☐ addition/subtraction Fact Triangles in an envelope

3 Options for Individualizing

Enrichment Children identify and solve multiplication problems found in literature. [Operations and Computation]

Extra Practice Children solve problems involving multiplication situations. [Operations and Computation]

- ☐ *Each Orange Had Eight Slices: A Counting Book*
- ☐ *Sea Squares*
- ☐ *Minute Math*®, p. 95

See Advance Preparation

Additional Information

Advance Preparation For the optional Enrichment activity in Part 3, obtain the books *Each Orange Had Eight Slices: A Counting Book* by Paul Giganti, Jr. (Greenwillow Books, 1992) and *Sea Squares* by Joy N. Hulme (Hyperion Books for Children, 1991).

Vocabulary • equal groups • multiplication • times • multiplied by

---

Getting Started

Mental Math and Reflexes

Pose comparison number stories like the following:

- Michael is $2\frac{1}{2}$ years old and weighs 30 pounds. Meredith is 10 months old and weighs 20 pounds. How much more does Michael weigh than Meredith? 10 pounds more
- Trung learned 26 new spelling words this week. Nicholas learned 6 fewer words than Trung. How many new spelling words did Nicholas learn? 20 new words
- Marque ran around the track for 15 minutes. Elizabeth ran for 7 minutes more than Marque. How many minutes did Elizabeth run? 22 minutes

Math Message

Jane bought 3 packs of gum. There are 5 sticks of gum per pack. How many sticks of gum did she buy?

Home Link 6.7 Follow-Up

Have children draw the different arrays they made with 24 Xs. Be sure to include the following arrays: 1 row of 24 Xs and 24 rows of 1 X each. Show children any other possible arrays that they do not suggest.

---

1 Teaching the Lesson

$$5 + 5 + 5 = 15$$

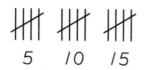

5   10   15

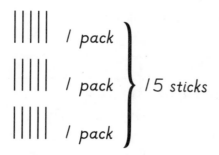

Some solution strategies for the Math Message problem

If children arrange their counters as shown here, they cannot "see" the 5 equal groups with 4 counters in each group.

This is a good arrangement of counters because children can clearly "see" the 5 equal groups.

✦ Math Message Follow-Up

WHOLE-CLASS DISCUSSION

Ask children to share their solution strategies. Expect a variety of strategies: Count by 1s; count by 5s; add 5s; double 5, and then add 5. Some children may draw pictures or use tallies. (See the margin.)

Use the Math Message problem to lead into a discussion about **equal groups.** The packs of gum are equal groups, because each pack has 5 sticks of gum in it. Six-packs of soft drinks are another familiar example of equal groups, because each 6-pack has 6 cans or bottles in it.

Tell children that combining equal groups to find the total number of things in all the groups is called **multiplication.** Emphasize that in a multiplication situation, each group must have the same number of things.

Show children what a number model for the number story looks like: $3 \times 5 = 15$. Mention that "3×5" is read "3 **times** 5" or "5 **multiplied by** 3."

✦ Solving Number Stories about Equal Groups of Things

WHOLE-CLASS ACTIVITY

Divide the class into groups of 4 or 5. Display several boxes of an item, such as pennies, paper clips, dominoes, or crayons. Each box should contain the same number of the item selected.

Example: Display 5 boxes, and put 4 pennies in each one. Tell the class that there are 4 pennies per box. Ask children to find the total number of pennies in all of the boxes by using counters to act out a solution.

Suggested questions

- How many groups of pennies are there? 5, because there are 5 boxes.

- How many pennies are in each group? 4 Are they "equal groups"? Yes, because there is the same number of pennies in each box.

- How many pennies are there in all? 20

Draw a diagram on the board that identifies the known and unknown quantities. Point out that the numbers in the diagram tell the quantities we know and that the question mark indicates the quantity we are trying to find. Once children have found the answer, erase the ?, write in the answer 20, and circle it. (See below.)

boxes	pennies per box	pennies in all
5	4	(20)

$$5 \times 4 = 20$$

Make up other stories by changing the number of boxes and the number of items per box. Emphasize the language of equal groups: for example, 3 boxes with 7 marbles *per* box and 3 boxes with 7 crayons *in each* box. (See margin.)

Children should continue using counters, pictures, doodles, or anything else that might help them to find the total number of items. As they share solution strategies, write number models on the board and read the models aloud. *For example:*

- $3 \times 7 = 21$ 3 times 7 is 21.

- $4 \times 6 = 24$ 6 multiplied by 4 equals 24.

Continue to fill in a diagram for each of the problems on the board. Write in the known quantities, and write ? for the unknown quantity. Ask children to help you complete the diagrams as you discuss problems, but do not expect children to come up with diagrams on their own. Repeated exposure to such diagrams will help children understand the meanings of multiplication and division.

Next, make up several number stories that do not require boxes of items as props. Fill in diagrams as before. As children share solutions, write number models on the board. *Suggestions:*

- 6 children have wet shoes. 2 shoes per child. How many wet shoes? 12

- 3 children took 4 crackers each. How many crackers? 12

- 4 packs of juice, 6 cans per pack. How many cans? 24

- 2 weeks, 7 days per week. How many days? 14

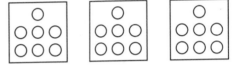

boxes	marbles per box	marbles in all
3	7	(21)

3 boxes, 7 marbles per box
$$3 \times 7 = 21$$

 Adjusting the Activity To challenge children, pose problems using larger numbers. *For example:*

- 3 hours, 50 miles per hour. How many miles? 150

- 5 toys, 99 cents per toy. Total cost? $4.95

Lesson 6.8   **397**

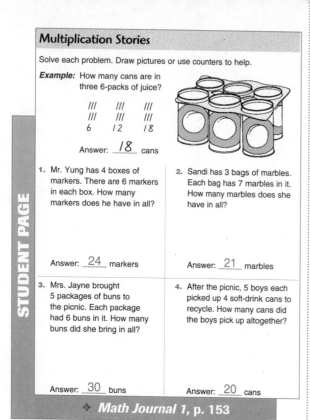

Multiplication Stories

Solve each problem. Draw pictures or use counters to help.

Example: How many cans are in three 6-packs of juice?

```
 ///    ///    ///
 ///    ///    ///
  6     12     18
```

Answer: _18_ cans

1. Mr. Yung has 4 boxes of markers. There are 6 markers in each box. How many markers does he have in all?

   Answer: _24_ markers

2. Sandi has 3 bags of marbles. Each bag has 7 marbles in it. How many marbles does she have in all?

   Answer: _21_ marbles

3. Mrs. Jayne brought 5 packages of buns to the picnic. Each package had 6 buns in it. How many buns did she bring in all?

   Answer: _30_ buns

4. After the picnic, 5 boys each picked up 4 soft-drink cans to recycle. How many cans did the boys pick up altogether?

   Answer: _20_ cans

◆ *Math Journal 1, p. 153*

◆ Solving Number Stories about Equal Groups
(*Math Journal 1*, p. 153)

PARTNER ACTIVITY

Partners act out and solve the multiplication stories on the journal page. Ask them to show how they solved the problems. Children might draw pictures or use counters.

2 Ongoing Learning & Practice

◆ Practicing with Addition/Subtraction Fact Triangles

PARTNER ACTIVITY

Have children work with a partner to use the Fact Triangles as flash cards.

✓ ONGOING ASSESSMENT

As children work, ask them to sort their triangles into two piles—one pile for facts they can recall quickly and one pile for facts they still need to practice. Have children record the facts they need to practice on a sheet of paper and give it to you. There are two reasons for recording these facts: First, children get additional practice. Second, you have a record of each child's progress.

Math Boxes 6.8

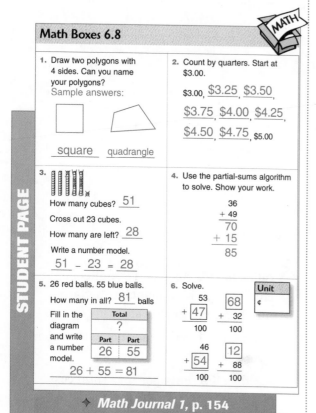

1. Draw two polygons with 4 sides. Can you name your polygons?
   Sample answers:

   square   _quadrangle_

2. Count by quarters. Start at $3.00.

   $3.00, $3.25, $3.50, $3.75, $4.00, $4.25, $4.50, $4.75, $5.00

3. How many cubes? _51_

   Cross out 23 cubes.

   How many are left? _28_

   Write a number model.
   _51_ – _23_ = _28_

4. Use the partial-sums algorithm to solve. Show your work.

   ```
     36
   + 49
     70
   + 15
     85
   ```

5. 26 red balls. 55 blue balls.

   How many in all? _81_ balls

   Fill in the diagram and write a number model.

Total	
?	
Part	**Part**
26	55

   _26 + 55 = 81_

6. Solve.

   ```
     53
   + [47]
    100
   ```
   ```
    [68]
   + 32
    100
   ```
   ```
     46
   + [54]
    100
   ```
   ```
    [12]
   + 88
    100
   ```

   Unit: ¢

◆ *Math Journal 1, p. 154*

◆ Math Boxes 6.8 (*Math Journal 1*, p. 154)

INDEPENDENT ACTIVITY

Mixed Review This journal page provides opportunities for cumulative review or assessment of concepts and skills.

◆ Home Link 6.8 (*Math Masters*, p. 321)

Home Connection Children can use objects, draw pictures, count, or use any other helpful device to solve problems about equal groups.

3 Options for Individualizing

◆ ENRICHMENT Equal Groups in Literature

SMALL-GROUP ACTIVITY **ⅰⅰⅰ**   15–30 min

Literature Link Read the following books to groups of children, or have children read the books themselves.

Each Orange Had Eight Slices: A Counting Book

Summary: Multiplication concepts are explored in this full-color book. In the first presentation, 3 red flowers are seen; each flower has 6 petals, and each petal has 2 black bugs. Questions are posed about the number of flowers, the number of petals, and the number of bugs.

Sea Squares

Summary: Text such as "Seven heavy pelicans diving for their dinner. Seven fish in every pouch can never make them thinner" reinforces equal groups and introduces square numbers.

◆ EXTRA PRACTICE Minute Math

SMALL-GROUP ACTIVITY **ⅰⅰⅰ**   5–15 min

To offer children more experience with solving multiplication problems about equal groups, see the following page in *Minute Math:*

Number Stories: p. 95

How Many?

Family Note In today's lesson, your child learned that multiplication is an operation used to find the total number of things in several equal groups. As you help your child solve the following problems, emphasize that each group has the same number of things. Your child can use objects, draw pictures, count, or use any other helpful devices to find the answers.

Please return this Home Link to school tomorrow.

Example

How many apples in 4 packages?

~~HHf~~   ~~HHf~~   ~~HHf~~   ~~HHf~~

5 + 5 + 5 + 5 = 20

There are 20 apples in 4 packages.

1. △ △ △ △ △ △

How many sides on each triangle? __3__ sides

How many sides in all? __18__ sides

2.

How many tires on each car? __4__ tires

How many tires in all? __16__ tires

3. How many fingers for each person? __10__ fingers

How many fingers in all? __80__ fingers

◆ *Math Masters,* p. 321

HOME LINK MASTER

6.9

Multiplication-Array Number Stories

OBJECTIVES To identify everyday examples of arrays; and to solve multiplication problems by using multiplication diagrams and array models.

summaries	materials

1 Teaching the Lesson

Children identify and describe familiar arrays; create and solve number stories about arrays using multiplication diagrams and array models; and complete number models to summarize solutions. [Operations and Computation; Patterns, Functions, and Algebra]

- ☐ *Math Journal 1,* pp. 155 and 156
- ☐ Home Link 6.8
- ☐ Teaching Masters (*Math Masters,* p. 115; p. 116, optional)
- ☐ Teaching Master transparency (*Math Masters,* p. 115; optional)
- ☐ 50 pennies or other counters per partnership (optional)

See **Advance Preparation**

2 Ongoing Learning & Practice

Children create and solve number stories about equal groups. [Operations and Computation]

Children practice and maintain skills through Math Boxes and Home Link activities.

- ☐ *Math Journal 1,* pp. 157 and 158
- ☐ Home Link Master (*Math Masters,* p. 322)

3 Options for Individualizing

Enrichment Children describe arrays found in the book *One Hundred Hungry Ants.* [Operations and Computation; Numeration]

Language Diversity Children create a display of arrays found in newspapers, magazines, and other sources. [Operations and Computation; Numeration]

- ☐ *One Hundred Hungry Ants*
- ☐ newspapers, magazines, and other sources of array pictures

See **Advance Preparation**

Additional Information

Advance Preparation In Part 1, choose one of the following to display a multiplication diagram and associated array:

▷ Make an overhead transparency of *Math Masters,* page 115.

▷ Draw and erase multiplication diagrams, arrays, and number models on the board as needed. You may use semipermanent chalk for the multiplication diagram.

For the optional Enrichment activity in Part 3, obtain the book *One Hundred Hungry Ants* by Elinor J. Pinczes (Houghton Mifflin, 1995).

Vocabulary • multiplication diagram • *x*-by-*y* array

Getting Started

Mental Math and Reflexes

Pose number stories about multiples of equal groups. *Suggestions:*

- Marcus can walk about 3 miles per hour. About how many miles can he walk in 4 hours? About 12 miles
- Each apple costs 25 cents. Jenna bought 5. How much did she pay? $1.25

Math Message

Egg carton: 2 rows of 6 eggs. Draw a picture. How many eggs in all?

Home Link 6.8 Follow-Up

Review answers. Ask children to write number models for each problem and to read them aloud.
$6 \times 3 = 18$; $4 \times 4 = 16$; $8 \times 10 = 80$

1 Teaching the Lesson

◆ Math Message Follow-Up
(*Math Masters,* p. 115)

WHOLE-CLASS DISCUSSION

Ask someone to draw the egg carton on the board. Remind children that an array is a rectangular arrangement of objects in rows and columns, and point out that the eggs form an array. There are 2 rows of eggs, with 6 eggs in each row; so there are 12 eggs in all.

Display a **multiplication diagram.** (See Advance Preparation.) Fill it in. Mark or draw a 2-by-6 array, and write a number model as shown below.

rows	*eggs* per row	*eggs* in all
2	6	? (12)

Number model: 2 × 6 = 12

◆ Identifying Familiar Arrays (*Math Masters,* p. 322)

WHOLE-CLASS DISCUSSION

Distribute Home Link 6.9. It includes pictures of six familiar arrays. For each array, ask children how many rows there

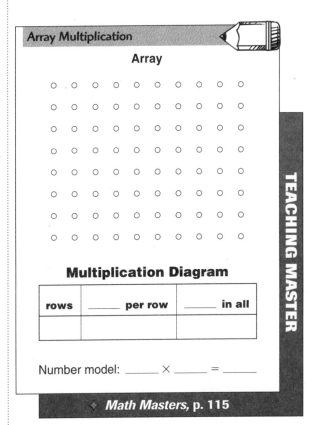

Array Multiplication

Array

Multiplication Diagram

rows	_____ per row	_____ in all

Number model: _____ × _____ = _____

◆ Math Masters, p. 115

TEACHING MASTER

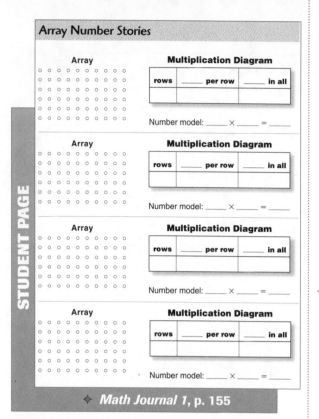

◆ Math Journal 1, p. 155

NOTE: *Math Masters*, page 116 is identical to journal page 155. Make copies of this master if children need more space to record number stories involving arrays.

○	○	○	○	○	○	○	○	○	○
○	⊗	⊗	⊗	○	○	○	○	○	○
○	⊗	⊗	⊗	○	○	○	○	○	○
○	⊗	⊗	⊗	○	○	○	○	○	○
○	⊗	⊗	⊗	○	○	○	○	○	○
○	⊗	⊗	⊗	○	○	○	○	○	○
○	○	○	○	○	○	○	○	○	○

rows	*keys* **per row**	*keys* **in all**
4	3	? ⑫

Number model: __4__ × __3__ = __12__

---

are and how many items there are in each row. Encourage them to talk about "**x-by-y arrays.**" *For example:*

▷ Telephone: 4 rows of keys, 3 keys *in each* row
                         a 4-by-3 array

▷ Checkerboard: 8 rows of squares, 8 squares *per* row
                         an 8-by-8 array

Array of Dots   Array of Squares

2-by-6 arrays: 2 rows, 6 per row

◆ Creating and Solving Number Stories about Arrays
(*Math Journal 1,* p. 155; *Math Masters,* p. 115)

WHOLE-CLASS ACTIVITY

Display a multiplication diagram.

You or the children make up number stories involving arrays of objects. (See the number-story suggestions at the top of the facing page.) For each story, children work alone or with a partner to do the following:

Solving Number Stories

1. Fill in the headings on the multiplication diagram on the journal page. For example, if the story is about rows of keys, fill in "keys" on the first line of the multiplication diagram.

2. Fill in the known numbers and write ? for the number to be found.

3. Make an array with counters to model the story.

4. Show the array next to the multiplication diagram by coloring the circles, drawing a ring around the circles, or marking the circles with Xs.

5. Write the answer on the diagram and circle it.

6. Write a number model.

As children solve each problem, fill in the displayed diagram, mark or draw an array picture, and ask for the answer. Help children to summarize by writing a number model. A sample solution is shown in the margin.

▷ Telephone: 4 rows of keys, 3 keys in each row. How many keys?

Number-story suggestions

▷ Carton of soup cans: 4 rows of cans, 6 cans *per* row. How many cans? 24

▷ Floor tiles: 5 rows of tiles, 9 tiles *in each* row. How many tiles? 45

▷ Tic-tac-toe: 3 rows of squares, 3 squares *per* row. How many squares? 9

▷ Math Boxes: 3 rows of problems, 2 problems *in each* row. How many problems? 6

▷ Calendar: 3 weeks, 7 days *in each* week. How many days? 21

Summary: Arrays are examples of equal groups of objects. The total number of objects in an array can be found using multiplication.

 Adjusting the Activity Pose more challenging problems like these:

- Theater seats: 15 rows of seats, 10 seats *per* row. How many seats? 150

- Cases of soda: 10 cases of soda, 24 cans *per* case. How many cans? 240

◆ Solving Array Multiplication Problems
(*Math Journal 1*, p. 156)

PARTNER ACTIVITY

Partners work together to draw arrays, solve problems, and write number models.

2 Ongoing Learning & Practice

◆ Creating and Solving Number Stories about Equal Groups (*Math Journal 1*, p. 157)

INDEPENDENT ACTIVITY

In Lesson 6.8, children solved stories about equal groups of things. Now they make up and solve their own stories.

 Adjusting the Activity Children who are not native English speakers may have some difficulty writing the words for number stories. You may want to pair these children with children who are proficient in English or allow them to simply draw pictures to "write" their number stories.

Multiplication Number Stories

For each problem:
- Use Xs to show the array.
- Answer the question.
- Fill in the number model.

1. The marching band has 3 rows with 5 players in each row. How many players are in the band?

There are ___15___ players in the band.

___3___ × ___5___ = ___15___

2. The orchard has 4 rows of trees. Each row has 8 trees. How many trees are there?

There are ___32___ trees in the orchard.

___4___ × ___8___ = ___32___

3. The sheet has 5 rows of stamps. There are 5 stamps in each row. How many stamps are there?

There are ___25___ stamps in all.

___5___ × ___5___ = ___25___

4. Mel folded his paper into 2 rows of 4 boxes each. How many boxes did he make?

He made ___8___ boxes.

___2___ × ___4___ = ___8___

◆ *Math Journal 1*, p. 156

 Adjusting the Activity If children are having difficulty with array multiplication, encourage them to make the arrays with counters first. Then they can record their arrays on the journal page.

More Multiplication Number Stories

Write your own multiplication stories and draw pictures of your stories. You can use the pictures at the side of the page for ideas.

For each story:
- Write the words.
- Draw a picture.
- Write the answer.

Example

There are 5 tricycles. How many wheels in all?

Answer: ___15 wheels___
(unit)

A person has 2 ears.

A tricycle has 3 wheels.

1. _____

Answer: Answers vary.
(unit)

A car has 4 wheels.

The box has 12 crayons.

2. _____

Answer: Answers vary.
(unit)

The box has 100 paper clips.

The juice pack has 6 cans.

◆ *Math Journal 1*, p. 157

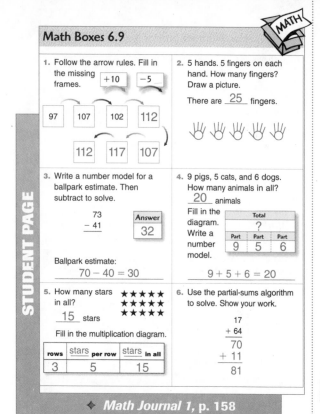

Math Boxes 6.9

1. Follow the arrow rules. Fill in the missing frames.

+10   −5

| 97 | 107 | 102 | 112 |

| 112 | 117 | 107 |

2. 5 hands. 5 fingers on each hand. How many fingers? Draw a picture.

There are __25__ fingers.

3. Write a number model for a ballpark estimate. Then subtract to solve.

```
  73
− 41
```

Answer
32

Ballpark estimate:
70 − 40 = 30

4. 9 pigs, 5 cats, and 6 dogs. How many animals in all?
__20__ animals

Fill in the diagram. Write a number model.

| Total |
| ? |

| Part | Part | Part |
| 9 | 5 | 6 |

9 + 5 + 6 = 20

5. How many stars in all? ★★★★★ ★★★★★ ★★★★★

__15__ stars

Fill in the multiplication diagram.

rows	stars per row	stars in all
3	5	15

6. Use the partial-sums algorithm to solve. Show your work.

```
   17
 + 64
   70
 + 11
   81
```

◆ *Math Journal 1, p. 158*

Adjusting the Activity To extend the Enrichment activity, children pick a number (such as 60) and draw each of its possible arrays on a separate piece of paper. They add a description to each page and combine them to create a "hungry ants" book of their own.

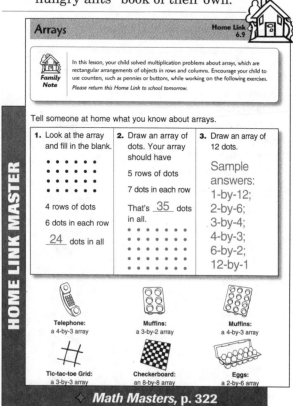

Arrays

Home Link 6.9

Family Note In this lesson, your child solved multiplication problems about arrays, which are rectangular arrangements of objects in rows and columns. Encourage your child to use counters, such as pennies or buttons, while working on the following exercises. Please return this Home Link to school tomorrow.

Tell someone at home what you know about arrays.

1. Look at the array and fill in the blank.

4 rows of dots
6 dots in each row
__24__ dots in all

2. Draw an array of dots. Your array should have
5 rows of dots
7 dots in each row
That's __35__ dots in all.

3. Draw an array of 12 dots.

Sample answers:
1-by-12;
2-by-6;
3-by-4;
4-by-3;
6-by-2;
12-by-1

Telephone: a 4-by-3 array
Muffins: a 3-by-2 array
Muffins: a 4-by-3 array
Tic-tac-toe Grid: a 3-by-3 array
Checkerboard: an 8-by-8 array
Eggs: a 2-by-6 array

◆ *Math Masters, p. 322*

HOME LINK MASTER

STUDENT PAGE

 ◆ **Math Boxes 6.9** (*Math Journal 1,* p. 158)

INDEPENDENT ACTIVITY

Mixed Review This journal page provides opportunities for cumulative review or assessment of concepts and skills.

◆ **Home Link 6.9** (*Math Masters,* p. 322)

Home Connection Children describe arrays and solve array problems.

3 Options for Individualizing

◆ ENRICHMENT **Arrays in Literature**

SMALL-GROUP ACTIVITY   **5–15 min**

Literature Link Read the following book to groups of children, or have them read the book themselves.

One Hundred Hungry Ants

Summary: One hundred ants arrange themselves in a variety of different arrays as they try to determine the most efficient way to get to a picnic.

◆ LANGUAGE DIVERSITY **Creating an Array Display or Booklet**

SMALL-GROUP ACTIVITY   **30+ min**

Encourage children to find pictures that show arrays in newspapers, magazines, and other sources. You may wish to use these pictures to build an "Arrays" bulletin-board display or booklet.

Adjusting the Activity Some teachers include a small section in the display titled "Almost an Array." This section contains items that aren't quite arrays, but are close to being arrays. For example, children might find rows of objects that do not all have the same number of objects. It is important to discuss why such a contribution is "almost an array," not a true array.

6.10

Multiplication with Arrays

OBJECTIVES To use arrays to develop multiplication concepts; and to begin recognizing multiplication facts.

summaries	materials

1   Teaching the Lesson

Children draw and name *x*-by-*y* arrays and practice finding the total number of items in an array by playing *Array Bingo.*
[Operations and Computation; Patterns, Functions, and Algebra]

- ☐ Home Link 6.9
- ☐ Teaching Masters (*Math Masters,* pp. 117–119)
- ☐ 2 six-sided dice, 1 twelve-sided die, or an egg-carton number generator per partnership or group
- ☐ all cards cut from *Math Masters,* p. 117
- ☐ 1 twenty-sided die or number cards with one card for each of the numbers 1–20 per partnership or group (from the Everything Math Deck, if available); optional
- ☐ 40 counters per partnership or group
- ☐ 40 overhead counters (optional)
- ☐ paper clip; envelope; scissors

***See* Additional Information**

2   Ongoing Learning & Practice

Children estimate differences and use the trade-first subtraction algorithm. [Operations and Computation]

Children practice and maintain skills through Math Boxes and Home Link activities.

- ☐ *Math Journal 1,* pp. 159 and 160
- ☐ Home Link Masters (*Math Masters,* pp. 323 and 324)

3   Options for Individualizing

Enrichment Children create larger arrays to play an extended version of *Array Bingo.* [Operations and Computation; Patterns, Functions, and Algebra]

Reteaching Children model multiplication by building arrays with pattern blocks. [Operations and Computation; Patterns, Functions, and Algebra]

- ☐ Teaching Masters (*Math Masters,* pp. 120 and 121)
- ☐ Pattern-Block Template; pattern blocks
- ☐ 16 index cards; paper clip; envelope
- ☐ 2 twenty-sided dice, 1 twelve-sided die, and 1 six-sided die

---

Additional Information

Background Information For additional information on egg-carton number generators, see the *Teacher's Reference Manual.*

Advance Preparation Before children play *Array Bingo* in Part 1, you may wish to have them cut out the cards on *Math Masters,* page 117.

Vocabulary • *x-by-y* **array**

Getting Started

Mental Math and Reflexes

Pose subtraction problems that feature multiples of 10.
Suggestions:

$54 - 10 = 44$	$54 - 20 = 34$
$54 - 30 = 24$	$58 = 68 - 10$
$48 = 68 - 20$	$18 = 68 - 50$
$96 - 20 = 76$	$57 - 40 = 17$
$79 - 60 = 19$	$42 = 92 - 50$

Math Message

*3 rows of window panes.
5 panes in each row.
Draw the array.
How many panes in all?*

Home Link 6.9 Follow-Up

Call on volunteers to draw their arrays of 12 dots on the board. For each array, ask: *How many rows? How many dots in each row?* Then write a number model under the array.

Continue until all possible arrays have been drawn. Be sure to include the 1-by-12 and 12-by-1 arrays.

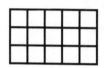

rows	panes per row	panes in all
3	5	? ⃝15

$$3 \times 5 = 15$$

Solution for Math Message

---

1 Teaching the Lesson

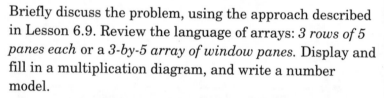

◆ Math Message Follow-Up

WHOLE-CLASS DISCUSSION

Briefly discuss the problem, using the approach described in Lesson 6.9. Review the language of arrays: *3 rows of 5 panes each* or a *3-by-5 array of window panes.* Display and fill in a multiplication diagram, and write a number model.

If you think children need more practice with array multiplication, pose some array number stories like those on journal page 156.

◆ Making *x*-by-*y* Arrays

WHOLE-CLASS ACTIVITY

Ask children to make a 5-by-2 array with counters to represent an arrangement of desks. Ask how many desks there are in all. As you discuss the solution, write a number model: $5 \times 2 = 10$.

Repeat with other *x*-by-*y* array problems as needed. Be sure to include some 1-by-*y* and *x*-by-1 arrays. You may wish to use overhead counters to model the arrays.

◆ Introducing *Array Bingo*
(*Math Masters,* pp. 117–119)

WHOLE-CLASS ACTIVITY

Read through the rules of *Array Bingo* with the class. Then, show children *Math Masters,* page 117 and say that these are the cards that are used to play the game.

Be sure to explain that arranging the cards "at random" means to arrange them in no pattern or order.

NOTE: Some teachers suggest that children glue their *Array Bingo* cards in a random arrangement (3-by-3 or 4-by-4) on cardstock paper. In this way, cards will not be lost. Instead of turning cards facedown while playing, children place counters on cards. The first player to cover a row, column, or diagonal with counters calls "Bingo!"

◆ Playing *Array Bingo*
(*Math Masters,* pp. 117–119)

PARTNER ACTIVITY

Divide the class into partnerships. After children have learned how to play the game, they may choose to play in small groups. The rules are on *Math Masters,* page 118.

Before the start of the game, each child should cut out the "A" cards from *Math Masters,* page 117.

After children finish playing, they should fasten their array cards with a paper clip and store them in their tool kits so that they can play the game again later.

Adjusting the Activity To make the game more challenging, players cut out and use all 16 array cards on *Math Masters,* page 117. The rules for extending the game are on *Math Masters,* page 119.

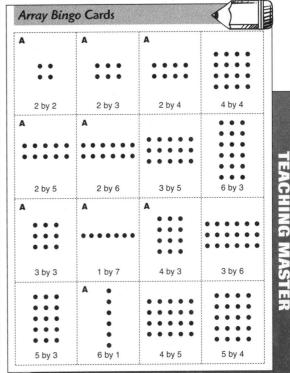

Array Bingo Cards

A 2 by 2	A 2 by 3	A 2 by 4	4 by 4
A 2 by 5	A 2 by 6	3 by 5	6 by 3
A 3 by 3	A 1 by 7	A 4 by 3	3 by 6
5 by 3	A 6 by 1	4 by 5	5 by 4

◆ *Math Masters,* p. 117

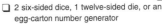

Array Bingo

Materials
☐ 2 six-sided dice, 1 twelve-sided die, or an egg-carton number generator
☐ 9 cards labeled "A" cut from *Math Masters,* p. 117 for each player

Players 2–5

Directions

1. Each player arranges the 9 cards at random in a 3-by-3 array.

2. Players take turns. When it is your turn:

   Generate a number from 1 to 12, using the dice, die, or number generator. This number represents the total number of dots in an array.

   Look for the array card with that number of dots. Turn that card facedown.

3. The first player to have a row, column, or diagonal of facedown cards calls "Bingo!" and wins the game.

◆ *Math Masters,* p. 118

TEACHING MASTER

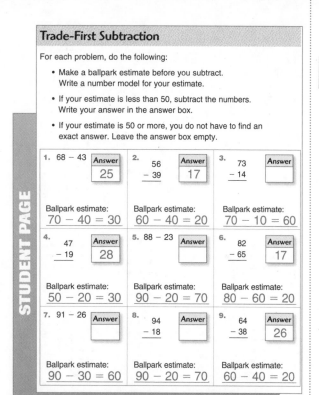

Trade-First Subtraction

For each problem, do the following:

- Make a ballpark estimate before you subtract.
  Write a number model for your estimate.

- If your estimate is less than 50, subtract the numbers.
  Write your answer in the answer box.

- If your estimate is 50 or more, you do not have to find an
  exact answer. Leave the answer box empty.

1. 68 – 43	Answer 25	2. 56 – 39	Answer 17	3. 73 – 14	Answer

Ballpark estimate:
70 – 40 = 30

Ballpark estimate:
60 – 40 = 20

Ballpark estimate:
70 – 10 = 60

4. 47 – 19	Answer 28	5. 88 – 23	Answer	6. 82 – 65	Answer 17

Ballpark estimate:
50 – 20 = 30

Ballpark estimate:
90 – 20 = 70

Ballpark estimate:
80 – 60 = 20

7. 91 – 26	Answer	8. 94 – 18	Answer	9. 64 – 38	Answer 26

Ballpark estimate:
90 – 30 = 60

Ballpark estimate:
90 – 20 = 70

Ballpark estimate:
60 – 40 = 20

◆ *Math Journal 1, p. 159*

NOTE: Many children don't recognize the value of making a ballpark estimate. However, most children should see the value of making an estimate if it will require them to do less work!

Math Boxes 6.10

1. 4 rows of 4 chairs. How many
   chairs in all? 16 chairs

   Draw an array
   to solve. Fill in
   the multiplication
   diagram.

rows	chairs per row	chairs in all
4	4	16

2. Solve.

   Unit
   ¢

   57 + 3 = 60

   40 = 35 + 5

   74 + 6 = 80

   120 = 111 + 9

3. Draw a line segment
   3 inches long.

   _____

   Now draw a line segment
   1 inch shorter.

   _____

4. Follow the rule. Fill in the table.

Rule +11	in	out
	73	84
	159	170
	85	96

   Answers vary.

5. Write 5 names for 28.

   28

   Sample answers:
   20 + 8, 30 − 2,
   twenty-eight, 18 + 10,
   veintiocho

6. Sue has $1.00 and spends
   73¢. How much change does
   she get?

   27¢

◆ *Math Journal 1, p. 160*

Ongoing Learning & Practice

◆ Using Estimation and the Trade-First Subtraction Algorithm (*Math Journal 1,* p. 159)

INDEPENDENT ACTIVITY

Children begin by making a ballpark estimate.

▷ If the estimated difference is less than 50, they should find an exact answer.

▷ If the estimated difference is 50 or more, they should not find an exact answer.

◆ Math Boxes 6.10 (*Math Journal 1,* p. 160)

INDEPENDENT ACTIVITY

Mixed Review This journal page provides opportunities for cumulative review or assessment of concepts and skills.

◆ Home Link 6.10 (*Math Masters,* pp. 323 and 324)

Home Connection Children draw arrays, complete number models, and answer questions about given arrays.

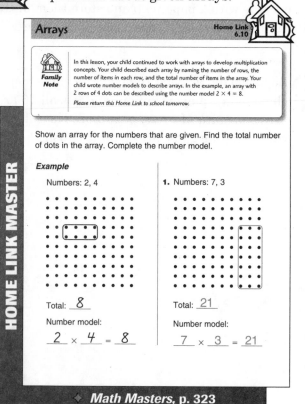

Arrays

Home Link 6.10

Family Note

In this lesson, your child continued to work with arrays to develop multiplication concepts. Your child described each array by naming the number of rows, the number of items in each row, and the total number of items in the array. In the example, an array with 2 rows of 4 dots can be described using the number model 2 × 4 = 8.

Please return this Home Link to school tomorrow.

Show an array for the numbers that are given. Find the total number of dots in the array. Complete the number model.

Example

Numbers: 2, 4

Total: 8

Number model:

2 × 4 = 8

1. Numbers: 7, 3

Total: 21

Number model:

7 × 3 = 21

◆ *Math Masters, p. 323*

3 Options for Individualizing

◆ ENRICHMENT Extending *Array Bingo*

PARTNER ACTIVITY 👥   15–30 min

Challenge children to create their own *Array Bingo* cards. Suggest that children draw arrays with up to 52 dots on 16 different index cards. Children generate numbers by rolling 1 twelve-sided die and 2 twenty-sided dice (or by rolling 1 twenty-sided die twice). The number, or sum of the numbers, face up represents the total number of dots in the array. The game is played using the rules described earlier in this lesson.

◆ RETEACHING Building Arrays
(*Math Masters*, pp. 120 and 121)

INDEPENDENT ACTIVITY 🧍   5–15 min

Children participated in an activity similar to this one in Lesson 5.3. However, some children may benefit from additional experiences manipulating actual objects into arrays.

Have children build arrays with pattern blocks. They determine the number of rows and the number of blocks in each row by rolling dice. They draw each array by using the Pattern-Block Template. Then children record the number of rows, the number of shapes in each row, and the total number of shapes in the array.

	How many rows?	How many shapes in each row?	How many shapes in all?
1.			
2.			
3.			
4.			
5.			

Table from *Math Masters,* page 121

Arrays (cont.)   Home Link 6.10

2. Numbers: 6, 10

Total: __60__

Number model:

__6__ × __10__ = __60__

Answer the questions about each array.

3.

How many rows? __5__

How many dots in each row? __6__

How many dots in the array? __30__

4.

How many rows? __3__

How many squares per row? __9__

How many squares in the array? __27__

5.

How many rows? __6__

How many squares in each row? __6__

How many squares in the array? __36__

◆ *Math Masters*, p. 324

Building Arrays ✏️

Materials   ☐ pattern blocks   ☐ Pattern-Block Template

         ☐ 1 six-sided die or number cube

         ☐ *Math Masters*, p. 121

1. Choose one of these blocks.

2. Roll the die 2 times.

The first number you roll tells how many rows to make in your array.

The second number you roll tells how many blocks to put in each row of your array.

Example

If you roll a 1 first and then a 5, you might make this:

3. Record the arrays you make on *Math Masters*, page 121.

Use the Pattern-Block Template. At the top of the page, draw the first array you made.

Fill in the table for Number 1 at the bottom of the page.

4. Make 4 more arrays. Follow the same steps. If you have room, draw the arrays you make. After you run out of room, fill in the table only.

◆ *Math Masters*, p. 120

6.11 Division Stories

OBJECTIVE To explore situations that require equal sharing or making equal groups of things.

summaries	materials
### 1 Teaching the Lesson	
Children use drawings or counters to find how a total number of items can be separated into an equal number of groups, or into groups of equal size. They also solve division number stories. [Operations and Computation]	☐ *Math Journal 1*, p. 161 ☐ Home Link 6.10 ☐ slate ☐ 30 counters for each group of 3 students
### 2 Ongoing Learning & Practice	
Children practice estimation and the trade-first subtraction algorithm. [Operations and Computation] Children practice and maintain skills through Math Boxes and Home Link activities.	☐ *Math Journal 1*, pp. 159 and 162 ☐ Home Link Master (*Math Masters*, p. 325)
### 3 Options for Individualizing	
Enrichment Children describe division situations found in the book *A Remainder of One*. [Operations and Computation] **Reteaching** Children are introduced to the modeling of equal-sharing and equal-grouping situations using a number line. [Operations and Computation]	☐ *A Remainder of One* **See** Advance Preparation

Additional Information

Advance Preparation For the optional Enrichment activity in Part 3, obtain the book *A Remainder of One* by Elinor J. Pinczes (Houghton Mifflin, 1995).

Vocabulary (teacher) • division • remainder

Getting Started

Mental Math and Reflexes

Write multiple-addend problems like the following on the board. Have children answer aloud or on their slates. Encourage them to look for combinations that will make the addition easier. *Suggestions:*

- 89 = 72 + 9 + 8
- 11 + 4 + 7 = 22; there isn't a particularly easy way to add these numbers.
- 43 + 7 + 15 = 65
- 90 = 4 + 25 + 36 + 25

Math Message

3 children share 12 pennies equally. How many pennies does each child get?

Home Link 6.10 Follow-Up

Review answers as necessary.

Before children turn in Home Link 6.10, consider asking them to respond to one of the following on the back of the Home Link:

• I think arrays are …

• Arrays are easy if …

• When solving array problems, I still don't understand …

Teaching the Lesson

◆ Math Message Follow-Up

SMALL-GROUP ACTIVITY

Divide the class into groups of 3. Start by having children act out the Math Message problem with pennies or other counters. As children share their solution strategies, draw a picture on the board to illustrate the problem.

Repeat the activity using 10 pennies. Elicit that when pennies are shared equally, it is not always possible to share all of them. Some pennies may be left over. Ask the following questions:

• If 10 pennies are shared equally by 2 people, will any pennies be left over? No, each person will get 5 pennies.

• What if 10 pennies are shared equally by 4 people? Each person will get 2 pennies, with 2 pennies left over.

• What if 10 pennies are shared equally by 5 people? Each person will get 2 pennies, with no pennies left over.

Ask children to make up other equal-sharing stories for one another to solve. Be sure they vary the numbers of pennies and children from story to story. They should act out the stories with pennies. Ask volunteers to share some of their stories.

Say that the operation called **division** can be used to solve equal-sharing problems. The number of things that are left over is called the **remainder.** Use these terms frequently, but do not expect children to use them.

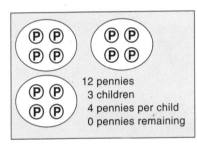

12 pennies
3 children
4 pennies per child
0 pennies remaining

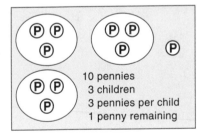

10 pennies
3 children
3 pennies per child
1 penny remaining

5 Children Sharing 12 Books

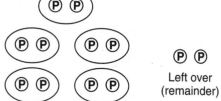

2 left

A simple drawing

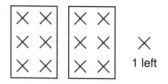

Left over
(remainder)

Modeling with counters

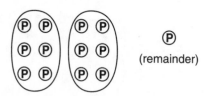

1 left

A simple drawing

P P P P
P P P P   P
P P P P   (remainder)

Modeling with counters

◆ Modeling Equal-Sharing Number Stories

WHOLE-CLASS ACTIVITY

Pose the following problem:

- 5 children share 12 books equally. How many books does each child get? 2 How many books are left over? 2

Ask children to solve the problem. Children can illustrate the story with a drawing or act it out with counters.

Discuss their methods and answers, and ensure that both strategies—drawings and counters—are presented. See the sample solutions in the margin.

Repeat this procedure with a few more division stories about equal sharing. *For example:*

- 18 chairs in 3 equal rows. How many chairs in each row? 6

- 4 friends share 14 apples equally. How many apples does each friend get? 3 How many apples are left over? 2

◆ Modeling Equal-Grouping Number Stories

WHOLE-CLASS ACTIVITY

Some division number stories involve making equal groups of things. It is not important that children distinguish these kinds of stories from equal-sharing stories since they can solve them using pictures or counters in very much the same way.

NOTE: Children have participated in several informal activities to explore the meanings of division. For example, in Lesson 5.2, children worked with equal-grouping situations by sharing "eggs" equally among "nests." In Lesson 6.7, children worked with equal-sharing situations by determining "how many children get *n* things."

Work together with children to solve an equal-grouping story. Then have them try several on their own. *For example:*

- There are 13 cans of soda. How many 6-packs is that? Two 6-packs, with 1 can left over

Begin by drawing a picture of a single 6-pack or by putting down 6 counters to represent a single 6-pack. Continue making additional 6-packs until the 13 cans are accounted for.

Other possible story ideas

- A building has 30 windows. There are 6 windows on each floor. How many floors does the building have? 5 floors

- 24 children want to play ball. How many teams can you make with 5 children on each team? 4 teams, with 4 children left over and not on a team

Summary: The operation called *division* can be used to solve equal-sharing and equal-grouping problems. The number of things left over is called the *remainder.*

✦ Solving Division Number Stories
(*Math Journal 1,* p. 161)

PARTNER ACTIVITY

Partners model each story with drawings or counters. Problems 1 and 2 are equal-sharing problems. Problems 3 and 4 involve making equal groups.

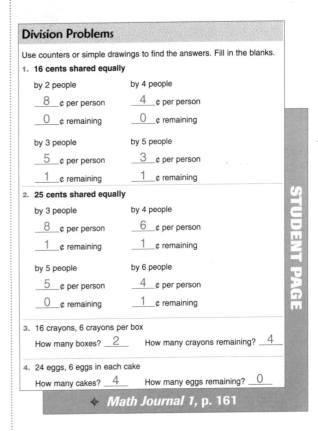

Division Problems

Use counters or simple drawings to find the answers. Fill in the blanks.

1. **16 cents shared equally**

   by 2 people
   __8__ ¢ per person
   __0__ ¢ remaining

   by 4 people
   __4__ ¢ per person
   __0__ ¢ remaining

   by 3 people
   __5__ ¢ per person
   __1__ ¢ remaining

   by 5 people
   __3__ ¢ per person
   __1__ ¢ remaining

2. **25 cents shared equally**

   by 3 people
   __8__ ¢ per person
   __1__ ¢ remaining

   by 4 people
   __6__ ¢ per person
   __1__ ¢ remaining

   by 5 people
   __5__ ¢ per person
   __0__ ¢ remaining

   by 6 people
   __4__ ¢ per person
   __1__ ¢ remaining

3. 16 crayons, 6 crayons per box

   How many boxes? __2__   How many crayons remaining? __4__

4. 24 eggs, 6 eggs in each cake

   How many cakes? __4__   How many eggs remaining? __0__

✦ *Math Journal 1,* p. 161

STUDENT PAGE

---

2 Ongoing Learning & Practice

✦ Using Estimation and the Trade-First Subtraction Algorithm (*Math Journal 1,* p. 159)

INDEPENDENT ACTIVITY

Children complete journal page 159 by calculating the remaining differences—those greater than or equal to 50. Children who did not have time to work on this page when it was assigned in Lesson 6.10 should do the whole page now.

Trade-First Subtraction

For each problem, do the following:

- Make a ballpark estimate before you subtract. Write a number model for your estimate.
- If your estimate is less than 50, subtract the numbers. Write your answer in the answer box.
- If your estimate is 50 or more, you do not have to find an exact answer. Leave the answer box empty.

1. 68 − 43   Answer: 25
   Ballpark estimate:
   70 − 40 = 30

2. 56 − 39   Answer: 17
   Ballpark estimate:
   60 − 40 = 20

3. 73 − 14   Answer:
   Ballpark estimate:
   70 − 10 = 60

4. 47 − 19   Answer: 28
   Ballpark estimate:
   50 − 20 = 30

5. 88 − 23   Answer:
   Ballpark estimate:
   90 − 20 = 70

6. 82 − 65   Answer: 17
   Ballpark estimate:
   80 − 60 = 20

7. 91 − 26   Answer:
   Ballpark estimate:
   90 − 30 = 60

8. 94 − 18   Answer:
   Ballpark estimate:
   90 − 20 = 70

9. 64 − 38   Answer: 26
   Ballpark estimate:
   60 − 40 = 20

✦ *Math Journal 1,* p. 159

STUDENT PAGE

STUDENT PAGE

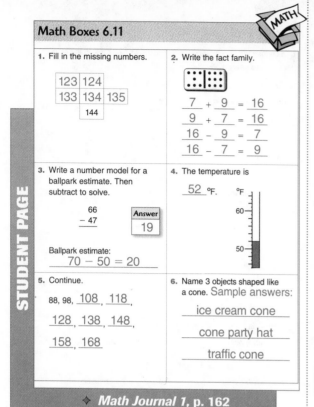

Math Boxes 6.11

1. Fill in the missing numbers.

123	124	
133	134	135
	144	

2. Write the fact family.

$7 + 9 = 16$

$9 + 7 = 16$

$16 - 9 = 7$

$16 - 7 = 9$

3. Write a number model for a ballpark estimate. Then subtract to solve.

$$\begin{array}{r} 66 \\ -\ 47 \\ \hline \end{array}$$

Answer **19**

Ballpark estimate:
$70 - 50 = 20$

4. The temperature is **52** °F.

5. Continue.

88, 98, **108**, **118**, **128**, **138**, **148**, **158**, **168**

6. Name 3 objects shaped like a cone. Sample answers:

ice cream cone

cone party hat

traffic cone

✦ *Math Journal 1, p. 162*

✦ **Math Boxes 6.11** (*Math Journal 1*, p. 162)

INDEPENDENT ACTIVITY

Mixed Review This journal page provides opportunities for cumulative review or assessment of concepts and skills.

✦ **Home Link 6.11** (*Math Masters*, p. 325)

Home Connection Using a group or handful of small items from home, children solve equal-sharing problems by acting them out.

3 Options for Individualizing

✦ **ENRICHMENT** Division in Literature

SMALL-GROUP ACTIVITY   **5–15 min**

Literature Link Read the following book to children, or have them read the book themselves.

A Remainder of One

Summary: Joe is an ant. When groups of ants are formed into an array, he is always left out—"a remainder of one." He tells the queen ant of an array design in which he won't be left out.

HOME LINK MASTER

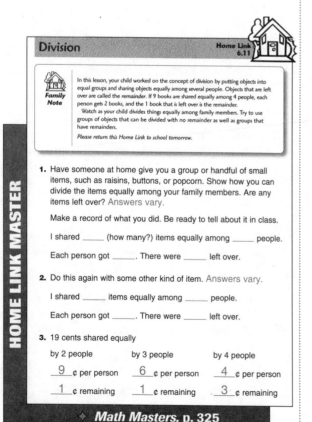

Division

Home Link 6.11

Family Note

In this lesson, your child worked on the concept of division by putting objects into equal groups and sharing objects equally among several people. Objects that are left over are called the *remainder*. If 9 books are shared equally among 4 people, each person gets 2 books, and the 1 book that is left over is the remainder.

Watch as your child divides things equally among family members. Try to use groups of objects that can be divided with no remainder as well as groups that have remainders.

Please return this Home Link to school tomorrow.

1. Have someone at home give you a group or handful of small items, such as raisins, buttons, or popcorn. Show how you can divide the items equally among your family members. Are any items left over? Answers vary.

Make a record of what you did. Be ready to tell about it in class.

I shared _____ (how many?) items equally among _____ people.

Each person got _____. There were _____ left over.

2. Do this again with some other kind of item. Answers vary.

I shared _____ items equally among _____ people.

Each person got _____. There were _____ left over.

3. 19 cents shared equally

by 2 people	by 3 people	by 4 people
9 ¢ per person	**6** ¢ per person	**4** ¢ per person
1 ¢ remaining	**1** ¢ remaining	**3** ¢ remaining

✦ *Math Masters, p. 325*

◆ RETEACHING Using a Number Line

INDEPENDENT ACTIVITY   **15–30 min**

Number lines are another way to model equal-sharing and equal-grouping situations. Some children may find the concepts easier to understand if you, or they, draw number lines and model problems as follows:

Equal-sharing situation

Consider a problem about 15 things shared equally by 3 people ($15 \div 3 = ?$). On a number line, the distance from 0 to 15 can be divided into 3 equal parts. The number of single "hops" in each part is equivalent to the number of things in each equal share. The total and the number of groups is known. The size of each group is to be determined.

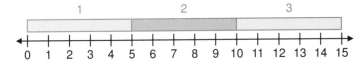

Three equal parts with 5 units in each part make a total of 15 units.

Equal-grouping situation

Now consider a problem in which 15 things are separated into equal groups of 3 things (also $15 \div 3 = ?$). On a number line, the distance from 0 to 15 (or from 15 to 0) is measured out in "hops" of 3. The number of "hops" of 3 is the total number of equal groups. The total and the size of each group is known. The number of groups is to be determined.

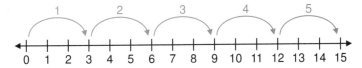

5 "hops" of 3 units each are measured out

6.12

Unit 6 Review and Assessment

OBJECTIVE To review and assess children's progress on the material covered in Unit 6.

1   Assess Progress

learning goals

6a   **Beginning/Developing Goal** Solve stories about multiples of equal groups. **(Lessons 6.8, 6.9, and 6.11)**

6b   **Beginning/Developing Goal** Solve equal-grouping and equal-sharing division problems. **(Lessons 6.11 and 6.12)**

6c   **Developing Goal** Use the trade-first method to solve 2-digit subtraction problems. **(Lessons 6.6, 6.10, and 6.12)**

6d   **Developing Goal** Make ballpark estimates of exact answers. **(Lessons 6.1, 6.4, 6.6, 6.7, 6.10, and 6.11)**

6e   **Developing Goal** Model multiplication problems with arrays. **(Lessons 6.9 and 6.10)**

6f   **Developing Goal** Add three 2-digit numbers mentally. **(Lessons 6.1, 6.6, and 6.11)**

6g   **Developing/Secure Goal** Add and subtract with multiples of 10. **(Lessons 6.1, 6.5, and 6.10)**

6h   **Developing/Secure Goal** Solve addition and subtraction number stories. **(Lessons 6.2–6.4 and 6.7)**

6i   **Secure Goal** Add three 1-digit numbers mentally. **(Lessons 6.1, 6.4, and 6.7)**

activities

- ❑ Oral Assessment, Problem 1

- ❑ Oral Assessment, Problem 2

- ❑ Oral Assessment, Problems 2–4
- ❑ Written Assessment, Problems 2–4

- ❑ Slate Assessment, Problem 1

- ❑ Oral Assessment, Problem 1
- ❑ Written Assessment, Problems 5 and 6

- ❑ Written Assessment, Problem 1

- ❑ Slate Assessment, Problem 2

- ❑ Slate Assessment, Problem 4
- ❑ Written Assessment, Problems 7 and 8

- ❑ Slate Assessment, Problem 3
- ❑ Written Assessment, Problem 1

materials

- ❑ Math Journal 1, p. 133
- ❑ Home Link 6.11
- ❑ Assessment Masters (*Math Masters*, pp. 428; and 438–440; optional)

- ❑ Teaching Masters (*Math Masters*, p. 22; and pp. 101 and 108; optional)
- ❑ slate; number cards 0–20 per partnership; 100 counters

2   Build Background for Unit 7

summaries

Children practice and maintain skills through Math Boxes and Home Link activities.

materials

- ❑ *Math Journal 1*, p. 163
- ❑ Home Link Masters (*Math Masters*, pp. 326–329)

Each **learning goal** listed above indicates a level of performance that might be expected at this point in the *Everyday Mathematics* K–6 curriculum. For a variety of reasons, the levels indicated may not accurately portray your class's performance.

Getting Started

Math Message
Share 18 dominoes equally among 4 children.
How many dominoes per child? 4
How many dominoes left over? 2
Draw a picture to show what you did.

Home Link 6.11 Follow-Up
Children name some of the items they divided equally among family members, the number of family members, how many items each family member received, and how many items were left over.

1 Assess Progress

◆ Math Message Follow-Up

WHOLE-CLASS ACTIVITY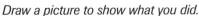

Children explain their solutions to the problem. Collect and evaluate responses.

◆ Oral and Slate Assessments

SMALL-GROUP ACTIVITY

If the list of suggested problems below is not appropriate for your class's level of performance, adjust the numbers in the problems or adjust the problems themselves to better assess your children's abilities.

Oral Assessment Suggestions

1. Encourage children to use counters or draw pictures to solve the following number stories about equal groups. **Goal 6a**

   - 3 shelves with books. 5 books per shelf. How many books? 15 books

   - 4 packages of pencils. 3 pencils in each package. How many pencils? 12 pencils

   - 8 puppies per pen. 2 pens. How many puppies? 16 puppies

   - 100 paper clips per box. 3 boxes. How many paper clips? 300 paper clips

NOTE: Many of these assessment suggestions relate to learning goals that have been addressed in previous units. Now is a good time to evaluate children's progress toward those goals.

2. Encourage children to use counters or draw pictures to solve the following equal-grouping and equal-sharing number stories. **Goal 6b**

- 18 children. 6 children per group. How many groups? 3 How many children remaining? 0

- 15 cents shared equally by 2 children. How many cents per child? 7 How much money remaining? 1 cent

- 25 sticks of gum shared equally by 5 children. How many sticks for each child? 5 How many sticks left over? 0

- 28 cups of flour. 5 cups of flour in each cake. How many cakes? 5 How many cups of flour left over? 3

Slate Assessment Suggestions

1. Have children make a ballpark estimate, with a number model, for each difference. **Goal 6d**

- $57 - 29 = ?$ $60 - 30 = 30$
- $92 - 41 = ?$ $90 - 40 = 50$
- $? = 63 - 49$ $10 = 60 - 50$
- $? = 89 - 22$ $70 = 90 - 20$

2. Pose addition and subtraction problems involving multiples of 10. **Goal 6g**

- $40 + 30 = ?$ 70
- $50 + 9 = ?$ 59
- $? = 60 + 14$ 74
- $? = 80 - 20$ 60
- $47 - 7 = ?$ 40
- $73 - 23 = ?$ 50

3. Write 1-digit multiple-addend problems on the board. Encourage children to look for combinations that will make the addition easier. **Goal 6i**

- $7 + 9 + 3 = ?$ 19
- $8 + 2 + 7 = ?$ 17
- $7 + 6 + 9 = ?$ 22; no easy combination
- $? = 4 + 4 + 6$ 14
- $? = 5 + 3 + 5$ 13
- $? = 6 + 7 + 4 + 3$ 20

4. Pose addition and subtraction number stories. **Goal 6h**

- Melodia brought 12 pieces of candy to school to share with friends. She gave 7 away during recess. How many does she have now? 5 pieces of candy

- Filip caught a fish that weighed 15 pounds. Jake caught one that weighed 8 pounds. How much less did Jake's fish weigh than Filip's? 7 pounds

- Mark planted 10 tulip bulbs in the garden. Allison planted 12. How many did they plant in all? 22 tulip bulbs

- Quentin scored 34 points in the basketball game. James scored 20 points. How many more points did Quentin score than James? 14 points more

- Jennifer had 12 bean-bag animals. She received 3 more for her birthday. How many bean-bag animals does Jennifer have now? 15 bean-bag animals

NOTE: Provide copies of *Math Masters*, page 108 for those children who would like to use a diagram to help them solve the problems.

✦ Written Assessment (*Math Masters*, p. 428)

INDEPENDENT ACTIVITY

Read through the problems with the class. You may want to do examples with the class for some of the problems.

If appropriate, work through the problems together. Wait for children to complete a problem before reading the next one.

If your class can work independently, have children work alone or with a partner on this review page. Circulate and assist.

- Choose a unit. Solve the problems. (Problem 1) **Goals 6f and 6i**

- Subtract. (Problems 2–4) **Goal 6c**

- How many rows? How many dots in each row? How many dots in all? Write a number model. (Problem 5) **Goal 6e**

- Draw an array with 3 rows and 5 dots in each row. How many dots in all? Write a number model. (Problem 6) **Goal 6e**

- Fish J weighs 24 pounds. Fish H weighs 14 pounds. How much more does Fish J weigh? (Problem 7) **Goal 6h**

- Fish K weighs 35 pounds. Fish G weighs 10 pounds. How much do they weigh together? (Problem 8) **Goal 6h**

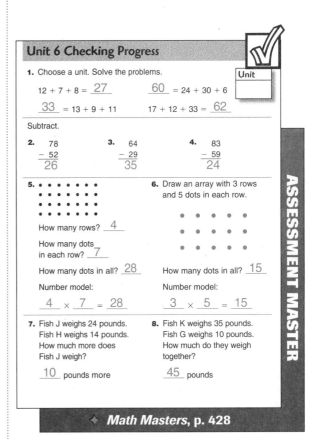

Unit 6 Checking Progress

1. Choose a unit. Solve the problems.

$12 + 7 + 8 =$ __27__   __60__ $= 24 + 30 + 6$

__33__ $= 13 + 9 + 11$ $17 + 12 + 33 =$ __62__

Subtract.

2.	3.	4.
78	64	83
− 52	− 29	− 59
26	35	24

5. How many rows? __4__

How many dots in each row? __7__

How many dots in all? __28__

Number model:

__4__ × __7__ = __28__

6. Draw an array with 3 rows and 5 dots in each row.

How many dots in all? __15__

Number model:

__3__ × __5__ = __15__

7. Fish J weighs 24 pounds. Fish H weighs 14 pounds. How much more does Fish J weigh?

__10__ pounds more

8. Fish K weighs 35 pounds. Fish G weighs 10 pounds. How much do they weigh together?

__45__ pounds

ASSESSMENT MASTER

✦ *Math Masters*, p. 428

◆ ALTERNATIVE ASSESSMENT OPTION
Describe a Method Used to Solve a Multidigit Subtraction Problem

INDEPENDENT ACTIVITY

Pose two subtraction problems, one of which requires a trade and one of which does not. For each problem, ask children first to solve it and then to describe the strategy that they used. In the descriptions of their strategies, look for children to display a clear understanding of place-value concepts.

◆ ALTERNATIVE ASSESSMENT OPTION
Play *Three Addends*
(*Math Journal 1*, p. 133; *Math Masters*, p. 101)

PARTNER ACTIVITY

Use this game to assess whether or not children understand the concept of looking for combinations of numbers that are easy to add. *Math Masters*, page 101 can be used to provide a written record of this game.

◆ ALTERNATIVE ASSESSMENT OPTION
Make Up and Solve Number Stories Involving Addition, Subtraction, Equal Groups, Equal Sharing, or Equal Grouping
(*Math Masters*, p. 22)

INDEPENDENT ACTIVITY

Children write number stories involving addition, subtraction, multiples of equal groups, equal sharing, or equal grouping. Children illustrate and solve their problems.

You may wish to compile children's number stories into books (either individual or whole-class). Children may look these over in their free time or check them out to take home.

Consider having children write addition and subtraction stories again at the end of the year. Comparing the books made now and those made later offers a clear picture of the progress children have made. Children also enjoy and are motivated by comparing stories and judging their own progress.

✦ Midyear Assessment
(*Math Masters*, pp. 438–440)

The Midyear and End-of-Year Assessment Masters
(*Math Masters*, pages 438–447) provide additional
assessment opportunities that you may want to use as
part of your balanced assessment plan. These tests cover
only some of the important concepts and skills in *Second
Grade Everyday Mathematics*. They should be used along
with ongoing, product, and periodic assessment
opportunities within the lessons and at the ends of the
units. Please see pages 91 and 92 of the *Assessment
Handbook* for answers to the Midyear Assessment.

2 Build Background for Unit 7

✦ Math Boxes 6.12 (*Math Journal 1*, p. 163)

INDEPENDENT ACTIVITY

Mixed Review This journal page provides
opportunities for cumulative review or
assessment of concepts and skills. The skill
in Problem 6 is a prerequisite for Unit 7.

✦ Home Link 6.12: Unit 7 Family Letter
(*Math Masters*, pp. 326–329)

Home Connection This Home Link is a
four-page newsletter that introduces parents
and guardians to Unit 7's topics and terms.
The letter also offers ideas for home-based
mathematics activities that are supportive of
classroom work.

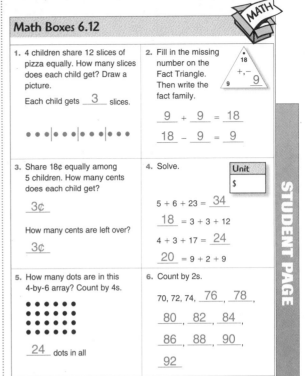

Math Boxes 6.12

1. 4 children share 12 slices of pizza equally. How many slices does each child get? Draw a picture.

Each child gets **3** slices.

2. Fill in the missing number on the Fact Triangle. Then write the fact family.

18
+,−
9   9

9 + 9 = 18
18 − 9 = 9

3. Share 18¢ equally among 5 children. How many cents does each child get?

3¢

How many cents are left over?

3¢

4. Solve.

Unit
$

5 + 6 + 23 = **34**
18 = 3 + 3 + 12
4 + 3 + 17 = **24**
20 = 9 + 2 + 9

5. How many dots are in this 4-by-6 array? Count by 4s.

24 dots in all

6. Count by 2s.

70, 72, 74, **76**, **78**,
80, **82**, **84**,
86, **88**, **90**,
92

✦ *Math Journal 1*, p. 163

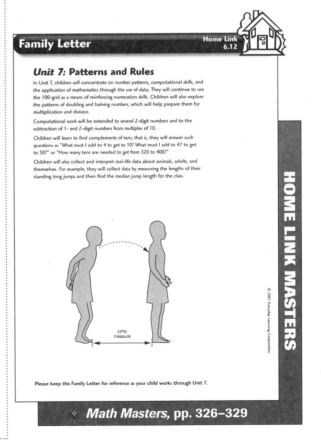

Family Letter Home Link 6.12

Unit 7: Patterns and Rules

In Unit 7, children will concentrate on number patterns, computational skills, and the application of mathematics through the use of data. They will continue to use the 100-grid as a means of reinforcing numeration skills. Children will also explore the patterns of doubling and halving number, which will help prepare them for multiplication and division.

Computational work will be extended to several 2-digit numbers and to the subtraction of 1- and 2-digit numbers from multiples of 10.

Children will learn to find complements of tens; that is, they will answer such questions as "What must I add to 4 to get to 10? What must I add to 47 to get to 50?" or "How many tens are needed to get from 320 to 400?"

Children will also collect and interpret real-life data about animals, adults, and themselves. For example, they will collect data by measuring the lengths of their standing long jumps and then find the median jump length for the class.

jump
measure

Please keep this Family Letter for reference as your child works through Unit 7.

✦ *Math Masters*, pp. 326–329

Appendices

contents

Title	Page
Projects	424
Second Grade Key Vocabulary	453
Scope and Sequence	467
Index	488

Boxes, Boxes, Beautiful Boxes

OBJECTIVES To name fractional parts; to practice following directions; and to use paper-folding techniques to make useful, open paper boxes.

background information

Recommended Use: During Unit 2 or Unit 7

See the discussion of Projects in the Management Guide section of the *Teacher's Reference Manual*.

materials

☐ several sheets of any rectangular and square pieces of paper (shiny magazine covers, pages from store catalogs, construction paper, and so on) per child

☐ large rectangular piece of paper for demonstration

☐ *Fun with Easy Origami: 32 Projects and 24 Sheets of Origami Paper*

☐ *Complete Origami: An A–Z of Facts and Folds, with Step-by-Step Instructions for Over 100 Projects*

See Advance Preparation

Project Information

Advance Preparation You may want to obtain the following books for the Extension Suggestions in Part 2:

▷ *Fun with Easy Origami: 32 Projects and 24 Sheets of Origami Paper* by John Montroll (Dover, 1993)

▷ *Complete Origami: An A–Z of Facts and Folds, with Step-by-Step Instructions for Over 100 Projects* by Eric Kenneway (St. Martin's, 1987)

1 Doing the Project

✦ Making Boxes

Mary Lewis of Carnegie School shared these directions for making an open paper box. She used them successfully many times with her students.

Model each step with a large rectangular piece of paper. After you complete a step, have children do that step with their papers.

1. Fold the paper in half lengthwise. Make sure that all corners are even. Unfold the paper.

   Ask, *How many parts are there?* 2 *Each part is what fraction of the whole paper?* Half, or one-half

2. Fold each long side so that the outside edge comes exactly to the middle line, as shown below.

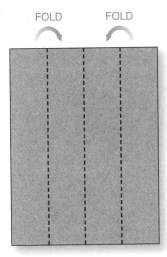

Unfold the paper. Ask, *How many parts are there now? 4 Each part is what fraction of the whole paper?* One-fourth, or one quarter

3. Fold the paper in half across the width. Unfold it.

Ask, *How many parts are there now? 8 Each part is what fraction of the whole paper?* one-eighth

4. Fold the short edges of the paper exactly to the middle width line, as shown below.

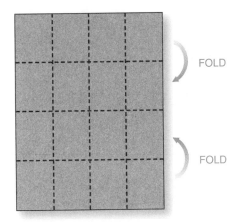

Unfold the paper. Ask, *How many parts are there now? 16 Each part is what fraction of the whole paper?* one-sixteenth

5. Fold the short edges back to the middle again. Crease the folds hard.

6. Fold a triangle at a corner. One side of the triangle should match up to the fold nearest the corner. Fold a triangle at the other corners. Crease the folds hard.

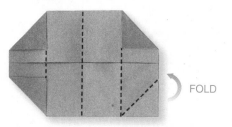

FOLD

7. Fold back the long edges at the center, over the corner folds, to form two cuffs, as shown below. Crease hard.

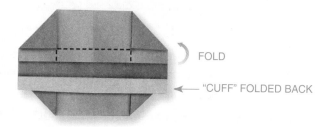

FOLD

← "CUFF" FOLDED BACK

8. Gently open the box by pulling apart the center of the cuffs. Recrease the four corners of the box.

A completed box

2 Extending the Project

◆ Extension Suggestions

1. Have children make a second box, slightly larger than the first, to use as a cover.

2. Have children make boxes from different-size rectangles or squares. They can use almost any kind of sturdy paper.

3. **Literature Link** Obtain a book on origami, such as *Fun with Easy Origami: 32 Projects and 24 Sheets of Origami Paper* by John Montroll (Dover, 1993) or *Complete Origami: An A–Z of Facts and Folds, with Step-by-Step Instructions for Over 100 Projects* by Eric Kenneway (St. Martin's, 1987), and have children make some of the figures.

◆ Home Link Suggestions

Children tell the box-making steps in order to a family member. Then they list the steps in order for making (or doing) something else with which they are familiar, such as making a sandwich, getting dressed, or using a computer program.

Weather Station

OBJECTIVES **To read thermometers using both the Fahrenheit and Celsius scales; and to observe and collect data on outdoor weather conditions and temperatures.**

background information

Recommended Use: During Unit 2 or Unit 8

See the discussion of Projects in the Management Guide section of the *Teacher's Reference Manual.*

materials

☐ Project Masters (*Math Masters,* pp. 211 and 212)

☐ class outdoor thermometer; scissors; tape or glue

☐ red crayon or marker

☐ clear, self-adhesive vinyl sheets (optional)

☐ weather reports from different parts of the country

☐ encyclopedia

☐ literature selections

☐ barometer (optional)

***See* Advance Preparation**

Project Information

Advance Preparation You may want to obtain the following books for the Extension Suggestions in Part 2:

▷ *Weather* by Tom Kierein (National Geographic, 1995)
▷ *The Magic School Bus Wet All Over: A Book about the Water Cycle* (Scholastic, 1996)
▷ *Weather Forecasting* by Gail Gibbons (Aladdin, 1993)
▷ *Weather,* edited by Lee Bennett Hopkins (HarperCollins, 1994)

1 Doing the Project

✦Assembling Paper Thermometers
(*Math Masters,* p. 211)

Science Link Guide children through the following steps to assemble their paper thermometers from *Math Masters,* page 211:

1. Color the bulb at the bottom of the thermometer red.

2. Color the strip marked "Color this red."

3. Cut out both strips and the thermometer.

4. Tape or glue the strips together on the space marked to make a single indicator strip.

    Optional: At this point, laminate the thermometers or cover them with clear, self-adhesive vinyl sheets to make them more durable.

5. Cut slits along the dashed lines at the top and bottom of the thermometer.

6. Insert the indicator strip (with the red part at the bottom) through the slits so that it slides down the face of the thermometer, as shown in the margin below.

◆ Reviewing Thermometers and Temperature Readings

Have available both the class outdoor thermometer and children's paper thermometers. The scales on the class outdoor thermometer and the paper thermometers may not be exactly alike. If they differ somewhat, focus on the paper thermometers.

Ask, *Which unit are temperatures reported in?* degrees

Point out the two scales: °F and °C. Ask, *What are the names of the two scales? What do F and C stand for?* Fahrenheit and Celsius *What does the small raised circle mean?* degrees

Ask a volunteer to explain why many thermometers have two different scales. The Celsius scale is used in most of the world; the Fahrenheit and Celsius scales are used in the United States. **Ask such questions as the following:**

• Are the two scales the same? No. On the Fahrenheit scale, water freezes at 32°. On the Celsius scale, water freezes at 0°.

• On each scale there are three different size marks. How many degrees are shown between a long mark and the next long mark? 10 degrees How many degrees are shown between a shortest mark and the next shortest mark? 2 degrees How many degrees are shown between a mark and the next mark? 1 degree

• What are temperatures below zero called? negative

• Which scale is more likely to record negative temperatures? Celsius, because all temperatures below freezing are negative Which scale is more likely to record 3-digit temperatures? Fahrenheit, because 3-digit Fahrenheit temperatures begin a little below 38 degrees Celsius

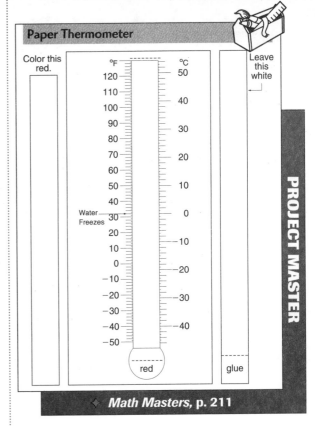

Paper Thermometer

◆ *Math Masters,* p. 211

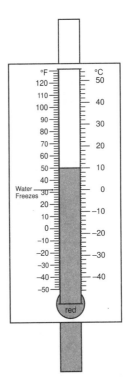

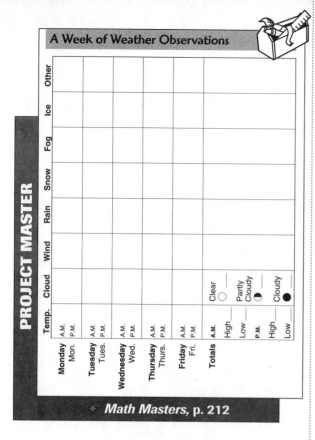

A Week of Weather Observations

Math Masters, p. 212

calm	light breeze	windy
strong wind	clear	partly cloudy
cloudy		

Say several temperatures. Have children display these temperatures on their paper thermometers as you circulate and check. Include some negative temperatures. Compare pairs of temperatures: Which is warmer, colder? Repeat this activity often over the next few days.

Give children two different temperatures in the same scale to compare. For example, *How much warmer is 50 degrees Fahrenheit than 30 degrees Fahrenheit?* 20 degrees Fahrenheit *How much colder is 5 degrees Celsius than 15 degrees Celsius?* 10 degrees Celsius Encourage children to share their solution strategies; record them on the board. Repeat this activity often as a review, especially during the week of this Project.

◆ Collecting Weather Data
(*Math Masters,* p. 212)

Examine the Project Master with the class. Point out the following:

▷ The rows are labeled at the left with the five days of the school week.

▷ The columns are labeled at the top with various weather conditions.

▷ The large row at the bottom is used to record information or summaries for the week.

Discuss how to fill in the chart for the current day. Help the class reach a consensus about how to describe the day—sunny, cloudy, windy, or something else. Design and record symbols as needed, such as those for wind and cloud cover shown in the margin.

Have a volunteer read and report the current outside temperature. Note that the temperature column has spaces for A.M. and P.M. readings. Recording morning and afternoon temperatures shows how the temperature changes during the day and provides real data for temperature-difference problems.

Each day for a week, allow a few minutes for children to fill in their weather observation chart for the day. Assign a pair of students to create a report for the class.

At the end of the week, children fill in the bottom row with the week's high and low morning and afternoon temperatures; the number of clear, partly cloudy, and cloudy days; and other comments or data.

⎇ Extending the Project

◆ Extension Suggestions

1. Repeat this activity during different seasons of the year.

2. Find out the temperatures in other parts of the country and compare them to the class readings.

3. ◯ Literature Link Read about weather and weather forecasting in an encyclopedia or in such books as *Weather* by Tom Kierein (National Geographic, 1995), *The Magic School Bus Wet All Over: A Book about the Water Cycle* (Scholastic, 1996), or *Weather Forecasting* by Gail Gibbons (Aladdin, 1993). *Weather,* edited by Lee Bennett Hopkins (HarperCollins, 1994), is a collection of poems about weather.

4. Have children read, watch, or listen to weather reports to find out amounts of rain or snow, wind speeds, and so on for the previous day. They then incorporate this information into their charts.

5. Have children read, watch, or listen to weather forecasts and compare them to the actual weather.

6. Introduce the barometer and its role in weather forecasting. Barometric pressure readings are part of many weather reports.

◆ Home Link Suggestions

Children and family members take turns making up and solving temperature-comparison number stories. These stories can be generated while the family watches a televised weather report for your local area or for the entire country.

PROJECT

3

Chinese Calendar

OBJECTIVES To count up and back by 12s using 4-digit numbers; and to become familiar with the Chinese 12-year animal cycle.

---

background information

Recommended Use: During Unit 2 or Unit 7

See the discussion of Projects in the Management Guide section of the *Teacher's Reference Manual*.

materials

☐ Project Masters (*Math Masters,* pp. 213 and 214)

☐ crayons or markers

☐ *The Greenwich Guide to Time and the Millennium*

See **Advance Preparation**

Project Information

Advance Preparation You may want to obtain the following book for the Extension Suggestions in Part 2:

▷ *The Greenwich Guide to Time and the Millennium* by Graham Dolan (Heinemann Library, 1999)

---

1 Doing the Project

◆Discussing the Chinese Calendar's 12-Year Animal Cycle (*Math Masters,* p. 213)

The ancient Chinese developed an accurate calendar based on the motion of the Sun and Moon. Beginning in the Zhou dynasty (1045 B.C.), the Chinese numbered years in a 12-year cycle. (*Source:* E. G. Richards, *Mapping Time: The Calendar and Its History* (Oxford University, 1998))

Social Studies Link In the Chinese calendar, each year of the 12-year cycle is represented by a different animal (6 wild and 6 domesticated), as shown below:

Number	Name	Animal
1	Zi	Rat
2	Chou	Ox
3	Yin	Tiger
4	Mao	Rabbit
5	Chen	Dragon
6	Si	Snake
7	Wu	Horse
8	Wei	Sheep
9	Shen	Monkey
10	You	Rooster
11	Xu	Dog
12	Hai	Pig

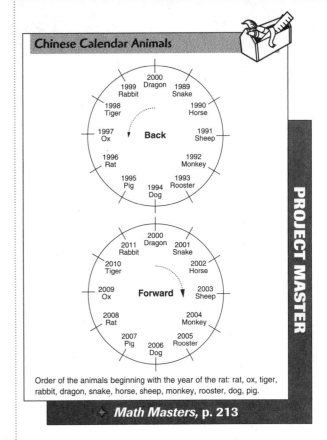

Chinese Calendar Animals

Order of the animals beginning with the year of the rat: rat, ox, tiger, rabbit, dragon, snake, horse, sheep, monkey, rooster, dog, pig.

◆ *Math Masters,* p. 213

PROJECT MASTER

The animals repeat in this order every 12 years. (According to legend, Buddha called all the animals to him before he left Earth. Only twelve came. He named a year after each in the order in which they arrived.) In addition to the 12-year cycle, there is a 60-year cycle (five 12-year cycles). The 79th cycle began in 1996.

The first circle on *Math Masters,* page 213 shows the cycle going back 12 years from 2000; the second circle shows it going forward 12 years from 2000.

Ask questions about the master.

Suggestions

- On our calendar, this is 2001 (use the actual current year.) Which Chinese year is it? snake

- When will the year of the snake come again? 2013 Besides using the Project Master, is there another way to figure out the next year of the snake? Add 12 to the current year

- When was the last year of the snake? 1989 How can you figure this out mathematically? Subtract 12 from the current year

Have children share their strategies for mentally adding and subtracting 12. For example, count up or back by 1s; count up or back by 10s and then add or subtract 2; count up or back by 6s; and so on. The years in the cycle can also be determined by counting up or back by 12s on the calculator.

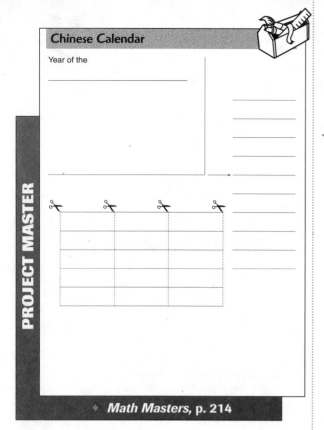

Chinese Calendar

Year of the

_____

✦ Math Masters, p. 214

Determine the birth years of different members of the class. Then have children find the animals that represent the years of those births. When will the years of those particular animals come again?

✦ Listing Past and Future Animal Years
(*Math Masters,* pp. 213 and 214)

If possible, assign two children to each of the animals represented in the cycle. Have them fill in the name of their animal and draw a picture of it in the blank space on *Math Masters,* page 214.

Children find their animal on one of the circles on *Math Masters,* page 213 and write the corresponding year on the line next to the arrow on *Math Masters,* page 214. Then they fill in the four years before (above) and four years after (below) their initial year by adding and subtracting 12 years from that line. That is, they are to count by 12 forward and back, using whichever method they wish. Encourage them to use scratch paper if they need to.

As you circulate, check the mathematics and talk about the methods children are using to determine the years into the future and the past.

If children are interested in making a scroll by extending their counts in either direction, have them cut out the columns on *Math Masters,* page 214 and glue or tape them to the bottom and/or top of their initial columns.

You can post the completed scrolls or lists on a bulletin board so that the entire animal cycle can be seen.

GONG XI FA CAI!

("Happy and Prosperous New Year")

Extending the Project

✦ Extension Suggestions

1. The date of the Chinese New Year varies from late January to the middle of February—February 5 in 2000, January 24 in 2001, February 12 in 2002, and so on. Children can investigate the Chinese New Year and how it is celebrated on the following Web sites:

   http://homex.s-one.net.sg/member/crescent/index.htm

   http://dir.yahoo.com/Society_and_Culture/Cultures_and_Groups/Cultures/Chinese/Holidays_and_Observances/Chinese_New_Year/

2. Help children read about calendars and timekeeping in such books as *The Greenwich Guide to Time and the Millennium* by Graham Dolan (Heinemann Library, 1999).

✦ Home Link Suggestions

Children take home copies of *Math Masters,* page 213. With the help of family members, they find the animal that represents their birth year. They then list the next three years represented by that particular animal.

Dates on Pennies

OBJECTIVES To gain experience working with 4-digit numbers within familiar yearly notation (1998, 1999, and so on); and to use tallies and graphs to compare data.

background information

Recommended Use: During or after Unit 3

See the discussion of Projects in the Management Guide section of the *Teacher's Reference Manual.*

materials

☐ small magnifying lenses (optional); about 1,000 pennies

☐ Class Data Pad (optional); coin collector's catalog

☐ literature selections

***See* Advance Preparation**

Project Information

Advance Preparation You may want to obtain the following books for the Extension Suggestions in Part 2:

▷ *Let's Find Out about Money* by Kathy Barabas (Scholastic, 1997)
▷ *Money* by Joe Cubb (Knopf, 1990)

1 Doing the Project

✦ Observing Dates on Pennies

Each child examines a few pennies to find the years the pennies were made (minted). Some dates have a "D" under the year, indicating that those pennies were minted in the Denver Mint. Make sure most children can find the dates easily. Small magnifying lenses may help.

Have children call out some of their pennies' years as you record them on the board in a systematic way. Continue until you have a range of years. Use a tally mark to record each reoccurrence. Ask, *In which year were the oldest pennies minted? The newest pennies?*

✦ Tallying Dates for a Large (Diverse) Collection of Pennies

In roughly equal batches, distribute the collection of pennies among pairs of children. Have partners record the year and make a tally mark for each penny in their collection. They can use the method you modeled on the board or devise their own recording scheme.

After all or most of the pennies have been recorded, bring the class together and record on the board or the Class Data Pad the total number for each year found. Compare the range of years and the various totals by asking questions about the data. *Suggestions:*

- What is the range of years?
- In which year were the fewest pennies minted? How many pennies were minted in that year? What is the difference between the fewest number of pennies minted and the most?
- Why are there fewer older pennies?
- Are there pennies older than class members? How much older?
- How much older is the oldest penny than the newest?

◆ Graphing the Data

Work with children to construct a bar graph showing the years in the class penny collection. After the class starts building the graph, assign each partnership one or two years to add to the graph by using the information on the board or the Class Data Pad. (See the margin.)

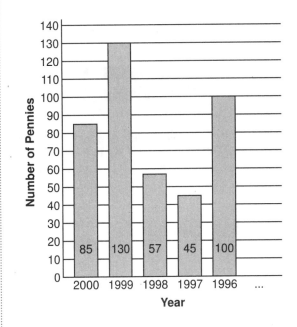

2 Extending the Project

◆ Extension Suggestions

1. Obtain a catalog of U.S. coins that features illustrations of pennies and other coins over the years and gives prices for them.

2. Literature Link Suggest that children read about money in such books as *Let's Find Out about Money* by Kathy Barabas (Scholastic, 1997) and *Money* by Joe Cubb (Knopf, 1990).

◆ Home Link Suggestions

Children tally the dates found on pennies at home. They explain to family members how to compare the data represented by these pennies. Children may also tally the dates found on nickels, dimes, and quarters found at home.

PROJECT 5

Snowflakes

OBJECTIVES To experiment with paper folding; and to create paper snowflakes that represent real 6-sided water crystals.

background information

Recommended Use: During Unit 4, Unit 6, or Unit 8

Children use lightweight paper in this Project because it is easy to fold and cut; 8" × 11" is a good size to begin with.

See the discussion of Projects in the Management Guide section of the *Teacher's Reference Manual.*

materials

☐ lightweight, white pieces of paper of various sizes

☐ scissors

☐ literature selections

***See* Advance Preparation**

Project Information

Advance Preparation If possible, ask at least two adults to help children with the initial paper folding. Or, if your school has a program in which your class is paired with an older class for certain activities, this is a good activity to incorporate older children. It's helpful if helpers know the folding routine in advance!

The paper needs to be square. You may want to cut square pieces yourself, or you can have children cut square pieces as the first step (see the second activity).

You may want to obtain the following books for the Extension Suggestions in Part 2:

▷ *Snow Crystals* by W. A. Bentley and W. J. Humphreys (Dover, 1931)
▷ *Snowflake Bentley* by Jacqueline Briggs Martin (Houghton Mifflin, 1998)
▷ *Snow* by Uri Shulevitz (Farrar Straus & Giroux, 1998)
▷ *The Snowy Day* by Ezra Jack Keats (Viking, 1962)

1 Doing the Project

◆ Talking about Snowflakes

Snowflakes are hexagonal (6-sided) crystals of water that form in clouds. Snowflakes come in many forms, from 6-sided clumps to lace-like, 6-pointed stars. The type that forms depends on the temperature and on the amount of moisture in the air.

It was once thought that no two snowflakes are alike, but identical snowflakes have been found. However, these are rare. Like the paper snowflakes children will make, most real snowflakes are unique.

✦ Making Paper Snowflakes

Follow these directions, or use other directions with which you are familiar.

1. If the paper is not already square, make it square by first folding it and then cutting it.

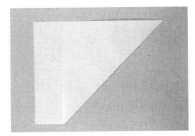

2. Fold a square sheet of paper in half along a diagonal to make a triangle. Place the fold at the bottom.

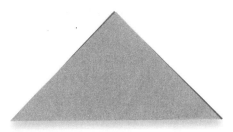

3. Fold the triangle into thirds. *Hint:* To fold into thirds, first find the center of the bottom edge. This will be the point of the triangular-shape folded paper. Put the tip of an index finger here while folding.

   Be careful to fold exactly into thirds. The edge of one side must match the fold on the other side.

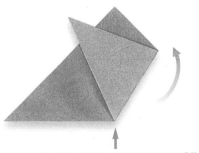

   CENTER OF THE BOTTOM EDGE

4. Fold in half again. *Hint:* Fold back so that an "ear" is on the outside top of the folded paper.

5. Cut off the "ears" along the straight edges on top. This makes each "arm" of the snowflake identical.

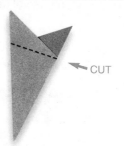

6. Draw a curved or jagged line to indicate the shape you would like the snowflake to be. Begin near the bottom point of the double-folded edge; end near the top of the single-folded edge. *Hint:* Do not draw too close to the bottom point or the snowflake will fall apart when it is cut out.

7. Cut along the line drawn.

8. Carefully unfold the snowflake. The darkened part of the snowflake in the picture is the part originally drawn.

Children cut out additional snowflakes as time permits. The beauty of making snowflakes is that it gets easier each time children do it! Encourage them to experiment with different shapes and to make small cutouts along the single fold or the spine of the points of the snowflake.

2 Extending the Project

◆ Extension Suggestions

1. Discuss features of children's snowflakes. For example, each snowflake is *symmetric*—it can be folded in half so that the two halves match. Ask, *In how many ways can a snowflake be folded so that the two halves match?* 3 The six "arms" are *congruent*—they all are the same shape and size.

Children go outside to observe actual snowflakes with a magnifying lens, weather permitting.

2. **Science Link** Read about snow in such books as *Snow Crystals* by W. A. Bentley and W. J. Humphreys (Dover, 1931), which contains over 2,000 illustrations of snowflakes. W. A. Bentley, who devoted his life to studying snow, is the subject of the biography *Snowflake Bentley,* written for children by Jacqueline Briggs Martin (Houghton Mifflin, 1998). The book includes sidebars describing Bentley's experiments and techniques for photographing snowflakes.

3. **Literature Link** Read stories about snow, such as *Snow* by Uri Shulevitz (Farrar Straus & Giroux, 1998). *The Snowy Day* by Ezra Jack Keats (Viking, 1962) is a beautifully illustrated, classic book for younger children.

◆ Home Link Suggestion

Children take one of their snowflakes home. They explain the process of making a paper snowflake to family members. With the assistance of an older child or adult, children make another snowflake or a different item (such as a boat or a hat) out of paper.

PROJECT

6

Time Capsule

OBJECTIVES To agree on, collect, and display information to be included in a time capsule; and to make predictions about life four years from now.

background information

Recommended Use: During or after Unit 7; possibly at the end of the year

Children gather information about themselves and make predictions which are then sealed in a "time capsule." The time capsule is left with the principal to be opened in sixth grade (or another appropriate grade) when children are about to leave the school.

See the discussion of Projects in the Management Guide section of the *Teacher's Reference Manual.*

materials

☐ shoe box or other "time capsule" container

☐ calculator

See **Advance Preparation**

Project Information

Advance Preparation Arrange ahead of time with the principal for delivery of the capsule to his or her care (preferably in front of the whole class).

1 Doing the Project

✦ Explaining the Purpose of the Time Capsule

Discuss the idea of a time capsule with the class. Explain that a time capsule is a container holding items that represent a group, such as the residents of a town, at a particular moment in history. The items might be handicrafts, commercial products, newspapers, books, photographs, audiotapes, videotapes, and so on. The time capsule is buried or otherwise preserved for the future. Time capsules are often placed in the cornerstones of new buildings to be opened after a certain time or when the buildings are remodeled or torn down.

The object shown in the margin was sent as a time capsule on two Voyager space probes that have left the solar system. It is a 12-inch gold-plated copper disk containing sounds and images selected to portray the diversity of life and culture on Earth. There are images, recorded sounds, musical selections from different cultures and eras, spoken greetings in 55 languages, and printed messages. The contents were chosen in order to represent civilization on Earth in a way that might be understood by a distant civilization.

The idea of a second grade time capsule is to have children seal information about themselves in a box and, instead of leaving it for a far distant age, leave it with the principal of the school until they are in sixth grade. When they open the time capsule, they will find instructions to help them determine what things have changed about the class and how accurate (or inaccurate) some of their predictions were.

✦ Deciding upon the Contents of the Time Capsule

Have children suggest items to include in the time capsule. List their suggestions on the board. *For example:*

▷ a class photograph with each person identified

▷ the median height and weight of the class

▷ surveys of favorite activities, sports teams, food, television shows, musical groups, school subjects, topics in mathematics, and so on

▷ the distance some of us can run in 10 seconds (see Project 8); the distance some of us can throw a ball

▷ a list of important world, national, and local events

Have the class choose about six topics about which to gather data for the time capsule. Each child might write a brief description of herself or himself—likes, dislikes, height, weight, and so on and seal it in an envelope to be put into the time capsule. Encourage children to include pictures and recordings that they think might be interesting additions to the time capsule.

✦ Preparing Information for the Time Capsule

Divide the class into small groups. Assign one or more data-gathering tasks to each group. Within the groups, let children decide how they are going to collect and display the information assigned to them.

Bring the class together and have each group present its plan. Work with the class as a whole to fine-tune the plans; children from other groups might have suggestions for improving or adding to some of the plans. Ask children what to tell the sixth grade class (themselves!) about comparing the data from second grade to the data from sixth grade.

Develop a schedule for carrying out each group's plans over the next few days. For example, if a survey of favorite foods is needed, the group takes a poll and carries out its plan for displaying that information. If predictions are made, these are written up with space allowed for the future sixth graders to compare predictions to reality in order to see how accurate those predictions were.

Encourage children to look ahead four years and make predictions to include in the time capsule. *For example:*

- How many members of the current class will be in the same classroom or at the same school in sixth grade?

- About how much will class members have grown—that is, what will be median number of inches grown or pounds gained?

- Will their favorite television shows still be on the air? Will their favorite musical groups still be together?

- What will computers and the Internet be like?

- Will the United States have the same president?

◆ Preparing the Time Capsule

After all of the information has been gathered, each group takes a few minutes to share its data with the rest of the class. Then seal all the information and other items in a shoe box or other appropriate container. Be sure to label the time capsule with instructions for opening at the appropriate time. Deliver the time capsule to the principal.

◆ Asking Time Capsule Questions

Ask the class the following questions: If the time capsule is opened the same day of the year in *sixth* grade ...

- How many years will have gone by since second grade?

- Will the date fall on a school day?

- How old will you be?

- How many months until then? (Use a calculator to help.)

- Will there be a leap year between now and then?

You and children will have more ideas. Discuss and share responses.

2 Extending the Project

✦ Extension Suggestions

1. Have children research the time capsule shown on page 443 at:

   http://vraptor.jpl.nasa.gov/voyager/gold.gif.

2. Suggest that children investigate time capsules that have been placed in cornerstones of buildings in your community.

✦ Home Link Suggestion

Children plan and create a time capsule with members of their family. They devise a plan, gather information, and prepare the time capsule. Encourage children to write a short paragraph describing their family time capsules.

Collections

OBJECTIVE To describe a collection in terms of number, size, age, and other attributes.

background information

Recommended Use: During Unit 7 or Unit 11

Children prepare an information sheet about a collection of their own, of someone in their family, or of someone they know well. They bring a selection from the collection to display. If the collection is too fragile or too valuable for classroom display, children represent it in some other way.

See the discussion of Projects in the Management Guide section of the *Teacher's Reference Manual*.

materials

☐ writing paper
☐ *A Kid's Guide to the Smithsonian*
***See* Advance Preparation**

Project Information

Advance Preparation You may want to explore the feasibility of this project in advance by surveying the class to find out if children have a collection of any particular objects or know someone who has.

Send a note home explaining the Project. If possible, children bring in a collection or a selection from a collection; alternatively, they bring in a representation of the collection (photos, drawings, lists, catalog pictures, and so on).

You may want to obtain the following book for the Extension Suggestions in Part 2:

▷ *A Kid's Guide to the Smithsonian* by Ann Phillips Bay (Smithsonian Institution, 1996)

1 Doing the Project

✦Talking about Collections

Many children have collections of different types of toys, rocks, hats, tropical fish, seashells, stamps, books, sports cards, and so on. Encourage them to talk about their collections as you list the different kinds on the board. Some children may feel they have no collections. Ask if they have several of one kind of toy (such as cars, dolls, or stuffed animals). They may have collections and not realize it!

The start of a collection

Children who have no collections can talk about a collection they know about—maybe a friend's or a family member's. Or they can work with a classroom partner who has a collection.

◆ Collecting Data about the Collections

Discuss what kinds of data or information about the collections might be of interest to other people. List responses on the board. *For example:*

▷ the size of the collection

▷ categories or organization within the collection, such as stamps by country, year, intended use, or denomination

▷ the approximate length of time since the collection began

▷ the smallest or largest item in the collection

▷ the source(s) of items in the collection

▷ items most prized (and why)

▷ reasons the collection was begun

◆ Preparing Information Sheets

Using the list on the board, children decide which data are appropriate for their collections. Then they prepare an information sheet to remind them of the data on which they wish to report.

Children take the information sheets home to complete. You may want to send them as Home Links. (See the next page). Children bring the information sheets back to school in 2–3 days. They also bring to class a few representative items from the collections they described, or a representation of several items—photos, drawings, lists, videotapes, catalog pictures, and so on.

◆ Reporting on the Collections

Over the course of the next few days, allow time for children to report on and display selections from their collections.

Extending the Project

◆ Extension Suggestions

1. Invite a parent, friend, or local expert (for example, a baseball card collector) to class to display and describe a collection.

2. Go on a field trip to a museum or art gallery featuring a particular collection.

3. Have children read about collections of diverse things, from dinosaurs to Dorothy's red shoes to the Apollo 11 command module that returned from the Moon in *A Kid's Guide to the Smithsonian* by Ann Phillips Bay (Smithsonian Institution, 1996).

◆ Home Link Suggestion

Children complete their information sheets. They discuss with family members which items, if any, they will take to school. Children take photos, draw pictures, or make a list of items in their collections.

8

How Far Can I Run in 10 Seconds?

OBJECTIVE To measure the distances children can run in 10 seconds.

background information

Recommended Use: During Units 10, 11, or 12

See the discussion of Projects in the Management Guide section of the *Teacher's Reference Manual*.

materials

☐ Project Master (*Math Masters,* p. 215)

Per group of 3:

☐ string or yarn

☐ masking tape, chalk, colored blocks, or another marker

☐ stopwatch or watch with second hand (optional)

☐ slip of paper or stick-on note

***See* Advance Preparation**

Project Information

Advance Preparation You may want to enlist the help of the physical education teacher in collecting the data.

Each group of three children will need a 10-foot piece of string or yarn marked off at 1-foot intervals. You may want to have several children help you prepare these. In addition, children will need some way of timing 10-second intervals. While this can be done by counting aloud using a clock, a watch, or a stopwatch that shows seconds will give more accurate results.

1 Doing the Project

✦ Finding out How Far Children Can Run in 10 Seconds (*Math Masters,* p. 215)

Plan for the actual data collection to take place outside, on the playground or other large, open space.

Children are to collect the data in groups of 3; they will take turns being "runner," "timer," and "spotter." Before you leave the classroom, explain the steps for collecting the data:

Data-Collecting Steps

1. The timer gives the runner the signal to start and begins timing.

2. The spotter follows the runner.

3. When 10 seconds are up, the timer says "Stop!" and drops a raised arm or gives some other prearranged signal.

4. The spotter marks the spot reached by the runner with masking tape, chalk, a colored block, or some other marker.

5. The group cooperatively uses a 10-foot string to measure the distance covered.

6. The runner records the distance run in 10 seconds on a slip of paper or stick-on note.

Once the class gets to the running location, have each group mark a starting line with chalk, masking tape, or some other marker. Be sure there is enough room between starting lines so that groups will not get in one another's way.

Before groups start running, have several volunteers demonstrate how to measure a distance greater than 10 feet by laying a 10-foot length of string end-to-end.

Also demonstrate how to time the runners. If children count to time the runners, remind them to do it aloud: 1,001, 1,002, 1,003, ...

2 Extending the Project

◆ Extension Suggestions

1. If children record their distances on stick-on notes, collect the notes and make a bar graph of the data on the wall. (See margin.)

2. Have children find the range of 10-second distances, as well as a middle 10-second distance.

◆ Home Link Suggestion

Children discuss with family members what they have learned about the speed at which children run. They investigate the speed at which adults run by conducting an activity similar to the one in the Project with adult volunteers.

How Far Can I Run in 10 Seconds?

1. Record the distance you ran in 10 seconds.

_____ feet

2. The range of 10-second running distance for our class is _____ feet.

3. A middle 10-second running distance for our class is _____ feet.

Follow-Up

Record your distance again on a stick-on note. Your teacher will use the notes to make a bar graph of the data on the wall. A sample is shown below.

		Shawna 31 ft		
		Raoul 31 ft		Yasuko 33 ft
Tamika 30 ft		Paola 31 ft		Dolores 33 ft

◆ *Math Masters*, p. 215

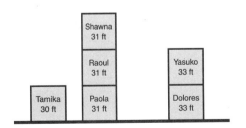

Second Grade Key Vocabulary

For a more extensive glossary that includes additional illustrations and references, please refer to the *Teacher's Reference Manual*.

addend   One of two or more numbers that are added.

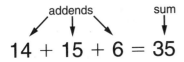

$$14 + 15 + 6 = 35$$

addition   A mathematical operation based on putting together two or more quantities.

addition fact   Two 1-digit numbers and their sum, such as $9 + 7 = 16$.

algorithm   A set of step-by-step instructions for doing something, such as carrying out a computation or solving a problem.

A.M.   The abbreviation for *ante meridiem,* which means "before the middle of the day"; from midnight to noon.

analog clock   A clock that shows the time by the positions of the hour and minute hands.

angle   A figure that is formed by two rays or two line segments with a common endpoint.

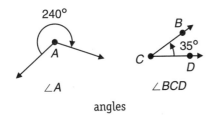

angles

area   The measure of a bounded surface.

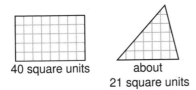

40 square units   about 21 square units

arm span   The distance from fingertip to fingertip of a person's outstretched arms.

array   A rectangular arrangement of objects in rows and columns.

arrow path   In *Everyday Mathematics,* a route to follow on a number grid.

arrow rule   In *Everyday Mathematics,* the operation that determines the number that goes in the next frame in a Frames-and-Arrows diagram. See *Frames and Arrows.*

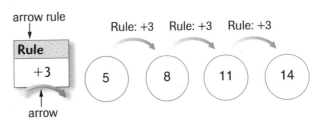

arrows   In *Everyday Mathematics,* the links representing the rule that determines which numbers go in the frames of a Frames-and-Arrows diagram. See *arrow rule.*

associative property   A property of addition and multiplication (but not of subtraction or division) that says that changing the grouping of the elements being added or multiplied will not change the sum or product. *For example:*

$$(4 + 3) + 7 = 4 + (3 + 7)$$

attribute   A feature of an object or a common feature of a set of objects. Examples of attributes include size, shape, color, and number of sides. See *property*.

ballpark estimate   A rough estimate used as a check on the reasonableness of an answer or when an exact figure is not necessary.

bank draft   A written order for the exchange of money. $1,000 bills are no longer in existence, so $1,000 bank drafts are issued. People can exchange $1,000 bank drafts for smaller bills (for example, 10 bills of $100 each).

bar graph   A graph that shows the relationships among variables by the use of bars to represent quantities.

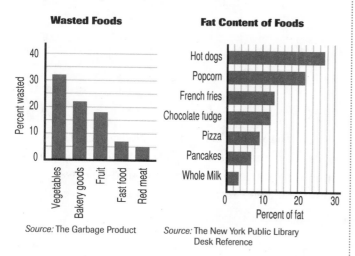

bar graphs

base   1. Any side of a polygon, usually used, along with the altitude perpendicular to it, for computing area.

Bases are shown in blue.

2. The flat face or faces that define the shape when classifying polyhedrons.

base-10 shorthand   In *Everyday Mathematics*, a system to represent base-10 blocks.

Name	Base-10 block	Base-10 shorthand
cube	▱	▪
long	▯	│
flat	▦	☐
big cube	▦	◱

big cube   In *Everyday Mathematics*, the term for the 10 cm by 10 cm by 10 cm base-10 block. A big cube is worth 1,000 cm cubes.

capacity   A measure of how much a container can hold, usually in units such as quarts, gallons, cups, or liters.

Celsius   The temperature scale on which 0° is the temperature at which pure water at sea level freezes and 100° is the temperature at which it boils. The Celsius scale is used in the metric system.

centimeter (cm)   In the metric system, a unit of length equivalent to 10 millimeters, $\frac{1}{10}$ of a decimeter, and $\frac{1}{100}$ of a meter.

centimeter cube   In *Everyday Mathematics*, the term for the smallest of the base-10 blocks, measuring 1 cm on each edge.

change diagram   In *Everyday Mathematics*, a diagram used to represent situations in which quantities are either increased or decreased.

14 − 5 = 9

circle   The set of all points in a plane that are equally distant from a given point in the plane called the *center* of the circle.

center

Class Data Pad   In *Everyday Mathematics,* a large pad of paper where data collected by the class can be stored for use (and reuse) throughout the year.

column   A vertical arrangement of objects or numbers in an array or table.

commutative property   A property of addition and multiplication (but not of subtraction or division) that says that changing the order of the elements being added or multiplied will not change the sum or product. For example, $5 \times 8 = 40$ and $8 \times 5 = 40$.

comparison diagram   In *Everyday Mathematics,* a diagram used to represent situations in which two quantities are compared.

Quantity
12

Quantity	Difference
9	?

$12 = 9 + ?$

cone   A 3-dimensional shape having a circular base, a curved surface, and one vertex, called the apex.

consecutive   Following one another in an uninterrupted order, such as A, B, C, D or 6, 7, 8, 9.

corner   See *vertex.*

counting numbers   The numbers used to count things. The set of counting numbers is {1, 2, 3, 4, ...}. Sometimes 0 is included with the counting numbers.

cube   A polyhedron with six square faces. One of the five regular polyhedra. See *regular polyhedron.*

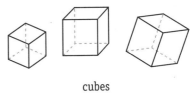

cubes

cubit   An ancient unit of length, measured from the point of the elbow to the end of the middle finger.

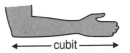

cubit

cup   In the U.S. customary system, a unit of capacity equal to 8 fluid ounces; $\frac{1}{2}$ pint.

curved surface or face   A surface which does not lie in a plane; for example, a sphere or cylindrical surface. Also, a nonbase face of a cone or cylinder.

customary system   The measuring system used most often in the United States, in contrast to the metric system used nearly everywhere else. See *U.S. customary system.*

cylinder   A 3-dimensional shape having a curved surface and parallel circular or elliptical bases that are the same size. A can is an object shaped like a cylinder.

data   Information gathered by observing, counting, or measuring. *Data* is the plural of *datum.*

deci-   Prefix meaning one-tenth.

decimal point   The mark that separates the whole number from the fraction in decimal notation; in expressing money, it separates the dollars from the cents.

decimeter (dm)   In the metric system, a unit of length equivalent to $\frac{1}{10}$ of a meter or 10 centimeters.

degree (°) A unit for measuring temperature. Also a unit of measure for angles based on dividing one complete circle (rotation) into 360 equal parts. The small raised symbol (°) is called the *degree symbol*.

denominator The number written below the line in a fraction. In a part-whole fraction, the number of equal parts into which the whole (ONE) is divided. Compare to *numerator*.

diagonal (of a table) A line of objects or numbers from upper left to lower right, or from lower left to upper right in an array or a table.

+, −	0	1	2	3	4	5	6	7	8	9
0	0	1	2	3	4	5	6	7	8	9
1	1	2	3	4	5	6	7	8	9	10
2	2	3	4	5	6	7	8	9	10	11
3	3	4	5	6	7	8	9	10	11	12
4	4	5	6	7	8	9	10	11	12	13
5	5	6	7	8	9	10	11	12	13	14
6	6	7	8	9	10	11	12	13	14	15
7	7	8	9	10	11	12	13	14	15	16
8	8	9	10	11	12	13	14	15	16	17
9	9	10	11	12	13	14	15	16	17	18

The diagonal is shown in blue.

difference The amount by which one number is greater or less than another number.

digit In the base-ten numeration system, one of the symbols 0, 1, 2, 3, 4, 5, 6, 7, 8, and 9 which can be used to write any number.

digital clock A clock that uses numbers to show the time in hours and minutes, with a colon used to separate them.

division The operation used to solve equal-sharing problems. It is used to find how a total amount can be separated into an equal number of groups, or into groups of equal size.

$$24 \div 4 = 6$$

doubles fact The addition and multiplication facts without turn-around partners. A doubles fact names the sum or product of a 1-digit number and itself, such as $4 + 4 = 8$ or $3 \times 3 = 9$.

edge A line segment where two faces of a polyhedron meet.

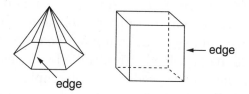

endpoint A point at the end of a line segment or a ray. A line segment is named by its two endpoints. "Segment *LT*" or "segment *TL*" is the line segment between points *L* and *T*.

equal-grouping story A number story that involves separating something into equal groups. In such a problem, the total and the number in each group are known. Division can often be used to solve equal-grouping stories.

equal groups Sets with the same number of elements.

equal-sharing story A number story that involves sharing something equally. In such a problem, the total and the number of groups are known. Division can often be used to solve equal-sharing stories.

equivalent names Different ways of naming the same number. For example, $2 + 6$, $4 + 4$, $12 - 4$, $18 - 10$, $100 - 92$, $5 + 1 + 2$, eight, VIII, and ~~HHt~~ /// are all equivalent names for 8. See *name-collection box*.

estimate 1. *n.* A close, rather than exact, answer. A number close to another number. 2. *v.* To make an estimate.

even number A whole number that can be evenly divided by 2. It has 0, 2, 4, 6, or 8 in the ones place. Compare to *odd number*.

Exploration In *Everyday Mathematics,* an independent or small-group activity that may involve concept development, manipulatives, data collection, problem solving, games, and skill reviews.

extended fact A variation of a basic arithmetic fact involving multiples of 10, 100, and so on. For example, $30 + 70 = 100$, $40 \times 5 = 200$, and $560 \div 7 = 80$ are extended facts.

face A surface that bounds a 3-dimensional shape. It may be curved (as on a cylinder or a cone) or flat (as on a prism).

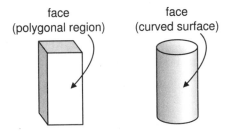

face
(polygonal region)

face
(curved surface)

fact extensions Calculations with larger numbers using knowledge of basic facts. For example, knowing the basic fact $5 + 8 = 13$ makes it easy to solve problems such as $50 + 80 = ?$ and $65 + ? = 73$. Fact extensions can also be applied to basic subtraction, multiplication, and division facts.

fact family A collection of related addition and subtraction facts, or multiplication and division facts, made from the same numbers. For 5, 6, and 11, the addition/subtraction family consists of $5 + 6 = 11$, $6 + 5 = 11$, $11 - 5 = 6$, and $11 - 6 = 5$. For 5, 7, and 35, the multiplication/division family consists of $5 \times 7 = 35$, $7 \times 5 = 35$, $35 \div 7 = 5$, and $35 \div 5 = 7$.

fact power In *Everyday Mathematics,* a term that refers to the ability to recall basic number facts automatically without having to figure them out.

Fact Triangle A triangular flash card labeled with the numbers of a fact family for practice with addition/subtraction and multiplication/division facts.

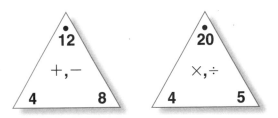

factors The numbers being multiplied in a multiplication number model. In the number model $4 \times 3 = 12$, 4 and 3 are factors.

Facts Table A chart of rows and columns, also known as an Addition/Subtraction Facts Table or a Multiplication/Division Facts Table, for use in finding addition and subtraction or multiplication and division facts.

Fahrenheit The temperature scale on which pure water at sea level freezes at $32°$ and boils at $212°$. The Fahrenheit scale is used in the U.S. customary system.

flat In *Everyday Mathematics,* the term for the base-10 block consisting of 100 cm cubes.

foot (ft) In the U.S. customary system, a unit of length equivalent to 12 inches, or $\frac{1}{3}$ of a yard.

fraction   A number in the form of $\frac{a}{b}$ or % that names part of an object or collection of objects, compares two quantities, or represents division. A fraction names equal parts of a whole.

Frames and Arrows   In *Everyday Mathematics,* diagrams used to represent number sequences—sets of numbers ordered according to a rule. The diagrams consist of *frames* in which numbers are written and *arrows* that represent rules for moving from one frame to another.

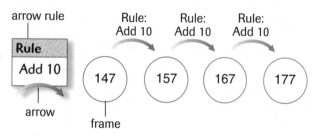

Frames-and-Arrows diagram

frequency   The number of times a value occurs in a set of data.

frequency graph   A graph showing how often each value in a data set occurs.

frequency table   A chart on which data is tallied to find the frequency of given events or values.

function machine   In *Everyday Mathematics,* a diagram of an imaginary machine programmed to process numbers according to a certain rule. A number (input) is put into the machine and is transformed into a second number (output) through the application of a rule.

in	out
1	2
2	4
3	6
5	10
10	20
20	40

function machine with input/output table

gallon (gal)   In the U.S. customary system, a unit of capacity equal to 4 quarts.

geometric solid   A 3-dimensional shape bounded by surfaces. Common geometric solids include the rectangular prism, square-based pyramid, cylinder, cone, and sphere.

geometry   The study of spatial objects and their properties and relationships. The word *geometry* is derived from the Greek words for "earth" and "measure."

gram (g)   In the metric system, a unit of mass equal to $\frac{1}{1,000}$ of a kilogram.

height   A measure of how tall something is.

heptagon   A 7-sided polygon.

hexagon   A 6-sided polygon.

Home Link   In *Everyday Mathematics,* a suggested follow-up or enrichment activity to be done at home.

inch (in.)   In the U.S. customary system, a unit of length equal to $\frac{1}{12}$ of a foot and equivalent to 2.54 centimeters.

input   A number inserted into an imaginary function machine, which processes numbers according to a designated rule. See *function machine.*

kilogram (kg)   In the metric system, the fundamental unit of mass; it is equal to 1,000 grams. 1 kilogram equals about 2.2 pounds.

kilometer (km)   In the metric system, a unit of length equal to 1,000 meters. One kilometer equals about 0.62 miles.

kite   A quadrilateral with two pairs of adjacent sides that are the same length. (A rhombus is not a kite.)

kite

label Descriptive word or phrase used to put numbers in context. Using a label reinforces the idea that numbers refer to something. Flags, snowballs, and scary monsters are examples of labels.

length Usually, but not necessarily, the longer dimension of a rectangle or a rectangular object.

line A straight path that extends infinitely in opposite directions.

line of symmetry A line that divides a figure into two halves that are mirror images.

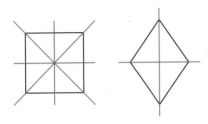

Lines of symmetry are shown in blue.

line plot A sketch of data in which checkmarks, Xs, or stick-on notes above a number line show the frequency of each value.

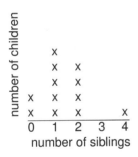

line plot

line segment A straight path joining two points.

liter (L) In the metric system, a unit of capacity equal to 1,000 milliliters. A liter is a little larger than a quart.

long In *Everyday Mathematics,* the term for the base-10 block consisting of 10 cm cubes.

Math Boxes In *Everyday Mathematics,* a format to provide review problems and to practice skills. A set of Math Boxes for each lesson are found in the student *Math Journals.*

Math Journal In *Everyday Mathematics,* a student record of mathematical discoveries and experiences. It provides visual models for conceptual understanding and problems, and includes activities for individuals and small groups.

Math Masters Pages ready for duplicating. Most of these are used by children in carrying out suggested activities. Some will be used more than once during the school year.

Math Messages In *Everyday Mathematics,* activities for children to complete at the start of each lesson. Math Messages may be problems that introduce the day's lesson, directions to follow, sentences to complete or correct, or reading assignments.

mathematics A study of relationships among numbers, shapes, systems, and patterns. It is used to count and measure things, to discover similarities and differences between them, to solve problems, and to learn about and organize the world.

measurement unit The reference unit used when measuring length, weight, capacity, time, or temperature. Ounces, degrees, and centimeters are examples of measurement units.

median The middle value in a set of data when the data are listed in order from least to greatest (or greatest to least). See *middle value.*

memory Mechanical or electronic storage of information for later recall, as in computers or calculators.

memory keys Keys to manage a calculator's memory. The memory keys are commonly labeled ⓜ⁺, ⓜ⁻, and ⓜⓡⓒ. The ⓜ⁺ key is used to add a number to the number stored in the calculator's memory; the ⓜ⁻ key is used to subtract a number from the number in memory. The ⓜⓡⓒ key, pressed once, displays the number currently stored in memory; when the key is pressed twice, the calculator's memory is cleared.

mental arithmetic Computations done by people "in their heads," either in whole or in part.

Mental Math and Reflexes In *Everyday Mathematics,* exercises (usually oral) suggested at the start of most lessons. They are designed to strengthen children's number sense and to review and advance essential basic skills.

meter (m) In the metric system, the fundamental unit of length, equal to 10 decimeters, 100 centimeters, or 1,000 millimeters.

metric system A measurement system based on the base-ten numeration system and used in most countries in the world. Units for linear measure (length, distance) include millimeter, centimeter, meter, and kilometer; units for mass include gram and kilogram; units for capacity include milliliter and liter; and the unit for temperature change is degrees Celsius.

middle value The number in the middle when a set of data is organized in sequential order. Also called the *median.*

mile (mi) In the U.S. customary system, a unit of length equivalent to 5,280 feet, 1,760 yards, or about 1,609 meters.

milliliter (mL) In the metric system, a unit of capacity equal to $\frac{1}{1,000}$ of a liter; 1 cubic centimeter.

millimeter (mm) In the metric system, a unit of length equivalent to $\frac{1}{10}$ of a centimeter or $\frac{1}{1,000}$ of a meter.

mode The value or values that occur most often in a set of data. For example, in the data set 3, 4, 4, 4, 5, 5, 6, 4 is the mode.

multiples Repeated groups of the same amount. Multiples of a number are the products of that number and whole numbers.

multiplication The operation used with whole numbers, fractions, or decimals to find the total number of things in several equal groups.

multiplication/division diagram Used to represent numbers in which several equal groups are being considered together. The diagram has three parts: a number of groups, a number in each group, and a total number.

boxes	candies per box	candies in all
3	6	18

$3 \times 6 = 18$

multiplication fact The product of two 1-digit numbers, such as $6 \times 7 = 42$.

name-collection box In *Everyday Mathematics,* a boxlike diagram tagged with a given number and used for collecting equivalent names for that number.

name-collection box

number family A triplet of numbers consisting of two addends and their sum or two factors and their product.

number grid A table in which consecutive numbers are arranged in rows of ten. A move from one number to the next number within a row is a change of one; a move from one number to the next number within a column is a change of ten.

number-grid puzzle In *Everyday Mathematics,* a piece of a number grid in which some, but not all, of the numbers are missing. Number-grid puzzles are used for practice with place-value concepts.

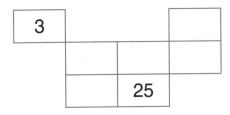

number-grid puzzle

number line A line on which equidistant points correspond to numbers in order. Used as a frame of reference for counting and numeration activities.

number model A number sentence that models or fits a situation. For example, the situation *Sally had $5 and then she earned $8,* can be modeled as $5 + 8 = 13$.

number scroll In *Everyday Mathematics,* number-grid pages taped together. See *number grid.*

number sequence A list of numbers often generated by some rule. See *Frames and Arrows,* which generate number sequences.

number story A story that contains a problem that can be solved using one or more of the four basic arithmetic operations or by sorting out relations such as equals, is less than, or is greater than.

numerator The number written above the line in a fraction. In a part-whole fraction, it names the number of equal parts of the whole being considered.

octagon An 8-sided polygon.

odd number A number that cannot be evenly divided by 2. It has 1, 3, 5, 7, or 9 in the ones place. Compare to *even number.*

ONE In *Everyday Mathematics,* a way of denoting the unit whole in part-whole fractions and other similar situations.

1-facts The sum of two 1-digit numbers where one of the numbers is one, such as $6 + 1 = 7$. If one is added to any number, or vice versa, the result is the next higher number. Also, the product of two numbers where one of the numbers is 1, such as $1 \times 3 = 3$. The product of 1 and any number is equal to that number.

operation An action performed on one or two numbers producing a single number result.

ordinal number A number used to express position or order in a series, such as first, third, and tenth.

ounce (oz) In the U.S. customary system, a unit of weight equal to $\frac{1}{16}$ of a pound. One ounce is 31.103 grams.

outcome A possible result of a random process. Heads and tails are the two outcomes of tossing a coin.

output The number resulting from the application of a rule used by an imaginary function machine to process numbers.

pan balance A device used to weigh objects or to compare their weights.

parallel Lines, rays, line segments, or planes that are equidistant at all points, no matter how far extended; never meeting.

parallelogram A quadrilateral that has two pairs of parallel sides and opposite sides that are congruent.

partial-sums algorithm An addition procedure in which sums are computed for each place separately and then added to yield the final sum.

	268
	+ 483
1. Add 100s.	600
2. Adds 10s.	140
3. Add 1s.	+ 11
4. Add partial sums.	751

parts-and-total diagram   In *Everyday Mathematics,* a diagram used to represent problems in which two or more quantities are combined to form a total quantity. It is often used when the parts are known and the total is unknown. It can also be used when the total and one or more parts are known, but one part is unknown.

Total	
13	
Part	Part
8	?

parts-and-total diagram

pattern   A model or plan by which objects or numbers can be arranged so that what comes next can be predicted.

Pattern-Block Template   In *Everyday Mathematics,* a sheet of plastic with geometric shapes cut out, used to draw patterns and designs.

pentagon   A 5-sided polygon.

per   *In each* or *for each,* as in ten chairs per row or six tickets per family.

percent (%)   Per hundred, or out of a hundred. Times $\frac{1}{100}$; times 0.01; 1 one-hundredth. 15% means $\frac{15}{100}$, or 0.15 of a number.

perimeter   The distance around a closed plane figure or region. *Peri-* comes from the Greek word for "around" and *meter* comes from the Greek word *metron* that means "measure"; perimeter means "around measure."

pictograph   A graph constructed with pictures or symbols. A pictograph makes it possible to compare at a glance the relative amounts of two or more counts or measures.

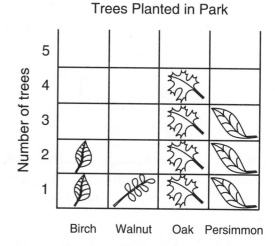

Trees Planted in Park

pint   In the U.S. customary system, a unit of capacity equal to 2 cups or 16 fluid ounces.

place value   The relative worth of each digit in a number, which is determined by its position. Each place has a value ten times that of the place to its right and one-tenth of the value of the place to its left.

point   An exact location in space. Points are usually labeled with capital letters.

polygon   A closed plane figure formed by three or more line segments that meet only at their endpoints. The word comes from Greek: *poly* means "many" and *gon* (from *gonia*) means "angle."

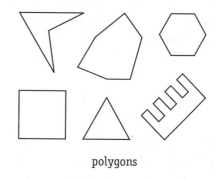

polygons

polyhedron A closed 3-dimensional shape, all of whose surfaces (faces) are flat. Each face consists of a polygon and the interior of the polygon.

poster In *Everyday Mathematics,* a page displaying a collection of numerical data. The poster may be referred to as a source of data for developing number stories.

pound (lb) In the U.S. customary system, a unit of weight equal to 16 ounces and defined as 0.45359237 kilograms.

prism A polyhedron with two parallel flat faces (bases) with the same size and shape. The other faces are bounded by parallelograms. Prisms are classified according to the shape of the two parallel bases.

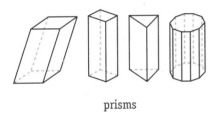

prisms

probability A number from 0 to 1 that indicates the likelihood that an event will happen. The closer a probability is to 1, the more likely it is that the event will happen. The closer a probability is to 0, the less likely it is that the event will happen. For example, the probability that a fair coin will show heads is 1/2.

product The result of doing multiplication. In the number model *4 × 3 = 12,* 12 is the product.

Project In *Everyday Mathematics,* a thematic activity to be completed in one or more days by small groups or by the whole class. Projects often involve collecting and analyzing data and are usually cross-curricular in nature.

property A feature of an object. For example, size, shape, color, and number of parts are all properties. Same as *attribute.*

pyramid A polyhedron (3-dimensional shape) in which one face (the base) is a polygon and the other faces are triangles with a common vertex called the apex. A pyramid is classified according to the shape of its base.

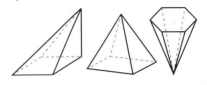

pyramids

quadrangle A 4-sided polygon. Same as *quadrilateral.*

quadrilateral A 4-sided polygon. Same as *quadrangle.*

quart In the U.S. customary system, a unit of capacity equal to 32 fluid ounces, 2 pints, or 4 cups.

quotient The result of dividing one number by another number; the number of equal shares. In the division number model *15 ÷ 5 = 3,* 3 is the quotient.

range The difference between the greatest and least numbers in a set of data.

rectangle A parallelogram whose angles are all right angles. See *parallelogram.*

rectangular prism A prism whose bases are rectangles.

rectangular pyramid A pyramid whose base is a rectangle.

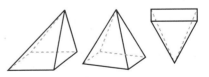

rectangular pyramids

regular polygon A polygon whose sides are all the same length and whose angles are all equal.

regular polyhedron   A polyhedron whose faces are all congruent regular polygons and with the same number of faces meeting at every vertex, all at the same angle.

cube   octahedron

relation symbol   A symbol used to express a relationship between two quantities. Some relation symbols used in number sentences are = (is equal to), < (is less than), and > (is greater than).

remainder   The amount left over when things are divided into equal shares. In the division number model *16 ÷ 3 → 5 R1*, the remainder is 1.

rhombus   A parallelogram with sides that are all the same length. The angles may be right angles, in which case the rhombus is a square.

rhombuses

right angle   A square corner; a 90° angle. See *angle*.

round   1. *v.* To express a number in a simplified way. Examples of rounding include expressing a measure of weight to the nearest pound and expressing an amount of money to the nearest dollar. 2. *adj.* Circular in shape.

rule table   In *Everyday Mathematics*, a table for displaying the input, output, and rule of a function in the "What's My Rule?" routine.

scale   The ratio of the distance on a map, globe, or drawing to the actual distance. On a thermometer, a vertical number line used for measuring temperature.

set   A collection or group of objects, numbers, or other items.

side   Any one of the line segments that make up a polygon. Sometimes a face of a 3-dimensional figure is called a side.

slate   Lap-size (about 8" × 11") chalkboard or whiteboard that children use in *Everyday Mathematics* for a variety of purposes, including recording responses during group exercises and informal group assessments.

sphere   A 3-dimensional shape whose curved surface is, at all points, a given distance from its center point. A ball is shaped like a sphere. A sphere is hollow; it does not include the points in its interior.

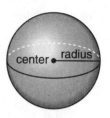

sphere

square   A rectangle whose sides are all the same length.

square number   A number that is the product of a whole number and itself. A square number can be represented by a square array.

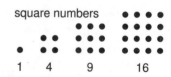

square of a number   The product of number and itself.

square pyramid   A pyramid with a square base.

square pyramid

square units   The units used to measure area. A square unit represents a square with the measure of each side being one of that unit. For example, a square inch represents a square that measures one inch on each side.

straightedge   A tool, such as a ruler, used to draw line segments. A straightedge does not need to have measure marks on it.

subtraction   A mathematical operation based on taking away one quantity from another or decreasing a quantity.

sum   The result of adding two or more numbers. For example, in *5 + 3 = 8,* 8 is the sum. See *addition.*

survey   A study that collects data. In *Everyday Mathematics,* surveys are used to generate data for graphing and analysis.

symmetry   The property of exact balance in a figure; having the same size and shape across a dividing line or around a point.

line symmetry   rotational symmetry

symmetry

tally marks   Marks (///// /////) used to keep track of a count.

tens   The place-value position equal to ten times the unit value.

tetrahedron   A polyhedron with four faces.

3-dimensional (3-D)   Objects that are not completely within a single flat surface; objects with thickness as well as length and width.

tiling   An arrangement of closed shapes that covers a surface completely without overlaps or gaps.

time line   A device for showing in sequence when events took place. A time line is a number line with the numbers naming years, days, and so on.

tool kit   In *Everyday Mathematics,* a bag or a box containing a calculator, measuring tools, and manipulatives often used in the program.

trade-first subtraction   A subtraction procedure in which all necessary trades are done before any subtractions are carried out. This simplifies the algorithm since the user can concentrate on one thing at a time.

trapezoid   A quadrilateral that has one pair of parallel sides. No two sides need be the same length.

trapezoid

triangle   A 3-sided polygon.

triangular prism   A prism whose bases are triangles.

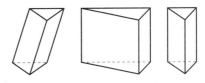

triangular prisms

triangular pyramid   A pyramid in which all faces are triangles, any one of which can be called the base.

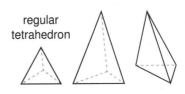

regular tetrahedron

triangular pyramids

turn-around facts   A pair of addition or multiplication (but not subtraction or division) facts in which the order of the addends or the factors is reversed. For example, 3 + 5 = 8 and 5 + 3 = 8 or 3 × 9 = 27 and 9 × 3 = 27. If a fact is known, its turnaround is also known.

2-dimensional (2-D) Objects completely within a plane; objects with length and width, but no thickness.

unit A label, descriptive word, or unit of measure used to put a number in context. Using a unit with a number reinforces the idea that numbers refer to something. Fingers, snowballs, miles, and cents are examples of units. Same as *label*.

unit box In *Everyday Mathematics,* a rectangular box displayed alongside a set of numbers or problems. It contains the unit or label for the numbers in use.

unit box

U.S. customary system The measuring system most frequently used in the United States. Units for linear measure (length, distance) include inch, foot, yard, and mile; units for weight include ounce and pound; units for capacity include cup, pint, quart, and gallon; for temperature change, degrees Fahrenheit.

vertex (vertices) The point at which the rays or line segments of an angle, sides of a polygon, or the edges of a polyhedron meet. Same as *corner*.

weight A measure of how heavy something is.

"What's My Rule?" In *Everyday Mathematics,* a routine that involves a set of number pairs in which the numbers in each pair are related to each other according to the same rule. The problems are usually displayed in table format in which two of the three parts (input, output, rule) are known and the goal is to find the unknown part.

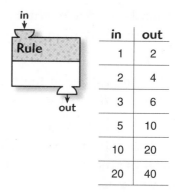

in	out
1	2
2	4
3	6
5	10
10	20
20	40

"What's My Rule?" problem

width of a rectangle Length of one side of a rectangle or rectangular object; often the shorter side.

x-by-y array An arrangement having *x* rows of *y* per row, representing *x* sets of *y* objects in each set.

Array of Dots   Array of Squares

2-by-6 arrays: 2 rows, 6 per row

yard (yd) Historically, the distance from the tip of the nose to the tip of the longest finger.

In the U.S. customary system, a unit of length equivalent to 3 feet or 36 inches.

zero facts The sum of two 1-digit numbers where one of the addends is zero, such as $0 + 5 = 5$. If zero is added to any number, or vice versa, there is no change in the number. Also, the product of two 1-digit numbers where one of the factors is zero, such as $4 \times 0 = 0$. The product of a number and 0 is always 0.

Scope and Sequence Chart

Throughout *Everyday Mathematics,* children repeatedly experience concepts and skills in each of the mathematical strands. Each exposure builds on and extends children's understanding. They study important concepts over consecutive years through a variety of formats. The Scope and Sequence Chart shows the units in which exposures occur and the developmental level of the skill or concept. The three levels of skill and concept development used in the chart are Beginning, Developing, and Secure. These levels refer here to unit content within the *K–6 Everyday Mathematics* curriculum rather than performance expectations for children.

The skills and concepts are divided according to the mathematical strands below.

Mathematical Strands	**Pages**
Numeration	468–471
Operations and Computation	472–474
Patterns, Functions, and Algebra	475–476
Geometry	477–479
Measurement and Reference Frames: Measurement	480–483
Measurement and Reference Frames: Reference Frames	484–485
Data and Chance	486–487

How to Read the Scope and Sequence Chart

Each section of the chart includes a mathematical strand title, three grade level columns divided by units, and a list of specific skills and concepts grouped by major concepts.

Numeration

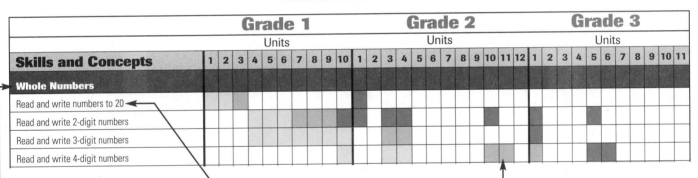

Skills and Concepts	Grade 1 Units 1	2	3	4	5	6	7	8	9	10	Grade 2 Units 1	2	3	4	5	6	7	8	9	10	11	12	Grade 3 Units 1	2	3	4	5	6	7	8	9	10	11
Whole Numbers																																		
Read and write numbers to 20																																	
Read and write 2-digit numbers																																	
Read and write 3-digit numbers																																	
Read and write 4-digit numbers																																	

Major mathematical concepts within each strand. A list of related skills and concepts appear below this head.

Find specific skills and concepts in this list and then follow across the row for units in which they appear at each grade level.

The shading in the cells indicates the skill and concept development level for a particular exposure. The lightest shading shows beginning exposures, the medium shading designates developing exposures, and the darkest shading indicates secure exposures.

Numeration

Scope and Sequence Chart

Skills and Concepts	Grade 1 — Units										Grade 2 — Units												Grade 3 — Units										
	1	2	3	4	5	6	7	8	9	10	1	2	3	4	5	6	7	8	9	10	11	12	1	2	3	4	5	6	7	8	9	10	11
Whole Numbers																																	
Read and write numbers to 20																																	
Read and write 2-digit numbers																																	
Read and write 3-digit numbers																																	
Read and write 4-digit numbers																																	
Read and write larger numbers																																	
Read and write ordinal numbers																																	
Order numbers to 20																																	
Order 2-digit numbers																																	
Order 3-digit numbers																																	
Order 4-digit numbers																																	
Order larger numbers																																	
Compare numbers to 20																																	
Compare 2-digit numbers																																	
Compare 3-digit numbers																																	
Compare 4-digit numbers																																	
Compare larger numbers																																	
Compare numbers using $<$, $>$, and $=$ symbols																																	
Perform rote counting																																	
Perform rational counting																																	
Skip count by 2s, 5s, and 10s																																	
Count by 25s																																	
Count by 100s, 1,000s and 10,000s																																	
Count using a calculator																																	

Whole Numbers (cont.)

Skill	1	2	3	4	5	6	7	8	9	10	11	12	13	14	15	16
Use Roman numerals																
Identify even and odd numbers				Developing				Secure							Developing	
Find equivalent names for numbers	Beginning	Beginning		Secure		Developing			Developing					Secure		Developing
Make and solve number-grid puzzles		Developing	Beginning		Secure	Secure		Developing	Developing							Developing
Explore place value using a number grid					Beginning	Developing	Secure									
Identify place value in 2-digit numbers					Secure	Developing	Beginning		Secure							Secure
Identify place value in 3-digit numbers						Beginning			Beginning							
Identify place value in 4-digit numbers							Developing			Secure			Developing	Secure		Secure
Identify place value in larger numbers						Secure	Beginning									
Make exchanges among place values				Secure	Developing				Beginning							
Find complements of 10																
Find complements for multiples of 10						Secure				Beginning						
Make least and greatest numbers with randomly selected digits																
Write numbers in expanded notation										Developing						
Display and read numbers on a calculator																
Explore magnitude of numbers						Beginning										
Identify square numbers	Beginning	Developing			Secure											

Money and Decimals

Skill	1	2	3	4	5	6	7	8	9	10	11	12	13	14	15	16
Use cents notation					Secure	Developing	Beginning		Developing							
Use dollars-and-cents notation					Secure	Developing			Beginning							
Display money amounts on a calculator					Developing			Secure								
Identify equivalencies and make coin exchanges				Developing	Beginning		Secure	Developing								
Identify equivalencies and make coin/bill exchanges					Beginning											
Show money amounts with coins					Secure				Developing						Secure	
Show money amounts with coins/bills					Developing				Secure							

Beginning   Developing   Secure

Numeration (cont.)

	Grade 1 Units										Grade 2 Units												Grade 3 Units										
Skills and Concepts	1	2	3	4	5	6	7	8	9	10	1	2	3	4	5	6	7	8	9	10	11	12	1	2	3	4	5	6	7	8	9	10	11
Money and Decimals (cont.)																																	
Compare money amounts using <, >, and = symbols																																	
Identify pennies and dimes as fractional parts of a dollar.																																	
Calculate the value of coin combinations																																	
Calculate the value of coin/bill combinations																																	
Explore uses for decimals																																	
Identify and name decimal numbers																																	
Identify place value in decimals through thousandths																																	
Model decimals with base-10 materials																																	
Compare and order decimals																																	
Read and write 1- and 2-digit decimals																																	
Read and write 3-digit decimals																																	
Count by tenths																																	
Relate decimals to metric measurement																																	
Count by thousandths																																	
Read and write decimals beyond thousandths																																	
Write decimals with expanded notation																																	
Fractions																																	
Understand the meaning of fractions																																	
Identify numerator and denominator																																	
Identify fractional parts of a region																																	
Identify fractional parts of a set																																	
Find equivalent fractions																																	

Fractions (cont.)

- Compare and order fractions
- Explore uses of fractions
- Use fractions in number stories
- Write fraction words
- Identify fractions on a number line
- Identify and name mixed numbers
- Convert between mixed numbers and fractions

Positive and Negative Numbers (Integers)

- Count back past zero
- Explore uses for positive and negative numbers (integers)
- Explore reference points for zero
- Use positive and negative numbers (integers) in number stories

Beginning   Developing   Secure

Notes on Scope and Sequence

Operations and Computation

Skills and Concepts	Grade 1 Units	Grade 2 Units	Grade 3 Units
	1 2 3 4 5 6 7 8 9 10	1 2 3 4 5 6 7 8 9 10 11 12	1 2 3 4 5 6 7 8 9 10 11
Addition and Subtraction			
Understand meaning of addition/subtraction			
Solve addition/subtraction number stories			
Make up addition/subtraction number stories			
Solve addition number stories with 3 or more addends			
Solve multi-step addition/subtraction number stories			
Find/use complements of 10			
Find/use complements of 100			
Solve change-to-more and change-to-less number stories/diagrams			
Solve parts-and-total number stories/diagrams			
Solve comparison number stories			
Find patterns in addition/subtraction facts			
Add/subtract using a number line			
Add/subtract using a number grid			
Add/subtract using a calculator			
Find sums of even and odd numbers			
Practice basic facts			
Practice extensions of basic facts			
Use mental arithmetic to add/subtract			
Investigate relationships between addition and subtraction			
Add/subtract multiples of 10			
Add/subtract multiples of 100			

Addition and Subtraction (cont.)

- Add/subtract money amounts/decimals
- Add 3 or more 1-digit numbers
- Add/subtract 2-digit numbers
- Add/subtract 2-digit numbers in number sentences containing parentheses
- Add 3 or more 2-digit numbers
- Add/subtract 3- and 4-digit numbers
- Investigate properties of addition/subtraction
- Use an Addition/Subtraction Facts Table
- Make change
- Use estimation to add/subtract
- Use addition/subtraction algorithms
- Estimate to check reasonableness of an answer
- Add/subtract positive and negative numbers
- Explore calculator functions

Multiplication and Division

- Understand meaning of multiplication/division
- Solve multiplication/division number stories
- Make up multiplication/division number stories
- Interpret a remainder in division number stories
- Solve multi-step multiplication/division number stories
- Solve problems involving ratios
- Investigate properties of multiplication/division
- Practice multiplication/division facts
- Explore square numbers
- Use arrays to model multiples of equal groups
- Use manipulatives to model multiplication

Beginning **Developing** **Secure**

Operations and Computation (cont.)

Skills and Concepts

Skills and Concepts	Grade 1 — Units										Grade 2 — Units												Grade 3 — Units										
	1	2	3	4	5	6	7	8	9	10	1	2	3	4	5	6	7	8	9	10	11	12	1	2	3	4	5	6	7	8	9	10	11
Multiplication and Division (cont.)																																	
Investigate relationships between multiplication and division																					■				■						■		
Multiply/divide using a number line																										■							
Find patterns in multiplication/division facts																					■				■	■			■				
Find patterns in multiples of 10, 100, and 1,000																					■				■	■	■	■	■	■	■		■
Multiply/divide with 2-digit numbers																										■					■		
Use estimation to multiply/divide																													■				
Multiply/divide with large numbers																													■				
Use a calculator to multiply or divide																										■							
Use a Multiplication/Division Facts Table																			■											■			
Multiply/divide 1- and 2-digit numbers in number sentences with parentheses																				■													
Use mental arithmetic to multiply/divide																			■										■				
Multiply/divide multiples of 10, 100, and 1,000 by 1-digit numbers																													■		■		
Multiply/divide money amounts																													■				
Use multiplication/division algorithms																													■		■		
Identify factors of a number																													■				
Use a multiplication algorithm to multiply 3-digit numbers by 2-digit numbers																																	
Solve missing factor number models																																	■

Patterns, Functions, and Algebra

Skills and Concepts	Grade 1 Units										Grade 2 Units												Grade 3 Units										
	1	2	3	4	5	6	7	8	9	10	1	2	3	4	5	6	7	8	9	10	11	12	1	2	3	4	5	6	7	8	9	10	11
Visual Patterns																																	
Create patterns with 2-dimensional shapes																																	
Sort and identify shapes/objects by attributes																																	
Explore and extend visual patterns																																	
Find patterns in the real world																																	
Find common attributes in objects and people																																	
Create patterns with 3-dimensional shapes																																	
Number Patterns																																	
Count up and back on a number grid																																	
Investigate even and odd number patterns																																	
Identify and use patterns on a number grid																																	
Add and subtract using a number grid																																	
Find patterns in addition and subtraction facts																																	
Find patterns in multiplication and division facts																																	
Find equivalent names for numbers																																	
Investigate square numbers																																	
Find number patterns that describe the relationship between similar figures																																	
Explore patterns in doubling numbers																																	
Plot points on a coordinate grid																																	
Find locations on a map																																	

Legend: ▢ Beginning ▨ Developing ■ Secure

Patterns, Functions, and Algebra (cont.)

Skills and Concepts	Grade 1 Units										Grade 2 Units												Grade 3 Units										
	1	2	3	4	5	6	7	8	9	10	1	2	3	4	5	6	7	8	9	10	11	12	1	2	3	4	5	6	7	8	9	10	11
Number Patterns (cont.)																																	
Find number patterns in data																																	
Sequences																																	
Count up and back on a number line																																	
Make/complete a number line																																	
Count by 2s, 5s, and 10s																																	
Count by numbers greater than 10																																	
Complete number sequences																																	
Solve Frames-and-Arrows problems with one rule																																	
Solve Frames-and-Arrows problems with two rules																																	
Explore counting patterns using a calculator																																	
Functions																																	
Solve "What's My Rule?" (function machine) problems																																	
Number Sentences																																	
Use symbols +, −, =																																	
Write/solve addition and subtraction number sentences																																	
Write/solve number sentences with missing addends																																	
Explore number properties (commutative, zero, identity)																																	
Use symbols x, ÷, =																																	
Write and solve multiplication number sentences																																	
Write/solve number sentences with missing factors																																	
Write and solve division number sentences																																	
Make up/solve number sentences with parentheses																																	
Inequalities																																	
Compare numbers using <, > symbols																																	

Geometry

Skills and Concepts	Grade 1 (Units)										Grade 2 (Units)												Grade 3 (Units)										
	1	2	3	4	5	6	7	8	9	10	1	2	3	4	5	6	7	8	9	10	11	12	1	2	3	4	5	6	7	8	9	10	11
2-Dimensional Shapes (Polygons)																																	
Identify 2-dimensional shapes																																	
Create/extend designs with 2-dimensional shapes																																	
Make 2-dimensional shapes on a geoboard																																	
Record geoboard shapes on dot paper																																	
Draw triangles and quadrilaterals																																	
Explore shape relationships																																	
Explore the relationship between diameter and circumference																																	
Identify characteristics of 2-dimensional shapes																																	
Compare 2-dimensional shapes																																	
Construct 2-dimensional shapes																																	
Solve 2-dimensional-shapes problems																																	
Record designs with 2-dimensional shapes																																	
Compare polygons and non-polygons																																	
Complete shape patterns																																	
Sort shapes by attributes																																	
Explore similarities and differences among quadrilaterals																																	
Form shapes by combining polygons																																	
Model polygons with rope																																	
Classify and name polygons																																	
Construct models of polygons with straws																																	

Legend: Beginning | Developing | Secure

Geometry (cont.)

Skills and Concepts	Grade 1 Units										Grade 2 Units												Grade 3 Units										
	1	2	3	4	5	6	7	8	9	10	1	2	3	4	5	6	7	8	9	10	11	12	1	2	3	4	5	6	7	8	9	10	11
3-Dimensional Shapes																																	
Identify 3-dimensional shapes							■								■													■					
Identify characteristics of 3-dimensional shapes									■				■											■				■					
Construct 3-dimensional shapes															■									■				■					
Explore similarities and differences among 3-dimensional shapes							■								■													■					
Explore the relationship among the number of faces, edges, and vertices of pyramids															■													■					
Identify faces, edges, vertices, and bases of prisms and pyramids																															■		
Identify the shapes of faces									■																						■		
Explore slanted 3-dimensional shapes									■																								
Symmetry											■												■										
Fold and cut symmetrical shapes														■	■												■						
Create/complete a symmetrical design														■	■	■											■						
Identify symmetrical figures								■	■					■	■												■						
Identify lines of symmetry								■	■					■	■												■						
Make symmetrical shapes on a geoboard								■							■												■						
Congruence											■												■										
Identify congruent figures															■												■						
Identify similar figures								■							■												■						
Points, Lines, and Angles											■												■										
Draw line segments with a straightedge															■												■	■					
Draw line segments to a specified length															■															■			
Identify parallel and nonparallel line segments																																	

Points, Lines, and Angles (cont.)

- Identify and name points
- Identify and name line segments
- Identify and name lines
- Identify and name intersecting lines
- Identify and name rays
- Draw lines and rays
- Model parallel lines on a geoboard
- Draw parallel lines with a straightedge
- Draw designs with line segments
- Model line segments, rays, and angles
- Model intersecting lines on a geoboard
- Identify and name angles
- Model clockwise and counterclockwise turns/rotations
- Draw angles to record rotations
- Measure angles with nonstandard units
- Measure angles with degree units
- Solve degree problems

Beginning **Developing** **Secure**

Notes on Scope and Sequence

Scope and Sequence Chart **479**

Measurement and Reference Frames: Measurement

Skills and Concepts	Grade 1 Units										Grade 2 Units												Grade 3 Units										
	1	2	3	4	5	6	7	8	9	10	1	2	3	4	5	6	7	8	9	10	11	12	1	2	3	4	5	6	7	8	9	10	11
Length																																	
Estimate and compare distances																																	
Estimate and compare lengths/heights of objects																																	
Measure lengths with nonstandard units																																	
Measure to the nearest foot																																	
Measure to the nearest inch																																	
Investigate the yard																																	
Measure to the nearest centimeter																																	
Investigate the meter																																	
Solve length/height number stories																																	
Name tools used to measure length																																	
Measure to the nearest $\frac{1}{2}$ inch																																	
Measure to the nearest $\frac{1}{2}$ centimeter																																	
Measure to the nearest yard																																	
Identify equivalent customary units of length																																	
Identify equivalent metric units of length																																	
Choose the appropriate unit of measure																																	
Measure to the nearest decimeter																																	
Investigate the mile																																	
Investigate the kilometer																																	
Solve distance number stories																																	
Measure to the nearest meter																																	
Use a map scale																																	

Length (cont.)

- Use a mileage map
- Use a scale drawing
- Measure to the nearest $\frac{1}{4}$ inch
- Measure to the nearest $\frac{1}{8}$ inch
- Read measurement to the nearest mile
- Measure to the nearest millimeter
- Measure diameter and circumference

Capacity and Volume

- Compare capacities of containers
- Name tools used to measure capacity
- Identify customary units of capacity
- Identify equivalent customary units of capacity
- Identify metric units of capacity
- Identify equivalent metric units of capacity
- Measure capacities of irregular containers
- Name tools used to measure volume
- Find volume
- Estimate volume
- Order objects by volume
- Investigate the relationship between volume and weight
- Choose the appropriate unit of measure
- Solve capacity number stories

Weight

- Use a pan balance
- Solve weight number stories

Beginning   Developing   Secure

Scope and Sequence Chart **481**

Skills and Concepts	Grade 1 Units										Grade 2 Units												Grade 3 Units										
	1	2	3	4	5	6	7	8	9	10	1	2	3	4	5	6	7	8	9	10	11	12	1	2	3	4	5	6	7	8	9	10	11
Weight (cont.)																																	
Identify customary units of weight																		■	■	■										■			
Identify metric units of weight																		■	■	■											■	
Use a spring scale																		■	■	■											■	
Name tools used to measure weight																		■	■	■												
Choose the appropriate unit of measure																		■	■	■												
Estimate and compare weights				■									■			■		■	■	■				■							■	
Use a bath scale																	■	■	■	■												
Identify equivalent customary units of weight																		■	■	■												
Identify equivalent metric units of weight																		■	■	■												
Choose the appropriate scale																		■	■	■												
Order objects by weight																		■	■	■												
Perimeter and Area																																	
Investigate area														■				■	■	■				■							■		
Estimate area												■						■	■	■				■									
Name tools used to measure area																		■	■	■												
Find the perimeter of irregular shapes																		■	■	■												
Find the perimeter of regular shapes																		■	■	■						■			■			■	
Find the area of regular shapes																		■	■	■					■	■					■	■	
Estimate perimeter																		■	■	■							■						
Compare perimeter and area																		■	■	■						■					■		
Find the area of irregular shapes																		■	■	■												

Money

- Recognize pennies and nickels
- Use cents notation
- Calculate the value of coin combinations
- Recognize dimes
- Use dollars-and-cents notation
- Compare values of sets of coins
- Recognize quarters
- Show money amounts with coins
- Show money amounts with coins/bills
- Recognize dollars
- Solve money number stories
- Make change
- Calculate the value of coin/bill combinations
- Calculate the value of bill combinations
- Identify equivalencies and make coin exchanges
- Identify equivalencies and make bill exchanges
- Add money amounts
- Subtract money amounts
- Estimate costs
- Identify pennies and dimes as fractional parts of a dollar
- Divide money amounts

Beginning   **Developing**   **Secure**

Measurement and Reference Frames: Reference Frames

Skills and Concepts — Time	Grade 1 Units 1-10	Grade 2 Units 1-12	Grade 3 Units 1-11
Use the calendar	1, 2	12	1
Compare the hour and minute hands	2, 3	2	
Tell time on the hour	4, 5, 6	2, 3, 4	6
Investigate A.M. and P.M.	4, 5	3	
Estimate the duration of a minute	5		
Investigate the duration of an hour			
Tell time on the half-hour	6, 7, 8, 9, 10	1, 2, 3, 4, 5	1
Tell time on the quarter-hour	7, 8, 9	1, 2, 3	1
Use digital notation	8, 9	2, 3, 10	1
Tell time to the nearest 5 minutes	9	2, 3, 4	1
Investigate the second hand			4
Solve time number stories	8, 9	1, 3, 4, 5, 7	1, 7, 8, 9, 11
Investigate 1-minute intervals			
Calculate elapsed time	4	1, 12	1, 6
Show days/events on a timeline	1, 2		
Number and name the months in a year		2, 12	1, 7
Write today's date		1	4
Tell time to the nearest minute		2	
Name tools used to measure time		9	
Identify time equivalencies		12	

Time (cont.)								
Read time in different ways								
Choose the appropriate unit of measure								
Temperature								
Use the Fahrenheit temperature scale								
Use a thermometer								
Solve temperature number stories								
Use a weather map								
Use the Celsius temperature scale								

Beginning   Developing   Secure

Notes on Scope and Sequence

Data and Chance

Skills and Concepts	Grade 1 Units										Grade 2 Units												Grade 3 Units										
	1	2	3	4	5	6	7	8	9	10	1	2	3	4	5	6	7	8	9	10	11	12	1	2	3	4	5	6	7	8	9	10	11
Collecting Data																																	
Collect data by counting																						●											●
Collect data by interviewing																							●										
Collect data from print sources																													●				
Collect data from posters																							●	●			●						
Collect data from a map																								●									
Make predictions about data													●												●								
Explore random sampling																																	
Conduct a survey									●																								
Recording/Displaying Data	●																						●										
Make a tally chart																	●						●	●									
Make a bar graph																	●														●		
Record data in a table/chart													●		●																		
Record data on a map																																	
Make a frequency table																													●		●		●
Make a line plot																																	
Evaluating Data																							●										
Find the range																								●									
Find the mode																								●									●
Find the median																											●						●
Find the mean																															●		●
Compare two sets of data																																	●

486 **Scope and Sequence Chart** *Data and Chance*

Evaluating Data (cont.)

- Compare the median and mean
- Find the minimum/maximum
- Read tables, graphs, and maps
- Use data in problem solving
- Summarize and interpret data

Probability and Chance

- Explore equal-chance events
- Predict outcomes
- Find combinations
- Classify events
- Use fraction notation to express probability
- Conduct experiments
- Explore *fair* and *unfair* games
- Solve problems involving chance outcomes
- Use an area model of probability

Beginning   Developing   Secure

Notes on Scope and Sequence

Index

Cylinders, 309, 320
  compared to cones, 321
  compared to rectangular prisms,
    322
  Exploration, 663

D

Data collection, organization, and
    analysis, 188–192
Data, set of
  median of, 528–532
  mode of, 864–868
Data day, 166–167, 188–192, 351
  four food groups, 366–371
  standing jumps and arm spans,
    545–549
Data representation and
    interpretation, 835
Data table, 368
Days, 26–30
Decade, 846
Decagon, constructing a, 331
Deci-, 639
Decimal notation
  for dollars-and-cents amounts, 174,
    696, 702–707
Decimal point, 704
Decimals, 688–756
Decimeter, 638, 645
  measuring in, 639
Degree marks, 236, 242
Degrees Celsius (°C), 236, 242
Degrees Fahrenheit (°F), 236, 242
Denominator, 581, 583
Devices, routines and, 10
Diagonal, 101
  on a table, 101–102
Diamond, 301
Dice
  dot, 36, 40, 48, 202, 295, 390, 405,
    528, 556, 562, 714, 727, 732,
    742, 752
  polyhedral, 118, 207, 290, 300, 528,
    545, 556, 562, 584
Dice-Roll and Tally Game, 9, 39
Differences, 144, 361
  comparisons with, 768
  finding on a number grid, 726
Digit, 44
Digital clock, 179, 180
Digital-clock notation, 92, 178–182,
    292–293
Digit Discovery game, 9, 69, 78
Digit Game, 163, 176, 695, 746
Dimes, 174
  as fractional parts of a dollar, 704
  relationship with other money,
    706–707
Directions
  Exploration, 292
  exploring, 290–294
Distances
  comparing, 861

finding median and range of,
    860–861
  measuring, 902–903
  measuring around shapes, 649
  measuring longer, 627, 652–655
  measuring with yardsticks,
    633–634
  on a number grid, 99, 229
  on a number line, 227
Divided by, 790
Division, 351–352, 411, 766–767,
    789
  arrays, 767
  equal-grouping situations, 393
  equal-sharing situations, 393
  exploring, 390–394
  facts, 767–768
  from multiplication, 853–857
  number models, 788–794, 790–791
  number stories, 410–415, 581, 791,
    792, 800, 811, 817, 824
Dollar, making a
  Exploration, 303
Dollars
  exchanges for, 174
  relationship with other money,
    706–707
Dollar Rummy game, 163, 186, 287,
    304
Dollars-and-cents
  decimal notation, 696, 702–707
  notation, 43, 174, 238, 709, 714,
    770
  number stories, 770–775
  subtraction number stories,
    776–781
Dominoes
  addition and subtraction facts, 116,
    117
  double 9, 73
  Exploration, 73
  exploring, 15, 70–74
  version of *Addition Top-It,* 112
Doubles facts, 100–104, 110–113
Doubling
  numbers, 534–536
  patterns in, 533–538
  visual images for, 538

E

Edge, 320
Elapsed time, 842
Endpoints, 307
Equalities, 69
Equal grouping, 412–413, 594
Equal groups
  and building arrays, 787
  Exploration, 121
  exploring, 90, 118–122
  multiples of, 395–399, 782–787,
    784–785
  number stories, 403, 564, 784–785,
    789

Equal parts
  dividing shapes into, 583
Equal parts of ONE (the whole), 576,
    578–583
  folding squares, 579–580
Equal sharing, 298, 412, 539–544,
    594
Equivalencies, 60, 174
  time, 84
Equivalent, 596
Equivalent fractions, 594–597
  display of, 595–596
  using Fraction Cards, 598–601
Equivalent Fractions Game, 575, 600,
    601, 604, 614, 623, 665, 695, 725
Equivalent Measures, Table of,
    638–639, 674
Equivalent metric units of capacity,
    675
Equivalent names for numbers,
    56–60, 128–132, 174
Equivalent U.S. customary units of
    capacity, 674
Estimates
  checking, 633–634
  safeguarding against errors, 766
Estimating
  costs, 720–721, 774
  regions, 605
Estimation
  ballpark estimates, 264, 270, 315,
    320, 339, 357, 385, 391, 408, 418
  to check answers, 263–268
  to compare sums of weight, 251
  discussing, 248
  number stories, 733
  seconds, 21
  solving problems by, 248–249, 375
  time, 28, 180
  and trade-first subtraction
    algorithm, 525, 531
  using to compare sums of weights,
    251
Even numbers, 50
Everything Math Deck, 32
Exact change, 203, 204
  buying with, 204
  buying without, 204
Exchange values, 699
Exploration
  area, 664, 728–729
  arrays, 587–588
  attribute blocks, 239, 260– 261,
    296–297
  attribute rules, 292
  base-10 structures, 73, 588
  centimeter cube arrays, 303
  clock booklet, 185
  Clock Concentration, 292–293
  coin-stamp booklets, 238
  cylinders, 663
  dollar, making a, 303
  dominoes, 73
  equal groups, 121, 392–393

H

Half-pictures of Pattern-Block
  Template shapes, completing, 334
Halving
  numbers, 534–536
  patterns in, 533–538
  visual images, 538
Heavier, 119
Height, 866–868
Height changes, 866–867, 868
Hepta-, 302
Heptagon, 302
Hexa-, 302
Hexagon, 302
History link, 160
Hit the Target game, 505, 524–525,
  526, 536, 543, 566, 765, 773, 781
Home Link, 14, 68,
Hour hand, 30, 180, 181

I

In balance, 119
Inch (in.), 638
  grid, 664
  measuring to nearest, 637–638, 639
  measuring to nearest half, 645, 646
  scales, 258–259, 262
In each, 784
Inequalities, 69
Input, 139–140
Inverse relationship, 123–127
Is equal to, 14, 65–69, 250
Is greater than, 14, 65–69, 250
  mnemonic devices for, 251
Is less than, 14, 65–69, 250
  mnemonic devices for, 251

K

Kilogram (kg), 680
  and pound collection, 682
Kilometer (km), 653
Kite, 316

L

Label, 93
Language arts link, 6, 29, 84, 180,
  185, 284, 302, 306, 346, 376,
  572, 609, 620, 649, 653, 692,
  704, 751, 762, 784
Language link, 84, 129, 692
Learning goals, 4, 82, 158, 214, 282,
  344, 500, 570, 618, 690, 760, 828
Length, 122
  Exploration, 259
  exploring, 257–262
  fish, 370, 686–687
  fractional units of, 626, 642–647
  measuring to nearest centimeter,
    545–549
  measuring to nearest inch, 545–549

measuring with a nonstandard unit,
  631–632
measuring with a ruler, 520
Lighter, 119
Line, 306
Linear measures, 626, 636–641, 657,
  659
  units of metric, 647
Line plot
  of arm spans, 558–559
  of height changes, 866–867
Line segments, 288, 305–309
  counting, 323
  drawing, 307, 309, 312, 323
  naming, 306–307
  parallel, 310–313
Lines of symmetry, 333
  finding, 333–334
Line symmetry, 289, 332–336
  with geoboards, 336
Liter (L), 675
Literature and art link, 284, 303, 323,
  335
Literature and history link, 160
Literature link, 6, 20, 84, 97, 104,
  132, 160, 177, 216, 238, 260,
  284, 302, 318, 346, 399, 404,
  414, 502, 538, 543, 572,
  582–583, 593, 620, 635, 641,
  673, 692, 701, 726, 762, 786,
  793, 802, 830, 863, 879, 883,
  889, 893
Long, 15, 169, 733
Lost-and-Found Box, 23

M

Magic squares, completing, 171
Making Change game, 163, 205,
  210–211
Maps, 654, 818–819
Materials, 8, 86, 162, 218, 286, 348,
  504, 574, 622, 694, 764, 832
Math Boxes, 13, 44–47
Mathematic modeling, 748, 751,
  788–794
Mathematics
  All Around bulletin board, 20
  sharing ideas about, 19
  writing about, 824
Math Journal, 18
Math Masters, 8, 86, 162, 218, 286,
  348, 504, 574, 622, 694, 764, 832
Math Message, 11–12, 16–21
Measurement, 616–687
  need for accurate, 643–644
  systems, 633, 638, 674, 680
  time, 834
  unit, 633, 638, 674, 680
Measures
  of capacity, 629, 657
  linear, 626, 636–641, 657, 659
  of volume, 657
  of weight, 629, 657

Measure sense, 625
Measures All Around, 627–628,
  656–660
  Museum, 625
Measuring
  in centimeters, 639
  in decimeters, 639
  distances, 902–903
  distances around shapes, 649
  in feet, 639
  in inches, 639
  longer distances, 627, 652–655
  with meters, 626, 630–635
  to nearest centimeter, 637–638
  to nearest half-centimeter, 645, 646
  to nearest half-inch, 645, 646
  to nearest inch, 637–638
  objects, 554
  perimeter in paces, 651
  tools booklet, 660
  with yards, 626, 630–635
Median, 190, 550–555, 557
  of distances, 860–861
  length of arm spans, 560
Mental arithmetic, 220–221, 291,
  296, 528–532, 713
Meter (m), 633, 638, 645
Meters, measuring with, 626, 630–635
Metric linear measure, units of, 647
Metric system, 633, 638
Middle number
  of pockets, 189–190
Middle value, 552, 818. *See also*
  Median
Mile (mi), 653
milli-, 645
Milliliter (ml), 645
Millimeter (mm), 645
Minuend, 124, 379
Minute hand, 30, 180, 181
Missing measurements story, 686
Mnemonic devices, 251
Mode, 191
  of a set of data, 864–868
Money, 164–165, 698–756
  amounts with a calculator, 708–713
  calculating sums of, 779
  comparing place value with, 734
  counting, 41
  decimal notation for, 702–707
  equivalent amounts, 701
  Exploration, 541–542
  exploring, 235–240
  Frames-and-Arrows problems, 181
  number stories, 276, 303, 606, 611,
    716, 776–781
  from other countries, 700
  using a calculator to solve problems,
    714–717
Money Exchange Game, 9, 42, 59, 695,
  735, 745
  with bank drafts, 43
  with base-10 blocks, 43
  with coins and $1 bills, 43